Morphology
of Plants

HARPER & ROW, Publishers
New York, Evanston and London

Morphology
of Plants

HAROLD C. BOLD

Professor of Botany
The University of Texas

SECOND EDITION

Morphology of Plants, Second Edition

Copyright © 1957 by Harper & Row, Publishers, Incorporated.

Copyright © 1967 by Harold C. Bold.

Printed in the United States of America. All rights reserved. No part of this book may be
used or reproduced in any manner whatsoever without written permission except in the
case of brief quotations embodied in critical articles and reviews. For information address
Harper & Row, Publishers, Incorporated, 49 East 33rd Street, New York, N.Y. 10016.

Library of Congress Catalog Card Number: 67–10790

Acknowledgments

Sources of figures used in this book and permission to reproduce them are as follows:

Fig. 3-4E: From the paper by R. A. Lewin and J. O. Meinhart, "Studies on the Flagella of Algae, III." Reproduced by permission of the National Research Council of Canada from the *Canadian Journal of Botany*, Vol. 31, pp. 711–717, 1953.

Fig. 3-34E: From P. W. Cook, "Variation in Vegetative and Sexual Morphology Among the Small Curved Species of *Closterium*," *Phycologia*, Vol. 3, pp. 1–18, Fig. 20.

Fig. 3-39: From G. M. Smith, *Cryptogamic Botany*, Vol. 1, Fig. 53 A, F, G. Copyright, 1955, McGraw-Hill Book Company, Inc. Reprinted by permission of the publishers.

Fig. 3-43A, B, C: From G. M. Smith, *Cryptogamic Botany*, Vol. 1, Fig. 65. Copyright, 1955, McGraw-Hill Book Company, Inc. Reprinted by permission of the publishers.

Fig. 3-43D: From G. M. Smith, *Cryptogamic Botany*, Vol. 1, Fig. 64B. Copyright, 1955, McGraw-Hill Book Company, Inc. Reprinted by permission of the publishers.

Fig. 4-8: From T. Kanda, "On the Gametophytes of Some Japanese Species of Laminariales," *Scientific Papers*, Institute Algological Research, Hokkaido Imp. Univ., Vol. 1, No. 2, pp. 221–260.

Fig. 4-9: From Gilbert M. Smith, *Marine Algae of the Monterey Peninsula*, p. 465. Reprinted by permission of the publishers, Stanford University Press. Copyright, 1944, by the Board of Trustees of Leland Stanford Junior University.

Fig. 4-11: Reprinted from *Marine Algae of the Monterey Peninsula*, by Gilbert M. Smith with the permission of the publishers, Stanford University Press. Copyright 1944 by the Board of Trustees of the Leland Stanford Junior University. Plate 26, *Macrocystis integrifolia*.

Fig. 4-16B: From W. Nienburg, "Die Entwicklung der Keimling von *Fucus vesiculosus* und ihre Bedeutung für die Phylogenie der Phaeophyceen." *Wissenschaftliche Meeresuntersuchungen*, Vol. 21: p. 51, Fig. 1.

Fig. 5-3: From E. Gantt and S. F. Conti, "The Ultrastructure of *Porphyridium cruentum*," reprinted by permission of the Rockefeller University Press from *J. Cell Biology*, Vol. 26, pp. 365–381, Fig. 1.

Fig. 5-4B-D: From K. M. Drew, "Studies in the Bangioideae. 1. Observations on *Bangia fuscopurpurea* (Dillw.) Lyngb. in Culture," *Phytomorphology*, Vol. 2: pp. 39–50. Parts of Fig. 2.

Fig. 5-7: From I. Iwasaki and C. Matsudaira, "Observation of the Ecology and Reproduction of the Free-Living *Conchocelis* of *Porphyra tenera*," *Biol. Bull.*, Vol. 124, pp. 268–276, Plate II, A, 1963.

Fig. 7-6C: From W. J. Koch, "A Study of the Motile Cells of *Vaucheria*," *Journal of the Elisha Mitchell Scientific Society*, Vol. 67: Plate 5, Fig. 18.

Fig. 7-7A: From G. M. Smith, *Cryptogamic Botany*, Vol. 1, Fig. 101 A, B. Copyright, 1955, McGraw-Hill Book Company, Inc. Reprinted by permission of the publishers.

Fig. 7-7B: From J. N. Couch, "Gametogenesis in *Vaucheria*," *Bot. Gaz.*, Vol. 94, pp. 272–296, Fig. 8, 1932.

Fig. 7-10A: From G. M. Smith, *Freshwater Algae of the United States*, Fig. 336B. Copyright, 1950, McGraw-Hill Book Company, Inc. Reprinted by permission of the publishers.

Fig. 7-13: From R. Subrahmanyan, "On Somatic Division, Reduction Division, Auxospore Formation and Sex-Differentiation in *Navicula Halophila* (Grun.)," Cl. *Journal of the Indian Botanical Society*, The M.O.P. Iyengar Commemoration Volume, pp. 238–266, Figs. 16, 17, 27, 28 and 39.

Fig. 7-16: From H. A. Von Stosch and G. Drebes, "Entwicklungsgeschichtliche Untersuchungen an zentrischen Diatomeen IV. Die Planktondiatomee *Stephanopyxis turris*— ihre Behandlung und Entwicklungsgeschichte, *Helgoland wiss. Meeresunters*, Vol. 11, pp. 209–257, Fig. 18, 1964.

Fig. 8-1A: From S. A. Tyler and E. S. Barghoorn, "Occurrence of Structurally Preserved Plants in Pre-Cambrian Rocks of the Canadian Shield," *Science*, Vol. 119, pp. 606–608, 1954. Copyright 1965 by the American Association for the Advancement of Science.

Fig. 8-1B-D: From E. S. Barghoorn and S. A. Tyler, "Microorganisms from the Gunflint Chert," *Science*, Vol. 147, pp. 563–577, Figs. 3 and 4, 1965. Copyright 1965 by the American Association for the Advancement of Science.

Fig. 8-2A. From J. Pia, "Die Siphoneae Verticillatae von Karbon bis zur Kreide," *Abh. Zool.-bot. Ges.* Bd. 11(2) Wien, Fig. 21, p. 112, 1920.

Fig. 8-3: From R. E. Peck and J. A. Eyer, "Pennsylvanian, Permian and Triassic Charophyta of North America," *J. Paleont.*, Vol. 37, pp. 835–844, Fig. 3–8, 1963.

Fig. 8-4: From *The Economic Importance of the Diatoms*, by Albert Mann. From the Annual Report of the Smithsonian Institution, 1916. Reprinted with permission from the Smithsonian Institution.

Fig. 9-4: From E. E. Clifton, *Introduction to the Bacteria*, Fig. 3-1. Copyright, 1950, McGraw-Hill Book Company, Inc. Reprinted by permission of the publishers.

Fig. 9-5: From W. B. Sarles, W. C. Frazier, J. B. Wilson, and S. G. Knight, *Microbiology: General and Applied*, 2nd ed., Harper & Brothers, p. 13, 1956. Reprinted by permission of W. D. Frost.

Fig. 9-8B: From G. Knaysi, R. F. Baker, and J. Hillier, "A Study, with the High-Voltage Electron Microscope, of the Endospore and Life Cycle of *Bacillus mycoides*," *Jour. Bact.*, Vol. 53, pp. 525–537, Fig. 5, 1947.

Fig. 9-9A, B: From F. Jacob and E. L. Wollman, *Sexuality and the Genetics of Bacteria*. Fig. 17. Reprinted by permission of Academic Press Inc., Publishers.

Fig. 9-10. From W. B. Sarles, W. C. Frazier, J. B. Wilson, and S. G. Knight, *Microbiology: General and Applied*, 2nd ed., Harper & Brothers, p. 59, 1956. Reprinted by permission of S. A. Waksman.

Fig. 10-7: From Dr. A. C. Lonert, "Dictyostelium," *Turtox News*, Vol. 43, No. 2, pp. 50–53. Reprinted by permission of General Biological Supply House, Inc. and A. C. Lonert.

Fig. 11-3: From R. M. Johns, "A New *Polyphagus* in Algal Culture," *Mycologia*, Vol. 56, pp. 441–451, Fig. 5, 1964.

Fig. 11-4: From R. M. Johns, "A New *Polyphagus* in Algal Culture," *Mycologia*, Vol. 56, pp. 441–451, Fig. 6, 1964.

Fig. 12-8A, D: From F. A. Wolf and F. T. Wolf, *The Fungi*, Vol. 1, Fig. 54 F, G. 1947.

Fig. 12-10: From B. O. Dodge, "Production of Fertile Hybrids in the Ascomycete Neurospora," *Jour. Agri. Res.*, Vol. 36, pp. 1–14, 1928.

Fig. 12-15A: From C. J. Alexopoulos, *Introductory Mycology*. Copyright, 1952, John Wiley & Sons, Inc. Reprinted by permission of the publishers.

Fig. 12-16: From H. C. I. Gwynne-Vaughan and H. S. Williamson, "Contributions to the Study of *Pyronema confluens*," *Annals of Botany*, Vol. 45, Figs. 8 and 22, 1931.

Fig. 13-13: From C. J. Alexopoulos, *Introductory Mycology*, p. 314. Copyright, 1952, John Wiley & Sons, Inc. Reprinted by permission of the publishers.

Fig. 14-3: From D. Pramer, "Nematode-trapping Fungi," *Science*, 144, pp. 382–388, 1964. Copyright 1964 by the American Association for the Advancement of Science.

Fig. 14-4, 14-6, 14-7: From "The Fungi of Lichens" by V. Ahmadjian. Copyright © 1963 by *Scientific American*, Inc. All rights reserved.

Fig. 14-12: From J. William Schopf, Elso S. Barghoorn, Morton D. Maser, Robert O. Gordon, "Electron Microscopy of Fossil Bacteria Two Billion Years Old," *Science*, Vol. 149, pp. 1365–1366. Copyright 1965 by the American Association for the Advancement of Science.

Fig. 14-14: From R. Kidston and W. H. Lang, 1917–1921. "On Old Red Sandstone Plants Showing Structure from the Rhynie Chert Bed, Aberdeenshire," *Trans. Roy. Soc., Edinburgh*, Vols. 51, 52. Plate I, Fig. 4; Plate III, Fig. 34.

Fig. 15-29B, C: From G. M. Smith, *Cryptogamic Botany*, Vol. 2, Fig. 9 F, G. Copyright, 1955, McGraw-Hill Book Company, Inc. Reprinted by permission of the publishers.

Fig. 15-29D, E: From G. M. Smith, *Cryptogamic Botany*, Vol. 2, Fig. 7 G, H. Copyright, 1955, McGraw-Hill Book Company, Inc. Reprinted by permission of the publishers.

Fig. 15-30A, B: From G. M. Smith, *Cryptogamic Botany*, Vol. 2, Fig. 10 A, F. Copyright, 1955, McGraw-Hill Book Company, Inc. Reprinted by permission of the publishers.

Fig. 15-50: From S. Hattori and M. Mizutani, "What is *Takakia lepidozioides?*" *Jour. Hattori Bot. Lab.*, Vol. 20, pp. 295–303. Parts of Fig. 1 and 2, 1958.

Fig. 15-64: From J. Walton, "Carboniferous Bryophyta; I. Hepaticae," *Annals of Botany*, Vol. 39, Plate 13, Fig. 1, 1925.

Fig. 16-12, 16-13: From N. S. Parihar, *An Introduction to Embryophyta*, Vol. 1, *Bryophyta*, Fig. 64, 1957.

Fig. 16-19: From D. H. Campbell, *Mosses and Ferns*, The Macmillan Company, Fig. 106A, 1928.

Fig. 16-28: From G. M. Smith, *Cryptogamic Botany*, Vol. 1, Fig. 64. Copyright, 1955, McGraw-Hill Book Co., Inc. Reprinted by permission of the publishers.

Fig. 16-29B: From G. M. Smith, *Cryptogamic Botany*, Vol. 1, Fig. 65B. Copyright, 1955, McGraw-Hill Book Company, Inc. Reprinted by permission of the publishers.

Fig. 17-2: From H. C. Bold, *The Plant Kingdom* (2nd ed.), Prentice-Hall, Fig. 5-2, 1964.

Fig. 17-3: From O. Schüepp, *Meristeme*, Vol. IV, Handb. Pflanzenanatonie 1 abt., 2 teil, Histologie, Fig. 16, 1926.

Fig. 17-11: From H. C. Bold, *The Plant Kingdom* (2nd ed.), Prentice-Hall, Fig. 5-5, 1964.

Fig. 17-12: From A. J. Eames and L. H. MacDaniels, *An Introduction to Plant Anatomy*, Fig. 121. Copyright, 1947, McGraw-Hill Book Company, Inc. Reprinted by permission of the publishers.

Fig. 17-14: From M. R. Darnley Gibbs, *Botany*, Fig. 154, 1950.

Fig. 17-16: From G. S. Avery, "Structure and Development of the Tobacco Leaf." *American Journal of Botany*, Vol. 20, pp. 565–592. Fig. 6, 1933.

Fig. 17-19: From H. C. Bold, *The Plant Kingdom* (2nd ed.), Prentice-Hall, Fig. 5-14, 1964.

Fig. 18-10: From D. W. Bierhorst, "Structure and Development of the Gametophyte of *Psilotum nudum, American Journal of Botany*, Vol. 40, Figs. 5, 6, 7, 1953.

Fig. 18-14, 18-15: From F. M. Hueber, "The Psilophytes and Their Relationship to the Origin of Ferns," *Torrey Bot. Club Memoir 21*, Fig. 1, 1964.

Fig. 18-16: From R. Kidston and W. H. Lang, 1917–1921, "On Old Red Sandstone Plants Showing Structure from the Rhynie Chert Bed, Aberdeenshire," *Trans. Roy. Soc. Edinburgh*, Vol. 52. Plate I, Fig. 4; Plate III, Fig. 34.

Fig. 18-17B: From R. Kidston and W. H. Lang, 1917–1921, "On Old Red Sandstone Plants Showing Structure from the Rhynie Chert Bed, Aberdeenshire," *Trans. Roy. Soc. Edinburgh*, Vols. 51, 52. Part I: Plate, IX, Fig. 62.

Figs. 19-12, 19-13, 19-14: From H. Bruchmann, "Die Keimung der Sporen und die Entwicklung der Prothallien von *Lycopodium clavatum, L. annotinum* und *L. selago*," *Flora*, Vol. 101, pp. 262, 263, 1910.

Fig. 19-20: From T. R. Webster and T. A. Steeves, "Developmental Morphology of the Root of *Selaginella Kraussiana* A.Br. and *Selaginella Wallacei* Hieron." Reproduced by permission of the National Research Council of Canada from the *Canadian Journal of Botany*, Vol. 42, 1665, 1964.

Fig. 19-32: From E. Steiner, A. S. Sussman, and W. H. Wagner, Jr., *Botany Laboratory Manual*, Holt, Rinehart and Winston, Inc. Fig. 22-2, 1965.

Fig. 19-35B: From D. J. Paolillo, "The Development Anatomy of Isoetes," *Illinois Biol. Monograph 31*, Fig. 1, 1963.

Fig. 19-38A: From J. Liebig, "Erganzungen zur Entwicklungsgeschichte von *Isoetes lacustris* L.," *Flora*, Vol. 125, p. 343, 1931.

Fig. 19-38B, C: From C. LaMotte, "Morphology of the Megagametophyte and the Embryo Sporophyte of *Isoetes lithophila*," *American Journal of Botany*, Vol. 20, Figs. 3, 10, 1933.

Fig. 19-40: From W. H. Lang and I. Cookson, "On a Flora Including Vascular Land Plants, Associated with *Monograptus*, in Rocks of Silurian Age from Victoria, Australia," *Phil. Trans. Roy. Soc. London*, Vol. 2.24B, pp. 421–449. Plate 29, Fig. 1, 1935.

Fig. 19-42: From R. Krausel and H. Weyland, "Pflanzenreste aus den Devon," *Senckenbergiana*, Vol. 14, Fig. 14, 1932.

Fig. 19-45: From M. Hirmer, *Handbuch der Palaobotanik*, Vol. 1, Figs. 200, 285, 1927.

Fig. 19-48A: From H. N. Andrews, Jr., *Studies in Paleobotany*, Fig. 8-14, 1961.

Fig. 19-48D: From G. M. Smith, *Cryptogamic Botany*, Vol. 2, Fig. 130A. Copyright, 1955, McGraw-Hill Book Company, Inc. Reprinted by permission of the publishers.

Fig. 19-49B, C: From J. H. Hoskins and M. L. Abbott, "*Selaginellites crassicinctus*, a New Species from the Desmoinesian Series of Kansas," *American Journal of Botany*, Vol. 43, pp. 36–46, Figs. 5, 7, 8, 1956.

Fig. 19-50: From M. Hirmer, "Paläophytologische Notizen: I. Rekonstruction von *Pleuromeia sternbergi* Corda, nebst. Bemerkungen zur Morphologie der Lycopodiales," *Palaeontographica.*, Vol. 78, p. 48, 1933.

Fig. 20-14B: From G. M. Smith, *Cryptogamic Botany*, Vol. 2, Fig. 160G. Copyright, 1955, McGraw-Hill Book Company, Inc. Reprinted by permission of the publishers.

Fig. 20-16: From S. Leclercq, "Contribution à L'Étude de la Flore du Dévonien de Belgique," *Academie Royale de Belgique Memoires Classe des Sciences*, IN40 S.2 12, Fig. 5, 1940.

Fig. 20-17: From R. Kräusel and H. Weyland, "Beiträge zur Kenntnis der Devon-flora II," *Abh., Senckenbergische Naturforsch Gesellschaft*, Vol. 40, Fig. 24, 1926.

Fig. 20-18A: From M. Hirmer, *Handbuch der Paläobotanik*, Vol. 1, Fig. 537, 1927.

Fig. 20-20: From M. Hirmer, *Handbuch der Paläobotanik*, R. Oldenbourg, Fig. 483, 1927.

Fig. 20-23A: From M. Hirmer, *Handbuch der Paläobotanik*, Vol. 1, Fig. 417, 1927.

Fig. 20-24: From M. Hirmer, *Handbuch der Paläobotanik*, Vol. 1, Figs. 553, 554, 1927.

Fig. 21-9B: From G. M. Smith, *Cryptogamic Botany*, Vol. 2, Fig. 185E. Copyright, 1955, McGraw-Hill Book Company, Inc. Reprinted by permission of the publishers.

Fig. 21-10A: From G. M. Smith, *Cryptogamic Botany*, Vol. 2, Fig. 186. Copyright, 1955, McGraw-Hill Book Company, Inc. Reprinted by permission of the publishers.

Fig. 21-13: From A. G. Stokey, "Gametophytes of *Marattia sambricina* and *Macroglossum Smithii*,".*Botanical Gazette*, Vol. 103, University of Chicago Press, Fig. 3, 1942.

Fig. 22-17B: From A. Haupt, *Plant Morphology*, Fig. 247D. Copyright, 1953, McGraw-Hill Book Company, Inc. Reprinted by permission of the publishers.

Fig. 22-19: From H. A. Gleason, *New Britton and Brown Illustrated Flora*, Vol. 1, parts of figures on *Osmunda*, p. 27, 1952.

Figs. 22-22B, 22-30: From H. N. Andrews, Jr., *Studies in Paleobotany*, Figs. 4-6A, B, D, 1961.

Fig. 22-28A: From D. S. Correll, *Ferns and Fern Allies of Texas*, Plate 10, Fig. 1.

Fig. 22-28C: From C. A. Brown and D. S. Correll, *Ferns and Fern Allies of Louisiana*, Fig. 37.

Fig. 22-29: From G. M. Smith, *Cryptogamic Botany*, Vol. 2, Fig. 197 A, B. Copyright, 1955, McGraw-Hill Book Company, Inc. Reprinted by permission of the publishers.

Fig. 22-31A: From G. M. Smith, *Cryptogamic Botany*, Vol. 2, Fig. 214. Copyright, 1955, McGraw-Hill Book Company, Inc. Reprinted by permission of the publishers.

Fig. 22-31B: From C. A. Brown and D. S. Correll, *Ferns and Fern Allies of Louisiana*, Fig. 5.

Fig. 23-6: From A. J. Eames, *Morphology of Vascular Plants*, Fig. 133B. Copyright, 1936, McGraw-Hill Book Company, Inc. Reprinted by permission of the publishers.

Fig. 23-8: From A. W. Haupt, *Plant Morphology*, Fig. 251, Copyright 1953. McGraw-Hill Book Company, Inc. Reprinted by permission of the publishers.

Fig. 23-10A: From L. W. Sharp, "Spermatogenesis in *Marsilia*," *Botanical Gazette*, Vol. 58, University of Chicago Press, Plate 33, Figs. 7, 8, 1914.

Fig. 23-12E: Reprinted by permission of the Rockefeller University Press from *J. Cell Biology*, Vol. 29, pp. 97–111, 1966.

Fig. 23-13A: From D. H. Campbell, *Mosses and Ferns*, The Macmillan Company, Fig. 250A, 1928.

Fig. 23-17: From R. Krausel and H. Weyland, "Die Flora des bömischen Mitteldevons." *Palaeontographica*, Vol. 78B, pp. 1–46, Fig. 8, 1933.

Fig. 23-18: From W. Goldring, "The Upper Devonian Forest of Seed Ferns in Eastern New York," *Bulletin N.Y. State Museum*, Vol. 25, pp. 50–92, Plate 1, Courtesy of N.Y. State Museum and Science Service, 1924.

Fig. 23-19: From R. Krausel and H. Weyland, "Beitrag zur Kenntnis der Devon-flora II," *Abh. Senckenbergische Naturforsch Gesellschaft*, Vol. 40, Fig. 24, 1926.

Fig. 23-20: From S. Leclercq and H. P. Banks, "*Pseudosporochnus nodosus* sp. nov., a Middle-Devonian Plant with Cladoxylalean Affinities," *Palaeontographica*, Vol. 110 (B), pp. 1–34, Fig. 7, 1962.

Fig. 23-21C: From M. Hirmer, *Handbuch der Paläobotanik*, Vol. 1, Fig. 580, 1927.

Fig. 23-22: From R. Wettstein, *Handbuch der Systematischen Botanik*, Franz Deuticke, and Asher and Co., Fig. 262-261, 1962.

Fig. 23-23: From J. Morgan, "The Morphology and Anatomy of American Species of the Genus Psaronius," *Ill. Biol. Monograph*, No. 27, pp. 1–108, frontispiece, 1959.

Fig. 23-24: From T. Delevoryas, *Morphology and Evolution of Fossil Plants*, Holt, Rinehart and Winston, Inc., Fig. 7-11A, 1962.

Figs. 24-1 to 24-3 and 24-5 to 24-10: From W. N. Stewart, "An Upward Outlook in Plant Morphology," *Phytomorphology*, Vol. 14, pp. 120–134, parts of Figs. 1-16.

Fig. 25-10: From F. Grace Smith, "Development of the Ovulate Strobilus and Young Ovule of *Zamia floridana*," *Botanical Gazette*, Vol. 50, University of Chicago Press, Figs. 9, 105, 1910.

Fig. 25-18: From G. S. Bryan, "The Cellular Proembryo of *Zamia* and Its Cap Cells," *American Journal of Botany*, Vol. 39, Fig. 5, 1952.

Fig. 25-24: From A. D. J. Meeuse, "The So-Called Megasporophyll of *Cycas*, etc." *Acta Bot. Neerlandica*, Vol. 12, pp. 119–128, Fig. 1, 1963.

Fig. 25-25: From H. N. Andrews, Jr., *Ancient Plants and the World They Lived In*, Comstock Publishing Co., Fig. 92, 1947.

Fig. 25-26A: From H. N. Andrews, "Early Seed Plants," *Science*, Vol. 142, p. 925, 1963. Copyright 1963 by the American Association for the Advancement of Science.

Fig. 25-26B: From A. G. Long, "On the structure of *Samaropsis scotica* Calder (emended) and *Eurystoma angulare* gen, et sp. nov., petrified seeds from the Calciferous sandstone series of Berwickshire," *Trans. Roy. Soc. Edinburgh*, Vol. 64, pp. 261–280, Fig. 1B; Fig. 6, 1960.

Fig. 25-29B: From C. A. Arnold, *An Introduction to Paleobotany*, Fig. 101A. Copyright, 1947, McGraw-Hill Book Company, Inc. Reprinted by permission of the publishers.

Figs. 25-30B and 25-31A: From W. N. Stewart and T. Delevoryas, "The Medullosan Pteridosperms.," *Bot. Rev.*, Vol. 22, pp. 45–80, Fig. 8, Fig. 9, 1956.

Fig. 25-32 A-C: From H. H. Thomas, "The Caytoniales, a new group of angiospermous plants from the Jurassic rocks of Yorkshire." *Phil. Trans. Roy. Soc. London* B, 213: p. 299, Text figures 1, 3, 7, 10B.

Fig. 25-32 D: From T. M. Harris, "The Fossil Flora of Scoresby Sound, East Greenland. Pt. 5," *Medelel. om Grönland* 112(2), Text figure 3G, F, 1937.

Fig. 25-34A, B: From T. Delevoryas, "Investigations of North American Cycadeoids: Cones of *Cycadeoidea*," *Amer. J. Bot.*, Vol. 50, pp. 45–52, Figs. 1, 13A, 1963.

Fig. 25-36: From R. Florin, "Studien über die Cycadales des Mesozoikums," *K. Svenska Vetenkapsakademiens Handlingar* Bd. 12 (5), Fig. 32C, 1933.

Figs. 26-16 and 26-17: From A. C. Seward, *Fossil Plants*, No. IV, Cambridge University Press, Figs. 639 and 650.

Fig. 27-22: From S. T. Buchholz, "Suspensor and Early Embryo of *Pinus*," *Botanical Gazette*, Vol. 66, University of Chicago Press, Plate VIII, Fig. 40, 1918.

Fig. 27-34C: From H. N. Andrews, *Studies in Paleobotany*, John Wiley & Sons, Inc., Fig. 11-1, 1961.

Fig. 27-35B: From C. Beck, "Reconstruction of Archaeopteris and Further Consideration of its Phylogenetic Position, *American Journal of Botany*, Vol. 49, pp. 373–382, Fig. 2, 1962.

Fig. 27-37A: From T. Delevoryas, "A New Male Cordaitean Fructification from the Kansas Carboniferous," *American Journal of Botany*, Vol. 40, pp. 144–150, Fig. 5, 1953.

Figs. 27-37B, C and 27-39A and B: From R. Florin, "Die Koniferen des Oberkarbons und des Unteren Perms," Palaeontographica, Vol. 85B. Figs. 58B, 45C (in part), Fig. 28, and Text-Fig. 33a, 1944.

Fig. 28-15B: From W. J. G. Land, "Fertilization and Embryogeny in *Ephedra trifurca*," *Botanical Gazette*, Vol. 44, University of Chicago Press, Fig. 17, 1907.

Fig. 28-17: From W. J. G. Land, "Fertilization and Embryogeny in *Ephedra trifurca*," *Botanical Gazette*, Vol. 44, University of Chicago Press, Figs. 4, 16, 21, 1907.

Fig. 28-20A: From *Gnetum* by P. Maheshwari and V. Vasil, *Botanical Monograph*, No. 4, CSIR, New Delhi, 1961.

Fig. 30-1: From J. E. Canright, "The Comparative Morphology and Relationships of the Magnoliaceae: IV. Wood and Nodal Anatomy," *Jour. Arnold Arboretum*, Vol. 36, pp. 119–140, Fig. 1, 1955.

Fig. 30-12A, C: From J. E. Canright, "The Comparative Morphology and Relationships of the Magnoliaceae: I. Trends of Specialization in the Stamen," *American Journal of Botany*, Vol. 39, pp. 484–497, Fig. 13 (in part).

Figs. 30-14, 30-15: From L. Benson, *Plant Classification*, Fig. VII. 1, 2, 1957.

Fig. 30-16: From L. Benson and R. A. Darrow, "The Trees and Shrubs of Southwestern Deserts," University of Arizona Press, Tucson, Fig. 74, 1954.

Fig. 30-33: Reproduced by permission from *Botanical Microtechnique*, Third Edition, by John E. Sass, Copyright 1958 by the Iowa State University Press, Ames, Iowa.

Figs. 30-35, 30-38, 30-40, 30-41: From R. M. Holman and W. W. Robbins, *Textbook of General Botany*, 4th ed., Figs. 216, 224, 242, 243, 283, 1934.

Fig. 30-42: From H. C. Bold, *The Plant Kingdom* (2nd ed.), Fig. 9-12, 1964.

Fig. 31-1A, B, C, D: From E. W. Berry, "Professional Paper 91," *U.S. Geological Survey*, Plate LI, Fig. 9-11; Plate CI, Fig. 2; Plate CVI, Fig. 4, 1916.

Fig. 31-3A, B: From A. G. Long, "On the Structure of *Samaropsis scotica* Calder (emended) and *Eurystoma angulare* gen. et sp. nov., Petrified Seeds from the Calciferous Sandstone Series of Berwickshire," *Trans. Roy. Soc. Edinburgh*, Vol. 64, pp. 261–280, Figs. 1B, 6, 1960.

Fig. 31-3B: From A. G. Long, "*Stamnostoma Huttonense*" gen. et sp. nov.—a Pteridosperm Seed and Cupule from the Calciferous Sandstone Series of Berwickshire," *Trans. Roy. Soc. Edinburgh*, Vol. 64, pp. 201–215, Fig. 4, 1960.

Fig. 31-3C: From J. Walton, "An Introduction to the Study of Fossil Plants," Fig. 110B, 1940.

Fig. 31-4A, B: From I. W. Bailey and B. G. L. Swamy, "The Conduplicate Carpel of Dicotyledons and Its Initial Trends of Specialization," *American Journal of Botany*, Vol. 38, Figs. 2, 3.

Fig. 31-4C: From K. Periasany and B. G. L. Swamy, "The Conduplicate Carpel of *Cananga odorata*," *Jour. Arnold Arboretum*, Vol. 37, pp. 366–372, 1956.

Fig. 31-5: From S. Tucker, "Ontogeny of the Inflorescence and the Flower in Drimys winteri var. chilensis," Plate 32. *Univ. of Calif. (Berkeley) Publ. in Botany*, Vol. 30(4), 1959.

Fig. 31-6: S. Tepfer, "Floral Anatomy and Ontogeny in Aquilegia formosa var. truncata and Ranunculus repens," Plate 59B; 60A. *Univ. of Calif. (Berkeley) Publ. in Botany*, Vol. 25(7), 1953.

Fig. 32-1: From R. N. Singh, "On Some Phases in the Life History of the Terrestrial Alga, *Fritschiella tuberosa* Iyeng. and Its Autecology," *New Phytologist*, Vol. 60, pp. 170–182, Fig. 1, 1941.

Contents

Preface
to the Second Edition

In the interim since the first edition of this book was submitted to the publisher (June, 1957), our knowledge of the morphology of plants and of related aspects of plant science has been rapidly augmented, and there is every indication that this will continue in accelerated fashion in the future. Accordingly, plant morphology, considered in certain circles to represent a static and conservative, if not oversaturated, area of biological science, has, in fact, undergone modification and enhancement by contributions from a wide spectrum of research effort. Insofar as possible, without incorporating burdensome detail, these recent advances have been incorporated in the present edition.

The author has continued to review and discuss with knowledgeable colleagues the system of classification he first proposed in 1956[1] and used in the first edition. The dismemberment of the division Tracheophyta, at the time considered by many to be radical, has been supported by the paleobotanical record, and the system of classification used, admittedly tentative as all phylogenetic classifications must be, has been adopted in its essentials by the authors of several texts. No *major* revisions have been made in the classification as first presented, with the exception of the supra-divisional groupings Prokaryota, Chlorota, and Mycota suggested in this edition.[2] A twenty-fifth division, the Deuteromycota, has been added to complete the classification of the fungi. It must be recognized, of course, in light of the compelling evidences of monphyleticism provided by comparative cytology and biochemistry, that our seemingly polyphyletic groupings are but imperfect conjectures regarding the real *pathways* of descent which occurred. As noted in the first edition, "No single system (of classification) can be accepted as final as long as a single fact concerning any kind of plant remains unknown."[3] There is every indication that at present the ultimate "facts" will be chemical and molecular, the structure and functions of plants, after all, being based upon this level of organization.

The present edition again is organized largely, but *not exclusively*, on the basis of a series of illustrative morphological type organisms, a practice not approved by some who plead instead for emphasis on "broader concepts and major principles." It is the author's experience that the latter must be built upon an indispensable minimum of rigorous and somewhat detailed body of data which can serve as a point of departure for more intensive and extensive comparative studies and generalizations. Excessive

---

[1] H. C. Bold, 1956. "Some Aspects of the Classification of the Plant Kingdom," *Bulletin Association of Southeastern Biologists*, 3:35–51.

[2] Page 518.

[3] C. A. Arnold, Classification of the gymnosperms from the viewpoint of paleobotany. *Bot. Gaz.* 110:2–12, 1948.

and premature emphasis on the latter too often provides the student with much shadow and little substance. Nevertheless, in the present edition, a serious effort has been made to broaden the account of the plant kingdom by including discussion of related organisms and principles in addition to the intensive treatment of the types.

In the first edition, the discussion of fossil organisms was segregated in a single chapter at the end of the text. This was done out of consideration for those users of the book with inadequate time to devote to both extinct and extant organisms. In the interim, the author has become convinced that concurrent study of both is indispensable. Accordingly, a somewhat expanded treatment of extinct groups has been interpolated at appropriate points in the account of extant plants.

While special effort was devoted in the first edition to providing new and original illustrations (and this effort has been maintained), the latter, for one reason or another, were not uniformly effective. In the present edition, a number of the earlier illustrations have been replaced by new ones and many others have been modified. Complicated figures in the present edition have been extensively labeled and their captions amplified. Similarly, there has been extensive modification of intra-chapter headings with the purpose of providing more readily apparent organization of the text.

The cited reference works have been modified and brought up to date. The majority are limited to major, synthetic works, although a number of primary sources in addition have been suggested in footnotes.

The appendix of the first edition containing data on methods and materials for laboratory work in plant morphology has been omitted from the present edition for two reasons. First, there has thus been provided space for an expanded treatment of the plant kingdom and for incorporation of new data. Second, an up-dated and expanded treatment of material in the appendix of the first edition will be incorporated in a brief laboratory "manual" or "syllabus."

In the Preface (to the teacher) to the first edition, the author indicated that an introductory course in biology was widely replacing one in introductory botany at the first-year college level. The "short shrift" given to the plant kingdom in general biology courses impelled the author to prepare *Morphology of Plants*.

While the author wholeheartedly supports the practice, at the freshman level, of replacing the introductory botany course with one in biology, he has observed increasingly that the emphasis in such courses is placed on the subcellular and cellular levels of biology with reduced consideration of organisms, especially their comparative morphology. The need for a text which covers this aspect of plant science has thus been enhanced.

As in the preparation of the first edition, a number of students, friends, and colleagues have generously read portions of the manuscript critically and have made valuable suggestions for improving it. In this connection the author acknowledges with deep gratitude especially the help of Professors C. J. Alexopoulos, David W. Bierhorst, Walter V. Brown, Margaret Fulford, Donald A. Larson, Edwin B. Matzke, H. Wayne Nichols, and Richard C. Starr. A number of colleagues have contributed to the improvements in the illustrations; in addition to those listed on pages v–xi and in the captions, the author would express his appreciation for aid from Drs. Howard J. Arnott, R. Malcolm Brown, Jr., Takashi Sawa, Patricia L. Walne, and Mr. Geza Knipfer.

Thanks are due, of course, to the many users of this book in its first edition, both teachers and students, who have written to suggest changes and improvements based on their experience.

Once again, the writer acknowledges with deep gratitude the continuing aid of his wife, Mary Douthit Bold, during the revision and for assistance in preparing the index and glossary. Finally, his thanks are due to Mrs. Frances Denny for expert proofreading and to Mr. and Mrs. Donald T. Knight for typing and other miscellaneous aids in preparation of the manuscript.

HAROLD C. BOLD

March, 1967

Preface
to the First Edition

To the Teacher

As a result of the widespread practice in our colleges in recent years of revising the curriculum with increasing emphasis on "general education," the full-year course in introductory botany has suffered one of several fates. It is sometimes condensed and incorporated in a year course of so-called general biology, either as a minor unit or in scattered segments, or it occupies a still less prominent part of a "survey course" in the sciences. The most usual result of these arrangements is that students who elect further work in plant science enter it poorly grounded in the fundamental aspects of the science in the field of morphology and in other areas. Thus they find themselves inadequately prepared to read the more advanced text and reference books in the field, and the treatment of groups other than the flowering plants in introductory texts is in most cases rather limited, of necessity. On the other hand, the more advanced treatises deal with only a limited number of plant groups rather than with a complete range of morphological types.

The present text has been prepared as a possible solution to these difficulties. It is designed to present a discussion of the morphology and reproduction of the more important plant types. The "type method" has been employed and the text is designed for a year's course, with parallel, integrated study of the types presented. Wherever feasible, every effort has been made to select types readily available or obtainable in most localities. Information regarding where these materials may be obtained and how they may be maintained is included in the appendix. Appropriate substitutions and amplifications will suggest themselves to the teacher.

The author cannot emphasize sufficiently the indispensability of providing the students with living laboratory materials whenever possible. It is true that the collection and maintenance of such a variety of living plants are taxing and time-consuming, but the reward in student interest will amply repay the teacher's effort in this connection.

One who attempts the task of summarizing the structure and reproduction of representatives of the entire plant kingdom within the covers of a single volume is faced constantly with the problems of scope and degree of coverage. He must satisfy certain minima, but at the same time avoid overwhelming the student with detail. He also is liable to criticism from his colleagues for what may seem to them drastically abbreviated presentations. The phycologist and mycologist, for example, will deplore the omission of certain organisms which they deem important, and the bryologist and phanerogamic botanist will condemn the treatment of the algae and fungi as too exhaustive. The writer can only protest that the present text is designed to serve as an introduction on the basis of which more specialized treatments of the several groups may become more intelligible.

The author has been decidedly polyphyletic in the classification of the representative types at the divisional level. He is convinced that this is a conservative point of view. Should the classification he has suggested not meet with approval, he can only cite the subjective nature of the higher categories and add, in his defense, that he has minimized the formal classification of the representative types in view of our inability to come to final conclusions in this connection.

Discussion Questions are included at the end of each chapter to summarize the important data and to prepare the student for oral and/or written exercises on the subject matter presented. References are listed for those who may wish to explore certain aspects of a subject more intensively.

A high percentage of the illustrations is original and based on living material and fresh preparations. Acknowledgment of the source of figures which are not original is made on pp. xix–xxiii; the author is grateful for permission to use them. He appreciates especially the care and accuracy with which several of the habit drawings have been prepared by his colleague, Professor James J. Friauf.

A number of friends and colleagues have read portions of the manuscript and have made valuable suggestions for its improvement. The author wishes to thank especially Professors E. B. Matzke, Elsie Quarterman, and Richard C. Starr in this connection. He is particularly indebted to Dr. Harold W. Rickett for stimulating discussion and criticism of a number of points. He also wishes to thank Mr. Neal Buffaloe and Mr. Francis R. Trainor for their assistance in reading proof. The author is grateful to his wife, Mary Douthit Bold, for her aid in reading proof and preparing the index. He also acknowledges herewith his indebtedness to the Natural Science Fund of Vanderbilt University for financial aid in preparing the manuscript. The author alone, of course, accepts complete responsibility for the text which follows.

To the Student

Many years ago, your author happened to glance at the preface of a textbook of elementary botany which he was studying at the time. He was somewhat mystified and disturbed when he read the following statements there: "The text is designed for the student beginning the subject. We trust that a study of it will bring him to the classroom prepared for a discussion of the topics and *we also trust that this work of preparation will tax him to the full measure of his intellectual capacity.* The author is old fashioned in his ideas of education. *Work that simply entertains or imparts information . . . can be of little permanent value or make for any considerable development.*"[1]

From a cursory perusal of these lines, it might appear that their author was implying in his preface that he had deliberately made his presentation difficult in order to tax the students' ability to interpret his meaning and that he smugly hoped he had succeeded. These lines have recurred frequently to the present writer, and his interpretation of them now is based upon years of experience which have convinced him of their truth. Facts easily memorized or crammed from textbooks, notes, or outlines to meet

---

[1] C. C. Curtis, *Nature and Development of Plants*, Henry Holt and Company, Inc., 1918. (Italics added.)

the immediate threat of an impending examination make little permanent addition to one's fund of knowledge, and they fail to supply material for reflection and to effect real understanding. The latter is achieved only as a result of active effort on the student's part. Superficial knowledge is of little value in the long run. Mediocrity of effort is rewarded only by mediocrity of achievement, and information crammed just before an examination is rarely retained after it is over.

The student should not regard this or any other textbook as a sort of bible in which the sum total of knowledge has been summarized for his convenience. He should consider it rather as a guide to his thinking, reading, and laboratory study of the plants themselves. It should supply many but not all of the facts for classroom discussion under the teacher's leadership. In this connection, the value of careful and critical laboratory study cannot be overemphasized. Many students look upon the laboratory as a penance or a drudgery devised by science instructors for unaccountable reasons. The true purpose of the laboratory is to afford the student an opportunity to obtain real understanding by verifying the knowledge gained from the text and classroom discussions, to add to it, and to explore unknown fields. The student's reading, class discussion, and laboratory work are mutually indispensable. Together they form an integrated whole, and slighting any one of them, by student or instructor, will jeopardize their potential values. As a final suggestion, the writer would enjoin the student to develop, by practice, the habit of applying his knowledge to plants in the field. The principles learned in connection with the type plants studied in classroom and laboratory should enable him to recognize and understand related plants which he sees outdoors.

The Discussion Questions at the conclusion of each chapter are included with the purpose of affording the student a readily available means of testing his retention and understanding of the material studied. They may be used as a basis for interstudent and classroom discussions. Relevant works by other authors are cited at the end of certain chapters for those who wish to read more widely.

HAROLD C. BOLD

June, 1957

Morphology
of Plants

CHAPTER 1

Introduction

The Divisions of Plant Science

If each of us were to attempt to summarize the treatment of plant science in the introductory botany or biology course in which he had been enrolled, we would probably agree that we had devoted the greater part of it to studying the structure and functioning of what is often referred to as the "higher plant" or "flowering plant." In some cases, this may have been supplemented by consideration of such topics, among others, as metabolism, transpiration, translocation, tropisms, and growth-regulating mechanisms. Some portion of the course might also have included a brief and cursory "survey" of other representatives of the plant kingdom from among the so-called "lower plants," and possibly, in addition, consideration of such important topics as organic evolution and inheritance. In such a course, as a matter of fact, we would have made brief excursions into several fields of plant science, namely, morphology, physiology, genetics, ecology, and others.

These brief excursions may have given us some insight into the nature and significance of these disciplines, but further discussion may afford us perspective as we begin a somewhat more intensive study of one of them, morphology. At the outset we must realize that these various divisions of plant science are not separate or mutually exclusive, but that most of the fundamental advances in our knowledge have been attained by correlation and synthesis of the contributions of the several fields. Furthermore, no one of them is intelligible without reference to the others. The physiologist, for example, would be hard-pressed to achieve real understanding of transpiration if he did not understand the structure of the leaf.

Conversely, the leaf structure described by the morphologist lacks significance until one considers the functions of that organ, the genetic factors involved in its differentiation, and the variations a leaf may undergo under different environmental conditions.

The classification of plant science into major and minor subdivisions depends in some measure on the biological vocation and interests of the classifier. Probably no one classification could be devised which would be acceptable to all botanists. However, it is possible to distinguish between the various fields of technological, economic, or applied botany, on the one hand, and those of pure botany, the basic science. Among the former may be listed such major divisions as **agriculture, horticulture, floriculture, plant breeding, forestry,** and **plant pathology.** The scope of each of these is well known or may be ascertained from the dictionary, encyclopedia, and other sources. In a sense these comprise the anthropocentric aspects of plant science—plants in their relation to man. Pure or basic botany is the study of plant life without exclusive interest in and reference to its relations to man. It includes such major divisions as **taxonomy, morphology, physiology, ecology, phytogeography,** and **genetics,** among others. In reality, it is often impossible to distinguish absolutely between pure and applied botany. The results of the researches in pure science achieved today often become the basis of applied science tomorrow.

Taxonomy is probably the oldest division of plant science, inasmuch as primitive man, in his survival efforts, must have learned early to distinguish between edible or other useful plants and poisonous or otherwise noxious species. Taxonomy or systematic botany, as it is often called, deals with the identification, naming, and classification of the diverse types of plants which populate the earth. Its goal, in the eyes of most modern taxonomists, is the achievement of a natural or phylogenetic classification which implies that the groupings indicate actual relationship by descent from common precursors. Until recently, classification of plants has been based largely on attributes of structure and form, i.e., on morphological attributes. Currently, however, in systematic studies of all plant (and animal) groups, a great range of additional data is being appraised, including chemical, genetical, physiological, cytological, and ecological attributes. Consideration of this broad spectrum of characteristics often modifies earlier taxonomic treatments based largely on morphological criteria.

Physiology is concerned with the fundamental nature of life itself, with vital activities and with the mechanisms by which the living plant maintains itself. More and more, the physiological aspects of plants and animals are being investigated and explained as chemical and physical phenomena. While these aspects of biological science are making impressive progress, they are not, as some of their more zealous proponents imply, the sole and final solution to all biological problems. The latter, of course, will always require study at different levels—organismal and cellular as well as molecular—with different tools and different techniques. In this connection, the words of the eminent biochemist, Sir Frederick Gowland Hopkins,[1] are especially relevant:

"It is only necessary for the biochemist to remember that his data gain their full significance only when he can relate them with the activities of the organism as a whole. He should be bold in experiment but cautious in his claims. His may not be the last word in the description of life, but without his help the last word will never be said." Modern biologists studying phenomena at the organismal level, however, are becoming increasingly impressed by the truth of the last clause of the preceding quotation.

Ecology deals with the interrelation of the plant and its environment and with the mutual

---

[1] From his Boyle Lecture in 1931.

effects involved. **Phytogeography** is the study of plant distribution on the earth. The mechanisms and laws governing the transmission of structural and functional attributes of individual plants to their offspring form the subject matter of **genetics,** but more recently the structure and code of the deoxyribonucleic acid (DNA) molecule and its relationship to enzymes have been added.

It is relatively easy for a morphologist to summarize or to define the scope of the other divisions of plant science, but more difficult for him to describe the nature of **plant morphology.** As understood by many botanists, modern morphology represents a study of the form and structure of plants, and, by implication, an attempt to interpret these on the basis of similarity of plan and origin. Morphology is comparative. Both the reproductive and nonreproductive organs are studied, as are the reproductive process, normal life cycles and deviations therefrom. Morphology embraces various levels of study of structure and organization, such as ultrastructure, cytology, histology and anatomy, between which the boundaries are daily becoming less clear. **Ultrastructure** and **cytology** are both studies of cellular organization, the former using electron microscopy and the latter, at least during its classical development, light microscopy. The study of aggregations of cells in groups or tissues and in organs comprises the fields of **histology** and **anatomy;** these are often considered jointly in plant science. These categories represent subdivisions of morphology. All of them have contributed richly to our understanding of the organization and reproduction of plants. The morphologist, in his preoccupation with studies of plant life cycles, reproduction and organization at different levels, appraises all these data for clues regarding the origin, development in time (evolution), and possible relationships (phylogeny) among plant groups. Furthermore, he has come to realize that the real significance of plants of the present must be sought, in part, in plants of the past which have been preserved as fossils. **Paleobotany** as a segment of paleontology, therefore, is an important adjunct to, if not an actual component of, plant morphology.

In addition to the areas just cited as comprising plant morphology, a somewhat different concept of its scope has been developed by certain botanists. To them, morphology is dynamic and experimental and they emphasize the development of the organism and the interplay of factors involved in its morphogenesis. In this area, especially, the morphologist has begun to use the methods of the biophysicist and biochemist. Although originally and still, of necessity, descriptive, morphology is becoming increasingly experimental in subject matter and method.

On the basis of the data derived from several divisions and subdivisions of plant science, the morphologist often augments the methods of direct observation, perception, and experiment and becomes a speculative philosopher. At this stage he constructs logical hypotheses regarding relationships among plants and their component structures and attempts to construct a **phylogeny** or history of the origin and development of extant plants in light of the past. The student must critically distinguish such speculations and hypotheses from verified conclusions based on direct observation and experiment; nevertheless, speculation and hypothesis enhance the progress of science and are essential aspects of its method.

The several divisions of plant science discussed in earlier paragraphs are based in each case on one or another aspect of plant life. In contrast, there have also developed a number of divisions of plant science which reflect investigators' interests in one or another plant *group.* Thus we have the areas of plant science known as **phycology, mycology,** and **bryology,** among others, and the corresponding vocations of **phycologist, mycologist,** and **bryologist,** among others.

One should not conclude from the foregoing discussion that modern botany is composed of categories or subdivisions which are sharply delimited and segregated like the cubicles in a warehouse. The cooperative investigations and methods of various specialists in plant science, together with those from other natural sciences, especially chemistry, physics, and geology, have resulted in the great advances of our knowledge of plant life. The student of biological science, no matter of what phase, is (or should be) first of all a biologist with a broad comprehension of living organisms; secondarily he may become a specialist in one or more of the several subdivisions of plant (botany) or animal (zoology) science.

The Origin and Development of Living Things

Man has always been interested in the question of the origin of all living organisms, although historically and for obvious reasons, he has been most interested in the origin of the human species. Inasmuch as the method of origin of the *first* living matter on this earth is no longer subject to observational verification, no explanation of the origin of life based exclusively on observation is possible. As a result, there have emerged a number of hypotheses and speculations regarding both the origin and course of development of life upon the earth.

Within the past 15 years, however, experimental procedures have produced molecules of biological significance (without the mediation of living organisms) in relatively simple systems and from such simple substances as water, methane, hydrogen, and ammonia; the experimental conditions simulated those of the earth's primitive atmosphere. These investigations indicate clearly that experimentation has an important role in our understanding of the origin of life and conditions under which it began. In the experiments referred to above, and by further study, it has been possible to synthesize amino acids and other essential molecules of living organisms, even the important nucleotides and the energy-rich compound, adenosine triphosphate (ATP). Still more significant are the polymerization and combination of the simpler units into increasingly complex macromolecules that constitute living matter, such as proteins, which have been achieved by the chemist.

Hypotheses which have been offered in solution to the question of the origin and development of life may be grouped into two categories, namely, creationism and evolution. To many, these categories seem to be in violent contradiction and mutually exclusive, whereas others do not find them so. Creationist hypotheses postulate that living organisms arose first by an act of intervention on the part of a force extraneous to the natural universe itself, and therefore, supernatural. Some of them imply, furthermore, that the present species of animals and plants in all their diversity were called into existence in their present form at approximately the same time and that they have persisted in essentially that form until the present. By further implication it would seem that the possibility is entirely excluded that new types of living things are appearing now or that they may appear in the future or that natural relationships exist between species and other taxa. These last points of view, perhaps, represent extremes in creationist theories.

Evolution, on the contrary, emphasizes the changes which have modified species of living organisms over long periods of time. The population of living things on the earth at a given instant is considered by the evolutionist to represent the more-or-less modified descendents of organisms which existed earlier. These processes of change and modification of extant species are continuing in the world today, and species are not fixed and immutable but rather are plastic and changing, according to the evolutionary hypothesis.

The evidence for evolution is incontrovertible. One can observe changes or mutations in living organisms occurring spontaneously in nature, and they can be evoked experimentally in the laboratory by means of chemical and physical agents. Mutations are transmissible from one generation to another. Their combination, subsequent segregation, and recombination in sexually reproducing populations result in variability among individuals. Mutations, their segregation, recombination, and natural selection by the environment, repeated and continuing through the approximately 3 billion years during which life has evidently existed on earth, are considered to be the explanation of the current diversity of living things.

While there can no longer be doubt that living species are changing constantly and that mutations are being transmitted and selected for in successive generations, it is quite a different matter to trace in detail and with assurance the *course* of the resulting diversification of species and especially of the larger groups (higher categories) such as genera, families, orders, classes, and divisions, categories which by extrapolation are postulated to have developed by the same mechanisms of change demonstrated at the individual and specific level. Although the evidences for such extrapolation are not as compelling as one would wish, no other satisfactory alternate hypothesis to explain the diversity of living things has as yet been suggested.

Schemes, diagrams, evolutionary "trees" and statements regarding the course of evolution and relationship among the higher categories are of necessity largely speculative. Accordingly, such phylogenetic syntheses often vary with the individual biologist who proposes them, and they are subject to continuing modification as new evidences become available.

What are the evidences on which evolutionary relationship is postulated? The most trustworthy are certainly the fossil record and the comparative morphology of both extinct and extant organisms. Comparative morphology includes, especially, comparative studies of the ontogeny or development of individual living plants. In addition, present, as compared with earlier, geographical distribution of plants is helpful in providing clues to relationship. Although classical phylogenetic pathways of the nineteenth and early twentieth century were postulated largely on morphological criteria, increasing attention is being devoted at present to comparative physiology, biochemistry, and serology of both living and extinct organisms as important data in constructing phylogenetic systems. Differences of opinion in interpretation of available evidence are reflected in differences in phylogenetic systems of classification, a topic to which we shall return in the next section.

In summary then, species are demonstrably changing and nonstatic and heterogeneous, and they differ increasingly from successively earlier precursors.

The difficulty experienced by many students when they first become aware of the hypothesis of organic evolution as an explanation for the diversity of living organisms is occasioned by the stated or implied mechanistic philosophy of most evolutionists. Mechanistic evolutionists state or imply that the changing manifestations of life have occurred without supernatural cause or intervention. They hold a similar view of the origin of life. To them, all life and living things do not differ fundamentally from inorganic matter and phenomena except in details of physical and chemical structure and activity. These physical and chemical attributes, they are convinced, ultimately will be completely understood as science progresses. Physical and chemical phenomena, they urge, will adequately explain life and all its manifestations. Mechanistic biologists neither require nor postulate final or supernatural causes. The immediate has become final for them.

In any event, we are confronted with a great diversity of living organisms which populate the earth, notwithstanding our speculations regarding their origin and history. It is the purpose of the present volume to survey this diversity in the plant world and to attempt to reduce the *apparent* chaos to some semblance of order.

The Classification of Plants

When one considers that more than 350,000 species of plants have been described, it is manifestly impossible for a single individual to familiarize himself with all of them. As a beginning, therefore, one is driven to the expedient of selecting representatives or types which illustrate fundamental attributes of larger groups or organisms. The more diversified the group of plants under consideration, the more representatives it will be necessary to study. However, in attempting to include a survey of the morphology of representatives from the entire plant kingdom in one volume, it is obvious that rigorous selection of some types and exclusion of others are necessary. It is hoped that familiarity with the chosen representatives of the diverse plant groups will form a sound foundation and perhaps kindle the student's interest in a more exten-

sive study of one or several of them.

In classifying plants and animals, it is possible to set up the categories in several different ways, depending on the purpose of the classifier. In the first place, **artificial systems** can be devised, the primary purpose of which is ease and convenience of grouping and segregation, other considerations being minor. The classification of vascular plants into trees, shrubs, and herbs, and into annuals, biennials, and perennials exemplifies an artificial system. **Phylogenetic systems** of classification, on the other hand, endeavor to arrange plants so as to indicate real relationship and affinity based upon evolutionary development. The closeness of the supposed relationships is implied by the proximity of the taxa to each other in the system. The system itself, of course, is (or should be) based on data available from paleobotany, comparative morphology, genetics, and all other possible lines of evidence.

Classification of plants is subjective in large measure. It is small wonder, therefore, that few students of plant science have reached unified conclusions regarding the proper classification of members of the plant kingdom. Furthermore, classifications are constantly altered by the discovery of new facts; they are fluid and dynamic, not static.

In spite of the subjective nature of classification, anarchy is no more desirable in the grouping of plants than it is elsewhere. If his efforts are to be recognized, the classifier is bound to make his taxonomic categories, called taxa, conform to the legislation of the International Botanical Congress,[2] which has stated that "every individual plant belongs to a species, every species to a genus, every genus to a family, every family to an order, every order to a class and every class to a division." In addition to this *prescription* which is binding regarding the hierarchy of taxonomic categories, there are *recommendations* regarding the endings of the names of the higher taxa (divisions and classes, among others) which have been followed in the present volume. The classification and arrangement of the plant types to be described

[2] International Code of Botanical Nomenclature. 9th International Botanical Congress, Montreal, 1959. Regnum Vegetabile 23. Kemink en Zoon. N. V.

here deviate to some degree from those in many other current texts. Table 32-2 (p. 516) summarizes the present and certain other systems of classification in comparative fashion.

While the relative merits of various systems of classification might be discussed at this point, profitable consideration of this subject presupposes considerable knowledge of the plants to be classified, knowledge which becomes available only after study of the plants themselves. For this reason, the system of classification presented here will receive minimum comment at this point, more extensive discussion being deferred to the final chapter (Chapter 32). In anticipation of this, it should be stated that the very existence of various systems of classification is eloquent evidence of divergence in interpreting data on relationship.

The system of classification here presented will serve also as a sort of table of contents, for the illustrative genera will be discussed in an order which approximates that in which the divisions and their component classes are listed in Table 1-1.

To those familiar with older systems of classification (Table 32-2, p. 516) in which the plant kingdom was divided into four divisions—Thallophyta (including the algae and fungi), Bryophyta (liverworts and mosses), Pteridophyta (ferns and their "allies"), and Spermatophyta (seed plants) —the classification summarized above will seem longer and more complicated. At first glance there is merit in this complaint, for the four divisions have here been replaced by twenty-five.

The student may well wonder on what criteria the divisions of the plant kingdom are defined. To some extent, the criteria vary with the classifier; but, in general, most botanists seem to agree that the division is the largest phylogenetic taxon in which should be grouped organisms which seem to be related because they possess common basic attributes. This definition itself probably will not satisfy all botanists.

When one examines the old division Thallophyta (Table 32-2, p. 516) in the light of this concept of the division, serious difficulties become apparent. For example, the division

Thallophyta, usually defined as a group of organisms lacking stems and leaves, nonetheless included such brown algae as the kelps, in some of which leaflike, stemlike, and rootlike organs are developed. It includes as well simpler unicellular, colonial, and filamentous algae and fungi. Furthermore, grouping the algae and fungi together in the same division is an indication that they are closely related groups. Modern study of these plants has not provided strong support for this view. In addition, there is good evidence that the several groups of algae, in the past included in a formal category (class) under the name (Algae) (Table 32-2, p. 516), are themselves diverse and fundamentally different from each other physiologically and biochemically.

The division Bryophyta, which in other systems (Table 32-2, p. 516) includes both liverworts and mosses, here is conceived in a more restricted sense. For reasons to be discussed in a later chapter, the writer is of the opinion that the liverworts and mosses are not such close "allies" as was implied by earlier views of the scope of the division Bryophyta. He has, therefore, segregated the liverworts in the division Hepatophyta and retains the division Bryophyta for the mosses alone.

It will be recalled that the old division Pteridophyta (Table 32-2, p. 516) included the ferns and their "allies." That these supposed alliances are as nebulous and untrustworthy as certain political groupings seems clear from a comparison of the morphology of the plants themselves. Divisions 5 through 8 have been proposed, therefore, in place of the old division Pteridophyta.

Probably no two botanists would agree regarding the disposition of the higher categories of plants which formerly comprised the division Spermatophyta (Table 32-2, p. 516), the seed plants. In many current textbooks they are included in the same division with the ferns (Table 32-2, p. 516, middle column). For reasons which can be presented profitably only after the student has become familiar with the groups involved, the present author has assigned the plants in the old division Spermatophyta to the five divisions listed as 9–13. A more detailed presentation

TABLE 1-1. **Classification of Plants^a Through the Level of Class**

Subkingdom I. **Prokaryota**^{a}

Division 1. Cyanophycophyta^b
Class 1. Myxophyceae (Blue-green algae)

Division 2. Schizomycota
Class 1. Schizomycetes (Bacteria)

Subkingdom II. **Chlorota**

Division 1A. Chlorophycophyta^b
Class 1. Chlorophyceae (Green algae)

Division 1B. Euglenophycophyta^b
Class 1. Euglenophyceae (Euglenoids)

Division 1C. Phaeophycophyta^b
Class 1. Phaeophyceae (Brown algae)

Division 1D. Chrysophycophyta^b
Class 1. Xanthophyceae (Yellow-green algae)
Class 2. Chrysophyceae (Golden-brown algae)
Class 3. Bacillariophyceae (Diatoms)

Division 1E. Pyrrophycophyta^b
Class 1. Cryptophyceae (Cryptomonads)
Class 2. Dinophyceae (Dinoflagellates)

Division 1F. Rhodophycophyta^b
Class 1. Rhodophyceae (Red algae)

Division 2. Charophyta
Class 1. Charophyceae (Stoneworts)

Division 3. Hepatophyta^c
Class 1. Hepatopsida (Liverworts)
Class 2. Anthocerotopsida (Horned liverworts)

Division 4. Bryophyta^c
Class 1. Sphagnopsida (Peat mosses)
Class 2. Andreaeopsida (Rock mosses)
Class 3. Mnionopsida (True or common mosses)

Division 5. Psilophyta^d
Class 1. Psilopsida (Whisk ferns)

Division 6. Microphyllophyta^d
Class 1. Aglossopsida (Eligulate lycopods)
Class 2. Glossopsida (Ligulate lycopods)

Division 7. Arthrophyta^d
Class 1. Arthropsida (Arthrophytes)

Division 8. Pterophyta^d
Class 1. Eusporangiopsida (Eusporangiate ferns)
Class 2. Leptosporangiopsida (Leptosporangiate ferns)

Division 9. Cycadophyta^e
Class 1. Cycadopsida (Cycads)
Class 2. Pteridospermopsida (Seed ferns)
Class 3. Cycadeoidopsida (Cycadeoids)

Division 10. Ginkgophyta^e
Class 1. Ginkgopsida (*Ginkgo* and precursors)

Division 11. Coniferophyta^e
Class 1. Coniferopsida (Conifers)
Class 2. Taxopsida (Taxads)

Division 12. Gnetophyta^e
Class 1. Gnetopsida (*Gnetum, Ephedra, Welwitschia*)

Division 13. Anthophyta^f
Class 1. Angiospermae (Flowering plants)

Subkingdom III. **Mycota**

Division 1A. Myxomycota^g
Class 1. Myxomycetes (Slime molds)
Class 2. Acrasiomycetes (Cellular slime molds)

Division 1B. Phycomycota^g
Class 1. Phycomycetes (Algalike fungi)

Division 1C. Ascomycota^g
Class 1. Ascomycetes (Sac fungi)

Division 1D. Basidiomycota^g
Class 1. Basidiomycetes (Club fungi)

Division 1E. Deuteromycota^g
Class 1. Deuteromycetes (Imperfect fungi)

---

^{a} The Prokaryota and Mycota are considered by some biologists to be so different from other plants as to exclude them from the plant kingdom.

^{b} These divisions comprise organisms commonly called "Algae"; the Charophyta are often included with Algae. (See Chapters 2–8.)

^{c} These divisions are often amalgamated in a single division, Bryophyta. (See Chapters 15 and 16.)

^{d} These divisions comprise the "vascular cryptogams." (See Chapters 18–24.)

^{e} These divisions comprise the "gymnosperms." (See Chapters 25–29.)

^{f} The flowering plants are treated in Chapters 30 and 31.

^{g} These divisions are called "fungi." (See Chapters 9–14.)

of the evidence on which the present system of classification is based is included in the discussion of the several groups and in Chapter 32.

The system of classification to be followed in this text is admittedly polyphyletic in that the divisions Thallophyta, Bryophyta, Pteridophyta, and Spermatophyta, and even certain classes (Algae and Fungi) of other systems (Table 32-2, p. 516) have been broken down into smaller units which themselves have been elevated to divisional rank. Polyphyletic classifications are those in which several seemingly independent evolutionary lines are recognized, in contrast to monophyletic systems in which the several divergent lines are considered to have had a common origin. To the writer, classifications at present are of necessity *tentative* and *speculative;* his relatively polyphyletic classification seems to him truly conservative in not classifying within the same division organisms the fossil records of which represent unconnected lines of development, *insofar as that record is currently known.*

The resolution of monophyletic vs. polyphyletic origin of living things, in the last analysis, is related to the origin of life itself. If, in fact, life arose only once in time and substance, as some biologists have concluded, then the present diversity of living things is unequivocally monophyletic in origin. Strong evidences of the unity of living things support the hypothesis of monophyletic origin. These evidences include organizational manifestations at several levels such as general cellular organization, mitochondria, Golgi bodies, plastids, vacuoles, endoplasmic reticulum, other membranes, and flagellar structure; and chromosomal, nuclear, and cellular organization and replication. Furthermore, basic biochemical patterns in metabolism and the widespread occurrence of such compounds as starch, cellulose, and chlorophyll a in a vast group of plants are evidences of common origin. On the other hand, those who speculate that life may have originated more than once would interpret the unifying phenomena listed above as evidences of parallel development. Although speculations regarding such ultimate questions as the origin of life at one time would have been considered well beyond experiment, advances in biochemical techniques, such as syntheses of DNA from its components in cell-free systems, indicate that resolution of the origin of life is more susceptible of solution than we used to think.

Finally, before leaving the subject of classification, for the present, the writer cannot emphasize too strongly the futility of attempting to memorize the system of classification at this point. The several divisions, together with their component taxa, will be learned more readily in connection with the discussion of their morphology, in each case.

DISCUSSION QUESTIONS

1. How might one define or explain the term "science"?

2. What aspects of science distinguish it from other fields of knowledge?

3. Are all phenomena subject to analysis by the methods of science?

4. Is a distinction between pure botany and applied botany always possible?

5. Do you have any reasons for believing that the study of one is more valuable than the study of the other?

6. Can you cite examples which indicate that the researches in pure botany have led directly to important applications?

7. How may one distinguish among the several divisions of plant science? Are they mutually exclusive? Explain.

8. What is meant by "creationism"? "evolutionism"? "mechanism"? "vitalism"?

9. Do you think that the various taxonomic categories or taxa like species, genus, etc., exist in nature? Explain.

10. What is meant by the "type method" of studying plant morphology? What are its disadvantages?

11. Should generic names of plants always be capitalized?

12. Do the names of plants have meaning? Where can one find their meaning?

13. What syllables usually end the name of the plant family? the order? Are these endings subject to change by individual botanists?

14. Where can one find a printed copy of the International Rules of Botanical Nomenclature?

15. Distinguish between the terms "monophyletic" and "polyphyletic."

16. What bearing do recent chemical experiments have on the origin of life?

CHAPTER 2

Introduction to Algae; Cyanophycophyta

Algae, General Features

Definition of Algae

As noted in the preceding chapter, the term "Algae" has been abandoned as a formal taxon or category in modern classifications of the plant kingdom (Table 32-2, p. 516). However, the word is still useful in grouping informally the series of algal divisions, which, in spite of marked diversity, have certain attributes in common which distinguish them from other plants. It is necessary to cite several technical aspects of the reproduction of algae if we are to delimit them reliably from other chlorophyllous plants. Algae differ from the latter in that: (1) the organisms (in the case of unicellular algae) themselves may directly function as sex cells or gametes and unite in pairs to form zygotes (Fig. 3-3A-E); or (2) the gametes may be produced in either unicellular (Fig. 3-26B) or multicellular (Fig. 4-3A) structures called gametangia; in the latter case, every cell is fertile, that is, every cell produces a gamete;[1] furthermore (3) the spores develop either in unicellular containers or sporangia or in multicellular ones in which every cell is fertile. Algal reproduction will be summarized more fully in the chapters which follow.

Habitat

Algae are largely aquatic in habitat, occurring in waters of a wide range of salinity, in fresh, brackish, and marine waters, and in brines so concentrated that their solutes are crystallizing. Some algae (certain unicellular types and *Enteromorpha,* for example) can tolerate diversified salinities, while others (desmids, *Spirogyra,* and *Oedogonium,* for example) are restricted to fresh waters.

An increasingly large number of algae (especially blue-green, green algae, and diatoms) are regular inhabitants of the soil surface and considerable depths below it, while many others occur on moist pebbles and rocks, tree bark, woodwork, and even on rocks which are subject to prolonged desiccation. Recent investigation of atmospheric dusts has revealed that these carry a rich algal flora, derived largely, of course, from soil.

A number of algae, the so-called **cryoflora,** live on and within permanent patches of snow. Several species live within and among the cells of other plants and animals; special instances of these are described later in this and in other chapters, as are other algae of more bizarre habitats.

Aquatic algae may be attached to rocks, wood, or other aquatic vegetation or may be free-floating. Attached algae in marine habitats often exhibit orderly zonation in the exposure of their substrates at low tides. A number of genera such as *Porphyra, Enteromorpha, Fucus,* and *Ascophyllum* grow in the intertidal zone; they are thus exposed to and able to withstand desiccation. In contrast, other attached algae, like the kelps and *Polysiphonia,* are usually sublittoral.

A vast array of unicellular, colonial, and delicate filamentous algae occur permanently suspended in water where they may be associated with bacteria, fungi, protozoa, and other minute animals to form a community known as the **plankton** (Gr. *planktos,* wandering). Planktonic algae, under unusually

---

[1] This is in contrast to the multicellular gametangia of liverworts, mosses, and ferns, etc., in which a sterile covering is associated with the fertile cells (Fig. 15-7). With respect to this attribute, some question exists in the Charophyta (p. 85).

favorable conditions, may multiply rapidly and become strikingly abundant as **water blooms,** of which "red tides" are an example. A variety of algae may be present in blooms or only a single organism may predominate. Planktonic organisms are of tremendous importance as the basis of the food chain for larger animals in aquatic environments. Thus, it has become routine practice to add commercial fertilizer to tanks and ponds stocked with fish; this stimulates the planktonic algae, which, in turn, augment the basic food supply for the smaller animals on which the fish feed. Other aspects of the economic importance of algae are discussed in Chapter 8.

Organization of the Plant Body

As a group, algae are paradoxical in that they include both minute organisms and probably the largest chlorophyllous plants. Thus, certain *Chlorella*-like cells approach the larger bacteria in size (2–5 μ^2), while certain species of the giant kelp (*Macrocystis*) from South America have been reported to be more than 600 feet long,[3] far surpassing the height of our largest *Eucalyptus* and redwood trees. Most Pacific coast kelps are less than 150 feet in length. Between 19,000 and 25,000 species of algae are known, and these exemplify a wide range in size and complexity of form. Several types of organization occur.

The simplest algae are unicellular (Figs. 2-3, 2-4, 2-5, 3-1), the cells cohering in groups only temporarily after cell division, after which they separate. A slightly more complex level of organization is the colonial type (Figs. 2-8, 3-6, 3-8) which probably arose through the failure of cells to separate at the conclusion of cell division. Colonies may be undifferentiated (Figs. 2-8, 3-6) or contain several kinds of cells (Fig. 3-8) exemplifying differentiation, specialization, and division of labor. Occurrence of cell division predominantly in one direction results in chains of cells called **trichomes** or filaments[4] (Figs. 2-10, 2-11, 3-25). Division of certain cells of

a filament in a new direction produces branching (Figs. 2-22, 3-28A). In a number of algae which are filamentous in their juvenile stages, abundant cell divisions in two or more planes result in a leaflike or membranous structure one or several layers of cells thick (Fig. 3-36A). Finally, in a large number of green (and a few yellow-green) algae, the plant body is composed of a vesicle or tube, with few, if any, septations. In these, a large central vacuole is surrounded by a thin layer of multinucleate protoplasm. These vesicles (Fig. 7-5) and tubes (Fig. 3-40) may be measured in terms of inches and feet, respectively, and are known as **coenocytes** (Gr., *coenos*, common + Gr. *kystos*, bladder, hence, cell, in biology). Thus, among algae, five major types of body form have developed, namely, unicellular, colonial, filamentous, membranous, and tubular or coenocytic.

Classification of Algae

As noted in the preceding chapter, most current systems classify the algae in seven or eight divisions. These divisions are segregated on the basis of pigmentation, storage products, chemical nature of the cell wall, and flagellar number and insertion (Table 2-1). Of these divisions, the four major ones are the Cyanophycophyta,[5] Chlorophycophyta, Phaeophycophyta, and Rhodophycophyta. Of these, the first will be summarized in the remainder of this chapter, while the others will be discussed in Chapters 3–5. Additional divisions of algae are treated in Chapters 6 and 7. Chapter 8 recapitulates the entire discussion of algae.

Division Cyanophycophyta

General Features

The division Cyanophycophyta (Gr. *kyanos*, blue + Gr. *phyton*, plant + Gr. *phykos*, seaweed, hence alga) contains only a single class, the Myxophyceae (Gr. *myxa*, slime +

---

[2] A micron is 0.001 mm or 1/25,000 inch.
[3] This requires confirmation.
[4] For a special use of these terms see p. 16.

---

[5] Although classified with the bacteria in the subkingdom Prokaryota, the Cyanophycophyta are treated here because of their algal attributes.

TABLE 2-1. Summary of Algal Divisions and Their More Noteworthy Attributes

Division	Common Name	Pigments	Stored Photosynthate	Cell Wall	Flagellar Number and Insertion[a]	Habitat[b]
Chlorophycophyta	Green algae	Chlorophyll *a, b*; α-, β-, and γ-carotenes + 5 xanthophylls	Starch	Cellulose	1, 2–8, equal, apical	f.w., b.w., s.w., t.
Charophyta	Stoneworts	Chlorophyll *a, b*; α-, β-, and γ-carotenes + 5 xanthophylls	Starch	Cellulose	2, equal, subapical	f.w., b.w.
Euglenophycophyta	Euglenoids	Chlorophyll *a, b*; β-carotene + 4 xanthophylls	Paramylon	Absent	1–3, apical subapical	f.w., b.w., s.w.
Chrysophycophyta	Golden algae (including diatoms)	Chlorophyll *a, c, e*, in some; β-carotenes + several xanthophylls	Oil, chryso-laminarin	Pectin, silicon dioxide	1–2, unequal or equal, apical	f.w., b.w., s.w., t.
Phaeophycophyta	Brown algae	Chlorophyll *a, c*; β-carotene + 7 xanthophylls	Mannitol, laminarin	Cellulose, algin, and pectin	2, unequal, lateral	f.w. (rare), b.w., s.w.
Pyrrophycophyta	Dinoflagellates, in part	Chlorophyll *a, c*; β-carotene + 4 xanthophylls	Starch, fats and oils	Cellulose or absent; pectin	2, 1 trailing, 1 girdling	f.w., b.w., s.w.
Rhodophycophyta	Red algae	Chlorophyll *a, d* (in some); phycocyanin, phycoery-thrin; α- + β-carotene + flavicin; + 1 xanthophyll	Floridean starch[c]	Cellulose, pectin	Absent	f.w. (some), b.w., s.w. (most)
Cyanophycophyta	Blue-green algae	Chlorophyll *a*; phycocyanin; phycoery-thrin; β-carotene + 2 xanthophylls	Cyanophycean starch[d]	Cellulose,[e] pectin	Absent	f.w., b.w., s.w., t.

[a] In motile cells, when these are produced.
[b] f.w. = fresh water; b.w. = brackish water; s.w. = salt water; t. = terrestrial.
[c] Stains wine-red with iodine.
[d] Glycogenlike.
[e] Recently questioned for some.

Gr. *phykos,* seaweed), commonly known as blue-green algae. Some authors prefer the class name Cyanophyceae, whereas others use Schizophyceae (Gr. *schizo,* cleave + Gr. *phykos*).

Myxophyceae are ubiquitous in distribution, occurring in aerial, terrestrial, and aquatic habitats. Approximately 150 genera with 1500 species have been described. Myxophyceae frequently form extensive strata on moist, shaded, bare soil and may appear as gelatinous incrustations on moist rocks, other inanimate objects, and plants. Aquatic species inhabit both marine and fresh waters; they are either attached to submerged objects or are free-floating. Blue-green algae often represent an important component of the plankton. As such, they are important, along with other planktonic algae and minute animals, as the direct or ultimate source of food for more complex aquatic animals. Blue-green algae like *Polycystis* and *Anabaena* occur frequently as dominant organisms in water blooms (Fig. 2-1). A few genera of Myxophyceae are **endophytes** living within cavities in other plants. Species of *Nostoc,* for example, occur within the plant bodies of such liverworts as *Blasia* and *Anthoceros,* and a species of *Anabaena* grows within the water fern, *Azolla,* and in the roots of cycads. Species of some genera, like *Calothrix* and *Chamaesiphon,* live as **epiphytes** on other algae or other aquatic plants. Members of the

Myxophyceae may serve as the algal components of lichens; these are discussed in Chapter 14. A number of blue-green algae grow in waters of hot springs, where they deposit rocklike strata composed of carbonates. Some of these are present in water which attains a temperature of 85° C.

Color alone is insufficient to distinguish Cyanophycophyta from other algae, for their color, especially *en masse,* may be blue-green, black, dark purple, brown, or even red. This range in color is occasioned by the presence of varying proportions of several pigments. These are chlorophyll *a* and carotenoid pigments, as well as three pigments, phycocyanin (Gr. *phykos,* seaweed + Gr. *kyanos,* blue), allophycocyanin, and phycoerythrin (Gr. *phykos* + Gr. *erythros,* red). These pigments are biliproteins and each has a different tetrapyrrole prosthetic group. Species of Myxophyceae which are reddish contain a large proportion of phycoerythrin, while dark-colored species contain a large preponderance of phycocyanin. Both the phycoerythrin and phycocyanin are water-soluble. They readily diffuse out of plants killed by boiling, leaving the unmasked chlorophyll. The relation of this pigment complex to the course of photosynthesis is being investigated currently in Myxophyceae grown in pure culture. These studies have demonstrated that a number of genera of Myxophyceae are autotrophic (Gr. *autos,* self + Gr. *trophe,* food), for they are able to grow and reproduce in culture media containing only inorganic compounds. The accessory pigment phycocyanin (perhaps also allophycocyanin and phycoerythrin) has been identified especially as a light absorber for one of the two photoreactions occurring in photosynthesis.

There is good evidence, educed through the use of isotopic techniques, that several species of *Nostoc, Anabaena,* and *Calothrix* can grow in the absence of combined nitrogen, provided that atmospheric nitrogen is present. These species, therefore, carry on **nitrogen fixation,** as do certain bacteria. Several endophytic algal species are probably nitrogen fixers.

The protoplast of myxophycean cells is surrounded by a delicate wall, reported to

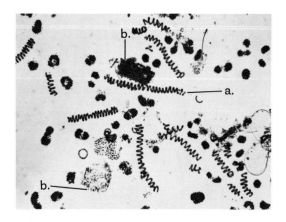

FIG. 2-1. Sample of a water bloom, living condition, as it appears under low magnification; a., *Anabaena flos-aquae* B. and F.; b., *Polycystis aeruginosa* Kütz. X 60.

contain cellulose,[6] external to which it frequently secretes a layer of slimy material of varying thickness and consistency (Figs. 2-2, 2-5, 2-13A). The presence or absence of this sheath may be demonstrated readily by immersing the organisms in diluted India ink or by staining them with dilute methylene blue. Masses of blue-green algae often are slimy to the touch because of the copious ensheathing substances, and this characteristic has suggested the group name Myxophyceae.

The cellular organization of blue-green algae differs markedly from that of other algae, and, in fact, from that of all other plants and animals, except that of bacteria (Chapter 9). The nuclear material DNA is not delimited from the cytoplasm by a nuclear membrane and often is dispersed as a network through it (Fig. 2-2). Furthermore, well-defined nucleoli are absent. This lack of membrane-bounded nuclei, and with it typical mitosis, has suggested the group names "Akaryota" or "Prokaryota"[7] for the Cyanophycophyta and bacteria. A second noteworthy feature of blue-green algal cells is that the chlorophyll-containing lamellae are not segregated from the cytoplasm by a membrane (Fig. 2-2) as in other chlorophyllous plants, so that true chloroplasts are absent. (The simple lamellae here correspond to the saclike structures of photosynthetic bacteria.) Although they occur largely in the periphery of the cell, the pigment-containing lamellae may be present in the central region as well. Large, central aqueous vacuoles, so characteristic of most algal cells, also are absent from those of Cyanophycophyta, as are endoplasmic reticulum, mitochondria, and Golgi apparatus;[8] both of the latter are absent also from bacterial cells. The excess photosynthate is stored as minute granules sometimes called "cyanophycean starch," the chemistry of which is still imperfectly known. There is evidence both

that it is glycogenlike and that it corresponds to the amylopectin fraction of green plant starches.

Illustrative Types

Three types of plant body structure occur in the Myxophyceae, namely, unicellular, colonial, and filamentous. In unicellular genera the plant is a single cell, either free-living or attached (Figs. 2-3, 2-6). As a result of more or less temporary coherence of several generations of recently divided cells, incipient colonial forms may arise. Permanently colonial genera are those in which a number of cells grow together within a common sheath which is augmented by the secretions of the individual cells (Figs. 2-7, 2-8). The cells of filamentous genera are joined in unbranched (Figs. 2-9, 2-10), branched (Fig. 2-22), or falsely branched (Fig. 2-17) chains. Unbranched filaments arise as a result of restrictions of cell division in only one direction. The unicellular and colonial types usually are considered to be primitive and the filamentous ones as derived from unicellular precursors.

UNICELLULAR GENERA
Chroococcus, Gloeocapsa, and Chamaesiphon

Chroococcus[9] (Gr. *chros*, color + Gr. *kokkos*, berry), *Gloeocapsa*[9] (Gr. *gloia*, glue + L. *capsa*, a box or case) and *Chamaesiphon*[10] (Gr. *chamai*, on the ground, hence sessile + Gr. *siphon*, a tube) will be described as representatives of the more simple unicellular types. *Chroococcus* (Figs. 2-3, 2-4) frequently occurs sparingly intermingled with other algae in the sludge at the bottoms of quiet bodies of water; *Gloeocapsa* (Fig. 2-5) along with *Chroococcus* is frequently encountered on moist rocks or on flower pots in greenhouses.

It is difficult sometimes to find single, isolated cells of *Chroococcus* and *Gloeocapsa* in a particular sample, because of the abundance of cell division and the tendency of the daughter cells to cohere at its conclusion. Cell di-

---

[6] This has recently been questioned. Instead, there is evidence that the walls are composed of mucopeptides which contain α,ε-diaminopimelic, muramic acids, and certain amino acids, substances occurring also in gram-positive bacterial cell walls.

[7] From the Greek, *karyon*, kernel or nut, referring to the nucleus.

[8] All representatives of the ultrastructural membrane systems of the cell.

[9] Included in the genus *Anacystis* by Drouet and Daily, 1956.

[10] Included in the genus *Entophysalis* by Drouet and Daily, 1956.

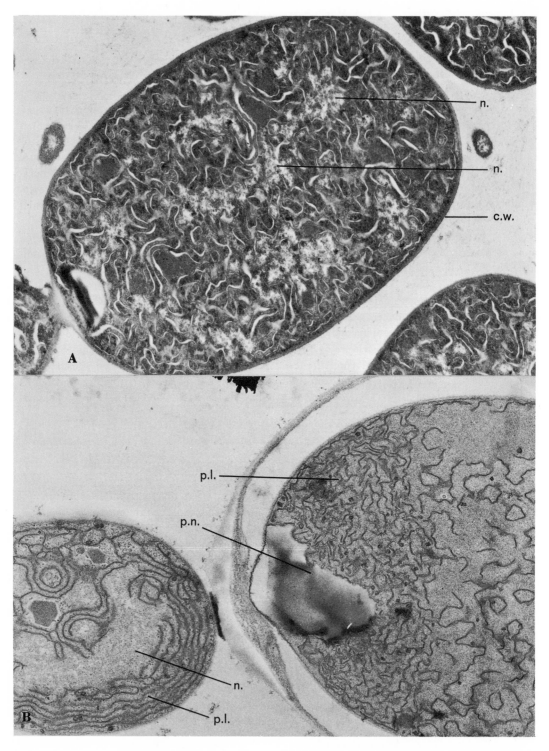

FIG. 2-2. *Anabaena* sp. Electron micrographs showing ultrastructure. A. Vegetative cell. B. Heterocyst (right) and segment of vegetative cell; c.w., cell wall; n., nuclear material; p.l., photosynthetic lamellae; p.n., polar nodule. X 9600. (*Courtesy of Dr. Norma J. Lang.*)

vision in both these genera is accomplished by the centripetal growth of a surface furrow which ultimately divides the cell (Fig. 2-3).

New walls are synthesized around the daughter protoplasts within the persistent wall of the mother cell, which becomes distended as the division products increase in size. The nuclear material apparently is divided into two portions at cytokinesis. Thus, as in most unicellular organisms, cell division effects reproduction or multiplication of the individual. Subsequent growth of the division products results in their achieving the size characteristic of the species.

The sheaths of *Gloeocapsa* may be colored in the living cells and usually are thicker and more prominent than in *Chroococcus;* the incipient colonies of *Gloeocapsa* generally are composed of more individual cells than in *Chroococcus.* Careful microscopic study of such aggregations of *Gloeocapsa* cells usually reveals that each cell has an individual sheath (which may be lamellated) at the conclusion of cell division. The sheaths of the parent cells stretch and persist (Figs. 2-3, 2-4, 2-5).

Chamaesiphon (Fig. 2-6) is epiphytic on other algae and aquatic flowering plants and is frequently present on such plants in aquaria. The cells of *Chamaesiphon* are attached to their hosts by **holdfasts.** The cells are enlarged distally from a tapering base. Cell division of one cell into two equal daughter cells does not occur in *Chamaesiphon.* Instead, a series of small, walled cells is delimited from the distal portion of the individual (Fig. 2-6), and these are gradually discharged through a terminal opening in the cell wall. These small cells are called **exospores** and presumably float to suitable substrata, where they germinate into new individuals.

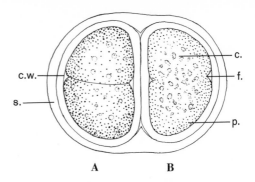

FIG. 2-3. *Chroococcus turgidus* (Kütz.) Näg. Dividing cell. A. Surface view. B. Median optical section; c., colorless central region; c.w., cell wall; f., incipient cleavage furrow; p., pigmented cytoplasm; s., sheath. X 1700.

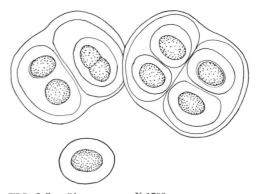

FIG. 2-4. *Chroococcus turgidus.* Living cells. X 1000.

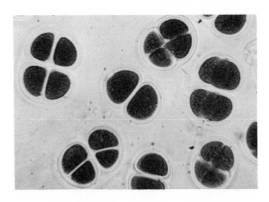

FIG. 2-5. *Gloeocapsa* sp. X 1700.

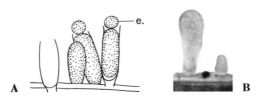

FIG. 2-6. *Chamaesiphon* sp. A. Epiphytic on a filamentous green alga. B. Photomicrograph of same; e., exospore formation. X 1500.

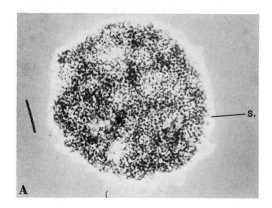

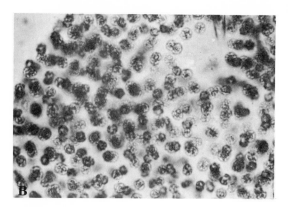

FIG. 2-7. *Polycystis aeruginosa*. A. Single living colony mounted in India ink. X 125. B. Portion of same under higher magnification; s., sheath. X 1600.

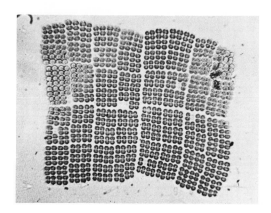

FIG. 2-8. *Merismopedia* sp. Living colony. X 250.

COLONIAL GENERA
Polycystis and Merismopedia

Polycystis[11] (Gr. *polys*, many + Gr. *kystis*, bladder, hence cell) and *Merismopedia*[12] (Gr. *merismos*, division + Gr. *pedion*, a plain) illustrate the colonial type of plant body among Myxophyceae. In both these genera the cells are surrounded by a common envelope. In *Polycystis* the densely cellular colonies vary in shape from spherical to irregular (Figs. 2-1, 2-7), whereas in *Merismopedia* the colony is a flattened or slightly curved plate (Fig. 2-8). *Polycystis aeruginosa* Kütz. frequently is a component of water blooms (Fig. 2-1). The individual cells are minute and

spherical and usually contain refractive pseudovacuoles which are filled with gas; their exact nature is not understood.

The ellipsoidal cells of *Merismopedia* are arranged in flat colonies in which the individual cells occur in rows (Fig. 2-8). This regularity of arrangement arises from the limitation of cell division to two directions. Numerous dividing cells often are visible within the colony. In these colonial genera, in contrast to strictly unicellular organisms, cell division results in increase in colony size rather than in multiplication of the individual. The latter is accomplished by fragmentation of larger colonies, the fragments continuing to increase in size by cell division.

FILAMENTOUS GENERA
Oscillatoria, Lyngbya, Anabaena, Nostoc, Scytonema, Rivularia, Gloeotrichia, Calothrix, and Hapalosiphon

The coherence of cells after completion of cell division results in the production of another type of plant body, the trichome[13] (Fig. 2-9). Where cell division is entirely restricted to a single direction, an unbranched trichome results, as in *Oscillatoria* (L. *oscillare*, to swing) and *Lyngbya* (in honor of *Lyngbye*, a Danish phycologist). *Oscillatoria* (Figs. 2-9, 2-10), which occurs floating in aquatic habitats or on damp soil, is a genus containing many species. In some of them the cells are

---

[11] Included in the genus *Anacystis* by Drouet and Daily, 1956.

[12] Included in the genus *Agmenellum* by Drouet and Daily, 1956.

[13] In the literature of the Cyanophycophyta the term "trichome" is limited to the chain of cells; the term "filament" refers to both the trichome and its enclosing sheath.

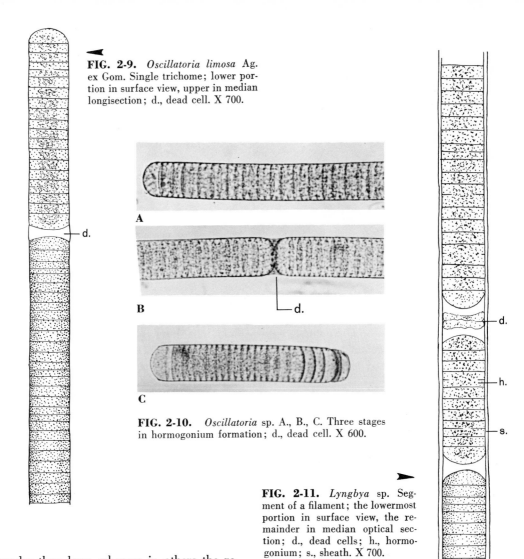

FIG. 2-9. *Oscillatoria limosa* Ag. ex Gom. Single trichome; lower portion in surface view, upper in median longisection; d., dead cell. X 700.

A

B

d.

C

FIG. 2-10. *Oscillatoria* sp. A., B., C. Three stages in hormogonium formation; d., dead cell. X 600.

d.

h.

s.

FIG. 2-11. *Lyngbya* sp. Segment of a filament; the lowermost portion in surface view, the remainder in median optical section; d., dead cells; h., hormogonium; s., sheath. X 700.

broader than long, whereas in others the reverse is true. In *Oscillatoria* and *Lyngbya* there is no differentiation among the component cells of a trichome, except that the apical cell may differ in shape from the other vegetative cells. Sheaths usually are not demonstrable around the trichomes of *Oscillatoria*. When they are observed in aqueous media, a number of the trichomes frequently exhibit an oscillating motion, as well as rotation and forward and backward movement along their long axes. The mechanism of these movements is not understood completely. It has been suggested that the movement of filamentous bluegreen algae is occasioned by the secretion of polysaccharides through pores in their cell walls. Electron microscopy has revealed the occurrence of such pores, but recent theoretical considerations of the rate of movement (forward and backward), which is 5–6 μ per

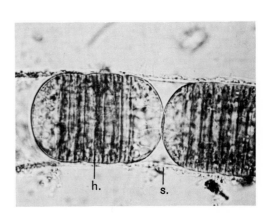

FIG. 2-12. *Lyngbya* sp. Living filament with hormogonium; h., hormogonium; s., sheath. X 1400.

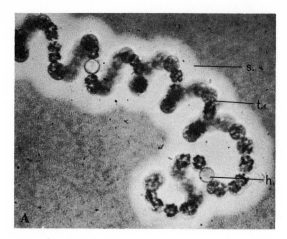

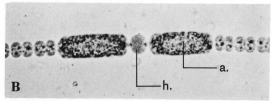

FIG. 2-13. *Anabaena flos-aquae.* A. Single filament mounted in India ink. B. *Anabaena* sp.; a., akinete; h., heterocyst; s., sheath; t., trichome. X 540.

second in a genus related to *Oscillatoria,* indicate that impossibly large amounts of colloids would have to be secreted to account for the movement.

Lyngbya (Fig. 2-11, 2-12), which occurs in both fresh and salt water, differs from *Oscillatoria* in that the trichomes are surrounded by rather firm, clearly visible sheaths. In both *Oscillatoria* and *Lyngbya,* cell division is generalized, all the cells of the trichomes being capable of division. Cell division here, as in colonial genera, results in increase in the size of the individual. Multiplication of the filaments takes place by a type of fragmentation called hormogonium (Gr. *hormos,* chain + Gr. *gonos,* reproductive structure) formation. In this process, either because of the death of one or more cells in the trichome (Figs. 2-10B, C; 2-12) or because of weakness at one point, the chains of cells break up into multicellular fragments, the **hormogonia.** These are usually motile and capable of forming new trichomes.

Anabaena (Gr. *anabainein,* to arise) and *Nostoc* (name used by Paracelsus), although unbranched like *Oscillatoria* and *Lyngbya,* possess several attributes not present in the latter. *Anabaena* (Figs. 2-13, 2-14), a genus which contains both planktonic species and some which form coatings on other aquatic vegetation, is widespread in bodies of fresh and salt water. *Nostoc,* "Starjelly" or "Witches' Butter" (Figs. 2-15, 2-16), includes a number of both aquatic and terrestrial or

rock-inhabiting species in which the tortuous, beadlike filaments are grouped together in matrices of macroscopically recognizable form. The plant mass may be spherical, ovoidal, or sheetlike. Cell division is generalized also in *Anabaena* and *Nostoc,* but two manifestations of differentiation occur. Certain cells, the **heterocysts** (Gr. *heteros,* different + Gr. *kystis,* cell), develop from some of the vegetative[14] cells. In this process, the

---

[14] The term "vegetative" cell is used by botanists in much the same sense that "somatic" is used in zoology, i.e., as the antonym to "reproductive" or "germ" cells.

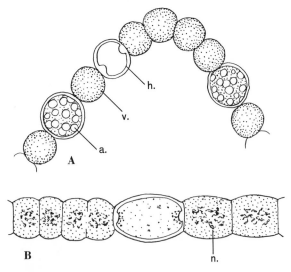

FIG. 2-14. *Anabaena circinalis* B. and F. A. Segment of living filament. B. *Anabaena* sp. Segment of acetocarmine-stained filament; a., akinete; h., heterocyst; n., nuclear material; v., vegetative cell. X 850.

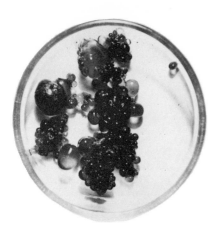

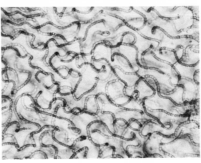

B

FIG. 2-15. *Nostoc microscopicum* B. and F. A. Living colonies. X ¾. B. Topographic view of crushed colony. X 135. C. Filaments with heterocysts. X 450.

A

C

cell destined to be a heterocyst becomes optically homogeneous, although electron microscopy reveals the presence of highly organized protoplasm and indications of active metabolism in the attached heterocyst. In the freed heterocyst, the protoplast seems to be disorganized. The heterocyst wall thickens uniformly, except in the region of contact with an adjacent cell. Here the wall is variously modified, often as a polar nodule (Figs. 2-13 to 2-16). It has been suggested that the formation of the heterocyst in *Anabaena* and *Nostoc* results in a weakness in the chain of cells, perhaps by destroying intercellular protoplasmic continuity, and the filaments break up readily into actively motile hormogonia. In a few cases, heterocysts have been observed to germinate into filaments. However, hormogonia in *Nostoc* may form in the absence of heterocysts and the latter may then differentiate from the terminal cells of the hormogonium. The function of heterocysts in such circumstances is not clear.

Other vegetative cells of *Nostoc* and *Anabaena* may become transformed into akinetes (Gr. *akinesia*, absence of motility). An **akinete** (Figs. 2-13, 2-14) is a thick-walled spore which, when set free from the parent plant, can germinate to form a new individual. As the akinete differentiates from the vegetative cell, certain changes take place. Refractive storage granules increase in number and the cell may enlarge. While these changes are occurring, an additional wall layer is formed

between the original cellulose wall of the vegetative cell and its protoplast. Akinetes are highly resistant to environmental adversities and have germinated after 70 years in air-dry storage.

Scytonema (Gr. *skytos*, hide or skin + Gr. *nema*, thread), a genus widely distributed on moist rocks and soil, where it forms dark, blackish, felty coatings, is of interest in two respects. Its sheaths are thick, firm, sometimes lamellated, and yellow-brown in older parts of the plant body (Fig. 2-17). Furthermore, there is a strong tendency for cell division to be restricted to cells near the apices of the filaments. However, heterocyst formation and renewal of cell division in intercalary vegetative cells between heterocysts often result in modifications of the trichome. Inasmuch as the heterocysts are firmly attached to the sheath, pressure generated by intercalary cell division results in the rupture of the sheath

FIG. 2-16. *Nostoc* sp. Single trichome, with heterocysts and vegetative cells, two of the latter dividing. X 850.

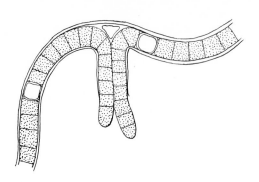

FIG. 2-17. *Scytonema myochrous* (Dillw.) Ag. Segment of filament showing false branching. X 450.

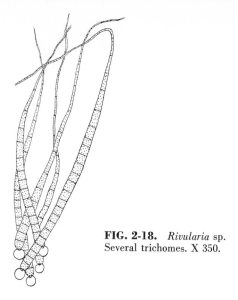

FIG. 2-18. *Rivularia* sp. Several trichomes. X 350.

and the emergence of pairs of trichomes (Fig. 2-17). In this way, although cell division is limited to one direction as in all the preceding filamentous genera, **false branching** takes place.

Rivularia (L. *rivulus,* a small brook) (Fig. 2-18) and *Gloeotrichia* (Gr. *gloios* gelatinous + Gr. *thrix,* hair) (Figs. 2-19, 2-20) also have falsely branched filaments but differ from *Scytonema* in that their filaments are united

in spherical, attached colonies, and their filaments taper from base to apex. The apices are composed of long, almost colorless, hairlike cells. The basal vegetative cell of each filament becomes transformed into a heterocyst (Figs. 2-18, 2-19). In *Gloeotrichia,* one or more enlarged akinetes usually are developed from the vegetative cells in the vicinity of the heterocyst; akinetes are lacking in *Rivularia.* In both these genera the sheaths of the individual filaments are partially confluent, thus contributing to the common matrix; however, remnants of the individual sheaths are usually apparent at the base of the plants.

The related genus *Calothrix* (Gr. *kalos,* beautiful + Gr. *thrix*) (Fig. 2-21) is frequently encountered as an epiphyte on aquatic plants, or grows abundantly on rocks and pilings exposed to sea water and spray, and on soil.

True branching, resulting from the division of certain cells of a trichome in a direction

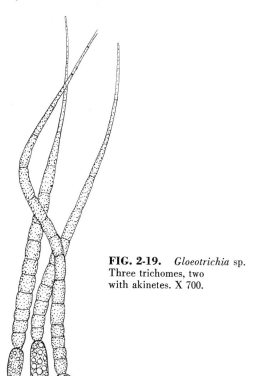

FIG. 2-19. *Gloeotrichia* sp. Three trichomes, two with akinetes. X 700.

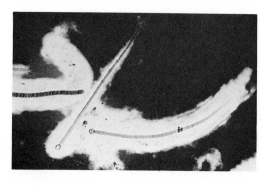

FIG. 2-20. *Gloeotrichia* sp. Long filaments mounted in India ink; note basal heterocysts. X 175.

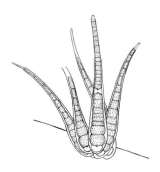

FIG. 2-21. *Calothrix fasciculata* Ag. epiphytic on *Enteromorpha*. X 385.

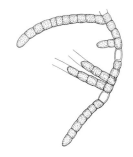

FIG. 2-22. *Hapalosiphon* sp. Segment of branching filament. X 205.

different from that of the majority, characterizes the genus *Hapalosiphon* (Gr. *hapalos*, gentle + Gr. *siphon*, tube) (Fig. 2-22). Species of *Hapalosiphon* often form extensive coatings on aquatic vegetation.

Summary and Classification

In summary, it should be emphasized that the blue-green algae represent a large but somewhat anomalous group among the algae. Their cellular organization is more nearly like bacterial cells than that of any other group of algae. Distinctive cyanophycophytan attributes, as compared with other algae, include the absence from the cells of definitely delimited plastids, of membrane-bounded nuclei, of large aqueous vacuoles, mitochondria, Golgi apparatus, and the presence of phycocyanin and phycoerythrin, in addition to chlorophyll and carotenoid pigments. Heterocysts do not occur in plants other than Myxophyceae. Their stored photosynthate, called "cyanophycean starch," a term which emphasizes our ignorance of its exact chemical nature, is different from that of other algae. Myxophyceae are of biological interest in their seemingly complete lack of sexuality, although some subtle method of exchange of genetic materials may yet be discovered.

A recent report[15] indicates strongly that

genetic recombinations may, in fact, occur in *Cylindrospermum majus* Kütz. When a clone of this organism which fails to produce akinetes and is streptomycin-resistant was grown together with an akinete-producing, penicillin-resistant clone in a medium containing both penicillin and streptomycin, growth occurred in two of forty-seven culture tubes. The algae in these tubes have been interpreted as recombinants since they produce akinetes and are resistant to both penicillin and streptomycin.

Reproduction in most blue-green algae is entirely asexual and is accomplished by cell division in unicellular genera and by various types of fragmentation in colonial and filamentous ones. In the latter, the filamentous fragments are known as hormogonia. Two special types of reproductive cells, namely, heterocysts and akinetes, are developed by many of the filamentous genera. With few exceptions, cell division in multicellular types is generalized, not localized. *Scytonema*, *Calothrix*, *Rivularia*, and *Gloeotrichia* differ from other filamentous genera in this respect. Growth in *Scytonema* is largely apical, whereas in *Calothrix*, *Rivularia*, and *Gloeotrichia*, it is basal. Although many Cyanophycophyta grow on damp soil, students of plant evolution do not look upon them with interest as possible progenitors of higher forms of plant life because of the anomalous attributes listed above, in all of which they differ markedly from other algae as well as from other plants. They have no clear kinship with other living organisms,

[15] Singh, R. N., and R. Sinha. 1965. "Genetic recombination in a blue-green alga, *Cylindrospermum majus* Kütz," *Nature*, 207: 782–783.

unless it is with the bacteria, a suggestion first made almost 100 years ago.

The classification of Cyanophycophyta is relatively uncontroversial. The orders and families, of which representative genera have been chosen for this chapter, may be classified as follows:

Division: Cyanophycophyta
  Class 1. Myxophyceae
    Order 1. Chroococcales
      Family 1. Chroococcaceae
        Genera: *Chroococcus, Gloeocapsa,*
              Polycystis, Merismopedia
    Order 2. Chamaesiphonales
      Family 1. Chamaesiphonaceae
        Genus: *Chamaesiphon*
    Order 3. Oscillatoriales
      Suborder 1. Oscillatorineae
        Family 1. Oscillatoriaceae
          Genera: *Oscillatoria, Lyngbya*
      Suborder 2. Nostochineae
        Family 1. Nostocaceae
          Genera: *Anabaena, Nostoc*
        Family 2. Scytonemataceae
          Genus: *Scytonema*
        Family 3. Stigonemataceae
          Genus: *Hapalosiphon*
        Family 4. Rivulariaceae
          Genera: *Rivularia, Gloeotrichia,*
             Calothrix

The orders are readily distinguishable from each other. The Chamaesiphonales alone produce endospores and exospores. The remaining unicellular and colonial Myxophyceae are members of the Chroococcales; the filamentous genera belong to the Oscillatoriales. Two series are distinguishable in the order Oscillatoriales, depending on the absence (suborder Oscillatorineae) or presence (suborder Nostochineae) of heterocysts. The several families of the Nostochineae are recognizable by the following unique attributes: The Nostocaceae are unbranched, with trichomes of uniform diameter; false branching occurs in the Scytonemataceae, which also have trichomes of uniform diameter. True branching characterizes the Stigonemataceae, while the trichomes of the Rivulariaceae, which may be falsely branched, are tapered.

DISCUSSION QUESTIONS

1. What attributes distinguish algae from other chlorophyllous plants?

2. Does habitat distinguish algae from other chlorophyllous plants?

3. It has been demonstrated that many algae retain their chlorophyll and multiply in darkness beneath the soil surface. What possible explanations are there for these observations?

4. What types of plant body occur among algae?

5. Define the terms "plankton" and "water bloom."

6. In what respects are plankton algae of biological and economic importance?

7. What organisms were formerly included in the group Thallophyta? (See Chapter 1, and Table 32-2, p. 516)

8. What attributes distinguish Cyanophycophyta from other algae?

9. For what reasons is the cell structure of Cyanophycophyta said to be "anomalous"?

10. What possible functions can you see for the copious sheaths of certain Cyanophycophyta?

11. What is meant by the following terms: growth, reproduction, vegetative reproduction, asexual reproduction, sexual reproduction, cytokinesis?

12. What types of growth can you distinguish on the basis of location in the plant body?

13. Explain how cell division is related to the form of the plant body of Cyanophycophyta, mentioning illustrative genera.

14. Define or explain the following terms: heterocyst, spore, akinete, vegetative cell, hormogonium, somatic, germ cell.

15. Do you consider colonies like *Polycystis* and *Merismopedia* multicellular organisms? Give reasons for your answer.

16. Where would you look for Cyanophycophyta in nature?

17. Are heterocysts empty at maturity? Explain.

18. Construct a dichotomous key to all the genera of Cyanophycophyta cited in this chapter.

19. What attributes do Cyanophycophyta share with bacteria?

REFERENCE WORKS ON ALGAE[16]

Bold, H. C., "The Cultivation of Algae," *Bot. Rev.* 8:69–138, 1942.

Boney, A. D., *A Biology of Marine Algae*, Hutchinson Educational Ltd., London, 1966.

Burlew, J. S. (ed.), *Algal Culture from Laboratory to Pilot Plant*, Publication 600, Carnegie Inst., Baltimore, Md., 1953.

Chapman, V. J., *Seaweeds and Their Uses*, Methuen and Co., Ltd., 1950.

Chapman, V. J., *The Algae*, Macmillan and Co., Ltd., London. St. Martin's Press, Inc., New York, 1962.

Chase, F. M., *Useful Algae*, Smithsonian Publication 3667, Smithsonian Inst., Washington, D.C., 1941.

Conger, P. S., "Significance of Shell Structure in Diatoms," *Smithsonian Report*, pp. 325–344, 1936.

Davidson, B., "Now—Bread from the Sea," *Colliers*, April 16, 1954.

Dawson, E. Y., *How to Know the Seaweeds*, Wm. C. Brown Co., Dubuque, Iowa, 1956.

Dawson, E. Y., *Marine Botany, An Introduction*, Holt, Rinehart and Winston, Inc., New York, 1966.

Drouet, F. R., and W. O. Daily, *Revision of the Coccoid Myxophyceae*, Butler University Botanical Studies XII, 1956.

Fritsch, F. E., *Structure and Reproduction of the Algae*, vol. 1 and 2, Cambridge Univ. Press, London, 1935 and 1945.

Jackson, D. F., *Algae and Man*, Plenum Press, Inc., New York, 1964.

Krauss, R. W., "Mass Culture of Algae for Food and Other Organic Compounds," *Am. J. Bot.* 49:425–435, 1962.

Lewin, R. A. (ed.), *Physiology and Biochemistry of Algae*, Academic Press, New York and London, 1962.

Lewis, J. R., *The Ecology of Rocky Shores*, The English Universities Press Ltd., London, 1964.

Milner, H. W., "Algae as Food," *Sci. Am.* 189:31–35, 1953.

Palmer, C. M., *Algae in Water Supplies*, Public Health Service Publication No. 657, 1959.

Papenfuss, G. F., "Classification of the Algae," *Century Progress Nat. Sci. 1853–1953* (pp. 115–224). Calif. Acad. Sciences, San Francisco, 1955.

Prescott, G. W., *How to Know the Fresh-Water Algae*, Wm. C. Brown Co., Dubuque, Iowa, 1954.

Prescott, G. W., *Algae of the Western Great Lakes Area*, Wm. C. Brown Co., Dubuque, Iowa, 1962.

Pringsheim, E. G., *Pure Cultures of Algae, Their Preparation and Maintenance*, Cambridge Univ. Press, London, 1946.

Round, F. C., *The Biology of the Algae*, St. Martin's Press Inc., New York, 1965.

Scagel, R. F., R. J. Bandoni, G. E. Rouse, W. B. Schofield, J. R. Stein, and T. M. C. Taylor, *An Evolutionary Survey of the Plant Kingdom*, Wadsworth Publishing Co., Inc., Belmont, Calif., 1965.

Setchell, W. A., and N. L. Gardner, *The Marine Algae of the Pacific Coast of North America*, Univ. California Publication in Botany 8: I. Myxophyceae, 1919; II. Chlorophyceae, 1920; III. Melanophyceae, 1925.

Smith, G. M., *Marine Algae of the Monterey Peninsula*, Stanford Univ. Press, Stanford, Calif., 1944.

Smith, G. M., *Freshwater Algae of the United States*, McGraw-Hill Book Co., New York, 1950.

Smith, G. M., *Cryptogamic Botany*, vol. 1, McGraw-Hill Book Co., New York, 1955.

Smith, G. M., *et al.*, *Manual of Phycology*, Chronica Botanica Co., Waltham, Mass., 1951.

Starr, R. C., "The Culture Collection of Algae at Indiana University," *Am. J. Bot.* 51:1013–1044, 1964.

Taylor, W. R., *Marine Algae of the Northeastern Coast of North America*, Univ. of Michigan Press, Ann Arbor, 1937.

Taylor, W. R., *Marine Algae of the Eastern Tropical and Subtropical Coasts of the Americas*, Univ. of Michigan Press, Ann Arbor, 1960.

Tiffany, L. H., *Algae, the Grass of Many Waters*, Charles C. Thomas, Springfield, Ill., 1958.

Tiffany, L. H., and M. E. Britton, *The Algae of Illinois*, Univ. of Chicago Press, 1952.

Tilden, J. E., *The Algae and Their Life Relations*, Univ. of Minnesota Press, Minneapolis, Minn., 1935.

---

[16] These references should be consulted in connection with Chapters 2 through 8.

CHAPTER 3

Division Chlorophycophyta

General Features

The division Chlorophycophyta (Gr. *chloros*, green + Gr. *phyton*, plant + Gr. *phykos*, alga), as here treated, includes a single class of algae, the Chlorophyceae (Gr. *chloros* + Gr. *phykos*, seaweed). The Chlorophycophyta include all plants usually designated "green algae," with the exception of the stoneworts, *Chara, Nitella,* and related genera, which in this text are grouped in a separate division, the Charophyta (see Chapter 6).

Like the Cyanophycophyta, green algae are widespread, occurring in both fresh and marine waters, on moist wood and rocks, and on the surface of and within soil. Many green algae have been recovered from airborne dusts. More than 400 genera and 6500 species of Chlorophycophyta have been described. They are well represented in the plankton and may occur in bodies of water which range in size from small, temporary pools to oceans. A number of species are epiphytic on other algae, on aquatic flowering plants and on animals, and still others (*Chlorella,* for example) are endophytic in the cells of certain protozoa, coelenterates, and sponges. Marine species are frequently attached to rocks, pilings, or larger algae, or grow on the sandy bottoms of quiet estuaries, often on shells. Planktonic species occasionally form water blooms.

The Chlorophycophyta are usually grass-green during their vegetative stages except for a few species with tannin-containing purple vacuolar pigments which mask their green color. The cells contain both chlorophylls *a* and *b* as well as α- and β-carotenes and certain xanthophylls (Table 2-1, p. 11). The predominance of chlorophyll pigments accounts for the typical green color of members of the division. Unlike the pigments of blue-green algae, those of the Chlorophycophyta are restricted to cytoplasmic organelles called **chloroplasts** which are delimited by double membranes (Fig. 3-1). The chloroplasts exhibit a great range of form, varying from large, urn-like structures (Figs. 3-1, 3-2) to plane or twisted ribbons (Fig. 3-31) to minute lens-shaped bodies (Fig. 3-16). **Pyrenoids** (Gr. *pyren,* fruit stone) are present in the chloroplasts of most Chlorophycophyta. They may well be centers of formation of the enzyme amylose synthetase which combines glucose molecules into starch. Golgi bodies, mitochondria and endoplasmic reticulum, all absent from the cells of Cyanophycophyta, are present in those of Chlorophycophyta (Figs. 3-1, 3-2E) and all other plants. Of all the algae, the Chlorophycophyta (and Charophyta, p. 84) are most like land plants in that their excess carbon compounds are stored within the plastids as starch. The nuclei of Chlorophycophyta are similar in organization to those of plants other than Cyanophycophyta and bacteria in having two-layered, perforate nuclear membranes (Fig. 3-1) and one or more nucleoli in addition to DNA. Mitotic nuclear division has been observed in many species. The nuclei (Figs. 3-1, 3-2E) are embedded in colorless cytoplasm and are always centripetal to the chloroplasts. Cell walls, when present, are cellulosic and in many cases are surrounded by colloidal sheaths or matrices which are pectinaceous. A few unicellular genera and

FIG. 3-1. *Chlamydomonas reinhardtii* Dang. A. Photograph of cell in motion prepared with interference microscope. X 1900. B. Electron micrograph of median longitudinal section of cell. X 23,000. C. Transection of flagellum; note two central fibrils surrounded by nine (double) ones. X 100,000. c.l., chloroplast lamella; c.w., cell wall; cy., cytoplasm; f., flagellum; n., nucleus; nu., nucleolus; py., pyrenoid; s., starch grain. (*Courtesy of Dr. David L. Ringo.*)

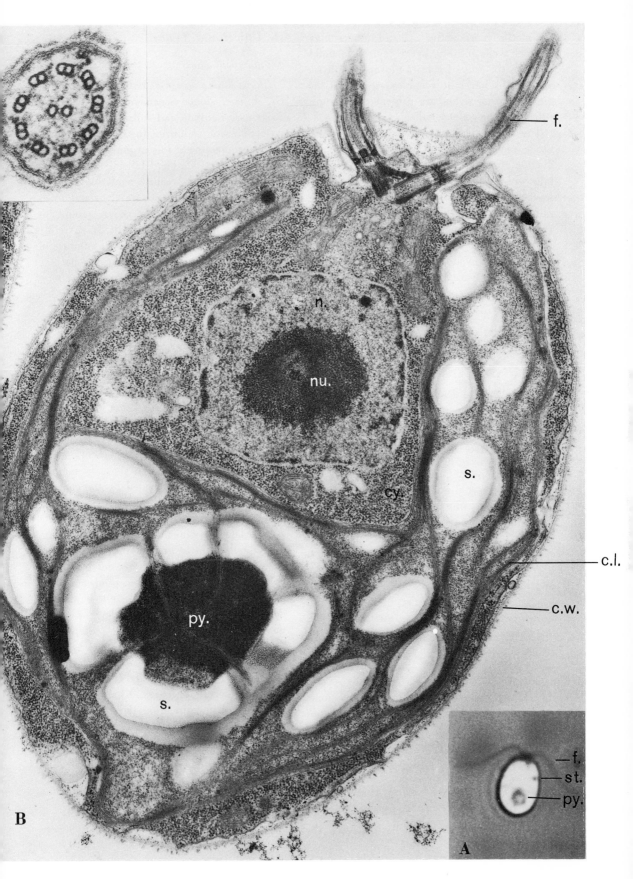

the motile reproductive cells of others may lack cell walls entirely. Large central vacuoles occur in the cells of many Chlorophycophyta, and small contractile vacuoles, which rid the cells of excess water, are present almost universally in their motile cells.

The Chlorophycophyta exhibit a wider range and complexity of structure and reproduction than the Cyanophycophyta. The details will be discussed in connection with the several illustrative genera. The latter exemplify five types of organization, as follows: (1) motile unicellular and colonial organisms; (2) nonmotile unicellular and colonial organisms; (3) filamentous organisms; (4) membranous organisms; and (5) coenocytic and tubular organisms.

I. Motile Unicellular and Colonial Organisms

A number of unicellular and colonial green algae are motile by means of flagella[1] throughout their existence. **Flagella** are protoplasmic extensions of the cell. In the Chlorophycophyta, the flagella always consist of a sheath surrounding a complex of fibrils which extend for a short distance beyond the sheath, much as a short whip extends from its handle. Accordingly, this type of flagellum is said to be of the "whiplash" type.[2] Electron microscopy has revealed a remarkable uniformity of flagellar organization throughout the plant and animal kingdoms in that each flagellum has been shown to consist of two central fibrils surrounded by nine similar double ones,[3] all surrounded by a sheath (Fig. 3-1C). In having flagella, motile algae resemble certain Protozoa with which they are sometimes classified. The occurrence of flagellate reproductive cells in the life cycles of many nonmotile algae suggests that the latter may have evolved from motile ancestral precursors. In this connection, two genera, *Chlamydomonas* and *Carteria*, are especially significant.

---

[1] Singular, flagellum (L. *flagellum*, a small whip).
[2] In other groups of algae the flagellum bears minute, hairlike lateral appendages in one or two rows. Such flagella are called tinsel flagella.
[3] Except bacterial flagella.

A. Unicellular Types

Chlamydomonas

Chlamydomonas (Gr. *chlamys*, mantle + Gr. *monas*, single organism) is widespread in aquatic habitats and soil and has been recovered from airborne dusts. The structure and reproduction of this organism will be described in considerable detail for a number of reasons: (1) it is readily available in pure cultures for laboratory study; (2) many of its attributes are shared by other genera of Chlorophycophyta; and (3) it is currently the experimental organism in a number of biochemical and genetical investigations.

The cells of most species of *Chlamydomonas* do not exceed 25 μ in length (Figs. 3-1, 3-2). The organisms are surrounded by a cellulose wall through which two flagella protrude anteriorly. Motility is effected by the lashing movements of these organelles. Each cell contains a single massive chloroplast which may be urn-, cup-, band- or H-shaped. The chloroplast may contain one or more pyrenoids, as well as a red pigment body often called the **eyespot** or **stigma** (Gr. *stigma*, mark or brand). With high magnification, one can frequently observe that there is an area of clear cytoplasm subtended by the concave stigma. It has been suggested that this functions as a primitive lens, and experiments with related organisms containing stigmata indicate that the stigma is indeed a site of light reception.[4] The single nucleus lies in the colorless cytoplasm and often is obscured by the chloroplast in living cells, but it may be demonstrated readily by staining. Two or more **contractile vacuoles** are present near the anterior pole of each cell (Fig. 3-2). There is good evidence that they play a role in the elimination of excess fluids from the cells. Electron microscopy (Figs. 3-1, 3-2E) reveals at increased magnification the complexity of the green algal cell as compared with that of the cyanophycophytan cell.

Multiplication of the plant is accomplished by cell division which involves nuclear and cytoplasmic division. The process is illus-

---

[4] It has been demonstrated that cells of *Chlamydomonas* with stigmata react with greater rapidity to the stimulus of light than those which lack them.

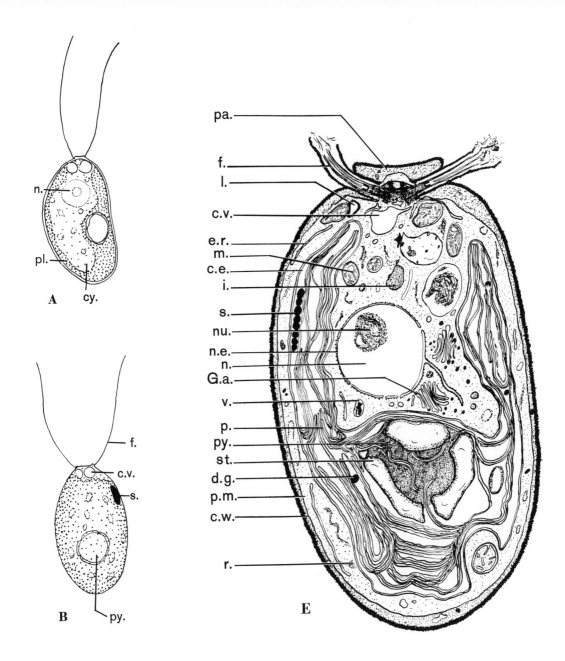

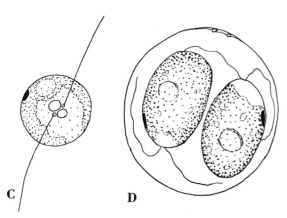

FIG. 3-2. *Chlamydomonas eugametos* Moewus. A–C. Motile individuals. (A. In median optical section. B. In surface view. C. In anterior polar view.) D. Asexual reproduction. E. Diagram of cellular organization as revealed by the electron microscope; ce., chloroplast envelope; c.v., contractile. vacuole; c.w., cell wall; cy., cytoplasm; d.g., dense granule; e.r., endoplasmic reticulum; f., flagellum; G.a., Golgi apparatus; i., inclusion; l., lipid body; m., mitochondrion; n., nucleus; n.e., nuclear envelope; nu., nucleolus; p., plastid; pa., papilla; pl., chloroplast; p.m., plasma membrane; py., pyrenoid; r., ribosomes; s., stigma; st., starch; v., vesicle. A–D. X 2250. E. X 8000. (E., *Courtesy of Dr. Patricia L. Walne*.)

trated, in part, in Fig. 3-2D. Two or more daughter cells may arise within a single parent cell by repeated bipartition. The flagella of the parent cell disappear at the beginning of division. The daughter cells emerge, after becoming motile within the mother cell, by the rupture or extreme hydration of the mother cell wall. The liberated individuals gradually grow to the size characteristic of the species, and then divide again.

Under a combination of suitable environmental and protoplasmic conditions, not yet completely understood, certain individuals undergo sexual reproduction. This process is made manifest in many species by the rapid aggregation of a number of individuals in **groups** or **clumps** (Fig. 3-4A-C). Careful study reveals that the individuals in a clump become paired (Figs. 3-3A, 3-4D, E) because of a chemical attraction between the flagella. Such pairs are held together by a delicate protoplasmic thread which connects them at the base of their flagella (Figs. 3-3A, 3-4E); the latter are not entangled, except briefly, after the cells have paired. As soon as the cells become united by the connecting strand of protoplasm, the paired flagella become free. In *Chlamydomonas moewusii* and in *C. eugametos*, the flagella of only one member of the gamete pair are motile and thus propel the pair in one direction. The cellulose walls of each member of the pair are ultimately dis-

solved at the anterior poles, and the protoplasts emerge, gradually uniting to form a single unit (Figs. 3-3B,C, 3-4D–F); the four flagella gradually shorten and disappear. Soon after union of the naked protoplasts, a new wall is formed around the fusion product. The discarded individual cell walls persist for some time in the vicinity of the fusion cell but finally disintegrate. Stained preparations of the uniting cells reveal that the two nuclei, which are thus brought together in one protoplast, unite to form one large nucleus (Fig. 3-3D).

The process just described represents the **sexual reproduction** of *Chlamydomonas*. It is characterized by the union of two cells, the union of their nuclei, and the association within the fusion nucleus of the chromosome complements (and genes) of the two uniting cells. Each of the uniting cells which undergoes union is called a **gamete** (Gr. *gamos*, marriage) or sex cell. The product of the sexual union is a **zygote** (Gr. *zygon*, yoke). In *Chlamydomonas* and many other algae, the zygote develops a thick wall, which may be variously ornamented (Figs. 3-3E, 3-4G), and undergoes a period of dormancy.

It is obvious that the zygote, a product of the union of two cells and their nuclei, will contain in its nucleus two sets of parental chromosomes and the genes they carry. Whenever this association of two sets of parental

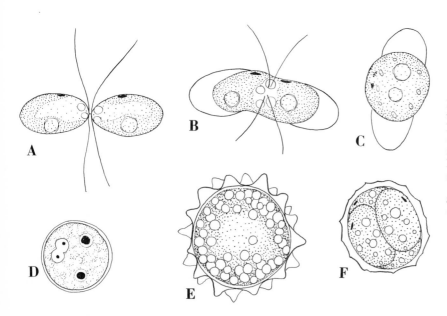

FIG. 3-3. Sexual reproduction in *Chlamydomonas*. A. Pair of isogametes recently emergent from a clump. B, C. Stages in plasmogamy. D. Karyogamy. E. Dormant zygote. F. Zygote germination. (All except D, *Chlamydomonas eugametos*. D, *C. chlamydogama* Bold.) X 1275.

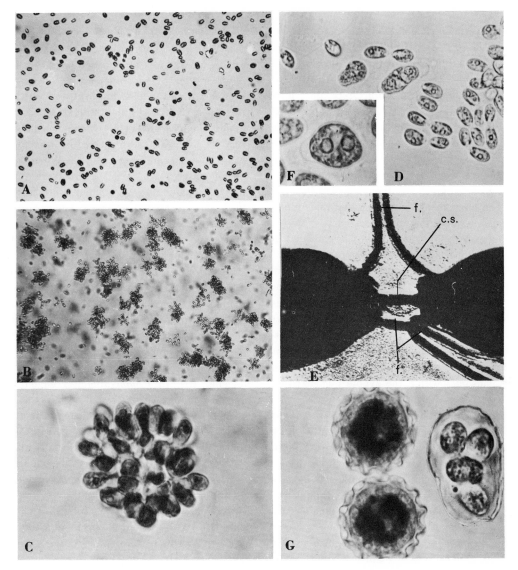

FIG. 3-4. Photomicrographs of sexual reproduction in *Chlamydomonas*. A. Motile individuals of one mating type. B, C. Clump formation after mixing of mating types. D. Paired gametes and plasmogamy. E. Electron micrograph of apices of paired gametes. F. Immature zygote. G. Dormant zygotes (left) and zygote germination; c.s., connecting strand; f., flagellum. (All except E, which is of *C. moewusii* [after *R. A. Lewin and Meinhart*], are *C. eugametos*.) A, B. X 125. C. X 750. D. X 500. E. X 37,000. F, G. X 1200.

chromosomes occurs, there follows inexorably, sooner or later in the life cycle, a phase in which the chromosomes and their genes are redistributed and segregated in different nuclei. The type of nuclear division which accomplishes this is known as **meiosis** (Gr. *meiosis*, diminution). Meiosis involves not only a quantitative reduction of the chromosome number by one-half, but a qualitative segregation of genes as well. That meiosis has taken place may often be inferred indi-

rectly from the occurrence of two rapidly successive nuclear divisions and cytokineses in which four daughter cells are produced from a single cell.[5] Cytological and genetical studies of *Chlamydomonas* indicate that meiosis occurs at the time the dormant zygote germinates. Meiosis in this case, therefore, is said to be **zygotic** with reference to its site of occurrence in the life cycle. The germinat-

[5] As, for example, in oogenesis and spermatogenesis in animals and in sporogenesis in many plants.

ing zygote of *Chlamydomonas* gives rise to four[6] motile cells (Figs. 3-3F, 3-4G) which are liberated by rupture and/or dissolution of the zygote wall. These cells are **haploid** as to chromosome constitution since they have received only a single basic set of chromosomes in meiosis. The zygote itself, having both sets of parental chromosomes before its meiosis, is said to be **diploid.** Accordingly, in the life cycle of *Chlamydomonas,* only the zygote is diploid; all other cells are haploid.

The phenomenon of sexual reproduction is relatively uniform in its essentials at the cellular level in most living organisms. It seems imperative, therefore, to emphasize certain of its significant features. Cytological investigation has demonstrated that the process usually involves four components, as follows: (1) the union of two cells (gametes) to form a zygote, a process known as **plasmogamy;** (2) the union of their nuclei or **karyogamy;** (3) the association of parental chromosomes within the zygote nucleus; and (4) their segregation in meiosis.

Primitive organisms like *Chlamydomonas* have recently been receiving intensive study with respect to their sexual reproduction, inasmuch as the process in unicellular organisms is not obscured or complicated by secondary morphological features. Although the origin of sexual reproduction remains unknown, it seems clear that the process is not as indispensable to the maintenance of the species as it is in land plants and in animals, for most unicellular organisms may multiply indefinitely by asexual means. It has been demonstrated that the sexual reproduction of *Chlamydomonas* is evoked by such factors as low available nitrogen, adequate light intensity, and abundance of carbon dioxide.

Figures 3-3A and 3-4D illustrate pairs of uniting gametes of *Chlamydomonas eugametos.* In this and many other species of sexually reproducing algae, the members of the pair are similar in size[7] and in other morphological attributes and are, therefore, said to be **isogamous** (Gr. *isos*, equal + Gr.

gamos, marriage). That isogamy is more apparent than real is indicated by three facts, among others: (1) In clonal cultures of isogamous species of *Chlamydomonas*, sexual reproduction may not occur. A **clonal culture** is one in which all the individuals of the population are genetically homogeneous and *really* similar, all being derived by asexual reproduction from a single cell. When such clonal cultures are mixed with other appropriate clonal cultures of compatible mating type, sexual reproduction will occur. This indicates that although they are similar in appearance, the gametes are, in fact, different. (2) Extracts of one of such compatible clonal cultures or of their flagella will cause agglutination or clump formation of the opposite mating type. This is a crude, but incontrovertible, manifestation that the isogametes differ chemically. It is evidence, furthermore, that gamete attraction resides, at least in part, in the complementary chemical nature of the flagella. (3) In *Chlamydomonas eugametos* and in *C. moewusii*, as stated earlier, the flagella of only one pair of gametes beat after their union; accordingly, the gamete pair moves in one direction; this also is a manifestation of difference between the gametes.

In still other species of *Chlamydomonas,* and in other algae (Fig. 3-39B,C), the uniting gametes are always different in size. This results from a difference in the number of nuclear divisions and cytokineses in the gamete-producing cells. Such gametes are known as heterogametes (Gr. *heteros*, different + Gr. *gamos*) or anisogametes (Gr. *anisos*, unequal + Gr. *gamos*); their union is called **heterogamy** or **anisogamy.** Probably on the basis of analogy with sexual reproduction in animals, the smaller of the gametes in heterogamy is referred to as male and the larger as female.

Finally, in other species of *Chlamydomonas,* and in other algae (Fig. 3-10H), the differences in the pairing gametes are more pronounced, one being small and motile and the other large and nonmotile; this condition is called **oogamy** (Gr. *ōon*, egg + Gr. *gamos*), and the smaller gamete is designated the **sperm** or **antherozoid** and the larger one, the **egg.** Within the single genus *Chlamydomonas,* therefore, there occur among the

---

[6] Additional mitoses after meiosis may result in the formation of more than four cells.

[7] In isogamous species, sporadic size differences in the uniting gametes are occasioned by the union of cells of different age.

numerous species isogamy, heterogamy, and oogamy.

Reference was made above to the fact that in clonal cultures of certain *Chlamydomonas* species, sexual reproduction would not occur unless the clonal culture were mixed with one of a compatible mating type. Such species are composed of unisexual individuals of two different types often designated + and −.[8] In other species of *Chlamydomonas*, and in other algae, sexual reproduction does take place within single clonal cultures. This indicates that compatible mating types are present in a single clonal population; the clone, accordingly is bisexual.[9]

The foregoing account of sexuality in *Chlamydomonas* is somewhat protracted and detailed, not only because it is designed to present specific information about a single alga, but also because the biological principles and terminology involved are of general application to other groups of plants and animals.

Carteria

The genus *Carteria* (Fig. 3-5) differs from *Chlamydomonas* in that its cells are quadri-

flagellate, and in certain ultrastructural details in wall, chloroplast, pyrenoid, and stigma; it is less frequently encountered in nature. The structure and asexual and sexual reproduction of *Carteria* are fundamentally similar to those of *Chlamydomonas*.

B. Colonial Types

The origin of the colonial type of algal organization probably resides in the tendency for recently divided cells of unicellular organisms to remain associated after cell division. Examples of this are abundantly evident in populations of *Chlamydomonas* and *Carteria*, among others.

Pandorina (mythology, reproduction like the opening of *Pandora's* box) and *Volvox* (L. *volvere*, to roll) (Figs. 3-6, 3-8) are two widely distributed genera which illustrate the motile colonial type of plant body. Both are sometimes present in water blooms. The individual cells, which are included in a common matrix, show many morphological features reminiscent of *Chlamydomonas*, such as massive chloroplasts, stigmata, and contractile vacuoles. Multiplication in all these genera is effected by repeated division of cells of the parent colony into miniature daughter colonies which are liberated ultimately by dissolution of the matrix of the mother colony (Fig. 3-7). The young colonies increase in cell size, but not in cell number, until the dimensions characteristic of the species have been attained.

Pandorina

The mature colonies of *Pandorina* (Figs. 3-6A, 3-7A) usually consist of sixteen cells arranged in an almost solid, ovoidal colony. Each cell is flattened at the anterior pole and narrowed posteriorly (Fig. 3-6B,C). The chloroplast is massive and contains a prominent stigma and basal pyrenoid. In anterior polar view (Fig. 3-6C), two alternately pulsating contractile vacuoles are visible in the opening of the plastid at the base of the two flagella. The single nucleus lies in the central colorless cytoplasm. Although all the cells of the colony are similar in size, a definite polarity is present, as evidenced by the fact that the stigmata of the more anterior cells

---

[8] The term heterothallic is sometimes used to describe this condition but is avoided here because of the confusion which is occasioned by its use at times in a morphological and/or physiological sense.

[9] The individual organisms of the population are, of course, unisexual.

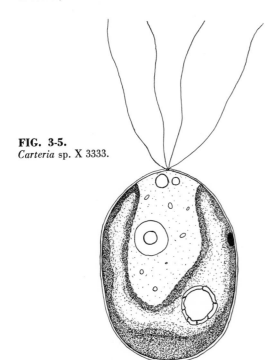

FIG. 3-5.
Carteria sp. X 3333.

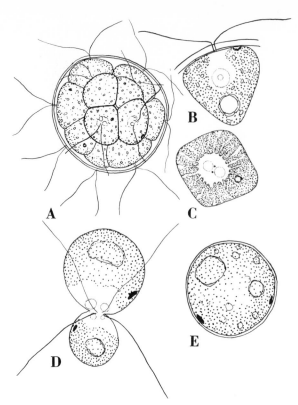

FIG. 3-6. *Pandorina* sp. A. Mature colony, surface view. B. Vegetative cell, median optical longisection. C. Vegetative cell, anterior polar view (flagella omitted). D. Gamete union (isogamy but gametes illustrated of different age). E. Zygote. A. X 700. B–E. X 1700.

colloidal matrix (Fig. 3-8). The plant is readily visible to the unaided eye and has been known for several hundred years. In a number of species of *Volvox*, the protoplasts of the individual cells are connected to their walls by delicate protoplasmic extensions. Those of contiguous cells are continuous through the cell walls (Figs. 3-9, 3-10A). In ontogeny, the young colonies turn themselves inside-out. The cells are entirely similar to each other during the early stages. However, a dimorphism soon becomes apparent in that certain cells enlarge and become slightly depressed beneath the surface (Fig. 3-10B,F). As the colonies move, it becomes evident that these larger cells lie in the posterior hemisphere. Here, too, the stigmata of the vegetative cells are smaller than those in the anterior hemisphere. These enlarged cells, the **gonidia,** alone are capable of dividing into daughter colonies (Figs. 3-8, 3-10B); the remaining cells are purely vegetative and disintegrate when the adult colony liberates its daughter colonies (Fig. 3-10B).

In some species of *Volvox, V. globator* L. for example, special enlarged cells give rise to gametes when the colonies become sexually mature. Sexual reproduction in *Volvox* is oogamous. In *V. aureus,* an interesting phenomenon has recently been described[11] in axenic laboratory cultures. Here the male colonies differ from the asexual and female colonies in that no gonidia are differentiated in the former (while they are in asexual and female colonies) before the colony is liberated from its parent. As the male colonies mature, two-thirds of the posterior cells divide repeatedly forming curved sperm

are larger than those in the posterior part of the colony.

After attaining the maximum size characteristic of the species, the colonies sink to the bottom of the pond or culture vessel and initiate daughter colony formation (Fig. 3-7B). Each of the component cells undergoes repeated nuclear and cytoplasmic division until miniature, sixteen-celled colonies are produced. The minute cells of these colonies then develop flagella and begin to move slowly within the parent colony until liberated by dissolution of its bounding membrane. Under certain conditions colonies of *Pandorina morum* Bory exhibit isogamous sexual reproduction (Fig. 3-6D).[10] It has recently been demonstrated that both unisexual and bisexual strains of *Pandorina morum* occur in nature. Meiosis is probably zygotic.

Volvox

Volvox is perhaps the most spectacular of the motile colonial Chlorophyceae, for its slightly ovoidal colonies may contain thousands of cells arranged at the periphery of a

---

[10] The difference in size of the uniting gametes in this instance is occasioned by differences in age.

[11] W. H. Darden, Jr., "Sexual differentiation in *Volvox aureus,*" *J. Protozool.,* 13:239–255, 1966.

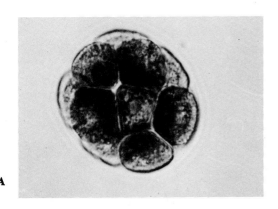

A

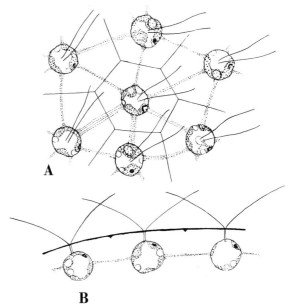

A

B

FIG. 3-9. *Volvox aureus.* Vegetative cells. A. In surface view. B. In vertical section. X 700.

B

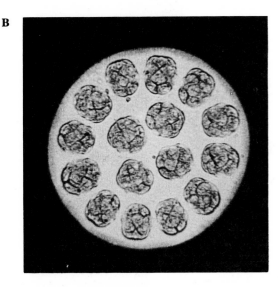

FIG. 3-7. *Pandorina morum* Bory. A. Living colony (flagella not visible). B. Daughter-colony formation (India-ink preparation). A. X 700. B. X 375.

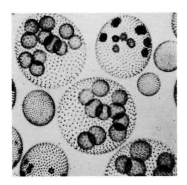

FIG. 3-8. *Volvox aureus* Ehr. Colonies containing daughter colonies of various ages. X 40.

platelets each with thirty-two sperms (Figs. 3-10D,E). Young female colonies are indistinguishable from the asexual colonies, each also having from four to twelve gonidia toward the posterior pole (Fig. 3-10B,F). When these are mixed with male colonies, the released sperm packets are chemotactically attracted to the female (potentially asexual) colonies (Fig. 3-10G), where they dissociate and individual sperms enter through dissolution of the female-colony surface membrane, fertilizing the numerous spherical gonidia which function as eggs (Fig. 3-10H). The zygotes enlarge, thicken their walls and are ultimately liberated when the parent colony disintegrates (Fig. 3-10I,J). At zygote germination (Figs. 3-10J,K), a single juvenile colony is formed.

The sperms of *V. globator* are borne in disc-like or spherical groups, each of which may contain as many as 512 male cells. The sperm groups are liberated from the parent colony, and are probably attracted chemically to colonies with eggs. Individual colonies of some strains may produce both sperms and eggs, whereas in others the individuals are unisexual. There the individual sperms are set

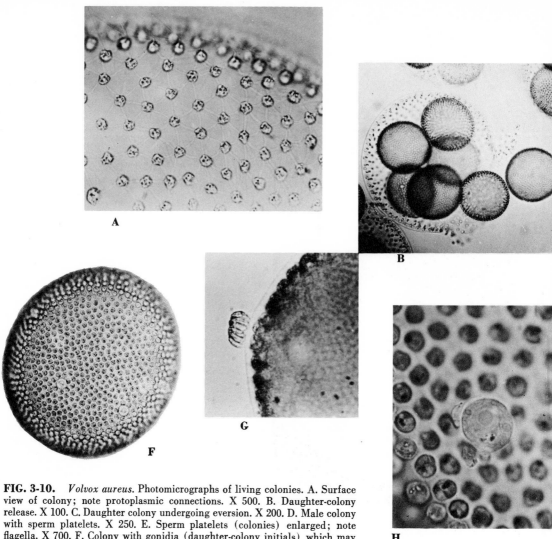

FIG. 3-10. *Volvox aureus.* Photomicrographs of living colonies. A. Surface view of colony; note protoplasmic connections. X 500. B. Daughter-colony release. X 100. C. Daughter colony undergoing eversion. X 200. D. Male colony with sperm platelets. X 250. E. Sperm platelets (colonies) enlarged; note flagella. X 700. F. Colony with gonidia (daughter-colony initials) which may function as eggs. X 250. G. Sperm colony approaching female colony. X 800. H. Fertilization; note sperm adpressed to egg. X 900. I. Female colony with mature zygotes. X 250. J, K. Stages in zygote germination. X 500. (*Courtesy of Dr. William A. Darden.*)

free and penetrate to the eggs. The latter differ from those of *V. aureus* in their pyriform shape. They too are fertilized within the parent colony. The zygotes of *V. globator* develop thick spiny walls after fertilization, undergo a period of dormancy after they are liberated by disintegration of the parent colony, and undergo meiosis during germination, forming a single colony.

In both *Pandorina* and *Volvox*, the number of cells in the colony is fixed before liberation of the daughter colonies from the parent, and it is not augmented by cell division later, even though one or more of the component cells may be injured or destroyed. Such a colony, in which the cell number is determined at origin, is known as a **coenobium.**

II. Nonmotile Unicellular and Colonial Organisms

A. Unicellular Types

Of the vast assemblage of commonly encountered unicellular, nonmotile green algae, two series may be distinguished on the basis of whether or not they produce flagellate cells (zoospores and/or gametes) in their life

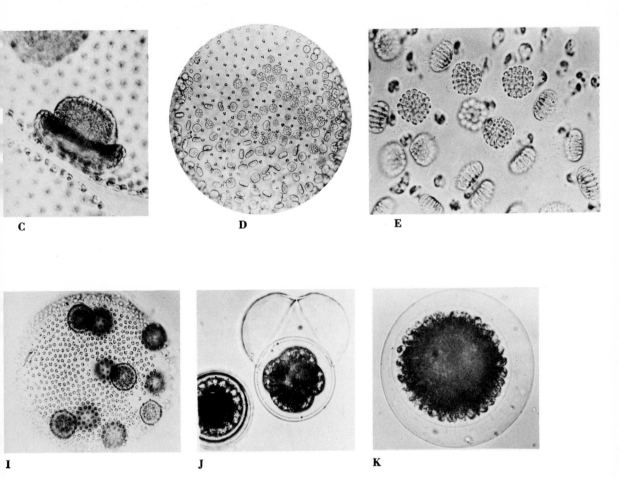

C   D   E

I   J   K

cycles. Flagellate asexual reproductive cells are called **zoospores.**

1. ZOOSPORE PRODUCERS

Tetracystis

The recently described soil-inhabiting genus *Tetracystis* is significant in its combination of seemingly primitive and advanced[12] at-

[12] In evolutionary biology, attributes present in ancient organisms or those clearly little modified from those of such organisms are said to be "primitive." Modifications of primitive attributes are designated as "advanced," "specialized," or "derived." Secondary simplification of an attribute is referred to as a "reduction," and the simplified attribute as "reduced."

tributes. *Tetracystis* produces biflagellate zoospores (Fig. 3-11A); the structure of the latter corresponds in all respects to that of *Chlamydomonas*. After motility, the zoospores lose their flagella, the cells enlarge, and sooner or later become partitioned so that two or four nonmotile daughter cells are formed (Fig. 3-11B). This cell partitioning is similar to that in multicellular plants in that the parental cell walls persist after the daughter cell walls have formed. The component cells of the tetrad enlarge and may again divide into tetrads, and this process may continue, thus giving rise to tissuelike complexes of

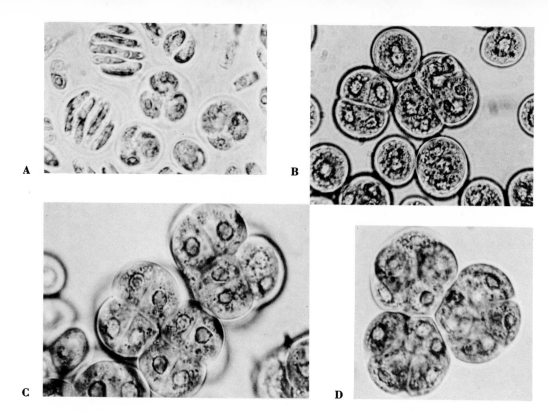

FIG. 3-11. *Tetracystis* sp. A. Stages in zoosporogenesis. B. Vegetative cells in tetrad formation. C. Mature tetrads. D. Tetrad complexes. X 560.

cells (Fig. 3-11D). We see in this unicellular green alga, accordingly, the potentiality of forming parenchymatous[13] aggregations of cells such as occur in membranous green algae (p. 53) and in the nonalgal groups of chlorophyllous plants. These cellular complexes of *Tetracystis* may dissociate into smaller cell clusters or even to the unicellular level by degradation and/or splitting of old cell walls. The individual cells of the complex may form zoospores (Fig. 3-11D) either before or after dissociation.

In some species of *Tetracystis*, the zoospores may function as isogamous gametes which unite to form zygotes. This occurs in many algae. Whether we consider such zoospores to be facultative gametes or whether we consider them to be gametes which may develop parthenogenetically[14] if they fail to unite with another gamete seems immaterial.

Sexuality in many algae seems to be incipient or sporadic, rather than obligate.

Chlorococcum

Chlorococcum (Gr. *chloros*, green + Gr. *kokkos*, berry) (Fig. 3-12) also is an inhabitant of fresh water and soils (both undisturbed and cultivated). More than nineteen species are known and available in culture.[15]

Chlorococcum is difficult to distinguish from other nonmotile spherical unicellular Chlorophycophyta, unless one cultivates it in unialgal cultures. The mature cells of *Chlorococcum* are spherical (Fig. 3-12A-3), unless they have become polyhedral by mutual compression. Each has a cellulose wall and a protoplast containing a hollow spherical chlo-

---

[13] Parenchymatous, adj. of parenchyma: plant tissue composed of thin-walled living cells.

[14] Parthenogenesis is the development of a gamete, without uniting with another gamete, into a new individual.

[15] Cultures are populations of microorganisms maintained in the laboratory. **Unialgal cultures** contain only one species of alga, although bacteria, fungi, or protozoa, or all three may be present. **Axenic** or **pure cultures** contain populations of only one species. **Clonal cultures** of a given organism are those in which the population has arisen from one individual by asexual reproduction.

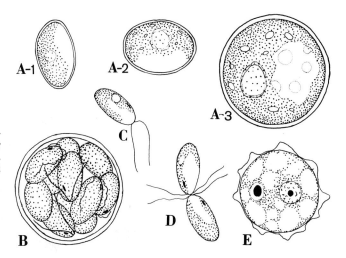

FIG. 3-12. *Chlorococcum echinozygotum* Starr. A1–3. Increasingly older vegetative cells. B. Zoospore formation. C. Zoospore. D. Isogamy. E. Dormant zygote (stained). X 1500.

roplast, usually with one aperture. One or more pyrenoids are embedded in the chloroplast, usually opposite the aperture. Both uninucleate and multinucleate species of *Chlorococcum* are known.

Division of one cell into two or four non-motile daughter cells, as in *Tetracystis* (Fig. 3-11B), is absent in *Chlorococcum*. Instead, the vegetative cells divide and form a number of biflagellate zoospores (Fig. 3-12B,C) which, again, are almost identical with cells of *Chlamydomonas*. A nonmotile cell which produces zoospores is called a **zoosporangium**. After a period of motility, the duration of which is affected by such environmental factors as light intensity, temperature, composition of the culture medium and its concentration, the zoospores aggregate in the most brightly illuminated portion of the culture vessel,[16] lose their flagella, and grow into new vegetative cells (Fig. 3-12A). During this process the stigma disappears, but in some species the contractile vacuoles persist. In *Chlorococcum, Tetracystis,* and other algae, production of zoospores by nonmotile vegetative cells is interpreted as a reversion to a primitively motile condition. This could be cited as an example of the biogenetic law which states that **ontogeny recapitulates phylogeny.**

Under certain circumstances in laboratory culture, and presumably in nature, the zoospores, instead of escaping from the zoospo-

rangia, omit the motile phase and begin their development into vegetative cells within the zoosporangial wall which is finally ruptured. Such potential zoospores, which have omitted a motile phase, are called **aplanospores.**

In some species of *Chlorococcum—C. echinozygotum* Starr, for example—the zoospores may function as isogametes and unite to form spiny-walled dormant zygotes (Fig. 3-12D,E). These give rise upon germination to four zoospores which, upon liberation, develop into vegetative cells. Meiosis is thought to be zygotic. The capacity of the motile cells of *Chlamydomonas, Tetracystis,* and *Chlorococcum* to function either sexually or asexually suggests a primitive grade of development, perhaps incipient sexuality, in contrast to those algae in which gametes and zoospores differ morphologically (Fig. 3-30C,E).

Protosiphon

Protosiphon botryoides Klebs (Fig. 3-13), a widespread soil alga, is included here because of its interesting morphology and life cycle and the marked modifications thereof evoked by environmental stimuli. *Protosiphon* is a terrestrial alga of cultivated soils (where it often grows intermingled with *Botrydium*) (Fig. 7-4, 7-5, p. 94). After rain, it forms dark-green patches, which become orange-red as the soil dries. The mature plants are saclike, with a single, basal, rhizoidal protuberance which penetrates the substrate (Fig. 3-13A). The upper, bulblike portion contains alveolar cytoplasm with a diffuse chloroplast containing many pyrenoids; the sacs are multinucle-

---

[16] Movements by organisms to or away from stimuli are **taxes**; the movement of the zoospores of *Chlorococcum* in the present instance exemplifies positive phototaxis.

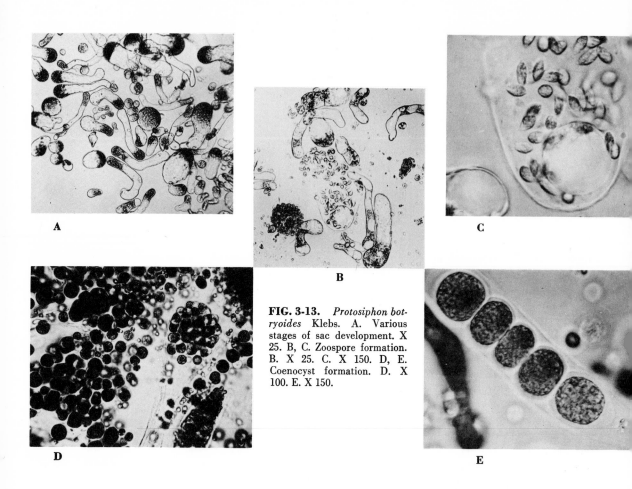

FIG. 3-13. *Protosiphon botryoides* Klebs. A. Various stages of sac development. X 25. B, C. Zoospore formation. B. X 25. C. X 150. D, E. Coenocyst formation. D. X 100. E. X 150.

ate (coenocytic) and, when adequate nitrogen is available, may exceed 1 mm. in length.

When it rains, or when agar cultures are submerged, the sacs form numerous biflagellate zoospores (Figs. 3-13B,C, 3-14) which, here again, may function as gametes. These zoospores, as in *Tetracystis* and *Chlorococ-*

cum, may be transformed into aplanospores if the moisture level falls.

On the other hand, sacs on drying soil or agar become subdivided into a small number of large multinucleate cells called **coenocysts** (Figs. 3-13D,E, 3-14). The walls of these thicken as the moisture level falls, and the

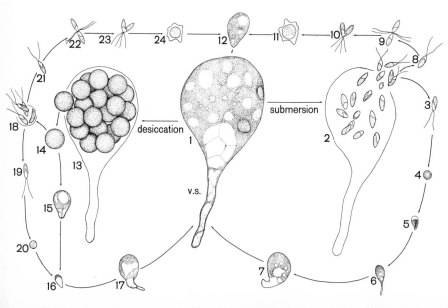

FIG. 3-14. The life cycle of *Protosiphon botryoides*. 1. Vegetative cell or sac. 2. Zoospore/gamete formation and release. 3–7. Stages in asexual development of sacs from zoospores. 8–12. Sexual cycle including gamete union (9, 10). 11, 12. Zygote and its germination. 13. Coenocyst formation. 14–17. Direct development of coenocysts into vegetative sac. 18–20. Asexual cycle of zoospores formed by coenocysts. 18–24. Sexual cycle of gametes from coenocysts.

chlorophyll is replaced or masked by an orange-red pigment, the chemical nature of which has not been determined. The coenocysts (and thick-walled zygotes) retain their viability during long periods of desiccation. When moisture again becomes available, they may become green and develop directly into new sacs, or the coenocysts may form zoospores or gametes. The complicated life cycle, as it is determined by availability of moisture, is summarized in Fig. 3-14. The occurrence of the coenocytic condition in *Protosiphon* has suggested to some its possible relationship to the coenocytic algae to be described later in this chapter.

2. FORMS LACKING ZOOSPORES

Chlorella

Chlorella (Gr. *chloros*, green + L. *ella*, diminutive) (Fig. 3-15) is widespread in fresh and salt water and also in soil. It appears often with surprising rapidity in laboratory vessels in which distilled water or inorganic salt solutions are stored. Like *Chlorococcum*, *Chlorella* is most successfully studied in unialgal cultures. *Chlorella* was the first alga to be isolated and grown in axenic culture; this was accomplished in 1890 by the Dutch microbiologist Beijerinck. The cells of most species of *Chlorella* are minute green spheres (Fig. 3-15) in which the details of cell structure are seen best under high magnification. The protoplast is composed of a cuplike chloroplast which may or may not contain a pyrenoid and of colorless central cytoplasm in which the minute nucleus is embedded. A series of bi-

partitions may occur, forming four or eight protoplasts endogenously. These develop delicate cell walls, and after they have begun to enlarge, they are liberated by rupture of the mother cell wall (Fig. 3-15B). Such asexual reproductive cells, which have no capacity for motility, are known as **autospores,** because they resemble, in miniature, the mother cells which produce them. Sexual reproduction has not been observed in *Chlorella*. A number of species of *Chlorella* have been grown in pure culture and have provided the material for experimental studies of photosynthesis.

Eremosphaera (Gr. *eremos*, solitary + Gr. *sphaira*, ball) (Fig. 3-16) is one of the largest and most spectacular unicellular green algae known. It occurs on the bottom of swamps and quiet ponds in which the water is at least slightly acid. It grows readily in laboratory culture. The individual cells of *Eremosphaera viridis* DeBary (Fig. 3-16) are large enough to be visible to the unaided eye. Each contains many small, pyrenoid-bearing chloroplasts and a prominent, central nucleus suspended by threads of streaming colorless cytoplasm. The only known method of reproduction is by the division of the parent cell into two, four, or eight (rarely) nonmotile daughter cells (autospores), which, unlike those of *Tetracystis*, are liberated promptly after division by rupture of the parent cell wall.

B. Nonmotile Colonial Organisms

The nonmotile colonial Chlorophycophyta parallel the nonmotile unicellular forms in that two series of genera are known. In one,

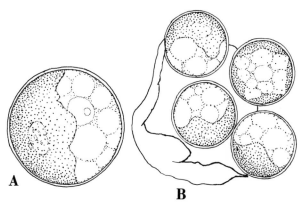

FIG. 3-15. *Chlorella* sp. A. Vegetative cell. B. Autospore liberation. X 3700.

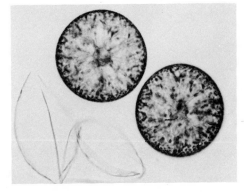

FIG. 3-16. *Eremosphaera viridis* DeBary. Two recently released young vegetative cells (autospores). X 2000. (*Courtesy of Dr. Richard L. Smith.*)

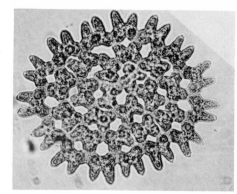

FIG. 3-17. *Pediastrum duplex* Meyen. X 300.

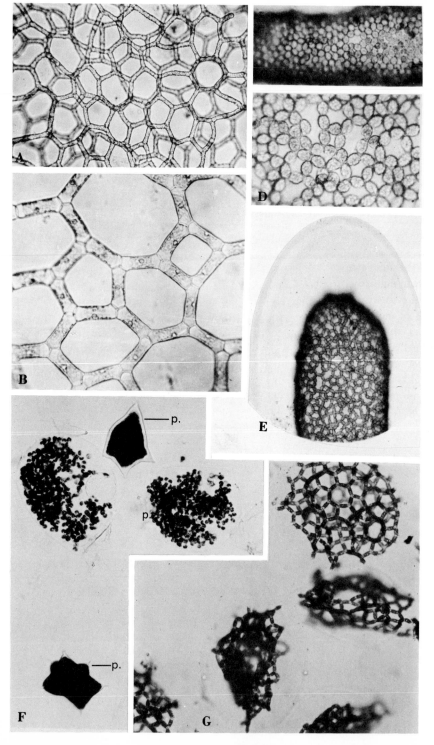

FIG. 3-18. *Hydrodictyon reticulatum* (L.) Lagerh. A. Portion of young net. X 125. B. The same. X 200. C. Zoospores within parent cell. X 250. D, E. Young nets within parent cell. D. X 500. E. X 125. F. Polyeders, two containing zoospores. X 300. G. Juvenile nets from polyeders. X 250; p., polyeder; p.z., polyeder containing zoospores. (F, G. *Courtesy of Dr. M. A. Pocock.*)

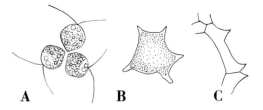

FIG. 3-19. *Hydrodictyon reticulatum.* A. Motile zoospores. X 700. B. Polyeder. X 300. C. Marginal cell of juvenile net; note *Pediastrum*-like protuberances. X. 700.

here represented by *Pediastrum* and *Hydrodictyon,* flagellate reproductive cells (zoospores and/or gametes) occur, while in the other, here illustrated by *Scenedesmus* and *Coelastrum,* motile cells are usually[17] absent.

1. ZOOSPORE PRODUCERS

Pediastrum and Hydrodictyon

The coenobic colonies of *Pediastrum* (Gr. *pedion,* plane + Gr. *astron,* star) (Fig. 3-17) and *Hydrodictyon* (Gr. *hydor,* water + Gr. *dictyon,* net) (Fig. 3-18) grow on the bottom of quiet pools and lakes as well as in their plankton and may readily be grown in laboratory culture. Both have multinucleate cells. The coenobia of *Pediastrum* are flat plates while those of *Hydrodictyon* are cylindrical. Both reproduce asexually by daughter colonies organized from zoospores and both have isogamous sexual reproduction.

Hydrodictyon reticulatum (L.) Lagerh., commonly known as the "water net," often appears in great abundance in pools, lakes, and quiet streams. The mature colonies are composed of large cylindrical cells joined together in polygonal configurations, the whole colony being cylindrical. The young cells (Fig. 3-18B) are uninucleate and delicate green. They ultimately enlarge many times, and develop numerous nuclei and large central vacuoles which force the cytoplasm into a peripheral position.

In asexual reproduction, the mature cells undergo a type of cytokinesis known as **progressive cleavage,** in which the multinucleate mass of protoplasm is gradually segmented into smaller and smaller portions until uninucleate segments result (Fig. 3-18C). Each of these functions as a zoospore (Fig. 3-19A). As motility abates, the zoospores are arranged in groups of four to nine, typically six, within the cylindrical parent cell (Fig. 3-19D) which

[17] See page 42.

serves as a mold for the young net of the next generation. After the flagella have disappeared, the cells begin to enlarge and assume a cylindrical form (Fig. 3-19E). By continuous increase in cell size and rupture of the parent wall, nets more than 30 inches in length may develop.

Sexual reproduction is isogamous. Unlike the zoospores which they resemble morphologically, the gametes are liberated from the parent cells. Meiosis is zygotic and the germinating zygotes develop four zoospores which grow into nonmotile polyhedral cells known as **polyeders** (Fig. 3-19B). These enlarge, undergo cleavage and zoosporogenesis, and liberate a number of actively swimming zoospores within a gelatinous vesicle (Fig. 3-18F). These zoospores arrange themselves as a hollow sphere (which may be flattened), or as a flat plate, lose their flagella, and grow into cylindrical cells typical of the adult plant. This juvenile colony (Fig. 3-18G), is not cylindrical as in the adult, although its component cells are cylindrical. Of great interest is the fact that its marginal cells may each bear two *Pediastrum*-like protuberances (Fig. 3-19C). These phenomena often are interpreted as evidence of a common ancestry for *Hydrodictyon* and *Pediastrum*. In this connection, it is of interest that two other species of *Hydrodictyon* have adult colonies which are flattened rather than cylindrical, possibly because they lack asexual reproduction.

2. COLONIAL ORGANISMS LACKING ZOOSPORES

Scenedesmus

With respect to zoospores, *Scenedesmus* stands in relation to *Pediastrum* and *Hydrodictyon* as *Eremosphaera* and *Chlorella* do to *Chlorococcum*. As in *Chlorella,* zoospores are not produced in *Scenedesmus*. This coenobic alga is ubiquitous, occurring abundantly in almost every fresh-water habitat and occasionally in soil. It consists of a colony composed of four or more component cells united laterally (Fig. 3-20). In some species, the terminal cells have spinelike processes. The uninucleate cells have a parietal chloroplast containing a single pyrenoid. Reproduction, which in many species is entirely asexual, is

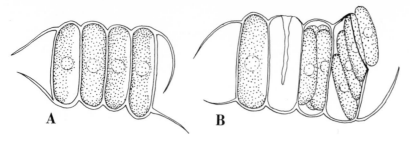

FIG. 3-20. *Scenedesmus* sp. A. Immature vegetative colony. B. Autocolony formation and liberation. X 770.

by the formation of **autocolonies** within each cell of the adult (Fig. 3-20B). These are liberated by the rupture of the parent cell wall and then gradually achieve the size and ornamentation characteristic of the species.

It has recently been demonstrated[18] that isogamous sexual reproduction occurs under certain conditions in *S. obliquus*. Clonal cultures are unisexual and the two compatible mating types must be mixed before clump formation and gamete union occur. The zygotes enlarge and later germinate to form forty or more cells. When these are taken into clonal culture, the clones are unisexual; this is genetic evidence of zygotic meiosis.

In light of these observations, it has been proposed that *S. obliquus* and other species which produce motile cells should be classified with coenobic algae like *Hydrodictyon* and *Pediastrum*.

Coelastrum

The coenobia of *Coelastrum* are hollow spheres of up to 128 cells, the latter contiguous or united by protuberances of the wall (Fig. 3-21). The sole method of reproduction is by autocolony formation in which the individual cells divide into miniature colonies which are liberated by the breaking of the parent cell wall.

---

[18] Trainor, F. R., and Carol A. Burg, 1965. "*Scenedesmus obliquus* sexuality," *Science*, 148:1094–1095, and personal communication.

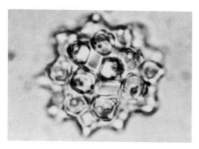

FIG. 3-21. *Coelastrum* sp. X 500.

III. Filamentous Organisms

As in the Cyanophycophyta, restriction of cell division to one direction and coherence of the daughter cells result in filamentous organisms among the green algae; division of certain cells in the filament in a plane at 90° or less, with reference to the prevailing direction, initiates branching.

The genera to be discussed in this section may be grouped into two categories on the criterion of whether or not they produce flagellate cells.

A. Filamentous Organisms with Flagellate Reproductive Stages

The illustrative genera in this group include both unbranched (*Ulothrix* and *Oedogonium*) and branched plants (*Stigeoclonium* and *Cladophora*).

Ulothrix

The unbranched filaments of *Ulothrix* (Fig. 3-22) grow attached to stones and other submerged objects in cold-water streams and lakes; several species are marine. In *Ulothrix* (Gr. *oulos*, wooly + Gr. *thrix*, hair), the cells of each filament are as similar to each other as are those of *Oscillatoria*, except that the basal cell is modified as an attaching structure, the holdfast (Fig. 3-22A). The cells contain partial or complete band-shaped chloroplasts (Fig. 3-22B) with more than one pyrenoid and are uninucleate.

After a period of vegetative growth by cell division and elongation, asexual reproduction by zoospores may occur (Figs. 3-22C, 3-23). Zoospores may be produced singly or in multiples of two from each vegetative cell. The liberated zoospores exhibit the usual attributes of motile cells such as stigmata, contractile vacuoles, and four flagella (Figs. 3-22C,

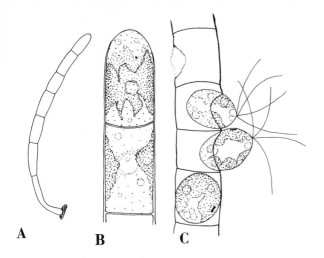

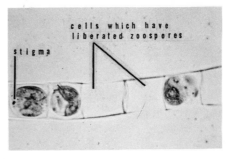

FIG. 3-22. *Ulothrix fimbriata* Bold. A. Young plant attached to particle of debris by a holdfast. X 215. B. Cellular organization at apex of filament; apical cell, three-dimensional, second cell in optical section. X 700. C. Zoospore formation. X 770.

FIG. 3-23. *Ulothrix fimbriata.* Zoosporogenesis. X 600.

3-24A) in which respect they resemble *Carteria* (Fig. 3-5). After a period of activity, the zoospores settle on submerged objects with their flagellate poles foremost (Fig. 3-24B,C), lose their flagella, and attach themselves. Elongation and division of the original zoospore (Fig. 3-24D) produce a vegetative filament.

Sexual reproduction by a union of biflagellate isogametes (Fig. 3-24E,F) also occurs. There is evidence that the sexual filaments are unisexual in some species. Meiosis, as in all other genera so far considered, occurs just prior to germination of the zygote. The latter gives rise to four zoospores each of which grows into a new filament.

Oedogonium

Oedogonium (Gr. *oedos*, swelling + Gr. *gonos*, reproductive structure) differs from *Ulothrix* in that its zoospores possess a crown of about 120 flagella (Figs. 3-25A,B, 3-26A). Furthermore, although the quadriflagellate and biflagellate cells of nonmotile algae suggest, respectively, the unicellular motile genera, *Carteria* and *Chlamydomonas*, no multiflagellate unicellular genus corresponding to the motile cells of *Oedogonium* is known. Growth is intercalary and localized in certain cells on which annular scars indicate the number of cell divisions which have occurred (Fig. 3-26B). The cells include segmented, netlike chloroplasts containing pyrenoids.

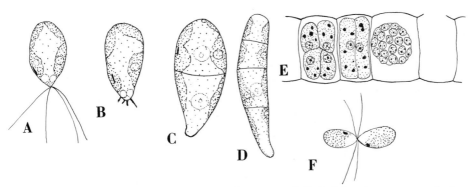

FIG. 3-24. *Ulothrix.* A–D. Development of zoospore of *U. fimbriata* into a young plant. A–C. X 700. D. X 400. E, F. *U. zonata.* E. Gametogenesis. F. Isogamy. X 315.

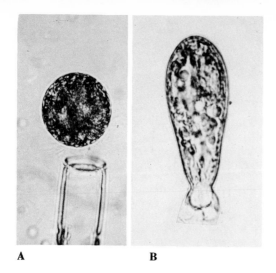

FIG. 3-25. *Oedogonium cardiacum.* A. Release of zoospore. B. Germling. X 500.

The life cycle of *Oedogonium* is like that of *Ulothrix*. Asexual reproduction is effected by the formation and liberation of single zoospores from vegetative cells (Figs. 3-25, 3-26A).

Sexual reproduction in *Oedogonium* is oogamous. The egg is produced in an enlarged gametangium, the **oogonium,** which opens by a pore or fissure just before fertilization (Figs. 3-26B, 3-27). The sperms arise in pairs in short, boxlike cells, the **antheridia** (Figs. 3-26 to 3-27). The sperms also are

multiflagellate (Fig. 3-27F). After fertilization, the zygote develops a wall composed of two or more layers, often becomes reddish, and enters a period of dormancy (Fig. 3-27G). It is liberated by the disintegration of the oogonial wall. The germination of the zygote[19] into four zoospores is preceded by meiosis.

Considerable variation occurs among the numerous species of *Oedogonium* with respect to the location of the sex organs.

Both antheridia and oogonia may occur on the same filament (Fig. 3-26B) in which case, of course, the organism is bisexual. In species with unisexual filaments, a plant which develops from a single zoospore produces either antheridia or oogonia (Fig. 3-27), never both. The male filaments may be slightly narrower than the female.

It has also been demonstrated that in unisexual types, the mature oogonia produce a substance which chemically attracts free-swimming sperm.

In a number of *Oedogonium* species, the male filaments are epiphytic dwarf filaments which develop from special androspores[20]

---

[19] The zygote formed in oogamous reproduction is often called an oospore.

[20] Zoospores which form dwarf-male plants.

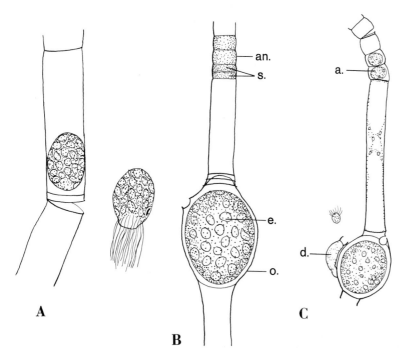

—— an.
—— s.

—— e.
—— o.

a. ——

d. ——

A

B

C

FIG. 3-26. *Oedogonium* sp. A. Zoospore formation and single, free-swimming zoospore. B. *Oedogonium foveolatum* Wittr., a bisexual species. C. *Oedogonium* sp., gynandrosporous; a., androspore; an., antheridium; d., dwarf male; e., egg; o., oogonium; s., sperm. X 315.

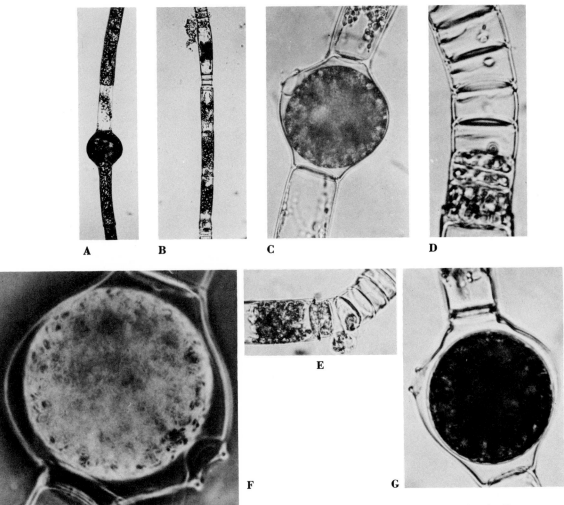

A   B   C   D

E

F   G

FIG. 3-27. *Oedogonium cardiacum.* A. Female filament with immature oogonium. X 150. B. Male filament with three series of antheridia. X. 150. C. Oogonium with egg ready for fertilization; note oogonial pore. X 700. D. Antheridia, two with sperm, the rest after sperm discharge. X 1500. E. Liberation of sperm. X 700. F. Prefertilization, sperm approaching oogonium. X 150. G. Young zygote (oospore). X 1000. (F. *Courtesy of Dr. L. R. Hoffman.*)

which attach themselves to the cell that divides to form the oogonium and its supporting cell (Fig. 3-26C). Recent research has demonstrated that these androspores are attracted to this site by a substance secreted by the oogonial mother cell. The direction of growth of the dwarf males, in turn, is determined by a hormone from the oogonium and its supporting cell only after the dwarf male has produced its antheridia. The dwarf males, accordingly, probably produce a chemical which evokes division of the oogonial mother cell.

Stigeoclonium

Occasional cell division in a second direction produces a branching filamentous plant body in *Stigeoclonium* and *Cladophora*.

Stigeoclonium (L. *stigens,* sharp + L. *clonium,* branch) is a plant widely distributed in lakes and streams, where it grows attached to stones and vegetation. In most species, the plant consists of two portions (Fig. 3-28A). A prostrate, and probably perennial, system of irregularly branched filaments or a disc is attached to the substratum. From this, elongate branching filaments grow out into the

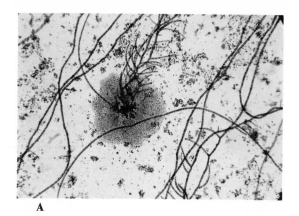

A

B

FIG. 3-28. *Stigeoclonium farctum* Kütz. A. Cultured plant showing heterotrichy; note prostrate basal and erect systems. X 75. B. Zoospore release. X 800. (*Courtesy of Dr. Elenor R. Cox.*)

water. These are attenuated and may end in hairlike branches. Because they have two branch systems, the plants are said to be heterotrichous. The cells of *Stigeoclonium* are uninucleate and contain single chloroplasts with one or several pyrenoids.

In asexual reproduction, quadriflagellate zoospores are liberated singly from the cells of the plant body (Fig. 3-28B). After a period of activity, these become attached to the substratum by the formerly flagellate pole, secrete a wall, and develop into new plant bodies.

Union of biflagellate gametes has been described for some species; in others the gametes are reported to be quadriflagellate. Apparently meiosis is zygotic in most species of *Stigeoclonium*. As in *Ulothrix*, the zygote germinates to form four zoospores which ultimately grow into new plants.

Cladophora

Cladophora (Gr. *klados*, branch + Gr. *phores*, bearer) (Fig. 3-29A) differs from *Stigeoclonium* in a number of respects, among them, larger size, multinucleate cells, and, especially, life cycle. Species of *Cladophora* are widespread in both fresh and salt water, where they may be free-floating or attached to rocks or vegetation. The plants often are anchored to the substratum by rhizoidal branches. The latter are perennial and persist through adverse conditions. Growth of the branching filaments is localized near the apices of the filaments, in contrast with the generalized growth of *Ulothrix*. In many species, the branches arise as eversions from the upper portions of the lateral walls of relatively young cells (Fig. 3-29A, arrow). When they have achieved a certain length, they are delimited from the parent cell by an annular ingrowth of the wall.

The cylindrical cells of *Cladophora* are much larger than those of *Stigeoclonium*, and their cell walls are thicker and stratified (Fig. 3-30A). The structure of the chloroplast varies with the age of the cell. In younger cells it is a continuous network, but in older ones it is largely peripheral and composed of irregular

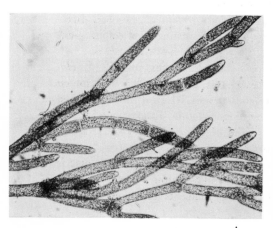

FIG. 3-29. *Cladophora* sp. A. Vegetative filaments. B. Zoospore formation. X 125.

A   B

46

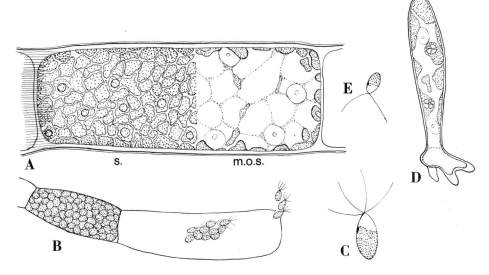

FIG. 3-30. *Cladophora*. A. Cellular organization; surface view at s., median optical section at m.o.s. X 770. B. Zoospore formation and liberation in a marine species. X 315. C. Zoospore. X 770. D. Germling from zoospore. X 550. E. Gamete. X 770.

segments in some of which pyrenoids are embedded. Segments of the chloroplast may extend toward the center of the cell. Frothy cytoplasm, with numerous nuclei (Fig. 3-30A) suspended in its meshes, fills the center of the cell. Mitosis and cytokinesis are entirely independent processes in *Cladophora*, in contrast with their rather close relationship in most plants and animals with uninucleate cells.

Asexual reproduction is accomplished by uninucleate, quadriflagellate zoospores (Figs. 3-29B, 3-30B-D). These arise by cleavage of the protoplasts of terminal and near-terminal cells into uninucleate segments. Each segment develops four flagella, and the mature zoospores are liberated through a pore in the zoosporangial wall. After a period of motility the zoospores grow into new plants. The young germlings are uninucleate, but the coenocytic (multinucleate) condition is soon initiated (Fig. 3-30D) by the continuation of mitosis without ensuing cytokinesis. *Cladophora* plants also produce biflagellate isogametes (Fig. 3-30E) in sexual reproduction. These also are formed in the terminal and near-terminal cells. The zygotes germinate without a period of dormancy and grow directly into new plants.

Cytological studies of plants in nature and in culture indicate that a complicated cycle occurs in *Cladophora*. In *Cladophora suhriana* Kütz., and other marine species, it has been shown that two types of plant occur in nature.

These are morphologically indistinguishable but differ in chromosome complement and nature of their reproductive cells. One type of plant is diploid and produces only zoospores from cells in which meiosis precedes the cleavage into zoospores. The latter develop into haploid plants, morphologically similar to the diploid ones. However, the haploid plants, which are probably unisexual, produce only biflagellate gametes at maturity. The gametes unite in pairs to form zygotes, which develop without meiosis into diploid filaments. Meiosis in *Cladophora*, therefore, is **sporic** rather than zygotic as in all the other green algae discussed up to this point.

Organisms with two distinct, free-living plants in the life cycle are **diplobiontic** (Gr. *diplóos*, double + Gr. *bion*, living) ; *Cladophora*, therefore, is diplobiontic. Other genera, in which only one free-living organism occurs in the life cycle, are **haplobiontic** (Gr. *haplóos*, single + Gr. *bion*), as are all the green algae discussed prior to *Cladophora*. Diplobiontic life cycles illustrate but one manifestation of the larger phenomenon of alternation of generations (see Chart 3-1). They are a specialized example of the latter in which the alternants are *free-living* individuals. In contrast, alternation of generations of another type, in which the alternants are physically connected, occurs in the liverworts, mosses, and in some vascular plants.

Haplobiontic life cycles may be thought of

CHART 3-1

Three Basic Types of Life Cycle in Algae[a]

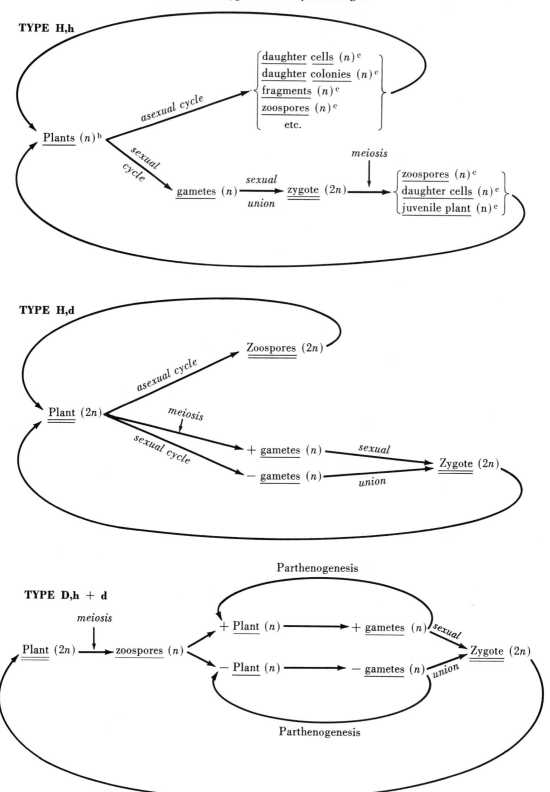

TYPE H,h

Plants (n)[b]

asexual cycle

$\begin{cases} \text{daughter cells } (n)\text{[c]} \\ \text{daughter colonies } (n)\text{[c]} \\ \text{fragments } (n)\text{[c]} \\ \text{zoospores } (n)\text{[c]} \\ \qquad \text{etc.} \end{cases}$

sexual cycle

gametes (n) — sexual union → zygote $(2n)$ →

meiosis

$\begin{cases} \text{zoospores } (n)\text{[c]} \\ \text{daughter cells } (n)\text{[c]} \\ \text{juvenile plant } (n)\text{[c]} \end{cases}$

TYPE H,d

Plant $(2n)$

asexual cycle → Zoospores $(2n)$

meiosis

sexual cycle

+ gametes (n)
− gametes (n)

sexual union → Zygote $(2n)$

TYPE D,h + d

Plant $(2n)$ — *meiosis* → zoospores (n)

+ Plant (n) → + gametes (n) *sexual*
− Plant (n) → − gametes (n) *union* → Zygote $(2n)$

Parthenogenesis

Parthenogenesis

[a] Haploid phases underlined once; diploid phases twice. Both the haploid and diploid plants may replicate themselves by asexual agents such as fragments and various types of spores.
[b] If plants are unisexual, + and − or male and female plants will be necessary.
[c] Alternate phases which characterize specific algae.

as exhibiting only alternation of nuclear (haploid and diploid) phases, one alternant, either the zygote or the gamete, consisting merely of a single cell and not of a free-living plant. This condition occurs in *Chlamydomonas* and *Ulothrix*, among others (Type H,h, Chart 3-1, p. 48). In these genera the entire life cycle consists of haploid individuals, with the exception of the diploid zygotes. It should be noted that the terms haploid and diploid are used with reference to chromosome constitution. Haploid organisms possess a single basic complement of chromosomes in their nuclei; diploid individuals have nuclei with two such sets.

A reverse type of haplobiontic life cycle (Type H,d, Chart 3-1, p. 48) is present in coenocytic green algae such as *Bryopsis* (p. 54) and *Acetabularia* (p. 56). In these, the diploid plant body is dominant and the haploid phase is represented only by the gametes.

Diplobiontic life cycles often are said to exhibit morphological (as well as cytological) alternation of generations, for in this type both the diploid and haploid phases occur as morphologically recognizable plants. The alternants may be equal in stature and morphologically similar, as in *Cladophora*. In this case, alternation is said to be **isomorphic**. When the alternating phases are dissimilar morphologically (as in *Laminaria*, a brown alga, p. 64, and in the fern, for example), the alternation is called **heteromorphic**.

Alternation of generations itself is the sequence in which a diploid phase gives rise by meiosis to haploid spores which initiate a haploid, gamete-producing phase. The zygote produced in sexual reproduction of the latter re-initiates the diploid phase.

One can compare the two alternating generations of *Cladophora* with the sporophytic and gametophytic phases of the land plants, for in origin, function, and position in the life cycle they seem to be fundamentally similar. The significance of these facts has not been appreciated as widely as it should have been by those interested in the problems of evolution and phylogeny of plants. While an alternation of generations like that described as Type D,h+d (Chart 3-1, p. 48) has long been known in the land plants, few students of these groups, in speculating about their origin, have considered the significance of the occurrence of a similar type of life cycle in the Chlorophycophyta. This problem will be discussed again in our consideration of the land plants.

B. Filamentous Organisms Lacking Flagellate Reproductive Cells

Finally, among the filamentous algae, representatives of two groups which lack flagellate

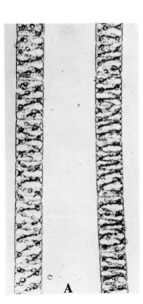  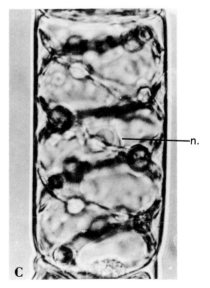

FIG. 3-31. *Spirogyra* sp. A. Vegetative filaments. X 450. B. Cell in surface view. C. The same cell in optical section; n., nucleus. B, C. X 1750.

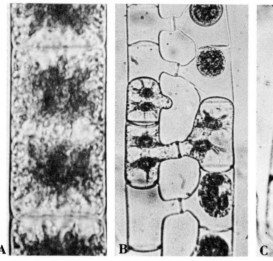
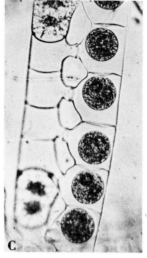

A B C

FIG. 3-32. *Zygnema* sp. A. Vegetative cells. X 1250. B, C. Stages in conjugation. X 500.

cells will be considered. In one of these groups, as exemplified by *Spirogyra* and *Zygnema*, the plants are unbranched filaments which under certain conditions may dissociate into the unicellular condition.

Spirogyra and Zygnema

Spirogyra (Gr. *speira*, a coil + Gr. *gyros*, curved) and *Zygnema* (Gr. *zygon*, yoke + Gr. *nema*, thread), but especially *Spirogyra* (Fig. 3-31), usually are familiar to everyone who has studied biology. These genera often form float-ing, bright green, frothy or slimy masses in small bodies of water in the spring of the year and are referred to frequently as "pond scums" by laymen. The unbranched filaments, generally unattached, grow by generalized cell division and cell elongation. Masses of the plants are slimy to the touch because the fila-ments are surrounded by watery sheaths, de-monstrable by India ink and methylene blue dye.

The cell structure of *Spirogyra* is familiar to many, at least superficially, because of the

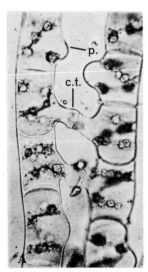
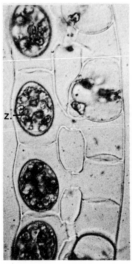

p.

c.t.

z.

z.

A C

FIG. 3-33. *Spirogyra*. A, B. Early and late stages in con-jugation. X 500. C. Zygote germination. X 250. D. Or-ganization of vegetative cell. X 1000; c.c., colorless cyto-plasm; chl., chloroplast; c.t., conjugation tube; n., nucleus; p., papilla; v., vacuole; z., zygote.

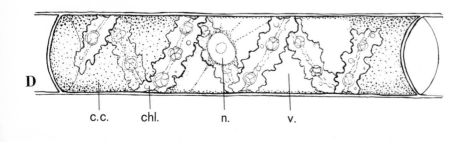

D

c.c.   chl.   n.   v.

spiral arrangement of the ribbonlike chloro-plast or chloroplasts (Figs. 3-31, 3-33D). How-ever, this familiarity and ability to recognize the plant readily often result in a failure to appreciate the many details of cell structure clearly observable by those who *will* to see them. A careful study of the cell structure of *Spirogyra* in the living condition, as revealed by an oil immersion objective, not only is a good test of one's powers of perception but also affords an opportunity for observation of detail in three-dimensional relations which can be transferred, with profit to the observer, to the study of all cells. Species containing one or a few chloroplasts in each cell are especially favorable for study of the cellular organiza-tion, which is illustrated in Figs. 3-31, 3-33D. The living cells of *Spirogyra* are excellent for observation of protoplasmic streaming or cy-closis. *Zygnema* (Fig. 3-32) differs from *Spiro-gyra* in having two stellate chloroplasts in each of its cells.

Aside from fragmentation of the filaments, no method of asexual reproduction occurs in *Spirogyra* and *Zygnema*. In *Spirogyra*, after a period of vegetative development, the fila-ments tend to become apposed. Adjacent cells of contiguous filaments produce papillate pro-tuberances which meet and elongate, thus forcing the filaments apart (Fig. 3-33A,B). Ultimately, the terminal walls of the contigu-ous papillae are dissolved, and one of the protoplasts of the pair of connected cells, both of which have lost much of the cell sap from their large vacuoles, initiates movement through the tubular connection. Contractile vacuoles, usually present only in flagellate cells, appear in the protoplasts during dehy-dration and play an important role in that process. The two protoplasts and their nuclei unite, and the resultant zygote develops a thick wall and enters a period of dormancy. There is evidence that the chloroplast of the migrant cell disintegrates subsequently. Sexual reproduction of this type is interpreted as morphological isogamy with physiological heterogamy, the migrant protoplast being con-sidered a male gamete.

At the conclusion of dormancy, the zygote, which has previously been liberated from the cell wall of the vegetative cell, germinates into a new filament (Fig. 3-33C). Meiosis precedes germination, but only one filament emerges from each zygote, because three of the four products of meiosis disintegrate before germi-nation. In one recently investigated species, meiosis occurred soon after karyogamy in the zygote and before its dormancy was initiated.

In some species of *Spirogyra*, papillae from adjacent cells of the same filament establish contact, and the protoplasts of alternate cells function as male gametes with respect to the next cell of the filament, so that zygotes occur in alternate cells. This is known as **lateral conjugation,** in contrast with the previously described **scalariform** or ladderlike pattern. As a matter of fact, lateral conjugation might more appropriately be called terminal. With respect to the life cycle, *Spirogyra* belongs to the H,h type (Chart 3-1, p. 48).

DESMIDS
Closterium, Cosmarium, Micrasterias

Although they are represented by both uni-cellular and filamentous genera, the desmids are similar to *Spirogyra* and its relatives be-cause of their cell structure and sexual repro-duction. The name **desmid** (Gr. *desmos,* bond) is ascribable to the fact that the cells of a majority of these plants are organized as two semicells which are mirror images of each other; the connecting region is known as the isthmus. As in *Spirogyra*, flagellate motile cells are absent. *Micrasterias* (Gr. *micros,* little + Gr. *asterias,* star) (Fig. 3-34A), *Closterium* (Gr. *kloster,* spindle) (Fig. 3-34B-E), and *Cosmarium* (Gr. *kosmos,* an orna-ment) (Fig. 3-35) are widely distributed genera representative of the unicellular des-mids, although *Micrasterias* cells sometimes are connected in chains. The two semicells of *Micrasterias* (Fig. 3-34A) are separated by a deep incision or sinus. The nucleus lies in the isthmus. The cell wall of a desmid is composed of several layers, the outermost of which is a rather diffluent pectin. It has been shown in some species that localized secretion of pectin through pores in the wall layers results in movement of the cells.

Asexual reproduction of unicellular genera is by cell division preceded by mitosis. In *Micrasterias* and *Cosmarium*, the two prod-

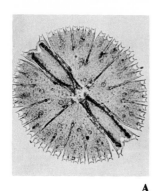

A

B

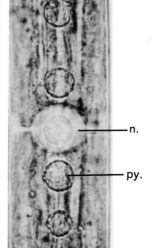

C

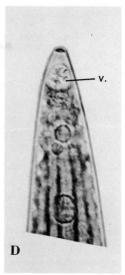

D

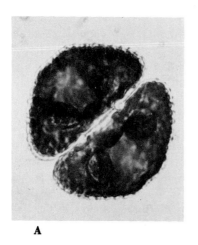

E

FIG. 3-34. Desmids. A. *Micrasterias thomasiana.* X 250. B–D. *Closterium* sp. B. Vegetative cell. X 250. C. Enlarged view of isthmus and adjacent area. D. Cell apex. C, D. X 750. E. *Closterium calosporum* Wittr. var. *maius* West and West; sexual reproduction; note dormant zygote between two empty cells. X 175; n., nucleus; py., pyrenoid; v., vacuole. (E. *After Cook.*)

ucts of cytokinesis, each containing a nucleus, regenerate a single semicell (Fig. 3-35B).

Cosmarium and *Closterium* (Fig. 3-34B-E) are ubiquitous desmids which have been receiving intensive genetic and cytological analysis. Both unisexual and bisexual strains are known in *Closterium* and *Cosmarium*. In some species of *Cosmarium* (Fig. 3-35), it has been demonstrated that the cells are unisexual. When abundant sexually compatible individuals are mixed in laboratory cultures provided with adequate carbon dioxide, the

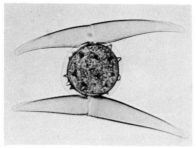

A

B

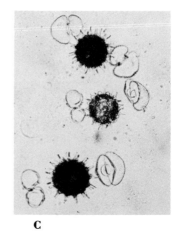

C

FIG. 3-35. *Cosmarium* sp. A. Vegetative cell. X 880. B. Late stage in cell division. X 440. C. Sexual reproduction; note dormant zygotes between pairs of empty cells. X 220.

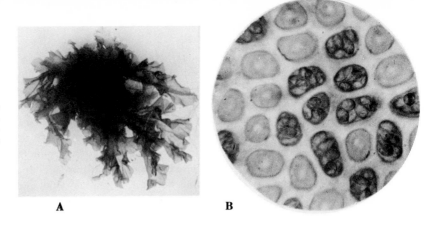

FIG. 3-36. *Ulva lactuca* L. A. Living plant. X ¹⁄₁₂. B. Zoosporogenesis; note emergence pores in empty zoosporangia. X 250.

A   **B**

cells pair within about 48 hours. This is accomplished through slow movements effected by secretion of pectin at one pole of the cell. The cells lie in a common mass of common pectin after they have paired. This is followed by opening of the cell walls at the isthmus and liberation of the protoplasts which unite to form a spiny zygote (Fig. 3-35C). After a period of dormancy, the zygote germinates, producing two daughter cells. Meiosis occurs during germination, but two of the four products of meiosis disintegrate. A similar mode of gamete union occurs in *Closterium* (Fig. 3-34E).

IV. Membranous Organisms

Ulva

The plant body of a membranous green alga like *Ulva* (L. *Ulva*, marsh plants) (Fig. 3-36A), since its life cycle is diplobiontic, may be initiated either by a haploid zoospore or by a zygote. In either case, the initial cell develops at first as an unbranched *Ulothrix*-like filament, from which longitudinal divisions later form in a flat blade. In addition, all the cells undergo one division parallel to the blade surface; thus the plant body becomes two-layered (Fig. 3-37A).

FIG. 3-37. *Ulva lactuca.* A. Transection of plant. B. Cellular organization. C. Zoosporogenesis; note liberation pores for zoospores. D. Zoospore. E, F. Germling from zoospores. G. Female gametangia and gametes. H. Male gametangia and gametes. I–K. Stages in heterogamous gamete union. L, M. Germlings from zygote. A, E, F, L, M. X 315. The remainder X 770.

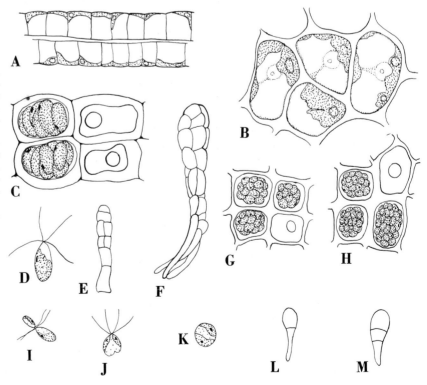

A **B** **C** **D** **E** **F** **G** **H** **I** **J** **K** **L** **M**

Ulva, the sea lettuce, is a familiar alga of marine and brackish waters. It is a widely distributed perennial alga which grows attached to rocks, woodwork, and larger marine algae in quiet estuaries. In *Ulva lactuca* L., the plant body is bladelike, often lobed and undulate; in some varieties it may exceed 3 feet in length. Each plant is anchored to the substratum by a small multicellular holdfast composed of cells with rhizoidal protuberances. The cell walls of *Ulva* (Fig. 3-37B,C) are rather thick, a probable correlative of the fact that the plant can withstand some desiccation when exposed at low tide. Each cell contains a single laminate chloroplast with one or more pyrenoids (Fig. 3-37A,B). The cells of the blade are uninucleate, but those of the holdfast may have several nuclei in their rhizoidal processes. Growth of the plant is generalized.

Ulva reproduces by zoospores (Figs. 3-36B, 3-37C,D) and heterogametes (Fig. 3-37G,H). If one gathers *Ulva* plants of sufficient maturity,[21] permits them to dry slightly, and then immerses them individually in dishes of sea water under strong unilateral illumination, such dishes soon become green with liberated motile cells. The latter manifest strong positive phototaxis. Careful microscopic examination of the motile cells of the several dishes reveals that three types are produced, each by different plants. Some of them liberate large zoospores (Figs. 3-36B, 3-37C,D) which are quadriflagellate; a second group shed biflagellate gametes of two distinct sizes (Fig. 3-37G-J). The small male gametes arise from plants other than those that produce the female ones so that plants of *Ulva lactuca*, therefore, are unisexual. Thus three types of plants, one zoosporic and two gametic, comprise a population of *Ulva*.

The zoospores grow directly into new plants (Fig. 3-37E,F). These plants are the male and female gametophytes which liberate the heterogametes at maturity. The zygotes develop into diploid, zoospore-producing plants (Fig. 3-37K-M). Meiosis occurs in the first two nuclear divisions in the cells that produce the zoospores, which accordingly are haploid, and one half of the zoospores of a given zoosporangium develop into male gametophytes and the other half into female; both, of course, are haploid. Gametes which fail to unite may grow parthenogenetically into new plants. The life cycle of *Ulva* is entirely similar to that of *Cladophora*, being diplobiontic and isomorphic; it clearly belongs to the D,h + d type (Chart 3-1, p. 48).

V. Coenocytic and Tubular Organisms

In addition to the unicellular, colonial, filamentous, and membranous types of plant bodies of Chlorophycophyta already described, brief mention must be made of one additional type, the coenocytic, tubular, or siphonaceous. Siphonaceous green algae are marine, with but a single exception. They may be simple, bilaterally symmetrical, tubular, pinnately branching plants like *Bryopsis* (Fig. 3-38) or radially symmetrical as in *Acetabularia* (Fig. 3-42). In all these plants, the unit of structure is a coenocytic tubular "cell," the multinucleate protoplasm of which is peripherally disposed around a large central vacuole. Transverse septa occur usually only at sites of injury or when reproductive organs are delimited from the vegetative branches.

Bryopsis

Bryopsis (Gr. *bryon*, a moss + Gr. *opsis*, appearance) (Fig. 3-38) grows attached to rocks in shallow marine waters. Growth is apical.

At maturity certain of the branches of *Bryopsis* become cut off from the main axis by septa and become transformed into gametangia (Fig. 3-39A). During this process, the numerous diploid gametangial nuclei undergo meiosis so that the heterogametes (Fig. 3-39B,C) are haploid. The motile zygote settles on the substrate and develops directly into the diploid *Bryopsis*[22] plant. The life cycle

---

[21] These are readily recognizable by their nongreen margins, an indication that reproductive cells have been liberated.

[22] It has been reported for the Mediterranean *Bryopsis halymeniae* Berth. that the zygotes develop into *Derbesia neglecta* Berth., the latter the diploid phase.

FIG. 3-38. *Bryopsis plumosa* (Hudson) C. Agardh. Apex of living plant. X 60.

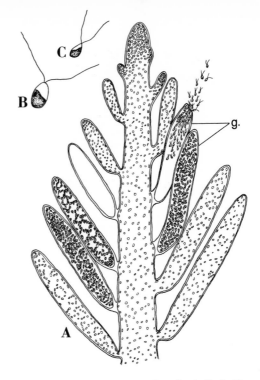

FIG. 3-39. *Bryopsis corticulans* Setchell. A. Shoot with gametangia (g.). X 30. B, C. Heterogamous gametes. X 550. (*Modified from G. M. Smith.*)

of *Bryopsis*, and all siphonaceous algae which have been studied, seems to conform to the H,d type (p. 48), with diploid plant bodies and gametic meiosis.

Caulerpa

In *Caulerpa* (Gr. *kaulos*, a stem + Gr. *herpo*, to creep) (Fig. 3-40), also haplobiontic and diploid, the coenocytic plant bodies are composed of large-diameter, sometimes flattened tubes, the vacuoles of which are traversed by supporting ingrowths of the wall. These tubes may colonize extensive areas and simulate the vascular plants with their stemlike, rootlike, and leaflike branches.

Codium

In *Codium* (Gr. *codion*, a fleece) (Fig. 3-41), the branched, ropelike plants are composed of a longitudinal axis of small-diameter tubes which bear vesicular branches all over their surface (Fig. 3-41C). At the bases of these, gametangia are delimited by walls as in *Bryopsis*.

FIG. 3-40. *Caulerpa* sp. A. Habit of growth. X ½. B. Slightly enlarged view of a branch. X 3. (*Courtesy of Drs. C. J. Alexopoulos and L. Almodovar.*)

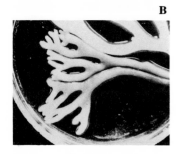

A

B

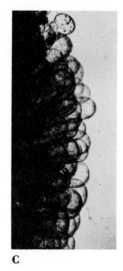

C

FIG. 3-41. *Codium.* A. Habit photograph of *C. fragile* (SW). Hariot. subsp. *tomentosoides* (Van Goor) Silva. X ⅓. B. *Codium tomentosum.* X ⅔. C. Surface view of branch of *C. tomentosum.* X 25.

Acetabularia

Finally, among the marine, coenocytic algae, mention must be made of *Acetabularia* (Fig. 3-42A), (L. *acetabulum*, vinegar cup), the "mermaid's wine goblet" or "mermaid's parasol," a calcified organism widely distributed in subtropical and tropical waters. The radially symmetrical plants arise from zygotes which become attached to calcareous substrates, differentiate slowly into a rhizoidal portion, an erect axis, and, ultimately, into the disclike cap. Throughout the major portion of this development, the zygote nucleus, although it enlarges, remains undivided in the rhizoidal portion. As the cap and its branching appendages (Fig. 3-43A-C) mature, the zygote nucleus divides, and the many diploid products become distributed throughout the plant.

In the chambers of the cap, each nucleus becomes the center about which cytokineses delimit a number of cysts (Figs. 3-42B, 3-43D). These become multinucleate later in development and their walls become calcified. Subsequent disintegration of the old plants liberates the cysts in which numerous biflagellate gametes arise (Fig. 3-43E) after meiosis and cytokineses. The zygotes formed by the union of the latter again initiate a new generation of plants.

Acetabularia, of which there are a number of species, has been intensively investigated with respect to morphogenesis and metabolism. Graft-hybrids between different species and nuclear-transplant studies have been made successfully and have provided basic information regarding the role of nuclei and cytoplasm in morphogenesis and in inheritance.

The existence of large and complex plant bodies composed of coenocytic tubes from which transverse septa are lacking, except during reproduction, has led to speculation regarding the relation of such plants to other types of plant body. To some, the extensive growths represent single giant, multinucleate cells. According to others, they are to be interpreted as acellular plant bodies, the individual nuclei and their surrounding cytoplasm being considered to represent cellular units not delimited by cell walls.

A

B

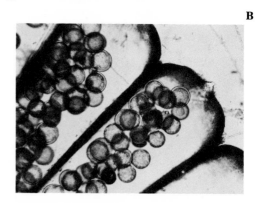

FIG. 3-42. *Acetabularia crenulata* Lamx. A. Group of plants on oyster shell, Rockport, Texas. X 1. B. Almost mature cysts of preceding. X 100.

MORPHOLOGY OF PLANTS

Summary and Classification

One may criticize the relative length of the discussion of the division Chlorophycophyta just concluded, but if he reviews the number and significance of the biological phenomena which they exhibit, no apology will seem necessary. The Chlorophycophyta are distinguished from the Cyanophycophyta (class Myxophyceae) by their pigments, nuclear organization, chloroplasts, mitochondria, and Golgi apparatus; by their flagellate cells and sexual reproduction.

The Chlorophycophyta comprise a series of genera with a wide range of body form, including motile unicellular and colonial organisms, nonmotile unicellular and colonial types, branched and unbranched filaments, membranous and tubular organisms. The component cells may be uninucleate or multinucleate.

The various genera may undergo asexual reproduction by cell division (unicellular forms), by fragmentation (colonial and filamentous types), or by the production of such special reproductive cells as zoospores, aplanospores, and autospores. Colonial genera reproduce by daughter colony formation.

Many genera of Chlorophycophyta exhibit sexual reproduction which involves the union of two cells, their nuclei, the association of their chromosomes and genes, and meiosis. Variations of sexuality such as isogamy, heterogamy, and oogamy may be observed in the several illustrative genera. In organisms like *Chlamydomonas* and *Chlorococcum*, in which gametes are morphologically indistinguishable from asexual cells, it is possible that sexuality is primitive and incipient. The gametes of both sexes may occur on one individual or be present in its asexual descendants, a clone, or they may be segregated in different individuals or clones. The Chlorophycophyta also illustrate a variety of reproductive cycles, as follows: Type H,h: Organisms which are haplobiontic and haploid, with zygotic meiosis. Type H,d: Organisms which are haplobiontic and diploid, with gametic meiosis. Type D,h + d: Organisms which are diplobiontic, with sporic meiosis (Chart 3-1, p. 48).

Alternation in the life cycle in the first two types (H,h and H,d) is often called **cyto-**

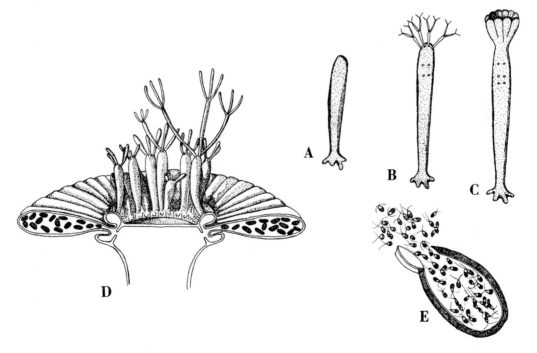

FIG. 3-43. *Acetabularia*. A–C. Successive stages in maturation of the plant, diagrammatic. D. Organization of mature cap; note cysts. X 8. E. Liberation of gametes by germinating cysts. (*Modified from G. M. Smith.*)

logical, in contrast with that of D,h + d, which is **morphological** (as well as cytological) in the sense that two plants are involved.

The genera of Chlorophycophyta discussed in the present chapter may be classified as follows[23]:

Division: Chlorophycophyta
Class 1. Chlorophyceae
Order 1. Volvocales
Family 1. Chlamydomonadaceae
Genera: *Chlamydomonas* (H,h);
Carteria (H,h)
Family 2. Volvocaceae
Genera: *Pandorina* (H,h); *Volvox* (H,h)
Order 2. Chlorosphaerales
Family 1. Chlorosphaeraceae
Genus: *Tetracystis*
Order 3. Chlorococcales
Family 1. Chlorococcaceae
Genus: *Chlorococcum* (H,h)[24]
Family 2. Hydrodictyaceae
Genera: *Pediastrum* (H,h);
Hydrodictyon (H,h)
Family 3. Oocystaceae
Genera: *Chlorella, Eremosphaera*
Family 4. Scenedesmaceae
Genera: *Scenedesmus, Coelastrum*
Order 4. Ulotrichales
Family 1. Ulotrichaceae
Genus: *Ulothrix* (H,h)
Family 2. Chaetophoraceae
Genus: *Stigeoclonium* (H,h)[24]
Order 5. Ulvales
Family 1. Ulvaceae
Genus: *Ulva* (D,h + d)
Order 6. Cladophorales
Family 1. Cladophoraceae
Genus: *Cladophora* (D,h + d)
Order 7. Siphonales
Family 1. Bryopsidaceae
Genus: *Bryopsis* (H,d)
Family 2. Codiaceae
Genera: *Codium* (H,d); *Caulerpa* (H,d)
Order 8. Dasycladales
Family 1. Dasycladaceae
Genus: *Acetabularia* (H,d)

Order 9. Oedogoniales
Family 1. Oedogoniaceae
Genus: *Oedogonium* (H,h)
Order 10. Zygnematales
Family 1. Zygnemataceae
Genera: *Spirogyra, Zygnema* (H,h)
Family 2. Desmidiaceae
Genera: *Micrasterias, Closterium, Cosmarium* (H,h)

The distinguishing attributes, on the basis of which the orders, families, and their component genera are delimited, are discussed in several of the specialized treatises listed at the conclusion of Chapter 2. Such characteristics as presence or absence of motility in the vegetative or reproductive phases, structure of the plant body, nature of the chloroplast, and other morphological aspects are involved in the segregation of the various taxa.

In concluding this account of the Chlorophycophyta, it should be emphasized that their pigmentation, cellulosic walls, and their storage of excess photosynthate as starch seem to link them (physiologically and biochemically) to the land plants more closely than do the attributes of any other group of algae, except the Charophyta (Chapter 6). For this reason, most speculations regarding the origin of the more complex groups always involve consideration of the morphology, physiology, and biochemistry of the division Chlorophycophyta.

DISCUSSION QUESTIONS

1. Cite the attributes which distinguish the Chlorophycophyta from the Cyanophycophyta.

2. On what basis is motility considered to be a primitive attribute?

3. Explain the meaning and use of the following terms: sexual and asexual reproduction; isogamy, heterogamy, and oogamy; zygote and oospore; zoospore and zoosporangium; haplobiontic, diplobiontic, haploid, diploid, meiosis, mitosis, and cytokinesis; plasmodesma; stigma, pyrenoid, contractile vacuole; flagellum; protoplast; coenocytic; coenobium; gamete and gametangium; antheridium, oogonium, sperm, and egg.

4. What evidence can you cite which indicates that sexuality in genera like *Chlamydomonas* and *Chlorococcum* may be incipient? How would you investigate this experimentally?

---

[23] The letters in parentheses after certain genera indicate type of life cycle; where these are absent, sexual reproduction is unknown.
[24] In certain species.

5. Can you make a statement regarding the relative advantages of isogamy and oogamy? Explain.

6. Why is the stigma sometimes called the "red eyespot"? Consult your instructor about the experiments of Engelmann, Mast, Hartshorne, Wolken, and Cobb.[25]

7. What significance do you attach to the fact that nonmotile organisms produce motile reproductive cells with two or four flagella?

8. What result would be realized, in your opinion, if the motile zoospores of *Hydrodictyon* were to be released from the parent cell? Verify by releasing some, if material is available.

[25] T. W. Engelmann. "Über Licht- und Farbenperception niederster Organismen," *Arch. f.d. ges. Physiol.*, 29: 387–400, 1882; J. N. Hartshorne, "The Function of the Eyespot in *Chlamydomonas*," *New Phytol.* 52: 292–297, 1953; S. O. Mast, "Structure and Function of the Eye-spot in Unicellular and Colonial Organisms," *Arch. f. Protistenk.*, 60: 197–220, 1928; J. J. Wolken, "Photoreceptors: Comparative studies" in *Comparative Biochemistry of Photoreactive Systems*. Symposia on Comparative Biology 1, Academic Press, New York, 1960; H. D. Cobb, "An *in vivo* absorption spectrum of the eyespot of *Euglena mesnili*," *Texas J. Sci.*, 15: 231–235, 1963; P. P. Batra, and G. Tollin "Phototaxis in *Euglena*. I. Isolation of the eye-spot granules and identification of the eye-spot pigments," *Biochim. Biophys. Acta*, 79: 371–378, 1964.

9. Give examples of cellular differentiation or division of labor in the Cyanophycophyta and Chlorophycophyta.

10. Describe cell division in *Micrasterias* or *Cosmarium*. Plan an experiment to obtain data on its frequency.

11. In scalariform conjugation in *Spirogyra*, conjugation tubes are often established between more than two filaments. What is the disposition of the zygotes when this occurs? What are the implications?

12. What genetic effect is produced by the disintegration of three of the four nuclei arising by meiosis in *Spirogyra?* Can you cite examples of a similar phenomenon elsewhere in the plant or animal kingdom?

13. Construct a dichotomous key to the genera of Chlorophycophyta discussed in this chapter.

14. Define the terms unialgal culture, axenic culture, pure culture, and clonal culture.

15. Define or explain the terms life cycle, alternation of generations, isomorphic and heteromorphic alternation, cytological and morphological alternation, alternant.

16. Do you consider *Bryopsis, Codium, Caulerpa,* and *Acetabularia* to be unicellular, multicellular, or acellular? Explain.

17. Place all the algae with sexual reproduction described in this chapter in Types H,h, H,d, or D,h + d with respect to life cycle.

Division Phaeophycophyta

General Features

The division Phaeophycophyta (Gr. *phaios,* dusky + Gr. *phyton,* plant + Gr. *phykos*) the brown algae, includes a single class, the Phaeophyceae (Gr. *phaios* + Gr. *phykos,* seaweed). The genera of Phaeophycophyta are marine in habitat almost without exception. They occur in the open ocean as well as in quiet estuaries and may be abundant on the muddy bottoms of salt marshes. Many grow attached to rocks, shells, or coarser algae like the kelps. Approximately 225 genera and 1400 species of Phaeophycophyta have been described. In general, brown algae flourish in colder ocean waters and on rocky coasts, where many grow attached in relatively shallow water in the intertidal and sublittoral zones. A number of genera are able to withstand exposure to the atmosphere during low tide, whereas others are sublittoral and continuously submerged. Some of the large genera live in shoal waters, and most thrive in waters with considerable current. Few brown algae occur at great depths. Both annual and perennial genera are known.

The brownish shades of the plant reflect the abundant presence in the plastids of the xanthophyll, **fucoxanthin,** which is dominant over chlorophylls *a* and *c,* the other xanthophylls, and β-carotene. The plastids are single, few (Fig. 4-2A) or numerous in each cell and may be elaborate in form. No starch occurs in Phaeophycophyta; instead, the excess photosynthate accumulates as a carbohydrate, **laminarin** (a mixture of polysaccharides), as **mannitol,** or in the form of fat droplets. The nuclei of Phaeophycophyta are prominent structures. In many genera, centrosomes and astral radiations appear during mitosis as in many animal cells. The protoplast is bounded by a primary wall and middle lamella composed of a gummy substance, alginic acid. This may represent 10–25% of the dry weight. Alginic acid is a polymer of D-mannuronic and L-guluronic acids. Alginic acid has considerable commercial importance as a stabilizer, emulsifier, and as a coating for paper.

The motile cells of brown algae are distinctive and differ from those of the Chlorophycophyta in that they are laterally biflagellate (Figs. 4-2E). The longer, usually anterior, flagellum is of the tinsel type and the shorter, posterior one is whiplash. Although it has been suggested that the Phaeophycophyta originated from unicellular motile organisms with similar lateral flagellation, no such organisms have yet been discovered.

The simplest type of plant body in the group is the branched filament (Fig. 4-1). Many Phaeophycophyta have considerable complexity of structure, as manifested in their leaflike, stemlike, and rootlike organs (Figs. 4-5, 4-17) which exhibit considerable histological differentiation. Certain brown algae, the giant kelps, which may attain a length of 50 meters, rival forest trees in stature.

Illustrative Genera

Filamentous Type: Ectocarpus

Ectocarpus (Gr. *ektos,* outside + Gr. *karpos,* fruit) (Figs. 4-1 to 4-3) is a relatively simple brown alga commonly growing on stones and shells or epiphytically on larger marine algae. *Ectocarpus* is a branching filamentous plant in which erect filaments arise from an attached prostrate branch system, much as in the green alga *Stigeoclonium.* The apices of the filaments in some species of

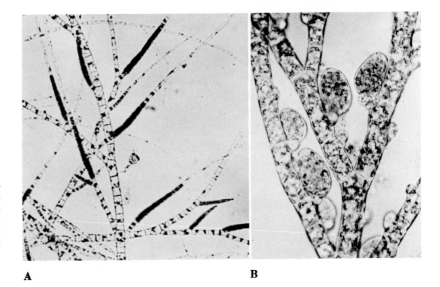

FIG. 4-1. *Ectocarpus siliculosus* (Dillw.) Lyngbye, living. A. Plant with plurilocular reproductive organs. X 135. B. Plant with unilocular zoosporangia in various stages of development. X 300.

A   B

Ectocarpus are colorless hairs (Fig. 4-1A). A zone of meristematic cells at the base of the hairs increases the length of both the filament and the hairs. This type of intercalary growth is said to be **trichothallic**. The mature cells contain band-shaped plastids with pyrenoid-like bodies (Fig. 4-2A); the function of the latter is not known.

The life cycle and reproduction of *Ectocarpus* are fundamentally similar to those in *Ulva* and *Cladophora*—namely, Type D,h + d (p. 48)—in that meiosis is sporic during an isomorphic alternation of generations. Two kinds of reproductive organs may be produced on the diploid sporophytic plants. The terminal cells of lateral branchlets enlarge, and their protoplasts segment into approximately 32–64 zoospores (Figs. 4-1B, 4-2C,D, 4-3B), each of which becomes pear-shaped and laterally biflagellate. These are discharged through an apical pore, and after a period of motility they begin to develop into new filaments. The organs producing these zoospores are called **unilocular zoosporangia,** inasmuch as the zoospores lie within a single cavity. It has been shown that meiosis occurs during the first two nuclear divisions in the unilocular zoosporangium, so that the zoospores produced from these structures are haploid.

By numerous transverse and vertical cell divisions, other lateral branches on the same plants may produce an aggregation of small cubical cells, the protoplasts of each of which also metamorphose into zoospores. Such zoosporangia are said to be **plurilocular** (Fig. 4-3A), inasmuch as each zoospore is borne in a separate cell. Zoospores from these plurilocular sporangia are diploid and germinate into filaments like those that produced them. This is a supplementary method of reproduction which increases the diploid generation.

Cultural studies indicate that the haploid zoospores from unilocular sporangia normally develop into haploid gametophytic plants which resemble the diploid plants in form; the gametophytes produce only **plurilocular gametangia** (Fig. 4-3A).

Motile cells (Fig. 4-2E) from these either may unite in pairs to form zygotes, or each may parthenogenetically produce a new gametophytic plant. Like the diploid, the haploid generation, therefore, is also increased asexually. Sexuality is isogamous, and the plants are unisexual. The zygote, without a period of dormancy, develops into a new diploid sporophyte. As in *Chlamydomonas*, sexuality here is not obligate, nor do the gametes differ markedly from the zoospores, for they may develop without sexual fusion into new plants. Both sporophyte and gametophyte may reproduce asexually, so that the alternation of generations is not obligate. Analogous asexual reduplication of sporophyte and gametophyte

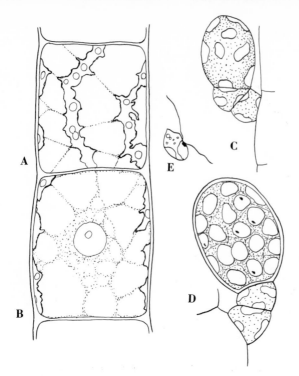

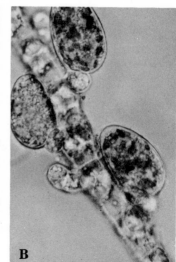

FIG. 4-2. *Ectocarpus siliculosus*. A. Surface and B. Median optical view of vegetative cell. C, D. Stages in development of unilocular zoosporangia. E. Motile cell from plurilocular organ. X 600.

FIG. 4-3. *Ectocarpus* sp., living. A. Plurilocular organ. X 450. B. Almost-mature zoosporangia. X 650.

is rather widespread among the land plants. The life cycle (Type D,h+d) of *Ectocarpus* is summarized in Chart 3-1 on page 48. The life cycle here described is that of *E. siliculosus*. Few other species have received adequate study. There is some indication that the life cycle of *Ectocarpus* varies with geographical location, being different in Naples and England from that reported above for the coast of Massachusetts.

The Kelps

The kelps are of interest not only because of the complexity of their vegetative structure, but also because their life cycle is representative of a type not yet clearly demonstrated in any of the Chlorophycophyta but similar in many respects to that of ferns and other vascular plants.

Laminaria

Laminaria (Figs. 4-4, 4-5) occurs attached to rocks which are usually submerged even at extreme low tide. The plant consists of a branching holdfast, a stipe, and an expanded blade. Growth occurs at the junction of the stipe and blade and is, therefore, intercalary. The oldest portion of the blade is the apex. Both blade and stipe are quite complex histologically. Only the more superficial cells of both stipe and blade are photosynthetic, other cells having very few plastids (Fig. 4-6). The central part of the blade is composed of elongate, colorless, filamentous cells comprising the **medulla.** Some of these, the trumpet hyphae, have flaring ends.

Late in the growing season, during the winter and spring on the East coast, certain superficial cells of the blade elongate and become transformed into unilocular zoosporangia (Fig. 4-7). These occur in extensive groups or **sori.** Between the zoosporangia occur sterile filaments called **paraphyses.** Paraphyses may occur among sex organs or sporangia. Meiosis is sporic and occurs in the unilocular zoosporangia, as in *Ectocarpus.* Each zoosporangium produces 32–64 zoospores which are liberated and develop asexually into prostrate, *Ectocarpus*-like branching filaments that ultimately produce gametangia (Fig. 4-8).

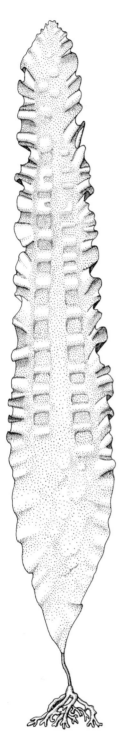

FIG. 4-4. *Laminaria agardhii* Kjellm. (young specimen). Note blade, stipe, and attaching organs. X ½.

A

B

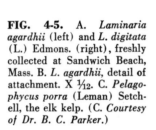

FIG. 4-5. A. *Laminaria agardhii* (left) and *L. digitata* (L.) Edmons. (right), freshly collected at Sandwich Beach, Mass. B. *L. agardhii*, detail of attachment. X ¹⁄₁₂. C. *Pelagophycus porra* (Leman) Setchell, the elk kelp. (C. *Courtesy of Dr. B. C. Parker.*)

C

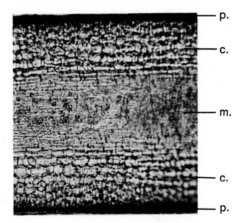

FIG. 4-6. *Laminaria agardhii.* Transection of blade; c., cortex; m., medulla; p., photosynthetic tissues. X 90.

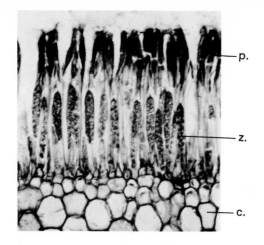

FIG. 4-7. *Laminaria* sp. Transection of fertile area; c., cortex; p., paraphyses; z., zoosporangium. X 300.

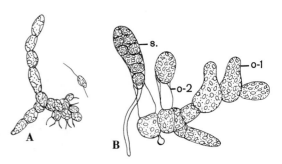

FIG. 4-8. *Laminaria japonica* Aresch. A. Male gametophyte; note cluster of antheridia and sperm. X 450. B. Female gametophyte; o-1, immature oogonium; o-2, oogonium with extruded egg; s., young sporophyte at mouth of oogonium. X 350. (*Modified from Kanda.*)

The *Laminaria* plant is diploid and sporophytic; the prostrate, branching filaments which develop from the haploid zoospores are gametophytic and haploid. The gametophytes are unisexual and sexuality is oogamous. The male gametophytic filaments are of smaller diameter than the female and often grow in close association with them. The antheridia (Fig. 4-8A) are produced as lateral cells on the male gametophyte; each antheridium produces a minute, laterally biflagellate sperm. The oogonia (Fig. 4-8B) produce single eggs which are released but remain attached to a tubular protuberance of the oogonium, so that fertilization and the development of the embryonic sporophyte occur *in situ* (Fig. 4-8B). Without undergoing a dormant period, the zygote grows into a new sporophyte which ultimately develops the form typical of the species. The life cycle[1] of *Laminaria* may be summarized as follows:

---

[1] Diploid phases are underscored with double lines, haploid with single lines.

The life cycle of *Laminaria* and other kelps is instructive in a number of respects. It is fundamentally similar to that of *Ulva*, the marine species of *Cladophora* and *Ectocarpus*, all of which have sporic meiosis and alternation of free-living, sporophytic and haploid, gametophytic generations (Type D,h + d, p. 48). However, in *Laminaria* and other kelps, the sporophyte and gametophyte differ markedly in size, structure, and longevity; alternation here is **heteromorphic.** The sporophyte is a large, complex, perennial plant, dominant in the life cycle, whereas the gametophytes are microscopic, few-celled, branching filaments and relatively ephemeral. It should be noted that both generations are free-living plants, presumably autotrophic by photosynthesis. In balance of the two generations, the life cycle of *Laminaria* is practically identical with that of ferns and related vascular plants. As a basis for theoretical discussions of the origin and relation of the alternating generations, it must be borne in

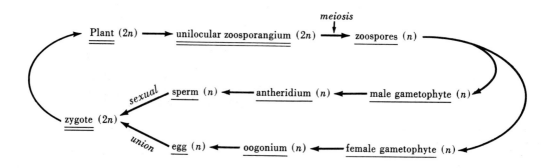

A   B

FIG. 4-9. *Macrocystis integrifolia* Bory. A. Portion of plant showing holdfasts and branching stipes with air bladders and blades. X ⅟₁₂. B, Single segment enlarged. X ¼. (*Modified from G. M. Smith.*)

mind that various genera of algae in the same aquatic environment illustrate alternation of both similar and dissimilar generations. Among the land plants, the alternating generations always are markedly dissimilar morphologically. The partial retention of the egg, and consequently the zygote, within the oogonium, which occurs in *Laminaria* and other kelps, represents an intermediate condition between their expulsion in many other algae and their permanent retention in the land plants. The significance of these features will be referred to later in our discussion of the land plants.

OTHER KELPS

Plants of *Macrocystis* (Gr. *makros*, long + *kystis*, bladder), the giant kelp (Fig. 4-9A), are among the largest of the brown algae, specimens 130–140 feet in length being common on the Pacific coast. The large plants are attached in deep water and the branching stipes bear leafy, *Laminaria*-like blades, at the base of each of which is a gas-filled bulb, the **pneumatocyst.** *Macrocystis, Nereocystis* (Fig. 4-11A), and *Pelagophycus* (Fig. 4-5C) are of interest in that they have specialized

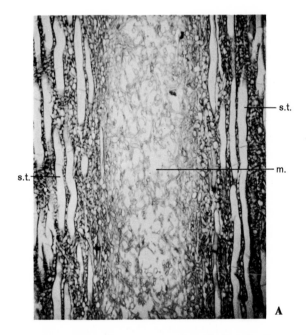

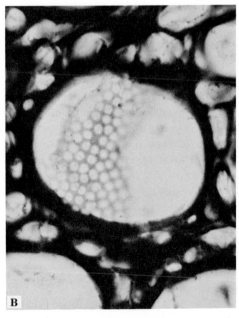

FIG. 4-10. *Macrocystis pyrifera.* A. Longisection of stipe showing central medulla and two groups of adjacent sieve tubes; m., medulla; s.t., sieve tubes.

X 75. B. Transection of same showing portion of sieve plate. X 700. (*Courtesy of Dr. B. C. Parker.*)

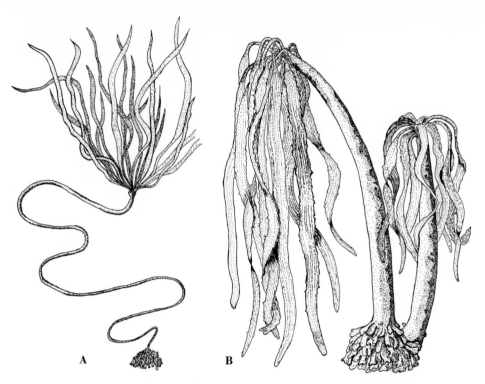

FIG. 4-11. A. *Nereocystis luetkeana* (Mert.) P. and R. X ⅓. B. *Postelsia palmaeformis* (Rupr.). X ⅓. (B. *Modified from G. M. Smith.*)

series of cells, called **sieve tubes,** in their stipes. These are very similar to the sieve tubes of phloem of the vascular plants. The word "sieve" refers to the pores which are present in the terminal walls (Fig. 4-10) of the adjacent cellular components of the sieve tube. The sieve tubes here, as in vascular plants, lack nuclei at maturity.

Although conduction by the sieve tubes themselves has not been demonstrated, it has recently been proven that C^{14}-labeled organic products of photosynthesis do move through the stipes of *Macrocystis* at rates comparable to movement of these substances in the phloem of vascular plants.

In *Nereocystis* (Gr. *Nereus*, god of the sea, + Gr. *kystis*, bladder) (Fig. 4-11A), a large kelp of the Northern Pacific, the stipe is usually unbranched and terminates in a large pneumatocyst which bears a profusion of blades.

Postelsia (after *A. Postels*, Russian naturalist), the sea palm (Fig. 4-11B) of the Pacific coast, grows in the intertidal zone. The stout and fleshy unbranched stipes are anchored to

the rocky substrate and may be 2 feet tall. Each bears distally a number of leaflike blades.

In *Macrocystis, Pelagophycus, Nereocystis,* and *Postelsia*, as in *Laminaria* and other kelps, the diploid plants become fertile and by meiosis produce haploid zoospores, which grow into microscopic, oogamous gametophytes; some of the latter bear eggs and others sperms. In all the kelps, accordingly, the life cycle is diplobiontic and heteromorphic.

The Rockweeds: Fucus *and* Sargassum

The widely distributed genera *Fucus* (L. *fucus* [from Gr. *phykos*, seaweed], rocklichen) (Fig. 4-12) and *Sargassum* (Sp. *sargazo*, seaweed) (Fig. 4-17) represent still a third type of life cycle which occurs among the Phaeophycophyta.

Fucus often grows attached to rocks in the intertidal zone (Fig. 4-13A) where the plants are exposed at low tide. The plant body, which may attain a length of 2 meters in certain species, is flattened and dichotomously branched.

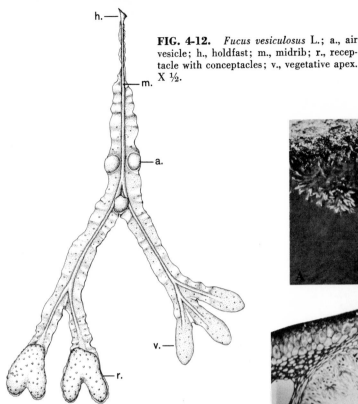

h. ——

m. ——

a. ——

v. ——

r. ——

FIG. 4-12. *Fucus vesiculosus* L.; a., air vesicle; h., holdfast; m., midrib; r., receptacle with conceptacles; v., vegetative apex. X ½.

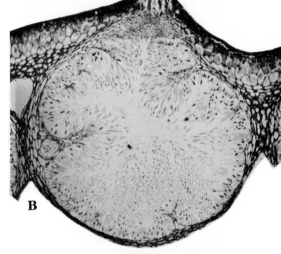

A

B

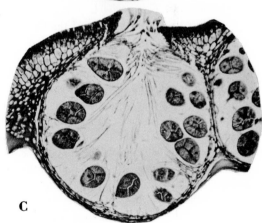

C

FIG. 4-13. *Fucus vesiculosus.* A. Plants (attached to rocks) emergent with falling tide. B. Male (antheridial) conceptacle in median section. X 60. C. Median section of female (oogonial) conceptacle. X 45.

Growth is initiated by the divisions of a clearly differentiated apical cell, derivatives of which, by subsequent division, enlargement, and differentiation, build up a rather complex plant body. The plants are attached by multicellular holdfast discs. Prominent **midribs** and **cryptoblasts** (probably sterile conceptacles, the latter described below), and **air bladders** occur in some species (Fig. 4-12).

The production of reproductive cells is localized at the tips of the branches in fertile areas called **receptacles,** which become enlarged and distended because of the internal secretion of large quantities of colloidal compounds (Fig. 4-12). The receptacles bear scattered pustulelike cavities, the **conceptacles,** which communicate with the surrounding water through narrow **ostioles,** through which tufts of colorless filaments protrude (Fig. 4-13B,C). At maturity the conceptacles bear eggs and sperms; these may be either in the same conceptacle, or those which produce the eggs may be on different plants from those producing sperms, depending on the species. Thus plants of *F. vesiculosus* L. are usually

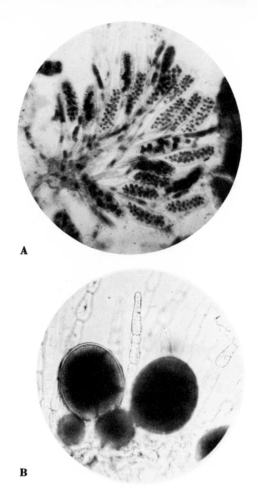

A

B

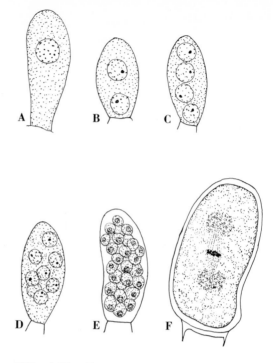

FIG. 4-15. *Fucus vesiculosus*. A–E. Stages in development of an antheridium. F. Young oogonium, first meiotic metaphase; note polar asters. X 770.

FIG. 4-14. *Fucus vesiculosus*. A. Stages in development of antheridia (acetocarmine preparation). X 320. B. Developing oogonia and paraphyses (living). X 135.

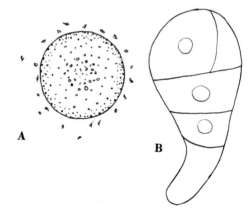

FIG. 4-16. A. *Fucus serratus* L. Egg surrounded by sperm. X 250. B. *Fucus vesiculosus*. Young plant from germinating zygote. X 300. (A. *After Thuret and Bonnet*. B. *After Nienburg*.)

unisexual (Fig. 4-13B,C); individuals of the Atlantic coast *F. spiralis* L. are bisexual, as in *F. furcatus* C. A. Agardh of the Pacific.

The sperms are laterally biflagellate and produced in groups of 64 from antheridia developed on branching filaments from the wall of the conceptacle (Figs. 4-13B, 4-14A). In *Fucus*, each oogonium, also an outgrowth from the conceptacle wall, produces eight eggs (Figs. 4-13C, 4-14B, 4-15F). The conceptacles contain colorless sterile filaments called paraphyses. Young oogonia and antheridia are uninucleate (Fig. 4-15A,F). Meiosis occurs during the first two nuclear divisions in these structures, the plants themselves being diploid.

Liberation of gametes is closely connected with tidal conditions in some species. At low tide, when the plants are exposed to the drying action of the air, shrinkage of the plant body may be accompanied by extrusion

of ripe oogonia and antheridia in slimy masses through the ostiole to the surface of the plant. The incoming tide, in submerging these droplets containing the sex organs, effects swelling and dissolution of their walls, so that the individual gametes are set free in the water. However, in other species, extrusion of gametes occurs in continuously submerged plants.

MORPHOLOGY OF PLANTS

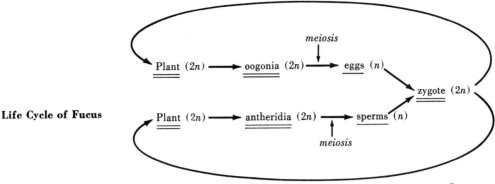

Life Cycle of Fucus

Plant (2n) ⟶ oogonia (2n) ⟶ *meiosis* ⟶ eggs (n) ⟶ zygote (2n)

Plant (2n) ⟶ antheridia (2n) ⟶ sperms (n) ⟶ *meiosis*

The eggs are large, spherical, and nonmotile and are penetrated by individual sperms, which swarm about the eggs in great numbers (Fig. 4-16A). Nuclear union follows, and the resulting zygote secretes a thin wall and germinates (Fig. 4-16B), without a period of dormancy, into a new *Fucus* plant. The life cycle of *Fucus* may be summarized as above.

It seems clear from this summary that the life cycle of *Fucus*, like that of *Bryopsis* and other siphonaceous green algae, falls into Type H,d (p. 48),[2] in which a diploid organism undergoes gametic meiosis and the zygote grows directly into the new plant.

Sargassum, unlike *Fucus*, is, with the exception of one or two species, largely a plant of warm marine waters. *Sargassum* is complex in having leaflike organs, stalked air bladders, and much-modified receptacles (Fig. 4-17). In *Sargassum*, seven of the eight nuclei disintegrate, so that each oogonium gives rise to but a single egg.

[2] The four nuclei present in the oogonia and antheridia at the conclusion of the first two nuclear divisions in these organs have been interpreted by some to be homologous with the nuclei of microspores and megaspores (produced in groups of four from their mother cells) in heterosporous land plants (p. 292). If this were true, one would have to look upon the "oogonium" and "antheridium," up to the four-nucleate stage, as a "megasporangium" and "microsporangium," respectively. The ensuing nuclear divisions, therefore, would be analogous to those that occur in microspores and megaspores in their production of gametophytes. In the case of *Fucus*, however, the gametophytic phase would be markedly abbreviated and would approach a condition most similar to that in certain seed plants, in which gametophytes complete development while the spores which produce them are still retained in their sporangia. According to this interpretation, the alternation of generations in *Fucus*, like that in the flowering plants, involves a dominant diploid sporophyte and a much-reduced gametophyte, the latter represented by only a few nuclear and cell generations.

FIG. 4-17. *Sargassum filipendula* C. Ag. Portion of plant; a., air vesicle; r., immature receptacles; v., leaf-like vegetative branch. X ¾.

Summary and Classification

The above account of the genera *Ectocarpus*, *Laminaria* (and other kelps), *Fucus*, and *Sargassum* summarizes the three types of life cycles and reproduction which occur among the Phaeophycophyta. Most of the remaining genera of this large alliance correspond in reproduction to one of the types described above; the generic differences are based largely on vegetative morphology. As a group, the Phaeophycophyta are sharply characterized and distinct from other algae in their pigmentation and photosynthate, in their almost exclusively marine habitat, their laterally biflagellate reproductive cells, and the complexity of the plant body in size and internal differentiation which are achieved in certain genera. Their life cycles have counterparts in certain Chlorophycophyta, on the one hand, and in certain vascular plants, on the other. However, no phaeophycean genus with zygotic meiosis has yet been described. The representative genera of Phaeophycophyta discussed in this chapter may be classified as follows:

Division Phaeophycophyta
   Class 1. Phaeophyceae
      Order 1. Ectocarpales
         Family 1. Ectocarpaceae
            Genus: *Ectocarpus*
      Order 1. Laminariales
         Family 1. Laminariaceae
            Genus: *Laminaria*
         Family 2. Lessoniaceae
            Genera: *Macrocystis, Nereocystis, Pelagophycus, Postelsia*
      Order 1. Fucales
         Family 1. Fucaceae
            Genera: *Fucus, Sargassum*

DISCUSSION QUESTIONS

1. Describe the life cycle and reproduction of *Ectocarpus, Laminaria,* and *Fucus.*

2. Compare these genera with respect to form of plant body and localization of growth.

3. What possible significance can you attach to the partial retention of the egg, zygote, and young embryo at the mouth of the oogonium of *Laminaria* and other kelps?

4. Do you think that Phaeophycophyta may have originated from the Chlorophycophyta? Give reasons for your answer.

5. If the Chlorophycophyta and Phaeophycophyta are not closely related in your opinion, how do you interpret the occurrence of the filamentous habit, holdfasts, zoospores, oogamous reproduction, and alternation of generations in both groups?

6. Distinguish between cytological, morphological, haplobiontic, diplobiontic, isomorphic, and heteromorphic alternation of generations, giving examples from genera of Phaeophycophyta.

CHAPTER 5

Division
Rhodophycophyta

General Features

The division Rhodophycophyta (Gr. *rhodon*, rose + Gr. *phyton*, plant + Gr. *phykos*) contains a single class, the Rhodophyceae (Gr. *rhodon* + Gr. *phykos*, seaweed), commonly called the red algae. About 400 genera and 3400 species are known. The Rhodophyceae, like the Phaeophyceae, are predominantly marine organisms; however, several genera like *Lemanea* (in honor of Dr. *S. Leman*, French botanist) (Fig. 5-1) and *Batrachospermum* (Gr. *batrachos*, frog + Gr. *sperma*, semen) (Fig. 5-12) are widely distributed in fresh-water streams, lakes, and springs. Marine Rhodophyceae flourish in both littoral and sublittoral zones. Rhodophyceae are very abundant in tropical seas, where they often grow at great depths in clear waters. A number of red algae precipitate calcium carbonate on their cell surfaces and become calcareous. These are important in reef formation. Many of the marine Rhodophyceae are strikingly beautiful, both in the living condition and when mounted on herbarium sheets.

In most genera, chlorophylls *a* and *d* (when present) and the carotenoids are largely concealed by a red pigment, phycoerythrin, and sometimes by the blue pigment, phycocyanin

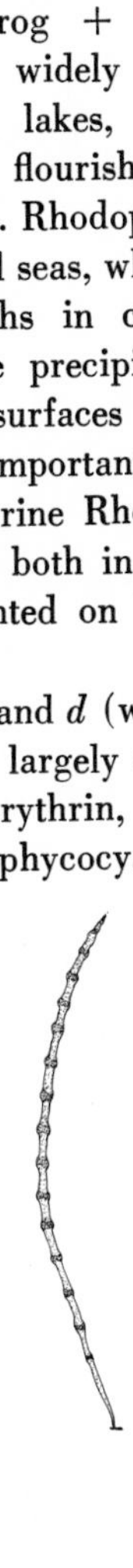

FIG. 5-1.
Lemanea australis Atk.
Single plant. X 1½.

(Table 2-1, p. 11). These pigments absorb light energy which they transfer to the chlorophylls. There is also evidence that, in addition, the accessory pigments may have a more direct role in the photosynthetic process. They are apparently associated with the surfaces of the plastid lamellae (Fig. 5-3). The numerous genera exhibit a range of color; various shades of red are common, and some plants are almost black. Some species of *Batrachospermum* (Fig. 5-12), on the other hand, are markedly blue-green. The pigments are localized in plastids which may be massive, with a single plastid in each cell (Fig. 5-11A), or the plastids may be numerous and disclike (Fig. 5-9A). The excess photosynthate is stored as a complex carbohydrate, called **floridean starch,** composed of approximately 15 glucose units; grains of this substance stain slightly red with iodine–potassium iodide solution. They usually occur at the surface of plastids rather than within them. The accumulated carbohydrate is often associated with the nucleus rather than with the pyrenoid when the latter is present. Floridean starch is similar to the amylopectin fraction of higher plant starches but differs in requiring prolonged boiling for gelatinization.

The vegetative cells of Rhodophyceae may be uninucleate (as in *Nemalion* and *Batrachospermum*) or multinucleate (*Polysiphonia* and *Griffithsia*). The vacuole of large, multinucleate cells is more prominent than in the uninucleate cells of genera like *Nemalion*. The cellulose cell wall is often surrounded by a slimy layer. In a number of genera, like *Nemalion*, the filaments are covered, in addition, by copious gelatinous material of rather firm consistency. The hydrocolloids of red algae have been classified as agars, carragheenins,[1] and gelans. Agars are of prime importance in biology as relatively inert agents for solidification of culture media. The walls between two adjoining cells in most of the Rhodophycophyta contain structures known as **pit connections** (Figs. 5-11F,G, 5-15A). The nature and function of these structures remain in doubt. They have been interpreted by some as evidence of protoplasmic continuity between contiguous cells.

Although a few unicellular and colonial rhodophycean genera have been described, a

[1] See also page 108.

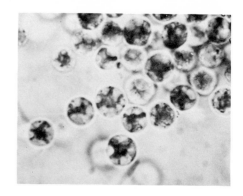

FIG. **5-2.** *Porphyridium cruentum* Näg. Living cells; note asteroidal plastids. X 1200.

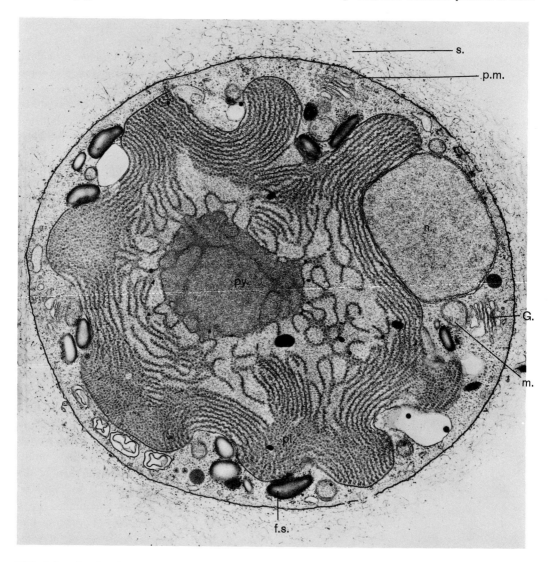

FIG. **5-3.** *Porphyridium cruentum.* Electron micrograph; f.s., floridean starch; G., Golgi apparatus; m., mitochondrion; n., nucleus; pl., plastid; p.m., plasma membrane; py., pyrenoid; s., colloidal sheath. X 7000. (*After Gantt and Conti.*)

vast majority are filamentous (Figs. 5-4, 5-10 to 5-15) or membranous and foliaceous plants. The basic pattern, however, is filamentous, and this can be demonstrated even in many membranous types. The development of the plant body is initiated by the activity of one or more apical cells. The membranous Rhodophyceae are less complex internally than similar types of Phaeophyceae.

Illustrative Genera

Porphyridium

The unicellular red alga, *Porphyridium* (Gr. *porphyra* + Gr. *idion*, similarity), is an inhabitant of moist soils, on which it forms crusts, and also occurs in fresh, brackish, and marine waters. The wall-less, spherical, uninucleate cells of *Porphyridium* (Figs. 5-2, 5-3) contain a stellate plastid with a central pyrenoid. The cells in mass may be blood-red or bluish-green, depending on the relative amounts of phycocyanin and phycoerythrin present. The cells have colloidal sheaths which, under some circumstances, may have stalklike protuberances. Reproduction is by cell division.

Bangia

Bangia (after *N. H. Bang*, a Danish botanist) (Fig. 5-4) is an unbranched, firmly sheathed, filamentous genus which may become pluriseriate as the filaments age. Here again, each uninucleate cell contains a massive, stellate plastid with a central pyrenoid. *Bangia fuscopurpurea* (Dillw.) Lyngbye grows on rocks and woodwork, is often exposed at low tide and hence is periodically wet by both fresh and salt water. Another species, *Bangia atropurpurea* (Dillw.) Ag., seems to be restricted entirely to fresh water.

In asexual reproduction, the protoplasts of cells in both uniseriate and pluriseriate filaments are liberated from their enclosing walls as **monospores** (Fig. 5-4B) which may be amoeboid. Cells which produce monospores are called **monosporangia.** The monospores germinate and grow into new plants (Fig. 5-4C,D).

Sexual reproduction, although reported for *Bangia*, is imperfectly known.

Porphyra

The genus *Porphyra* (Gr. *porphyra*, purple) also is representative of a group of genera which are considered to be primitive Rhodophyceae. The dark, brown-purple or rose-tinted, *Ulva*-like plant bodies of *Porphyra* (Fig. 5-5) grow attached to rocks or to larger marine algae. They are often inhabitants of the intertidal zone. The fronds may become more than a foot in length. They are composed of one or two layers (depending

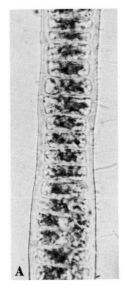

FIG. 5-4. *Bangia fuscopurpurea.* A. Uniseriate and pluriseriate portions of one strand. X 550. B–D. Monospore liberation and germination. X 435. (B–D. *After Drew-Baker.*)

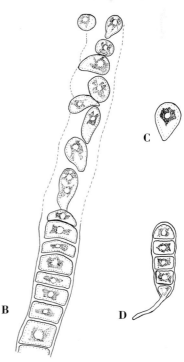

FIG. 5-5. *Porphyra umbilicalis*
(L.) J. Ag. Living plant. X ⅙.

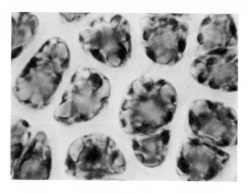

FIG. 5-6. *Porphyra umbilicalis*. Vegetative cells; note asteroidal plastid. X 350.

on the species) of cells which are surrounded by thick, colloidal cell walls (Fig. 5-6). The plants are attached to the substratum by rhizoidal holdfasts.

The uninucleate cells of *Porphyra* contain one or two[2] prominent, starlike chloroplasts which are central (Fig. 5-6). The cells lack the pit connections characteristic of so many Rhodophyceae. *Porphyra* deviates further in that its growth is generalized, that is, cell

---
[2] Depending on the species.

division is not restricted to a certain region of the maturing plant body.

A number of careful and intensive investigations in field and laboratory have failed so far to elucidate satisfactorily the complete life cycle of *Porphyra*. It is known with certainty that in several species spores shed from the membranous plants germinate into branching filaments (Fig. 5-7) long ago described, from examples growing on discarded mollusk shells, as a distinct genus, *Conchocelis* (Gr. *conche*, conch + Gr. *kēlē*, tumor). Cultures of the *Conchocelis* phase have given rise, in turn, to the membranous *Porphyra* phase.

It also has been reported that spores of *Porphyra* may germinate directly into new

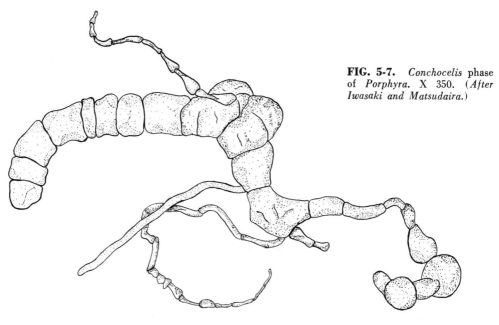

FIG. 5-7. *Conchocelis* phase of *Porphyra*. X 350. (*After Iwasaki and Matsudaira*.)

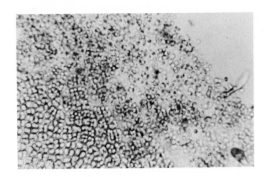

FIG. 5-8. *Porphyra umbilicalis.* Spermatium formation and discharge. X 300.

Porphyra plants and that spores of the *Conchocelis* phase may replicate that phase.

Several reports of sexual reproduction in *Porphyra* are inadequately supported, so that our knowledge of the life cycle is incomplete. The role of the minute, spermatiumlike "spores" (Fig. 5-8) is especially puzzling. The use of *Porphyra* in the Orient is discussed on p. 108.

Nemalion

Nemalion (Gr. *nema,* thread) differs from *Porphyra* in a number of important respects. In *Nemalion* growth is strictly apical and traceable to several apical cells. Prominent pit connections are present (Fig. 5-11D-F).

Nemalion multifidum (Weber and Mohr) J. Ag. is a marine organism which grows attached to rocks that may be exposed at low tide; the living plants have the appearance and texture of gelatinous, wormlike branching cylinders (Fig. 5-9); they are anchored to rocks by discoidal bases. In median longitudinal sections or in crushed preparations of apices, it is apparent that the plant body is composed of a number of colorless, central, longitudinal filaments, the tips of which elongate through the activity of apical cells. From the central filaments, tufts of lateral photosynthetic filaments arise in dense whorls (Fig. 5-10A). The axial and photosynthetic systems are both embedded in a rather firm colloidal material. The uninucleate photosynthetic cells are beadlike, each with a single starlike chloroplast in which a single pyrenoid is embedded (Figs. 5-10A, 5-11A). The function of the

latter and its relation, if any, to floridean starch have not yet been ascertained. The apices of the photosynthetic filaments may terminate in hairlike cells.

The reproductive organs of *Nemalion* and those of most Rhodophycophyta are unlike those of other algae. In some respects, however, they resemble those of certain ascomycetous and basidiomycetous fungi (Chapter 12). *Nemalion* is bisexual. The female reproductive organ, here called the **carpogonium,** is an oogonium with a more or less well-developed protuberance, the **trichogyne** (Gr. *thrix,* hair + Gr. *gyne,* female). The carpogonia are borne on almost colorless lateral branches which arise near the center of a tuft of photosynthetic filaments (Figs. 5-10B, C, 5-11B). Other branches on the same plant by successive divisions produce male sex organs, the **spermatangia** (Figs. 5-10D, 5-11C), which are analogous to the unicellular antheridia of other algae. Each spermatangium produces a single **spermatium,** the male gamete, which is discharged at maturity. The spermatia, which are produced and liberated in large numbers, are transported by water currents; these bodies may be slightly amoeboid. When a spermatium makes contact with the trichogyne (Figs. 5-10C, 5-11D), its nucleus divides. The walls then dissolve at the point of contact and one of the spermatial nuclei enters the trichogyne, migrating to the base of the carpogonium (Fig. 5-11D) where union of a spermatial nucleus with the carpogonial nucleus ensues.

Soon after fertilization in *N. multifidum,*[3] the zygote nucleus undergoes meiosis[4] and the

---

[3] Union of sperm and egg in oogamous sexual reproduction is often called fertilization.

[4] It has been reported for *Nemalion helminthoides* (Velley) Batters that meiosis does not occur in the zygote because the carpospores are diploid; the exact site of meiosis is not known for this species.

FIG. 5-9. *Nemalion multifidum.* Living plants. X ½.

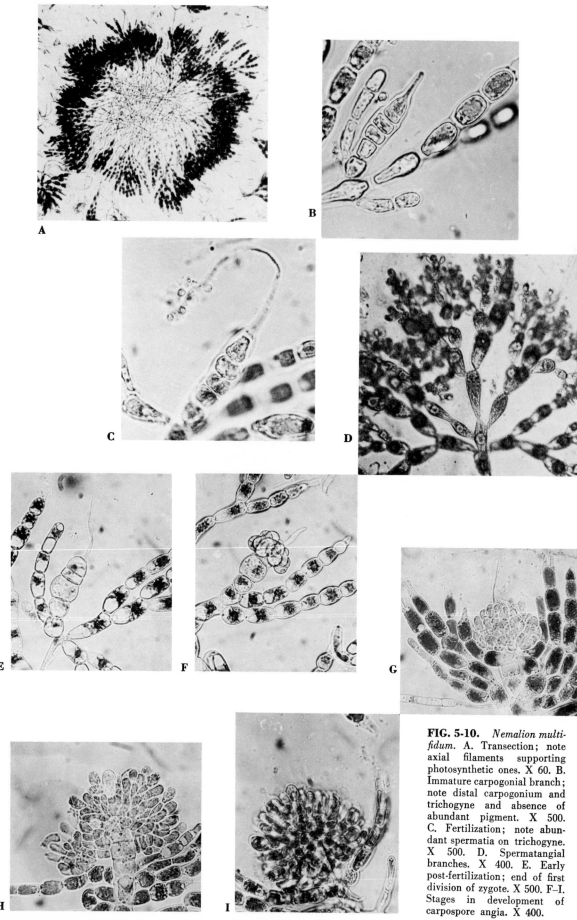

FIG. 5-10. *Nemalion multifidum.* A. Transection; note axial filaments supporting photosynthetic ones. X 60. B. Immature carpogonial branch; note distal carpogonium and trichogyne and absence of abundant pigment. X 500. C. Fertilization; note abundant spermatia on trichogyne. X 500. D. Spermatangial branches. X 400. E. Early post-fertilization; end of first division of zygote. X 500. F–I. Stages in development of carpospore angia. X 400.

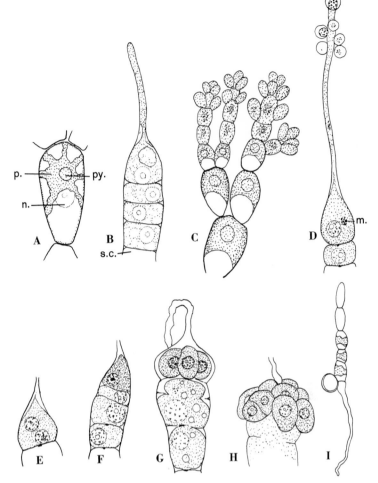

FIG. 5-11. *Nemalion multifidum.*
A. Organization of a cell of photosynthetic filament. B. Mature carpogonial branch; note rudimentary plastid in carpogonium. C. Branch with spermatangia. D. Fertilization. E. End of first meiotic division in zygote. F. Completion of first cytokinesis of zygote. G, H. Early stages in development of carposporangia. I. Germinating carpospore. A–C. living; the remainder from acetocarmine preparations; m., spermatial nucleus; n., nucleus; p., plastid; py., pyrenoid; s.c., supporting cell. A–H. X 770. I. X 315.

trichogyne withers. A series of mitoses and cell divisions follow, which result in the production of a tuft of short haploid filaments (Figs. 5-10E-I, 5-11E-H), the cells of which become **carposporangia** (Fig. 5-11H); the protoplasts of the latter are liberated as wall-less **carpospores.** The haploid carpospores ultimately germinate (Fig. 5-10I) and develop into gametophytic plants. The life cycle of *Nemalion* (H,h, p. 48) may be summarized as follows:

Batrachospermum

Batrachospermum (Fig. 5-12) also is reported to be haplobiontic and haploid,[5] but differs from *Nemalion* in vegetative structure. Instead of the numerous axial filaments and apical cells of the latter, *Batrachospermum* develops from a single apical cell which develops an axial filament and tufts of photosynthetic filaments that are loosely verticillate

---

[5] This also has been disputed.

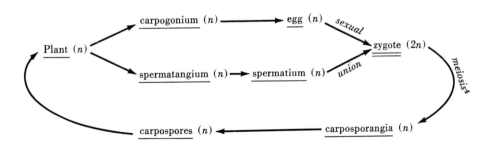

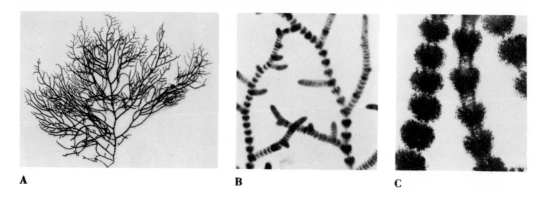

A   B   C

FIG. 5-12. *Betrachospermum* sp. at increasingly greater magnification. A. X 1.5. B. X 8. C. X 45.

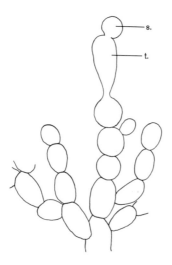

FIG. 5-13. *Batrachospermum* sp. Outline drawing of carpogonial branch at fertilization; s., spermatium; t., trichogyne. X 580.

and embedded in slime. Plants of *Batrachospermum* may be blue-green or deep wine-red, depending on the ratios between phycocyanin and phycoerythrin.

The carpogonial branches of *Batrachospermum* (Fig. 5-13) occur near the base of photosynthetic filaments. The spermatia (Fig. 5-14A) are larger than those of *Nemalion*. Huge masses of carpospores (Fig. 5-14B) develop after fertilization. These germinate, developing into prostrate branching filaments which, in turn, produce the erect plants.[6] Their further development has not been followed in laboratory cultures.

Polysiphonia and Griffithsia

Polysiphonia (Gr. *polys*, many + Gr. *siphon*, tube) and *Griffithsia* (after Lady Griffiths) illustrate the second of two types

---

[6] Unpublished data, Professor H. Wayne Nichols.

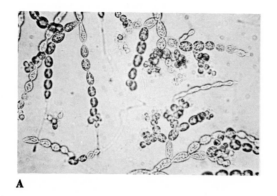

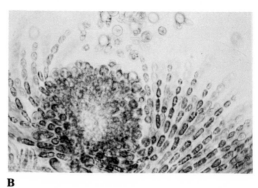

A   B

FIG. 5-14. *Batrachospermum* sp. A. Spermatangial branches. B. Carpospores. X 770.

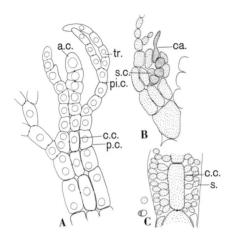

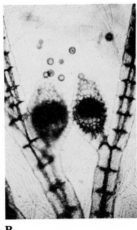

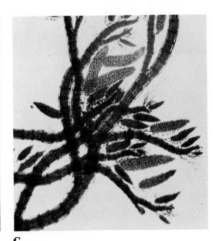

of life cycle which characterize the Rhodophycophyta.

Polysiphonia (Figs. 5-15, 5-16) is a branching filamentous plant which frequently grows attached to larger marine algae or to rocks. Growth is strictly apical, and the derivatives of the apical cell segment in a regular pattern (Fig. 5-15A) thus forming the multiseriate axis, which in some species achieves considerable complexity through superficial cortication. Delicate hairlike branches, the **trichoblasts,** may be present (Fig. 5-15A) in some species.

Polysiphonia is diplobiontic in life cycle. The gametophytes are unisexual, spermatia and carpogonia being produced on different individuals. The sex organs arise from derivatives of the apical cell near the tips of the branches (Figs. 5-15B, 5-16C). The curved carpogonial branch of *Polysiphonia* (Fig. 5-15B) at fertilization consists of four almost

FIG. 5-15. *Polysiphonia harveyi* Barl. A. Apex, showing ontogeny. X 388. B. Carpogonial branch (stippled). C. Median longitudinal section of spermatangial branch; a.c., apical cell; ca., carpogonium; c.c., central or axial cell; p.c., pericentral cell; pi.c., pit connection; s., spermatangium; s.c., supporting cell; tr., trichoblast. B, C. X 770.

A

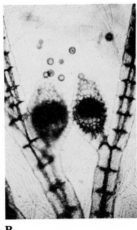

B

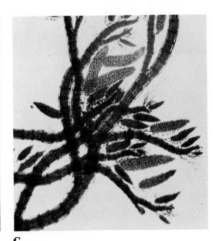

C

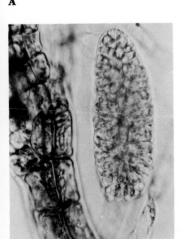

D

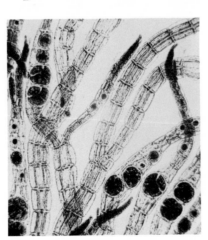

E

FIG. 5-16. *Polysiphonia.* A. Habit. X ¾. B. Female plant with two cystocarps liberating carpospores. X 125. C. Male plants with spermatangial branches. X 125. D. Young spermatangial branch, enlarged. X 500. E. Tetrasporophyte with tetrasporangia and tetraspores. X 125.

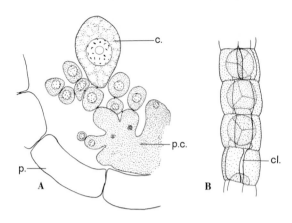

FIG. 5-17. *Polysiphonia harveyi.* A. Portion of cystocarp with placental cell and developing carposporangia. X 500. B. Portion of tetrasporic plant. X 125; c., carposporangium; cl., cleft through which tetraspores were liberated; p., pericarp cell; p.c., placental cell.

colorless cells, the most distal one of which develops a trichogyne. This branch arises from a pericentral cell which is known as the **supporting cell.** Certain cells at the base and above the carpogonial branch grow up around it, forming an urn-shaped envelope, the **pericarp** (Gr. *peri*, around + Gr. *karpon*, fruit) (Fig. 5-16B). The spermatangia and spermatia are borne on lateral branches (Figs. 5-15C, 5-16C), the pericentral cells of which produce spermatangial mother cells which give rise to large numbers of colorless spermatangia that are abscised and function directly as spermatia (Fig. 5-15C). As in all Rhodophycophyta, the spermatia are borne passively to the trichogyne by water currents. After attachment of spermatia to the tri-

chogyne, their contents flow into the latter. The spermatial nucleus migrates down through the trichogyne and ultimately unites with the carpogonial nucleus as in *Nemalion.*

Postfertilization development is rather complicated in detail. It involves extensive cell fusions, degeneration of the carpogonial branch, and migration of the zygote nucleus into an **auxiliary cell** which arises after fertilization. Meiosis does not occur, but mitotic divisions of the zygote nucleus give rise to a number of diploid nuclei which are present in a large fusion cell, the **placental cell.** Carposporangia, each with a diploid nucleus, are abstricted from this cell and develop seriatim (Fig. 5-17A).

The mature carposporangia are liberated through the terminal opening of the urnlike pericarp (Fig. 5-16B) and germinate into diploid plants under suitable conditions. These plants, the **tetrasporophytes,** are similar in size and general appearance to the male and female gametophytes, but at maturity they produce **tetrasporangia** (Figs. 5-16E, 5-17B) which arise on short stalk cells. Cytological investigation has demonstrated that the two successive nuclear divisions in the tetrasporangium accomplish meiosis, so the four spores produced are haploid. The tetrasporangial wall breaks open and the **tetraspores** are shed through clefts between the pericentral cells (Fig. 5-16E, 5-17B). It has been shown by culture methods that tetraspores develop into gametophytic plants. This rather complicated life cycle of *Polysiphonia* may be summarized as follows:

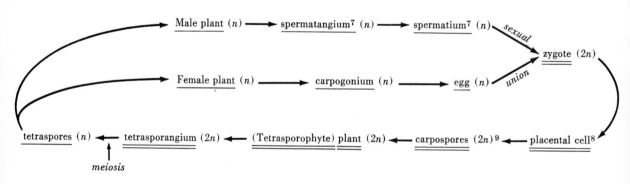

Male plant (n) ⟶ spermatangium[7] (n) ⟶ spermatium[7] (n) *sexual*

Female plant (n) ⟶ carpogonium (n) ⟶ egg (n) *union*

zygote $(2n)$

tetraspores (n) ⟵ tetrasporangium $(2n)$ ⟵ (Tetrasporophyte) plant $(2n)$ ⟵ carpospores $(2n)$[9] ⟵ placental cell[8]

meiosis

---

[7] In *Polysiphonia* and *Griffithsia*, unlike *Nemalion*, the entire spermatangium is abscised and functions as a spermatium.

---

[8] Contains a number of haploid and diploid nuclei.
[9] Complicated cell fusions occur at this point.

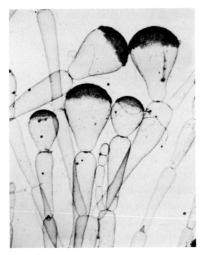
A

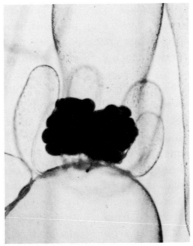
B

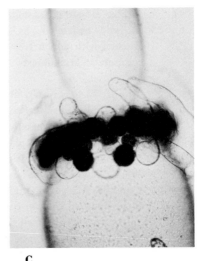
C

FIG. 5-18. *Griffithsia globulifera.* Living plants. A. Male plants with spermatangial caps. X 12.5. B. Female plant with carposporophyte; note involucral cells. X 60. C. Node of tetrasporic plant with tetrasporangia. X 60.

Griffithsia is similar in life cycle to *Polysiphonia*, but its vegetative structure is simpler, because the branching filaments are composed of large cells which are not covered by pericentral cells or cortications (Fig. 5-18). *Griffithsia globulifera* Harvey, an Atlantic coast species, appears during the summer when the water temperature is relatively high. The bushy growths are attached to stones and pilings in sublittoral habitats and are rosy pink in color. The multinucleate cells are very large, those near the base of the branches attaining a length as great as 5 mm. Growth is apical, from a multinucleate cell with dense cytoplasm and without a vacuole. The apparently dichotomous branching develops because of the upgrowth of the lateral surface of the cell below an apical cell to form a new growing point. In mature cells the cytoplasm is peripheral; it contains beautiful, ribbonlike, segmented plastids which are arranged in curved mosaics (Fig. 5-19A,

FIG. 5-19. *Griffithsia globulifera.* A. Portion of living vegetative cell, surface view. B. Detail of single spermatangial branch. C, D. Details of female reproductive branches and fertilization. E. Tetrasporangium mother cell with three tetrasporangia. F. Germinating carpospore; n., nucleus; p., plastid; s.c., supporting cell; t., tetrasporangium; te., tetraspore; t.m.c., tetrasporangium mother cell; tr., trichoblast; tri., trichogyne with spermatia attached. A, B. X 700. C–F. X 300.

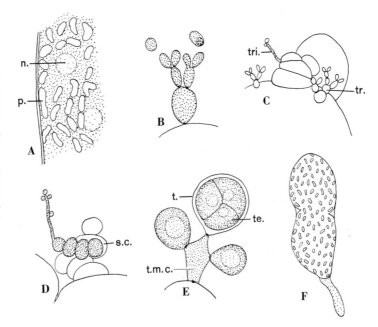

F). The attaching system of *Griffithsia* is weak and restricted, as evidenced by the frequency with which free-floating plants are encountered. Trichoblasts are present on the axes.

The life history of *Griffithsia* involves three free-living plants, as in *Polysiphonia*, namely, male and female gametophytes and tetrasporophytes, the female plants bearing **cystocarps** at maturity. The male plants are readily recognizable (Fig. 5-18A) because of their cap-like mantles of spermatangial filaments which produce spermatia (Fig. 5-19B) in enormous numbers and because cell size decreases from apex to base. The carpogonial branches arise from special three-celled, short, lateral branches which originate on the free distal surface of vegetative cells (Fig. 5-19C, D). The earliest stages in the development of these branches, and of the carpogonial branches they produce, occur near the growing point of each main axis. The supporting cell generates a four-celled carpogonial branch which is recurved, as in *Polysiphonia*. After fertilization, the supporting cell gives rise to the auxiliary cell, with which the fertilized carpogonium becomes united. The zygote nucleus passes from the carpogonium into the auxiliary cell, after which the carpogonial branch withers and is abscised. Further development involves extensive cell fusions and the ultimate formation of a placental cell, as well as generation of diploid nuclei within the auxiliary cell and the contiguous regions of the placental cell. Later, the formation of carposporangia is initiated. These are borne in groups (Fig. 5-18B). Meanwhile, soon after fertilization, the basal cell of the short lateral axis which bears the carpogonial branch gives rise to a number of curved, elongate, sausage-shaped pericarp cells that partially conceal the developing carposporangia. The latter are shed at maturity and then germinate (Fig. 5-19F).

There is good evidence that the carposporangia germinate into plantlets which mature as tetrasporophytes. In these, the distal portions of vegetative cells bud off a circle of tetrasporangial mother cells which give rise to three tetrasporangia each (Fig. 5-18C, 5-19E). Meiosis occurs in these while they are small, and each tetrasporangium is finally divided

into four tetraspores. When these have been liberated, they germinate, ultimately developing into male and female gametophytes. A circle of involucral cells surrounds each fertile, tetrasporangium-bearing node (Fig. 5-18C).

The *Polysiphonia* and *Griffithsia* type of life cycle is most similar to that observed among such Chlorophycophyta as *Cladophora* and such Phaeophycophyta as *Ectocarpus* (D, h + d, p. 62). It differs, however, in one important respect. In *Polysiphonia* and *Griffithsia* there is intercalated, between fertilization and the developing tetrasporophyte, a series of cell generations consisting of the placental cell and the carposporangia. This phase has been interpreted by some as still a third alternating phase, the **carposporophyte.** According to this point of view, alternation in *Polysiphonia* and *Griffithsia* involves the haploid gametophytes, the diploid carposporophyte,[10] and finally the diploid tetrasporophyte. There is no phase similar to the carposporophyte in groups of algae other than Rhodophycophyta nor does it occur among the land plants; the moss sporophyte is somewhat analogous. The closest approach to it, perhaps, is found in the postfertilization development in certain ascomycetous fungi, a feature which will be considered in the treatment of that group (Chapter 12). It should be emphasized that interpolation of the diploid carposporophyte makes possible the development of many tetrasporophytes (rather than only one) as a result of a single act of fertilization and from one zygote.

Summary and Classification

The genera of Rhodophycophyta described in this chapter exhibit three distinct types of life cycle. *Nemalion* and *Batrachospermum* are haplobiontic with zygotic meiosis (H, h, p. 48), while *Polysiphonia* and *Griffithsia* are diplobiontic (D, h + d) with sporic meiosis occurring in the tetrasporophyte. A third type of life cycle, diplobiontic with heteromorphic

---

[10] Even when the carpospores are haploid, as in *Nemalion multifidum*, the mass of carpospores is often referred to as a carposporophyte.

alternants, is probably exemplified by *Porphyra* and *Bangia*, although complete elucidation of their life cycles is not yet complete.

As a group, the Rhodophycophyta are sharply segregated from other algae by their pigmentation, their storage photosynthate (floridean starch), and their characteristic reproductive structures which appear elsewhere in the plant kingdom only in the ascomycetous fungi.

The development of a special series of terms for the reproductive organs and cells of the Rhodophycophyta is unfortunate in some ways, because it occasions confusion in the minds of those approaching the study of the group for the first time. It seems clear that the carpogonium and spermatangium correspond in function to the oogonium and antheridium, respectively, of other oogamous algae. The permanent retention of the zygote upon the gametophyte, however, marks a deviation rarely seen in other groups of algae, although suggested in the kelps. The continued production of carpospores for considerable periods following fertilization possibly is correlated with this retention, for although the postzygotic cells may contain pigments, they are nourished largely as a result of their organic connection with the parent gametophyte. Thus, a single act of fertilization, with retention of the zygote, results in the potential production of many more individuals than in those plants in which the zygotes are promptly separated from the gametophyte.

The genera of Rhodophycophyta discussed in this chapter may be classified as follows:

Division. Rhodophycophyta
  Class 1. Rhodophyceae
    Order 1. Porphyridiales
      Family 1. Porphyridiaceae
        Genus: *Porphyridium*
    Order 2. Bangiales
      Family 1. Bangiaceae
        Genera: *Bangia* and *Porphyra*
    Order 3. Nemalionales
      Family 1. Helminthocladiaceae
        Genus: *Nemalion*
      Family 2. Batrachospermaceae
        Genus: *Batrachospermum*
      Family 3. Lemaneaceae
        Genus: *Lemanea*
    Order 4. Ceramiales
      Family 1. Ceramiaceae
        Genus: *Griffithsia*
      Family 2. Rhodomelaceae
        Genus: *Polysiphonia*

DISCUSSION QUESTIONS

1. How does the life cycle of *Polysiphonia* or *Griffithsia* differ from that of diplobiontic Phaeophycophyta and Chlorophycophyta?

2. Can you see any advantage to the plant in carpospore production?

3. The sex organs of the Rhodophycophyta are called spermatangia and carpogonia, although they are similar to the antheridia and oogonia seen in other oogamous algae. Can you suggest a reason for this?

4. If one were to isolate and cultivate separately the four tetraspores from a single tetrasporangium, what result could be expected? Can you cite similar phenomena from other groups of plants or animals?

5. While most Rhodophycophyta are marine, a few genera like *Batrachospermum* and *Lemanea* are common in fresh-water streams. What might account for this?

6. Yamanouchi counted 20 chromosomes in nuclear division in the vegetative cells of the female gametophyte of *Polysiphonia violacea*[11] (Roth.) Grev. What would be the chromosome number in the nuclei of the following structures in this plant: spermatium, carpospore, carpogonium, apical cell of the tetrasporophyte, an undivided tetrasporangium, the pericarp, the basal cell of the carpogonial branch?

7. What is the explanation of the words "(Roth.) Grev." after *Polysiphonia violacea* in Question 6 above? Why is Roth. in parentheses? Why is Roth. not so written in "*Batrachospermum moniliforme* Roth."? Search for similar examples in other chapters.

8. Summarize the life cycle of *Porphyra*. How does it differ from that of other Rhodophycophyta discussed in this chapter?

---

[11] Now *P. flexicaulis* (Harv.) Collins.

Divisions Charophyta, Euglenophycophyta, and Pyrrophycophyta

Introduction

The preceding four chapters have presented an account of representatives of the four major groups of algae, namely, the divisions Cyanophycophyta, Chlorophycophyta, Phaeophycophyta, and Rhodophycophyta. The present chapter includes brief discussions of representative genera of three other divisions of algae[1] which are of widespread occurrence. The groups they represent are treated in most current phycological treatises as coordinate in rank with the four groups already considered. Other genera, in addition to the types here selected, are known in each group, but space does not permit a more extensive treatment of them.

Division Charophyta

The stoneworts and brittleworts, division Charophyta, here represented by the genera *Chara* (Latin name) and *Nitella* (L. *nitella*, splendor), are sometimes classified in the division Chlorophycophyta as a class coordinate with the Chlorophyceae. This reflects the point of view that their morphological deviations from the Chlorophyceae are of insufficient magnitude to warrant their removal to a separate division. In this text, however, for reasons which will be enumerated below, the stoneworts are considered to represent a group of divisional rank coordinate with the Chlorophycophyta. The division Charophyta contains the single class Charophyceae, order Charales and family Characeae.

Chara (Fig. 6-1, 6-2) and *Nitella* grow in the muddy or sandy bottoms of clear lakes and ponds, or in limestone streams and quarry basins. In such habitats, certain species have the capacity of precipitating calcium carbonate from the water and covering themselves with calcareous surface layers. This last attribute has suggested the names stoneworts and brittleworts. Calcareous casts of the oogonial and vegetative branches of stoneworts have been preserved abundantly as fossils (Fig. 8-3).

Unlike most fresh-water algae, the Charophyta are plants with macroscopically dis-

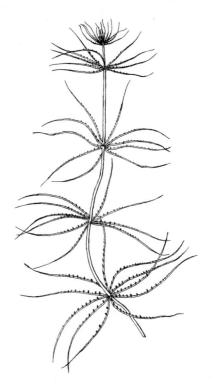

FIG. 6-1. *Chara sejuncta* A. Br. Portion of axis. X 1.

---

[1] Charophyta may not be algae in spite of their traditional association with that group (see p. 88).

FIG. 6-2. *Chara contraria* A. Br. ex Kütz. Bacteria-free culture; note vegetative propagation by rhizoids. X ⅓ (*Courtesy of Dr. Eugene Shen.*)

tinctive features. The markedly whorled branching (Figs. 6-1, 6-2), the organization of the plant body into regular nodes and internodes, and its geometrically regular pattern of ontogeny from the single apical cell (Fig. 6-3) all are features which suggest the Arthrophyta (Chapter 20 and *Ephedra* (p. 449) among the vascular plants.

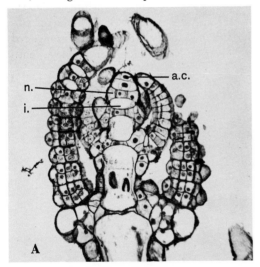

FIG. 6-3. *Chara sejuncta.* A. Median longitudinal section of apex. X 135. B. Transection of internode with cortications. X 90; a.c., apical cell; i., internodal cell; n., nodal cells.

The plant consists of a branching axis on which arise whorls of smaller branches of limited growth, often called "leaves." The lower portions of the axes are anchored to the substratum by branching filaments, the **rhizoids.** The rhizoids serve as organs of vegetative propagation, giving rise to erect, green shoots. Branches arise at the nodes among the leaf bases.

Median longitudinal sections through the apex of the axis (Fig. 6-3A) reveal the very regular manner of development which occurs in the stoneworts. All the cells have their origin from the descendants of a prominent, dome-shaped **apical cell** which cuts off derivatives in a transvere direction, parallel to its basal wall (Fig. 6-3A). Each of these segments divides again transversely into a nodal and internodal cell. The internodal cells elongate tremendously and may remain uncovered, as in *Nitella;* or, as in most species of *Chara* (Fig. 6-3), the internodal cells become clothed with corticating cells which arise from the node above and below a given internode. The protoplasm of the internodal cells streams rapidly in a direction parallel to the long axis of the cell; the minute peripheral chloroplasts are embedded in stationary cytoplasm. A prominent vacuole occupies the central portion of the elongate internodal cells which are multinucleate. The nodal initials divide in such fashion as to form two central cells surrounded by one or more rings of cells (Fig. 6-3B). The outermost of these are the precursors of the whorled lateral branches of "leaves." The latter develop nodes, internodes, and cortications like those of the main axes in *Chara;* in *Nitella* the leaves are uncorticated.

Reproduction in the Charophyta is strictly oogamous and the gametes are produced in specialized complex structures usually called antheridia[2] and oogonia.[2] Both unisexual and bisexual species are known. The reproductive structures are borne on the leaves (Figs. 6-1, 6-4). A fruiting plant furnishes a rather complete series in the ontogeny of the sex organs, if one examines leaves of successively

[2] Sometimes called globule and nucule, respectively.

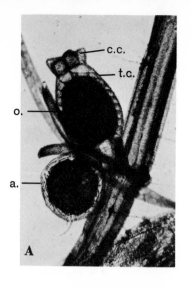

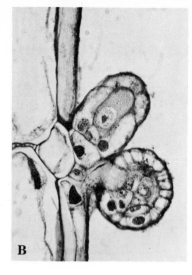

FIG. 6-4. *Chara* sp. A. Segment with oogonium and antheridium. X 60. B. Section of early stages in development of oogonium and antheridium (below). X 125. a., antheridium; c.c., crown cells; o., oogonium; t.c., tube cells.

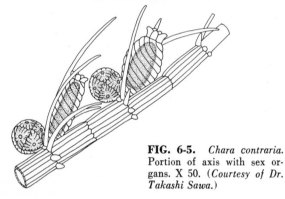

FIG. 6-5. *Chara contraria.* Portion of axis with sex organs. X 50. (*Courtesy of Dr. Takashi Sawa.*)

older nodes. The younger sex organs are green; but as development proceeds, the antheridia become orange-red and the oogonia rather blackish-brown (after fertilization) in many species.

The mature male reproductive organ (Figs. 6-4 to 6-7) consists of chains of colorless cells, each of which produces a single sperm, surrounded by several types of sterile accessory cells; the whole structure is stalked. Its surface is composed of eight large, epidermislike **shield cells** which are orange-red at maturity and contain incomplete, anti-

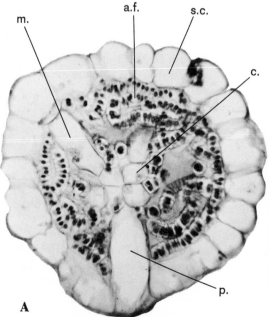

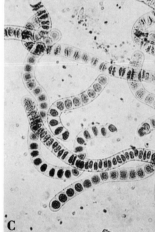

FIG. 6-6. *Chara.* Organization of the antheridium. A. Longitudinal section. X 250. B. Crushed antheridium showing mass of antheridial filaments. X 100.

C. Antheridial filaments in nuclear division. X 200; a.f., antheridial filament; c., capitulum; m., manubrium; p., pedicel; s.c., shield cell.

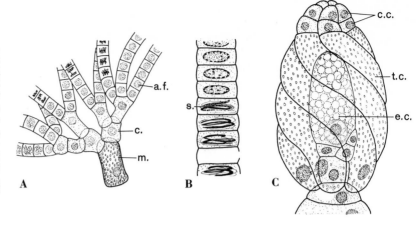

FIG. 6-7. *Nitella opaca* Ag. A. Manubrium with capitula and antheridial filaments. X 500. B. Segment of antheridial filament enlarged; note empty cell which has released its sperm. X 1800. C. Living, immature oogonium. X 400; a.f., antheridial filament; c., capitulum; c.c., crown cells; e.c., egg cell; m., manubrium; s., sperm; t.c., tube cell. (*Courtesy of Dr. Takashi Sawa.*)

clinal[3] septa (Figs. 6-4, 6-6A). To the inner tangential surface of each of these is attached a prismatic cell, the **manubrium** (L. *manus*, hand), which bears one or more isodiametric cells, the **primary capitulum** (L. *caput*, head) (Fig. 6-6A). The primary capitula are all contiguous at the center and give rise to secondary and, in some cases, to tertiary capitular cells, which generate the colorless **antheridial filaments** (Figs. 6-6B, 6-7A, B). These are composed of chains of boxlike cells coiled up within the cavities formed in the male organ by the enlargement of the developing shield cells. A single sperm emerges through a pore in the wall of each antheridial cell at maturity. The sperms are liberated by the partial separation of contiguous shield cells.

The female reproductive organ of the Charophyta is less complicated (Figs. 6-4, 6-5, 6-7C). It, too, consists of a fertile cell, the oogonium proper, surrounded by spirally elongate sterile cells, the tube cells. The apices of these are delimited to form the five cells (*Chara*) (Fig. 6-4A) of the **corona** or crown; there are two tiers or ten crown cells in *Nitella* (Fig. 6-7C). The female reproductive organ also is pedicellate. At maturity the tube cells separate from each other immediately under the corona, thus providing pathways for the entrance of sperms. The single large egg is uninucleate and contains abundant starch grains.

After fertilization, the zygote develops a thickened wall, and the oogonium is abscised from the leaf. The inner walls of the tube cells also thicken and persist as spiral markings on the dormant zygote (oospore) surface (Fig. 6-8).

After a period of dormancy, which is probably followed by meiosis, the zygote germinates (Fig. 6-8) into a juvenile plantlet, all the nuclei of which are the descendants of one of the products of meiosis, as in *Spirogyra*.

Comparison of the morphology of *Chara* and *Nitella*, and other genera of Charophyta, with that of the Chlorophycophyta, provides few points of similiarity. The complexity of the plant body in the Charophyta is unparalleled among the Chlorophycophyta, except, perhaps, in certain marine, siphonalean genera. Furthermore, such features as division into nodes and internodes, cortication of the

FIG. 6-8. A. *Nitella* sp. Germination of the oospore (zygote). X 10. B. *Chara* sp. Oospore germination. X 12. (A. *Courtesy of Dr. John Dodd.*)

---

[3] Perpendicular to the surface.

axes and leaves, and the occurrence of special cellular sheaths around the sexual organs are absent among Chlorophycophyta.[4] These reasons, among others, suggest that the stoneworts represent a distinct phyletic line and that, as such, they should be placed in a division separate from the Chlorophycophyta. It is argued by some that their sex organs suggest affinity with the Hepatophyta (liverworts, Chapter 15) or Bryophyta (mosses, Chapter 16). This claim is denied by others on the ground that the sex organs of the Charophyta are really unicellular, while those of the Hepatophyta and Bryophyta are multicellular. It is not clear to the writer, however, why the egg protoplast enclosed in a cell wall and surrounded by tube cells in the Charophyta should all together be considered "unicellular," while the egg protoplast of a liverwort or moss, enclosed in its cell wall and surrounded by venter, neck canal, and neck cells, should be considered "multicellular." Even if they are not homologous, both are apparently multicellular organs. If the term antheridium is applied in the Charophyta to one of the colorless cells of the antheridial filament because it produces one sperm, application of similar reasoning would restrict the use of the term antheridium to what is now called a spermatogenous cell or, possibly, an androcyte, in liverworts, mosses, and other plants. Is this not, perhaps, an eloquent example of the statement that "Nature mocks at human categories"? The divisional name Charophyta (rather than Charophycophyta) emphasizes the author's uncertainty that these plants are algae.

Division Euglenophycophyta

The Euglenophycophyta comprise a small group of organisms, some of which exhibit both plant- and animallike attributes. Approximately 25 genera and 335 species are known. The Euglenophycophyta contain chlo-

rophylls a and b, a- and β-carotene, and several xanthophylls (Table 2-1, p. 11). A number of colorless, protozoanlike genera are classified in this division, but only the cholorophyllous types are emphasized in the following brief discussion. *Euglena* (Gr. *eu*, good + Gr. *glené*, eye ball), *Phacus* (Gr. *phakos*, lentil), and *Trachelomonas* (Gr. *trachelos*, neck + *mona*, single organism) are widely distributed in fresh-water pools, often in such abundance as to form water blooms. At first glance, one would be inclined to classify *Euglena* and *Phacus* (Figs. 6-9 to 6-11) as members of the Chlorophycophyta, but closer study indicates a number of respects in which they differ. In the first place, the protoplast in these genera is unwalled, bounded only by a living, clearly differentiated (punctate, striate, etc.) plasma membrane called the **periplast;** a cellulose wall is absent. Furthermore, the granules of reserve photosynthate, **paramylum,** although similar in appearance to starch grains, fail to give the starch reaction with iodine. Paramylum is a β 1:3-linked glucan. Finally, uniflagellate genera are rare among the Chlorophycophyta. The lack of a cell wall, along with the possession of a nonrigid periplast in some species of *Euglena* and *Trachelomonas*, permits considerable change in body form, a phenomenon readily observable in the laboratory and often referred to as euglenoid movement.

The cellular organization of *Euglena* (Fig. 6-9) is typical of the group. In the individual cells a single prominent flagellum is inserted in the anterior portion of the protoplast in a slightly subapical invagination consisting of a tubular canal which leads into a broader reservoir (Fig. 6-9). A relatively large stigma is adpressed to the canal. It has recently been shown that the wavelengths of light which evoke positive phototaxis of *Euglena* correspond to those absorbed by the stigma pigments. These are composed largely of lutein and cryptoxanthin, with some β-carotene. The single nucleus is frequently obscured by the chloroplasts, the shape of which varies in different species. The chloroplasts may contain pyrenoids with associated grains of paramylum. Large annular grains of paramylum lie free in the colorless cytoplasm of some

---

[4] Segregation into nodes and internodes may be observed in members of the Chlorophycophyta, such as *Chaetophora, Draparnaldia,* and *Draparnaldiopsis.* Sterile cellular sheaths grow around the oogonia of *Coleochaete* after fertilization.

FIG. 6-9. *Euglena* sp. Living individual; ca., canal; chl., chloroplast; c.v., contractile vacuole; f., flagellum; n., nucleus; pa., paramylum; pe., periplast; r., reservoir; s., stigma. X 250.

f.

ca.

s.

r.

c.v.

chl.

pa.

n.

pe.

species of *Euglena*. A contractile vacuole empties into the reservoir. Special methods of staining reveal that the flagellum consists of an axial filament surrounded by a sheath; the flagellum is attached to a basal granule which lies within the apical canal.

There has been considerable discussion regarding whether these organisms, particularly *Euglena*, are plants or animals. Their chief plantlike attribute is the presence of chlorophyll and with it the capacity for photosynthesis. The occurrence of motility, the presence of a possible receptor for light stimuli (the stigma), and the anterior invagination (the canal and reservoir) are usually interpeted as animallike characteristics. Careful study of species of *Euglena* in bacteria-free cultures indicates that in spite of having chlorophyll, relatively few are completely autotrophic. Several have an absolute requirement for vitamin B_{12} and thus can be and are used as assay organisms to test for the presence of that vitamin. One may regard *Euglena*, therefore, as an organism descended from animallike ancestors and developing in the direction of the photosynthetic self-sufficiency of plants. According to this view, its animallike attributes would be considered to be vestigial. However, as seems to be the case in many phylogenetic speculations, there is also evidence that evolution may sometimes be retrogressive rather than progressive.

Experiments in which strains of *Euglena gracilis* were grown at high temperatures (34°–35° C.) and/or in the presence of the antibiotic, streptomycin, resulted in the development of a colorless race which could grow and reproduce when provided with suitable organic substrates. This colorless form of *Euglena* is strikingly like the (colorless) protozoan *Astasia*.

Multiplication of *Euglena*, *Phacus*, and *Trachelomonas* is effected by cell division (Fig. 6-10, 6-12) which follows mitosis. Un-

FIG. 6-10. *Euglena mesnili.* Living specimens. A. Mature individuals. B, C. Division stages; f., flagellum. X 175.

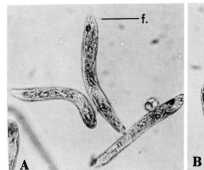

f.

A

B

C

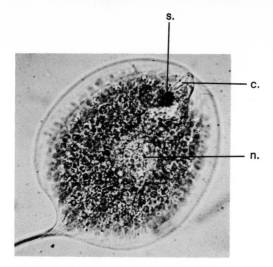

FIG. 6-11. *Phacus pleuronectes*. Living individual; c., canal; n., nucleus; s., stigma. (Flagellum not visible.) X 2400.

der certain conditions, the cells of *Euglena* may withdraw their flagella, secrete a thicker surface layer and copious slime, and remain nonmotile. Multiplication by cell division may occur in this "*Palmella*" condition,[5] which may be of long duration. Conclusive evidence for the occurrence of sexual reproduction among the Euglenophycophyta is not available.

Species of *Phacus* (Fig. 6-11) differ from *Euglena* in having rigid periplasts, so the cell form is fixed and constant. Many species of *Phacus* are flattened and slightly curved. The protoplasts of *Trachelomonas* (Fig. 6-12) are surrounded by a delicate periplast and a polysaccharide layer, the **lorica.** The latter is variously ornamented and generally impregnated with iron salts.

The division Euglenophycophyta usually is considered to contain but a single class, the Euglenophyceae, and a single order, the Euglenales, which includes three families. These are delimited on the basis of cytological features such as flagellum structure. The three genera here described are members of the family Euglenaceae, which includes all the chlorophyllous genera.

---

[5] Many algae may pass through a "*Palmella*" stage. This term is derived, by analogy, from the genus *Palmella* of the Chlorophycophyta in which the cells are nonmotile, surrounded by slime which they have secreted, and capable of reverting directly to a motile condition.

Division Pyrrophycophyta

Like the Euglenophycophyta, the division Pyrrophycophyta (Gr. *pyrrhos*, reddish + Gr. *phyton*, plant + Gr. *phykos*) contains both chlorophyllous and colorless organisms. The Pyrrophycophyta represented in this account by the single class Dinophyceae (Gr. *dinein*, to whirl + Gr. *phykos*), the dinoflagellates, formerly were considered to be members of the Protozoa; they are still so classified by many protozoologists. However, nonmotile unicellular and filamentous genera have been discovered that produce motile stages in which the cells are dinoflagellate in character; this indicates an affinity with plantlike organisms.

Dinoflagellates are abundant in both fresh and salt water, where they frequently form an important constituent of the plankton. Marine water blooms of one of these organisms, *Gonyaulax*, in the Gulf of Mexico have been known to form "red tides" and to result

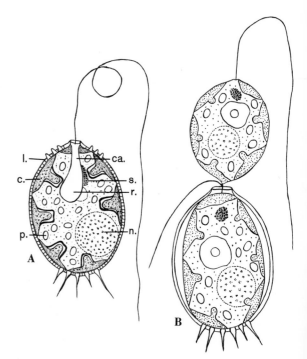

FIG. 6-12. *Trachelomonas armata* (Ehrbg.) Stein. A. Longisection of a single individual. B. Reproduction; c., chloroplast; ca., canal; l., lorica; n., nucleus; p., paramylum; r., reservoir; s., stigma. X 700. (*Courtesy of Dr. Kamala Prasad Singh.*)

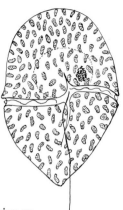

FIG. 6-13. *Gymnodinium* sp. Single individual from freshwater plankton. X 770.

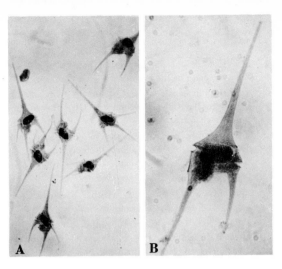

FIG. 6-14. *Ceratium* sp. stained to show nuclei. A. X 125. B. X 250.

in widespread destruction of fish. A number of marine dinoflagellates are luminescent.

The motile genera as well as the motile cells of nonmotile genera are characterized by the arrangement of their flagella (Fig. 6-13). One flagellum is elongate, usually extending posteriorly with reference to the direction of motion. The second flagellum, which emerges from the same point as the first, lies in a transverse groove in which it undergoes undulating movement. This furrow divides the cell into anterior and posterior portions which may be unequal in size in some genera. A few dinoflagellates, like *Gymnodinium* (Gr. *gymnos*, naked + Gr. *dinein*, to whirl) (Fig. 6-13), lack a cell wall, but in others the wall is prominent (Fig. 6-14) and composed of regularly arranged platelike segments. Genera with walls of the latter type are often said to be "armored." The walls probably contain cellulose; the empty walls persist for some time after the death of the protoplasts.

Ceratium (Gr. *keration*, little horn) (Fig. 6-14), *Gymnodinium*, and *Peridinium* (Gr. *peridines*, whirled around) are representatives of the motile type of dinoflagellates of common occurrence in the plankton in bodies of cold water or during the colder seasons of the year. The protoplasts contain discoid plastids which are yellow-brown to dark brown. The excess photosynthate is stored as starch or oil. Each cell has a single prominent nucleus and most genera have prominent

stigmata as well. Small, noncontractile vacuoles are frequently visible. There is some evidence that certain species of dinoflagellates, although photosynthetic, may undergo phagotrophic nutrition and ingest solid foods, but the exact mechanism of ingestion is not clearly understood.

Asexual reproduction is by cell division, frequently of cells in a motile condition. In plate-walled genera, each daughter cell receives a portion of the original cell wall. Sexual reproduction has been reported occasionally, but its occurrence requires further substantiation.

DISCUSSION QUESTIONS

1. Summarize the features which distinguish the following groups of algae: Charophyta, Euglenophycophyta, and Pyrrophycophyta from each other and from each of the four "major" divisions of algae.

2. Why are the Charophyta known as stoneworts and brittleworts? To what other algae might this name also be applied for a similar reason?

3. Describe the ontogeny of the plant body of *Chara* from the apical cell.

4. Describe the structure of the male and female reproductive organs of *Chara*. How does the female organ of *Nitella* differ from that of *Chara*?

5. How do the sperms reach the egg of *Chara?* What becomes of the zygote?

6. Do you consider the Charophyta to be closely related to the Chlorophycophyta? Give the reasons for your answer.

7. Why are the Euglenophycophyta placed in a division other than the Chlorophycophyta?

8. Summarize the plantlike and animallike attributes of *Euglena.*

9. How would you prove whether or not a given species of *Euglena* is autotrophic?

10. What facts concerning the occurrence of *Euglena* in nature might lead one to question its capacity for autotrophic nutrition?

11. How do you interpret the presence of a canal and reservoir in *Euglena?*

12. Suggest methods for making the platelike structure of dinoflagellate cell walls more readily observable.

13. Why are bacteria-free cultures necessary for study of physiological problems in algae?

14. How would you interpret the fact that there are a number of species of colorless dinoflagellates?

15. What significance do you attach to the observation, by a European phycologist, that a brownish, branching, filamentous alga produced zoospores with transverse furrows and with one girdling and one trailing flagellum?

CHAPTER 7

Division Chrysophycophyta

Introduction

The division Chrysophycophyta includes three classes of algae; in their plastids carotenes and xanthophylls are dominant (Table 2-1, p. 11). Therefore, the cells are varying shades of yellow-green and brown. Their excess photosynthate is never stored as starch but, instead, in the form of another carbohydrate or oil. The cell walls are often silicified and composed of two articulated portions. The Chrysophycophyta are usually subdivided as follows:

Class 1. Xanthophyceae, the yellow-green algae

Class 2. Chrysophyceae, the golden-brown algae

Class 3. Bacillariophyceae, the diatoms

A brief account of representatives of these three classes is given in the present chapter. More than 325 genera and 6000 species of Chrysophycophyta have been described.

Class Xanthophyceae

The Xanthophyceae (Gr. *xanthos*, yellow + Gr. *phykos*) are called the "yellow-green algae" because their color is distinctly that hue, especially if they are compared directly with members of the Chlorophycophyta. They were classified formerly among the Chlorophyceae, until it was recognized that several of their attributes differ markedly from those of that group. The yellow-green color results from a combination of pigments, among them chlorophylls *a* and *e*, β-carotene and several xanthophyll pigments. The pigments are localized in plastids which are usually lens- or disc-shaped. Droplets of oil and granules of a substance called **leucosin** or **chrysolaminarin**, related chemically to phaeophy-

cean laminarin, are frequently observable in cells of Xanthophyceae. In many genera—*Tribonema* (Fig. 7-2), for example—the cell wall is not homogeneous but is composed of overlapping segments. This attribute is not demonstrable in all Xanthophyceae, however, except by special chemical treatment. The cell wall is silicified in some genera. The flagella of Xanthophyceae are of unequal length (Fig. 7-1D), the longer tinsel and the shorter whiplash in organization.

The Xanthophyceae are predominantly fresh-water organisms, but they may be aerial (moist rocks and other vegetation) or terrestrial in habitat. A few are marine. A number of species have been isolated into culture from subterranean soil samples. The genera of Xanthophyceae, now grouped in a separate class, formerly were distributed among the orders and families of Chlorophyceae, the members of which they resemble in body structure. Removal of these xanthophycean genera into a separate class revealed that they comprise a series of body types largely parallel to those described in the Chlorophyceae. Space does not permit discussion of a complete array of parallel genera, but four commonly occurring and readily available xanthophycean organisms will be described.

Botrydiopsis

Botrydiopsis (Gr. *botrydion*, in clusters + Gr. *opsis*, resemblance), the simplest of these, is unicellular. *Botrydiopsis* (Fig. 7-1) occurs on and in soil, from which it may be readily isolated into unialgal culture. The spherical cells are thin-walled and contain an increasingly large number of lenticular plastids as the cells grow older and larger. The cells are multinucleate (Fig. 7-1B). As in *Chlorococcum*, each cell undergoes cleavage to form a number of zoospores (Fig. 7-1C, D), the

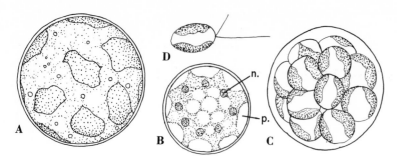

FIG. 7-1. *Botrydiopsis arhiza* Borzi. A. Vegetative cell, surface view. B. Stained cell. C. Zoospore formation. D. Single liberated zoospore; n., nucleus; p., plastid. X 1500.

number varying with the size of the cell. The zoospores are unwalled and have two flagella of unequal length. After a short period of motility, they become spherical, develop walls, and grow. Sexual reproduction has not been observed in *Botrydiopsis*.

Tribonema

Tribonema (Gr. *tribein*, to rub + Gr. *nema*, thread) is representative of the unbranched, filamentous Xanthophyceae (Fig. 7-2). *Tribonema* is cosmopolitan and occurs as floating masses and as overgrowth on submerged sticks and aquatic vegetation during the cooler months of the year. The uniseriate cells are often shaped like slightly inflated cylinders. Each contains a single nucleus and several discrete, discoidal, decidedly yellow-green plastids (Fig. 7-2B). *Tribonema* clearly illustrates the fact that certain Xanthophyceae have walls composed of overlapping halves. When the filaments break apart or dissociate, the wall sections may readily be observed to consist of H-shaped segments (Figs. 7-2B,

7-3), as viewed in optical section. They actually consist of segments of cylinders joined together by a plane, disclike wall. At the conclusion of cytokinesis in a given vegetative cell, the two daughter protoplasts form such a wall segment within the original wall of the parent cell. As in *Ulothrix* among the Chlorophyceae, *Tribonema* reproduces by forming zoospores which arise within the vegetative cells; *Tribonema* zoospores have flagella of unequal length. The germling produced by a zoospore has a holdfast, but the mature filaments are rarely encountered in an attached condition. Union of isogamous gametes has also been reported in *Tribonema*.

Botrydium

The terrestrial genus *Botrydium* (Gr. *botrydion*, in clusters), of widespread occurrence on damp soil, often grows in association with *Protosiphon*, its chlorophycophytan counterpart, with which it was long confused. The cells of *Botrydium* (Figs. 7-4, 7-5A) consist of an inflated epiterranean vesicle and a rhizoidal system; the latter is usually richly branched. In many localities and under appropriate conditions of laboratory culture, the vesicular portion of the plant may attain a size of 2 mm., and it is frequently ornamented with granules of calcium carbonate. Mature

A

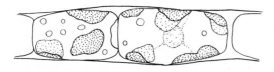

B

FIG. 7-2. *Tribonema* sp. A. Outline drawing of a segment of a filament. X 75. B. Two vegetative cells, the one at the left in surface view, the other in median optical section. X 500.

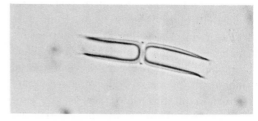

FIG. 7-3. *Tribonema* sp. H-shaped wall segment. X 1000.

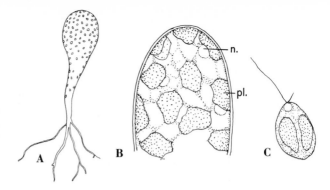

FIG. 7-4. *Botrydium granulatum* (L.) Grev. A. Small vegetative plant. X 60. B. Apex of young sac. C. Zoospore; n., nucleus; pl., plastid. B, C. X 1500.

plants of *Botrydium* contain a thin peripheral layer of protoplasm surrounding an extensive central vacuole. The protoplasm is composed of a superficial layer of chloroplasts (Fig. 7-4B) and slightly centripetal to these are numerous minute nuclei embedded in colorless cytoplasm. The rhizoidal portion of the plant contains few if any plastids and is filled with highly vacuolate protoplasm. *Botrydium* reproduces by zoospore and aplanospore formation. The zoospores (Fig. 7-4C, 7-5C) arise by cleavage of the protoplast when the vesicles are submerged in water. The zoospores are facultative isogamous gametes which may unite in pairs to form zygotes. Zoospores may also develop into new plants without union. Meiosis in *Botrydium* is probably zygotic.

Vaucheria

Vaucheria (in honor of *Vaucher*, a Swiss phycologist) the "water felt" is a widely distributed member of the Xanthophyceae; until recently, the genus was included among the Chlorophycophyta. Careful examination of its pigments, of its photosynthetic storage products, and of the flagellation of its motile cells (Fig. 7-6C) has demonstrated that the affinities of *Vaucheria* are probably with the Xanthophyceae. Species of *Vaucheria* may be amphibious like certain liverworts. Some flourish as dark green mats in running water or floating or submerged in quiet pools or on moist, undisturbed soil like that in greenhouse flower pots. The plant body consists of an elongate, sparingly branched tube (Figs. 7-6A,

A

FIG. 7-5. *Botrydium granulatum*. A. Portion of agar culture. X 5. B. Sacs from same culture. X 25. C. Zoosporogenesis. X 50.

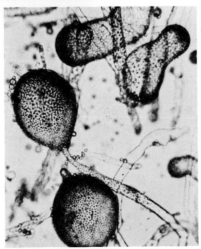

B

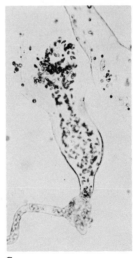

C

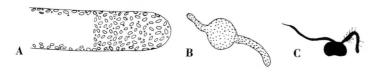

FIG. 7-6. *Vaucheria* sp. A. Apex of plant; the tip in surface view, the remainder in optical section. X 350. B. Germinating zoospore. X 75. C. Stained sperm of *V. pachyderma* Walz. X 1750. (*C. From Koch.*)

7-8A) from which septations are absent except in the reproductive stages or as a response to injury. The central portion of the tube is occupied by a large, continuous vacuole, which is separated from the wall by a delicate peripheral layer of protoplasm. Numerous discoidal plastids, which overlie the minute nuclei, occur in this layer. Growth of the siphonlike tubes is apical.

Asexual reproduction in the coenocytic *Vaucheria* plant is effected by the formation of large zoospores at the tips of the filaments, which are delimited by septa as zoosporangia (Fig. 7-7A). The protoplast in the sporangium contracts and an interchange of position between nuclei and plastids occurs, so that the nuclei are now nearer the surface. A pair of equal or slightly unequal flagella is then generated from the surface of the protoplast in the region of each beak-shaped nucleus (Fig. 7-7A). The large compound zoospore is liberated from the terminal zoosporangium and undergoes rather slow, narrowly circumscribed movements. It soon loses its flagella and germinates frequently from both poles, to form a new *Vaucheria* siphon (Fig. 7-6B).

Sexual reproduction, which is oogamous, is rather striking in *Vaucheria* because of the large size of the sex organs (Figs. 7-7B, 7-8B). These may be sessile on the main siphons or they may occur in groups on special reproductive branches. Both sex organs arise as protuberances into which the streaming protoplasm carries numerous nuclei and plastids.

They become segregated from the subtending branch relatively late in their ontogeny. The oogonium is at first multinucleate, but prior to formation of the delimiting septum, all the nuclei except one migrate back into the subtending siphon. At maturity, each oogonium contains a single, uninucleate egg cell. The sperms enter through a pore in the oogonial wall in a special receptive region. The antheridium, which is multinucleate when it is delimited by a septum from its subtending branch, produces a large number of minute, almost colorless, unequally flagellate sperms (Figs. 7-6C, 7-7B). In nature, these are liberated early in the morning. The zygote develops a thick wall soon after fertilization and loses its green pigment. The oogonium containing the zygote often is abscised from the parent branch. Germination into a new filament, after a period of dormancy, probably involves zygotic meiosis.

This brief account of the genera *Botrydiopsis*, *Tribonema*, *Botrydium*, and *Vaucheria* has been presented in order to provide some insight into the attributes of the yellow-green algae, the Xanthophyceae. In spite of the paucity of genera described, it should be apparent that the Xanthophyceae exhibit parallelisms with the Chlorophyceae, insofar as body form is concerned. This parallelism is reflected in the classification of the Xanthophyceae into orders which correspond to those of the Chlorophyceae. The genera described above may be classified as follows.

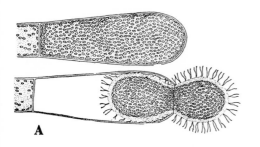

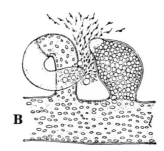

FIG. 7-7. A. *Vaucheria* sp. Zoospore formation. X 286. B. *V. sessilis* (Vauch.) DC. Mature antheridium (left) and oogonium. X 185. (*From G. M. Smith after Couch.*)

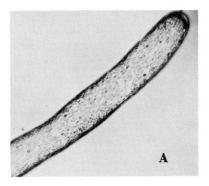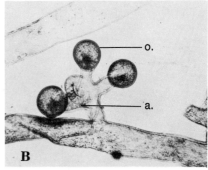

FIG. 7-8. *Vaucheria geminata.* A. Vegetative branch. B. Lateral branch with sex organs; a., antheridium; o., oogonium. X 200.

Division Chrysophycophyta
  Class 1. Xanthophyceae
    Order 1. Heterococcales
      Family 1. Pleurochloridaceae
        Genus: *Botrydiopsis*
    Order 2. Heterotrichales
      Family 1. Tribonemataceae
        Genus: *Tribonema*
    Order 3. Heterosiphonales
      Family 1. Botrydiaceae
        Genus: *Botrydium*
      Family 2. Vaucheriaceae
        Genus: *Vaucheria*

The Heterococcales correspond to the Chlorococcales of the Chlorophyceae; similar pairs of orders are the Heterotrichales and Ulotrichales and the Heterosiphonales and Siphonales. In spite of the parallelisms, the Xanthophyceae are clearly recognizable by their lack of starch, their pigmentation, their unequal flagellation, and by the overlapping construction of the cell walls in many genera. There is no sound evidence of relationship between the Xanthophyceae and the Chlorophyceae.

Class Chrysophyceae

The Chrysophyceae (Gr. *chrysos*, gold + Gr. *phykos*), or golden-brown algae, are widely distributed in fresh and salt water, but with the exception of a few genera, they are rarely encountered in any great number. Many of the species are planktonic and flourish in bodies of cold water or only in the colder months of the year. The golden-brown color is the result of a combination of pigments including chlorophyll *a*, β-carotene, and two xanthophylls; the abundance of β-carotene and the xanthophylls masks the chlorophyll in most species. The excess photosynthate is stored in the form of oil droplets or as granules of chrysolaminarin, the chemical composition of which is not known with certainty. In a great majority of genera the cells contain one or two parietal plastids and are uninucleate. The surface of the protoplast is often ornamented with small siliceous scales.

The Chrysophyceae, like the Xanthophyceae, represent a series in which types of plant body have developed in a manner parallel to that observed in the Chlorophyceae. In addition, in spite of the fact that the cells possess pigmented plastids, a number of motile genera carry on phagotrophic nutrition. Many Chrysophyceae are capable of forming siliceous cysts which are often ornamented in various ways. Although a considerable number of genera and species of Chrysophyceae have been found in this country and abroad, with few exceptions they do not seem to be organisms that appear with frequency in collectors' jars. Furthermore, few of them have been grown in culture in the laboratory. For these reasons, only three relatively widely distributed genera—*Ochromonas* (Gr. *ochros*, pale yellow + Gr. *monas*, single organism), *Synura* (Gr. *syn*, together + Gr. *oura*, tail), and *Dinobryon* (Gr. *dinos*, whirling + Gr. *bryon*, moss)—will be described.

Ochromonas

Ochromonas (Fig. 7-9A) is a unicellular motile organism which varies from spherical to a somewhat irregular shape. The unwalled cells contain one or two pale-yellow plastids

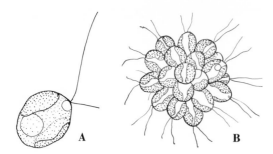

FIG. 7-9. A. *Ochromonas* sp. Single vegetative cell. X 1500. B. *Synura uvella* Ehrbg. Single colony. X 700.

which are curved and parietal. Two very unequal flagella, the longer tinsel and the shorter whiplash, emerge from the anterior portion of the protoplast. Each cell contains a single nucleus; contractile vacuoles and stigmata are present in the cells of certain species. Actively photosynthetic cells usually contain a single large posterior grain of excess photosynthate, called leucosin. Reproduction is by cell division. The cells may form siliceous cysts with prominent pores.

Various species of *Ochromonas* differ physiologically. In two species of *Ochromonas*, *O. danica* and *O. malhamensis*, distinct metabolic differences occur which are directly reflected in the relative amounts of growth. Growth of *O. danica* is fairly rapid in inorganic medium, while *O. malhamensis* will not grow well unless organic carbon sources (sugars, etc.), amino acids, and vitamins are added to the growth medium. The mode of nutrition also varies between the above species, for *O. malhamensis* has the capacity to ingest particulate food materials, like protozoa.

Synura

Synura (Fig. 7-9B) is a motile colonial organism in which the individual cells are stipitate and united into spherical clusters. The cells are ovoid and the anterior pole is broader than the stipitate posterior pole. Each is biflagellate and covered with delicate siliceous scales. The protoplast contains two parietal concave plastids, a single nucleus, and contractile vacuoles. Cell division augments the number of individuals in a colony. Multiplication is accomplished by fragmentation of the colony and continued growth of the fragments.

Dinobryon

The colonies of *Dinobryon* (Fig. 7-10) are branching and composed of a series of urn- or bell-like loricas, usually widely separated from their contained protoplasts except at the base. Each protoplast has two apical flagella (one of which, a tinsel flagellum, is markedly longer than the other which is of the whiplash type), usually two plastids, a single nucleus, contractile vacuoles, and a stigma. After longitudinal division, one of the daughter cells moves to the mouth of the lorica, becomes fixed there, and forms a new lorica. Continuation of this process through a number of divisions results in the formation of dendroid colonies. These fragment readily and the fragments continue to grow as individual colonies. Isogamous union of two vegetative individuals has recently been reported in *D. borgei* Lemm.

In addition to the genera described above, nonmotile unicellular colonial and filamentous forms of Chrysophyceae are known. One group of unicellular forms has cells which are amoeboid; the production of pseudopodia effects their movement and is involved in the ingestion of solid foods, an animallike attribute. The motile Chrysophyceae are most abundant in numbers of genera and species. However, the occurrence of filamentous types indicates that the group contains plantlike organisms as well as flagellates. The organisms

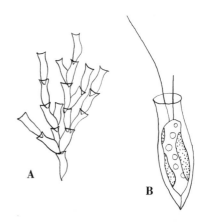

FIG. 7-10. *Dinobryon setularia* Ehrbg. A. Arborescent colony. X 225. B. Single lorica with protoplast enclosed. X 625. (A. *From G. M. Smith.*)

considered in the present account are usually classified as follows:

Division Chrysophycophyta
    Class 2. Chrysophyceae
        Order 1. Chrysomonadales
            Family 1. Ochromonadaceae
                Genera: *Ochromonas, Dinobryon*
            Family 2. Synuraceae
                Genus: *Synura*

Class Bacillariophyceae

The **diatoms,** Bacillariophyceae, are at once the best-known, the most numerous (in number of genera, species, and individuals, about 200 genera, 5000 species), and economically the most important members of the division Chrysophycophyta. Diatoms are the despair of the amateur and the joy of the professional microscopist with respect to their structural complexity. Their great beauty and perfection of design rival those of the desmids, but the beauty of diatoms is perhaps more subtle, for it is mostly confined to their cell walls. To appreciate this beauty in full measure, it usually is necessary to dissolve the protoplast with acid and to mount the cells in a highly refractive medium, a process known as "cleaning" the diatoms.

Although some diatoms are bottom dwellers and epiphytes in salt and fresh water, a great number occur in the plankton, where they are of inestimable and basic value in the nutritional cycle of aquatic animals. They have been extant at least since the Jurassic period (Table 32-1). The abundance of diatoms in earlier geological periods is attested by the finding of great deposits of their cell walls— "shells" or frustules, as they are often called. As individual diatoms died in certain bodies of water, they sank to the bottom; here the protoplasts disintegrated, leaving the siliceous cell walls. In this way there were built up great deposits which were exposed in later geological periods and which are now mined

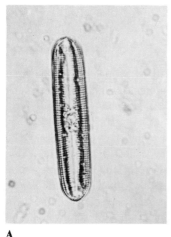

A

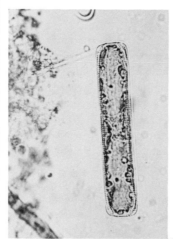

B

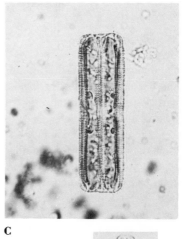

C

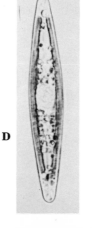

D

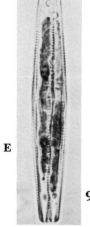

E

FIG. 7-11. Living pennate diatoms. A. *Pinnularia* sp., valve view. B. *Pinnularia* sp., girdle view. C. *Pinnularia* sp., recently divided cells. D. *Navicula* sp., valve view. E. *Navicula* sp., recently divided cells, girdle view. X 500.

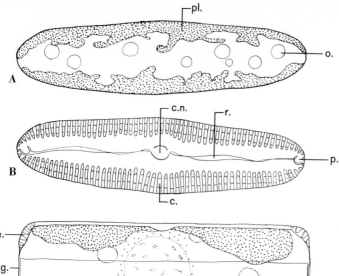

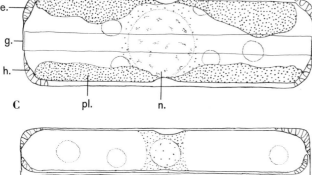

FIG. 7-12. *Pinnularia streptoraphe* Hustd. Organization of living cells. A. Valve view. B. Valve view, protoplast omitted. C. Girdle view. D. Recently divided cells; c., costae; c.n., central nodule; e., epitheca; g., girdle band; h., hypotheca; n., nucleus; o., oil droplet; pl., plastid; p.n., polar nodule. X 600.

as "diatomaceous earth" for use in industrial and technical processes. The economic importance of this substance is tremendous and its uses are many.[1]

At the present time, living diatoms are ubiquitous and important components of algal vegetation. In bodies of fresh water, they seem to be more abundant when the temperature is low. In marine habitats they often cover other algae with a heavy epiphytic growth. In running water, they often form a brownish coating on submerged rocks and other vegetation.

Diatoms may be strictly unicellular, colonial, or filamentous. They are divided into two types on the basis of symmetry. In the first, the pennate diatoms, exemplified by such genera as *Navicula* (L. *navicula*, small ship) and *Pinnularia* (L. *pinna*, feather) (Figs. 7-11, 7-12), the symmetry is bilateral. The second group, the centric diatoms, to which many marine genera belong, is characterized by radial symmetry. *Melosira* (Gr. *melos*, jointed + Gr. *seira*, rope) (Fig. 7-14), a common genus in fresh and salt water, and *Coscinodiscus* (Gr. *koskinon*, sieve + NL *discus*, disc) (Fig. 7-15A), usually marine, illustrate this type.

The taxonomy of diatoms is based almost exclusively on differences in the structure and ornamentation of the cell walls or frustules, rather than on attributes of the living protoplasts. The wall is impregnated with polymerized opaline silica ($SiO_2 \cdot nH_2O$) which is assimilated by the surface (plasma) membrane of the cell from the silicic acid of the environment. The diverse types of

[1] For a fascinating and informative account of this and other aspects of diatoms, see Paul S. Conger, *Significance of Shell Structure in Diatoms*, Smithsonian Report, 1936, pp. 325–344. For an advanced taxonomic treatment, see Ruth F. Patrick and Charles W. Reimer, *The Diatoms of the United States*, Monographs of the Academy of Natural Sciences of Philadelphia No. 13, 1966.

marking represent thin places or minute pores in the walls; these are rather constant in arrangement and form the basis for species delimitation. The transverse lines seen on the values of many pennate diatoms represent lines of pores which can be resolved as such with good oil immersion lenses as well as with the electron microscope.

The cell wall in all diatoms is composed of two overlapping portions, the **valves;** one is usually slightly larger than the other, much like the bottom and cover of a box (Figs 7-11 to 7-12). The larger, coverlike portion is called the **epitheca** (Gr. *epi*, over + Gr. *theke*, case); the smaller is known as the **hypotheca** (Gr. *hypo*, under + Gr. *theke*). The two valves, instead of overlapping each other directly, frequently are attached to a **girdle band** (Fig. 7-12C); this is composed of two overlapping portions. Supernumerary bands may be intercalated between the valves and girdle band segments; hence the epitheca and hypotheca may be quite widely separated in certain species. The cells are shaped like oblong boxes in *Navicula* (Fig. 7-11D) and *Pinnularia* (Fig. 7-12). When viewed from either above or below (valve view), *Pinnularia* cells usually have parallel sides and rounded polar portions (Fig. 7-11A, 7-12A,B). A prominent line, the **raphe** (Gr. *raphe*, a seam) traverses each valve (Fig. 7-12B). When observed in lateral aspect (girdle view) (Figs. 7-11B, 7-12C), the same cells appear rectangular. Each valve of *Pinnularia* is marked by two series of prominent riblike lines, the **costae** (Fig. 7-12B). In *Navicula*, rows of pores or **punctae** extend from the margin toward the central region of the wall, which, as in *Pinnularia*, is traversed by the raphe (Fig. 7-11D). This is connected to a **central nodule** and to two **polar nodules,** all of which open to the external aqueous medium. The **raphe** is wedge-shaped as viewed in transverse section. It has been reported that the continued secretion of a substance emergent through the central and polar nodules, accounts for movement of the diatom, at least in one direction.

The most conspicuous structures of the diatom protoplasts are the brownish plastids (Figs. 7-11), which are reported to contain, in addition to chlorophylls *a* and *c*, β-caro-

tene and a number of xanthophylls, including fucoxanthin; the latter is also present in Phaeophycophyta. The plastids may be few in number and massive, as in the pennate diatoms, or numerous and discoidal, as in the centric types. The excess photosynthate is stored in the form of oil or chrysolaminarin, which is frequently conspicuous in the living cells. The single nucleus is usually readily observable in the center of the cells in pennate genera. In addition to the nucleus, which lies in a bridge of colorless cytoplasm, the central portion of the cell is occupied by a large central vacuole.

Asexual reproduction in unicellular diatoms is effected by nuclear and cell division. Immediately after cytokinesis, the original wall contains two protoplasts, each approximately half the volume of the parental one. As the daughter protoplasts enlarge, each develops a new wall, using the half wall of the parent cell as the epitheca (Figs. 7-11C, 7-12D). It is obvious, therefore, that one of the daughter cells thus formed will be slightly smaller than the mother cell, and that if this process were to continue, some of the progeny would become progressively smaller. While there is evidence that this may occur, there is apparently a compensating ability of the girdle band and valve to increase slightly in size.

Sexual reproduction in pennate diatoms results in the formation of **auxospores** (Gr. *auxo*, increase + Gr. *spora*, spore). These are so called because they are naked protoplasts which increase markedly in size after their formation. Sexuality is superficially similar to that in certain desmids, because the

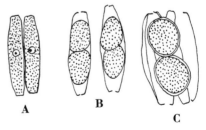

FIG. 7-13. *Navicula halophila* (Grun.) Cl. Stages in sexual reproduction. A. Pairing of cells. B. Formation of two gametes in each cell. C. Two auxospores (zygotes) formed. D. Elongation of auxospores. A–C. X 175. D. X 260. (*After Subrahmanyan.*)

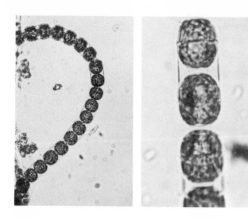

FIG. 7-14. *Melosira* sp. A living marine species, girdle view. A. X 150. B. X 450.

protoplasts of two cells may escape from their walls and unite directly to form a zygote. It differs, however, in that the pennate diatoms are diploid during their vegetative stages, and sexual reproduction is immediately preceded by meiosis. In some species—*Navicula halophila* (Grun.) Cl., for example—each member of the pair of vegetative cells forms

two gametes, so that two zygotes are formed (Fig. 7-13). In others, each cell forms but one gamete. The zygotes increase rapidly in size and become auxospores which are larger than the parent cells whose protoplasts functioned as gametes. In this way, when the auxospore has formed new cell walls it again achieves the maximum size characteristic of the species and functions as a vegetative cell (Fig. 7-13D).

The centric diatoms (Figs. 7-14, 7-15) are largely marine but a few also occur in fresh water. Of these, the filamentous genus *Melosira* (Fig. 7-14) is by far the most widely distributed. It is frequently present in the plankton in sufficient abundance to color the water, but benthic species are also common. The

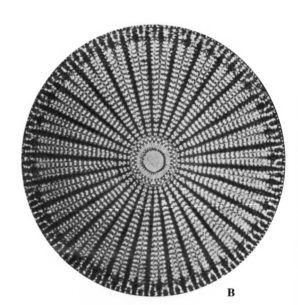

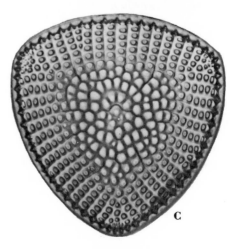

FIG. 7-15. Frustules of marine, centric diatoms. A. *Coscinodiscus radiatus* Ehrbg. X 700. B. *Arachnodiscus indiscus* Ehrbg. X 180. C. *Strictodiscus johnsonianus.* X 540. (*Courtesy of Dr. Ruth F. Patrick, Jay Sacks, and the Academy of Natural Sciences of Philadelphia.*)

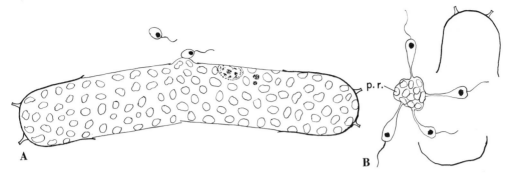

FIG. 7-16. Sexual reproduction in *Stephanopyxis turris* (Grev. et Arn.) Ralfs, a centric diatom. A. Protoplast of vegetative cell functioning as an oogo-nium, sperm making contact. X 000. B. Liberation of sperm; p.r., plastid remnant. Diagrammatic. (*After von Stosch and Drebes.*)

elongate cells, when joined together, are observed in girdle view. The cells contain many small brownish plastids and are uninucleate. The epitheca and hypotheca are joined by connecting bands which seem scarcely to overlap. The valve view of *Melosira* cells, which is circular, becomes apparent when the filaments dissociate into individual cells.

Coscinodiscus (Fig. 7-15A) is representative of numerous marine species of centric diatoms. Its cells are markedly flattened in the manner of extremely shallow petri dishes. Sexual reproduction, in some cases oogamous, has been reported for a number of centric forms. Our knowledge of sexual reproduction in centric diatoms has been greatly augmented by recent studies of certain marine species, like *Stephanopyxis turris* (Grev. et Arn.) Ralfs, in laboratory culture. In this organism (Fig. 7-16) the large eggs are fertilized by uniflagellate sperms. Both eggs and sperms arise as a result of (gametic) meiosis.

As a group, diatoms are perhaps economically the most important of the algae because of their role in the food cycle of aquatic animals and because of the many uses of diatomaceous earth. While diatoms have received considerable taxonomic study, many other aspects require further investigation. The Bacillariophyceae are clearly delimited from other Chrysophycophyta by their specialized wall structure, method of wall formation, and sexual reproduction.

The genera of diatoms discussed in the preceding account may be classified as follows.

Division Chrysophycophyta
    Class 3. Bacillariophyceae
        Order 1. Centrales
            Family 1. Coscinodiscaceae
                Genera: *Melosira, Coscinodiscus, Stephanopyxis*
        Order 2. Pennales
            Family 1. Naviculaceae
                Genera: *Navicula, Pinnularia*

Summary

In concluding this account of the division Chrysophycophyta, the question remains regarding the propriety of grouping the three classes Xanthophyceae, Chrysophyceae, and Bacillariophyceae into one division, a practice which implies their relationship. Among the attributes which these classes share in common may be listed the brownish color of the plastids that results from predominance of carotenes and xanthophylls, the frequent deposition of siliceous material in the cell membranes, and the storage of the excess photosynthate as oils. Furthermore, in all genera of one class (Bacillariophyceae) and many of the other two, it has been demonstrated that the cell wall is composed of two overlapping segments. Finally, in some genera of all three classes there has been observed the formation of a unique type of silicified resting cyst, which is not found among other algae. In view of these common attributes, the tentative grouping of these classes into one division, Chrysophycophyta, seems to be justified.

DISCUSSION QUESTIONS

1. What features distinguish the Xanthophyceae from the Chlorophycophyta?

2. Cite instances of parallel body structure in these two algal classes.

3. Do you think that Xanthophyceae, like the terrestrial *Botrydium,* may be like the ancestors of the "higher" land plants? Give the reasons for your answer.

4. What rapid laboratory technique can you suggest for distinguishing Xanthophyceae from Chlorophyceae?

5. In what location and under what conditions would you attempt to collect members of the Chrysophyceae?

6. List the respects in which diatoms are of economic importance.

7. Describe asexual reproduction in unicellular diatoms such as *Pinnularia.*

8. How could you prove that diatom cell walls are impregnated with silicon?

9. Speculate on what might happen if you cultivated diatoms in a silicon-free medium.

10. Distinguish between "pennate" and "centric" diatoms.

11. Why is the zygote of diatoms called an auxospore?

12. To what genera of Chlorophyceae are the pennate diatoms similar in respect to type of life cycle?

13. On the basis of supplementary reading, discuss the economic importance of both living and fossil diatoms.

CHAPTER 8

The Algae: Recapitulation

Classification

Chapters 2 through 7 have presented a brief account of the several divisions of algae and their component classes, as exemplified by certain illustrative genera. In the discussion of the classification of the plant kingdom in Chapter 1, it was pointed out that the algae, classified in this volume in eight separate divisions, formerly were grouped together in a single class, Algae, in the division Thallophyta. Now that the reader has gained some degree of familiarity with the organisms themselves through mastery of the material in the intervening chapters and especially through laboratory study of the living plants, it may be profitable to re-examine the question of classifying the algae and to present a general comparative summary of their attributes.

A **phylogenetic[1] classification** is one in which the arrangement of the various groups or taxa—namely, the genera, families, orders, classes, and divisions—signifies degree of kinship. To include all the algae in a single class, Algae, implies that they all had a common ancestry, in spite of their present divergences. This would signify, for example, that the blue-green algae, which lack plastids, Golgi apparatus, mitochondria, endoplasmic reticulum, and the type of nuclear organization characteristic of other algae, nevertheless arose from the same stock. Furthermore, it would imply that the range of variations (Table 2-1, p. 11) described in the preceding chapters with respect to pigmentation, type of reserve photosynthate, flagella number and insertion, cell wall structure, habitat, body organization, and structure of the sex organs and gametes is of insufficient magnitude to

---

[1] Sometimes called "natural."

indicate multiplicity of origin. Most modern phycologists are unwilling to accept these implications. The formal class Algae was erected more than 80 years ago, when the diversity of the morphological and physiological attributes of the algae had not been clarified by the studies of many botanists and biochemists. The various types of pigmentation (Table 2-1, p. 11) and associated photosynthates are now considered to be characteristics of sufficiently fundamental importance to separate the old class Algae into distinct phyletic lines or divisions. The remaining attributes—namely, flagellation, wall structure, habitat, body organization, and structure of the sex organs—have been used as criteria on the basis of which to delimit taxa lower than the division. For example, the orders Oedogoniales and Ulotrichales among the Chlorophyceae are segregated on such criteria as cell wall structure and flagellation. It must be emphasized once again, and it should be clear from the discussion in earlier chapters, that the classification of plants is to some extent subjective. The classification represents a system of presumed relationship carefully elaborated by one or more individuals on the basis of evaluation of the available evidence. The scheme frequently is cemented together by the classifier in a framework of speculation. In a group like the algae, for which the fossil record has not demonstrated the lines of development clearly, the classifier is bound to rely heavily upon the comparative morphology and physiology of the extant genera. It is quite possible, however, that genetic study of physiological attributes of algae may yet furnish evidence that the diversities of pigmentation and photosynthate, currently considered to be of such fundamental importance as to delimit divisions among algae, may represent merely small mutations from an ancestral type. Should this possibility be realized, it might be necessary to replace our currently polyphyletic interpretation of the algae by a more conservative one.

Pigmentation and Storage Products

Review of the type of pigmentation in the several taxa of algae reveals that all contain chlorophyll *a*, but that only the Chlorophycophyta and Euglenophycophyta have chlorophyll *b* as well. All the algae examined contain β-carotene; the greatest variations occur in the types of xanthophyll pigment present in the cells (Table 2-1, p. 11).

Reserve photosynthates and metabolites may be stored in either soluble or insoluble form. The Chlorophycophyta and Charophyta are similar to higher green plants in their almost universal storage of the excess photosynthate as starch. Oil is frequently present in addition, in such resting cells as zygotes and cysts. Some of the Dinophyceae also store starch, but a number of genera contain oils. Oil is present as visible droplets in the cells of Chrysophycophyta. Carbohydrate reserves occur in the cells of Cyanophycophyta, Phaeophycophyta, and Rhodophycophyta, but the exact chemical nature of the storage products is not known completely in each case. Lack of exact knowledge is evidenced by such names as "cyanophycean starch" and "floridean starch" for the reserve carbohydrates of Cyanophycophyta and Rhodophycophyta, respectively.

Organization of the Plant Body

Comparison of the several groups of algae with reference to the degree of organization of the plant body is instructive. In every division except the Charophyta and Phaeophycophyta, unicellular genera have been described. Of the divisions containing unicellular genera, flagellate motile forms are absent only in the Cyanophycophyta and Rhodophycophyta. Gelatinous and nongelatinous cell aggregates, namely, colonies, occur in several classes of algae. There is evidence that colonial plant bodies represent unicellular types in which the products of cell division have failed to separate. Similarly, the unbranched filament characteristic of a number of genera of Cyanophycophyta, Chlorophycophyta, Xanthophyceae, Bacillariophyceae, and a few Rhodophycophyta may arise in ontogeny from a single cell in which cytokinesis is restricted to one direction. Initiation of cell division in a second direction by certain cells of unbranched filaments results in the branched filamentous type of algal plant body (*Stigeoclonium, Cladophora, Ectocarpus, Griffithsia*). In such genera as *Ulva* and some species of *Porphyra*, continuous cell division in two directions perpendicular to each other and one division in a third direction by each of the cells have resulted in two-layered, sheetlike expanses. Such plant bodies may also arise ontogenetically by continuous branching of primarily filamentous axes in certain Rhodophyceae. Of all the algae, the Phaeophycophyta have the largest and most complex plant bodies.

Growth in algae may be generalized (*Merismopedia, Oscillatoria, Spirogyra*) or localized. In the latter case, three types of localization are present in the representative genera which have been described. Apical growth occurs in such plants as *Cladophora, Chara, Nemalion, Batrachospermum, Polysiphonia*, and *Griffithsia*. Intercalary growth is characteristic of *Oedogonium*, filamentous brown algae like some species of *Ectocarpus*, and of kelps. Finally, basal growth is illustrated by *Calothrix, Gloeotrichia*, and *Rivularia* among the Cyanophycophyta.

Reproduction

The preceding chapters have cited examples of a number of methods of asexual reproduction. Among these may be mentioned cell division, which occurs in a majority of unicellular genera; fragmentation, in colonial and multicellular types; and formation of specialized types of asexual reproduction cells. These may be motile zoospores or nonmotile aplanospores or autospores. All of these possess in common the negative attribute that no union of cells and nuclei is involved in their development into new individuals.

Sexual reproduction—the union of protoplasts and nuclei and the association of chromosomes—is absent only in the Euglenophycophyta and Cyanophycophyta[2] of the major groups of algae. In the other taxa, sexuality ranges through isogamous, heterogamous, and oogamous types. The Charophyta and Rhodophycophyta are unique in having only oogamous reproduction. The male gamete is actively motile by means of flagella in every group but the Rhodophycophyta. Both flagellate (*Chlamydomonas*) and nonflagellate (*Spirogyra*) gametes may display evidence of amoeboid activity during union. In algae as in animals, certain secondary characteristics may accompany sexuality. Among the motile unicellular genera, the gametes may be morphologically indistinguishable from vegetative cells. However, in other algae, the gametes are markedly differentiated from vegetative cells, and they may be produced frequently in specialized structures, the gametangia. The gametangia in oogamous reproduction are known as antheridia and oogonia. Both sex potentialities may occur on the same individual or each may be present on a separate individual.

The product of sexual union, the zygote, is free-floating in the water in many algae (*Chlamydomonas, Ulothrix*, etc.). In others—*Spirogyra, Oedogonium*, and the *Charophyta*, for example—the zygote is formed within the protective envelope of a parent cell which, however, ultimately disintegrates, thereby freeing the zygote. In *Laminaria* and in all the Rhodophycophyta, it is retained on the gametophyte after fertilization.

The behavior of the zygote after fertilization varies in different genera of algae, and this is associated with the development of several types of life cycle, shown in Chart 3-1. In what is regarded as the most primitive and simplest cycle (Type H, h, p. 48), the zygote undergoes meiosis, often after a period of dormancy, so that the product or products of its germination are haploid (*Chlamydomonas, Spirogyra, Nemalion*, etc.), and the

zygote represents the only diploid cell in the life cycle. At the other extreme is the condition (Type H,d, p. 48) in which the zygote, without undergoing dormancy, grows directly into a new individual which is diploid; meiosis occurs in this case when the diploid individual forms gametes (*Codium, Acetabularia, Caulerpa*, and diatoms). Here the gametes alone, of all the cells involved in the life cycle, are haploid. Both of these types of life cycle may be termed haplobiontic, because only one recognizable plant body type is present in nature. Haplobiontic organisms undergo alternation only of cytological states, for the diploid or haploid phase, as the case may be, is represented only by a single cell, the zygote or gamete.

Intermediate between these two extremes are the various modifications of diplobiontic life cycles (Type D, h + d). In these, the zygote, without undergoing meiosis, develops into a diploid individual. Meiosis takes place in these cells in connection with the formation of asexual reproductive cells which, therefore, are haploid. These develop into haploid, sexual gamete-producing individuals; union of their gametes gives rise to zygotes. In this type of life cycle two sets of independent individuals occur in nature. These may be morphologically similar (*Ulva, Cladophora, Ectocarpus, Griffithsia*) or divergent (*Laminaria, Porphyra*). Hence in morphological alternation, the cycle may be isomorphic or heteromorphic. The diplobiontic Rhodophycophyta have a life cycle like that summarized in Type D, h + d, with the interpolation of diploid spores between the zygote and the diploid plant. The origin and relationship of the alternating generations have been alluded to briefly in preceding chapters. This is a question of fundamental importance in any speculation dealing with the development of the so-called higher plants, and it will be referred to repeatedly in the following chapters.

Economic Aspects of Algae

Although this volume is devoted primarily to morphological data, brief mention must be made of the relation of algae to other

---

[2] See, however, p. 21.

organisms, and especially of their economic importance. That the algae have a twofold basic biological role becomes clear at once if we speculate regarding the outcome if all aquatic algae were to disappear from the earth. It is clear that all aquatic animal life would also soon be eradicated, for ultimately it is dependent on algal green pastures, not only as a link in the food chain, but because of the role of algae in maintaining an adequate level of oxygen in the animals' environment. The widespread presence of algae in soils suggests that their occurrence there is not fortuitous, and, as a corollary, that they must play some presently undiscovered role in the society of soil organisms. A number of species of soil-inhabiting Cyanophycophyta have been proven capable of fixing atmospheric nitrogen.

Several algae live in intimate association with other organisms. Noteworthy among these are the nitrogen-fixing species of *Anabaena* (and *Nostoc*) which occur within the liverworts, *Azolla,* and the roots of cycads. *Chlorella*-like algae occur within *Hydra* and certain fresh-water sponges where their role is not entirely clear. A number of algae live in intimate association with corals where the photosynthesis and oxygen production of the algae are of fundamental importance in the biology of the reef community. It has recently been reported that larvae of *Convoluta roscoffensis,* a flatworm, do not survive unless they become infected with a *Carteria*-like alga.

The value of algae directly as food, indirectly as vegetable manure, and for a variety of other purposes, has been appreciated for centuries in Oriental countries and to a more limited extent in the Western world. Many species of algae are regularly used in the diet of Oriental peoples. For example, a species of *Porphyra* known as "laver" has long been cultivated in Japan by sinking nets attached to bamboo poles in shallow estuaries; the *Porphyra* spores settle on the nets and develop into the bladelike plants which are subsequently harvested.

Various products of alginic acid, derived from the cell walls of coarser Phaeophycophyta, are used for several purposes in the textile industry, among them waterproofing cloth. Alginic acid has also been used to improve the texture of commercial ice cream.

Colloidal extracts from a number of marine Rhodophycophyta, but in this country especially *Gelidium cartilagineum* (L.) Gaillon, are the basis for the purified product known as agar-agar or simply agar. This substance is of paramount importance as the relatively inert agent of solidification of microbiological culture media, but it has a number of additional commercial and medicinal applications. Another red alga, *Chondrus crispus* (L.) Stack, Irish moss, often called "carragheen," is used in certain coastal localities in this country and abroad as the basis for blancmange and other confections. Colloids extracted from *Chondrus* are widely used in food products such as chocolate milk and ice cream. More than 3 million pounds (dry weight) of *Chondrus* were harvested commercially in Nova Scotia in 1960 and Japan alone harvested 285,000 metric tons of marine algae the same year. These examples indicate the importance of algae in the economy of certain populations.

In addition to the uses of these living algae or products derived from them, algae are important in many other connections. Reference has already been made to the numerous uses of the fossil remains of diatoms known as diatomaceous earth.

Finally, unicellular algae (*Chlorella*, etc.) are currently the experimental organisms in several very important lines of research which have obvious implications for human welfare. The first concerns the mechanism and energy relations of photosynthesis. The second concerns the large-scale cultivation of the organisms in a controlled environment, for the purpose of obtaining maximum yields to provide possible supplementary sources of food and fuel and as a source of oxygen in spacecraft. Furthermore, algae are extremely important organisms for the study of such life processes as differentiation, nutrition, etc. More extensive discussions of the topics and organisms alluded to in this chapter and in Chapters 2–7 will be found in the reference works listed at the end of Chapter 2.

Fossil Algae

There is both direct and indirect evidence that algae were present on the earth in Pre-

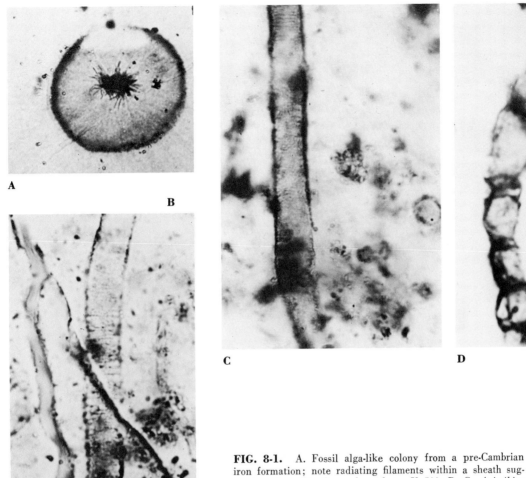

FIG. 8-1. A. Fossil alga-like colony from a pre-Cambrian iron formation; note radiating filaments within a sheath suggestive of certain Cyanophycophyta. X 500. B, C. *Animikiea septata* Barghoorn. B. X 1250, C. X 1100. D. *Gunflintia grandis* Barghoorn. X 2600. (A. *After Tyler and Barghoorn*; B–D. *After Barghoorn and Tyler*.)

cambrian (Table 32-1, p. 512) times. It is generally believed that algae were responsible (by removing carbon dioxide from water during photosynthesis) for the precipitation of large quantities of calcium carbonate which became limestone rock. Especially prominent deposits, presumably of algal origin, are visible at Glacier National Park. This process of carbonate precipitation is continued today by green and red algae in coral reefs and by blue-green algae which precipitate travertine rock in the waters of hot springs like those of Yellowstone National Park.

More direct evidence of the antiquity of algae is the discovery of blue-green algalike colonies (Fig. 8-1A) in Precambrian strata of the Gunflint chert on the shores of northern Lake Superior from Minnesota to Ontario.

The most recent report of these ancient algae includes descriptions of an *Oscillatoria*-like, unbranched filament, *Animikiea septata* Barghoorn (Fig. 8-1B, C) and of two species of the *Ulothrix*-like genus *Gunflintia* (Fig. 8-1D). The strata in which these algal remains occur are 1.9–2 billion years old. Other blue-green algae, among them one that is *Gloeocapsa*-like, occur in Ordovician and Devonian deposits.

Tubular, coenocytic green algae (Fig. 8-2), related to *Codium* and *Acetabularia*, are abundantly preserved in calcium carbonate encrustations of Ordovician strata. Fossil Charophyta (Fig. 8-3) are known in the middle Devonian and through Mesozoic and Cenozoic deposits.

Siliceous diatom frustules occur in abun-

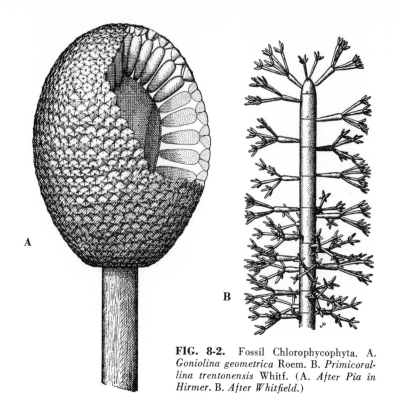

FIG. 8-2. Fossil Chlorophycophyta. A. *Goniolina geometrica* Roem. B. *Primicorallina trentonensis* Whitf. (A. *After Pia in Hirmer*. B. *After Whitfield*.)

dance (Fig. 8-4) from the Jurassic through the Mesozoic and Cenozoic. Finally, calcareous red and green algae are well known from the Ordovician through Mesozoic and Tertiary strata.

Ten genera and twenty-two species of noncalcareous marine algae have been described recently by Drs. Parker and Dawson from Miocene and Pliocene (Table 32-1, p. 512) deposits in Los Angeles County, California. These include one member of the Chlorophycophyta, four genera of the Phaeophycophyta, and five genera of Rhodophycophyta. All of the described species are extinct.

FIG. 8-4. Fossil marine diatoms from Hungary, grouped for illustration. X 45. (*After Mann*.)

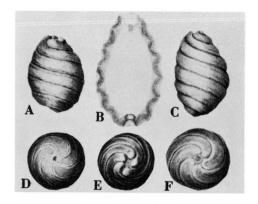

FIG. 8-3. Oogonia of the Pennsylvanian fossil charophyte, *Catillochara moreyi* Peck. A, C. in lateral aspect. B. Median longisection. D–F. Anterior polar view. X 60. (*After Peck and Eyer*.)

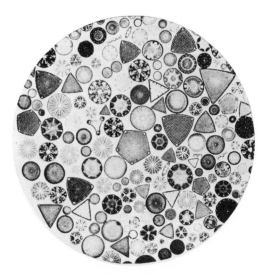

These statements indicate the antiquity of algae and also the early existence of diversities among them. Inasmuch as fossilized algae are in almost every case largely similar to extant genera, it is clear that our present-day algae are of ancient lineage and that they are relatively little modified from their progenitors. The fossil record thus sheds little light on the origin and course of evolution of algae, but does indicate that all the major divisions of algae had evolved by the beginning of the Paleozoic era (Table 32-1).

DISCUSSION QUESTIONS

1. What plants are usually included in the division Thallophyta? What does this practice imply?

2. Define or explain the terms ontogeny, phylogeny, monophyletic, polyphyletic.

3. What evidence can you cite to indicate that the algae are a polyphyletic group?

4. Discuss pigmentation and reserve photosynthates as they occur in algae. Compare with the land plants in these respects.

5. List the divisions and classes of algae and the attributes which distinguish them.

6. Summarize the types of life cycle that are present in algae and name illustrative genera.

7. Speculate regarding the possible development and relationships of the various types of plant body structure observed in the algae.

8. Discuss sexual reproduction with respect to possible origin, significance, gradation, and distribution of the sexes.

9. a. Where may the algal zygote be located during its formation and at maturity?

b. What correlations can you make between its location and further development?

10. Distinguish between morphological and cytological alternation of generations, between isomorphic and heteromorphic alternation, between haplobiontic and diplobiontic life cycles, between haplonts and diplonts, between haploid and diploid.

11. Discuss the algae with respect to habitat.

12. How would you go about proving that aquatic animals depend on algae (or other submerged plants) for their existence?

13. State the biological importance of algae.

14. In what respects are algae of economic importance?

15. What is meant by a "culture" of algae? What are pure cultures, unialgal cultures, clonal cultures?

16. In agricultural areas in many parts of the country it has become the practice to excavate for tanks or ponds in which to raise fish for food. Once the water has filled these artificial ponds, commercial fertilizer is added. Exactly how does this affect the fish?

17. What significant data are contributed by the fossil record of the algae?

CHAPTER 9

Introduction to Fungi; Division Schizomycota

Introduction

The algae, representatives of which have been described in Chapters 2–8, formerly were grouped as a class, Algae, coordinate with a class, Fungi, in a single division of the plant kingdom, the Thallophyta (Table 32-2, p. 516). Although this classification has been superseded, the concepts "algae" and "fungi" have persisted, and they serve useful functions. The fungi, in the broadest sense of the term, are sometimes considered to include all the nonphotosynthetic organisms in the plant kingdom other than a few colorless liverworts, mosses, and vascular plants. Although the various organisms thus delimited possess in common the attribute of nonphotosynthetic metabolism, they are divergent in so many other important morphological, cytological, and physiological aspects that they no longer are classified in a single group. Instead, they are here treated as six separate phyletic series or divisions, namely, Schizomycota, Myxomycota, Phycomycota, Ascomycota, Basidiomycota, and Deuteromycota. Discussion of the possible relationships between members of this series is deferred to Chapter 14.

Approximately 80,000 species of fungi are known; they thus comprise a much larger assemblage than the algae (19,000–25,000 species).

The plant bodies of fungi are unicellular, colonial, or filamentous. Although such fruiting structures as mushrooms and those of shelf and cup fungi may be quite complex, the vegetative phase is always simple. No fungus approaches in complexity of structure that of the brown and red algae.

Nutrition

With the exception of a small number of bacteria, the fungi are nonphotosynthetic and lack chlorophyll. They are, accordingly, for the most part dependent in their nutrition on metabolites provided by other organisms; this type of nutrition is called **heterotrophism.** In contrast, *relatively* self-sufficient organisms, which can synthesize their protoplasm from low-energy inorganic sources such as salts, carbon dioxide and water are classified nutritionally as **autotrophic** (Gr. *autos*, self + Gr. *trophe*, nourishment). Autotrophic organisms differ in the source of energy which drives their syntheses. **Photoautotrophic** organisms use the sun's energy through the agency of their chlorophyll.

A number of bacteria are photoautotrophic. These organisms are green, brown-red, or purple and can be cultivated in an entirely inorganic medium in the absence of oxygen, provided the cultures are illuminated. They contain a magnesium porphyrin compound which is similar to but not identical with chlorophyll. Their photosynthesis differs from that of chlorophyllous organisms in two respects: oxygen is not liberated during the process and the hydrogen donor is not water, but usually a sulfur compound. The photosynthesis of the green and purple bacteria involves a photochemical oxidation of hydrogen sulfide into sulfur or sulfuric acid.

A small number of autotrophic bacteria are **chemosynthetic,** in that (lacking chlorophyll) they use chemical energy freed by them in the oxidation of inorganic compounds such as ammonia, nitrite, and sulfur in synthesizing their protoplasm. Among these may be mentioned *Nitrosomonas,* which oxidizes ammonium salts to nitrites; *Nitrobacter,* which oxidizes nitrites to nitrates; and *Thiobacillus thioxidans* which oxidizes sulfur under acid conditions.

Although microorganisms may be shown to lead a purely autotrophic existence in the laboratory test tube, since they may be made to multiply in the absence of organic substances, it is doubtful that many lead an exclusively autotrophic existence in nature, because their environment usually contains many soluble organic substances, some of which certainly are used by the organisms. In connection with photoautotrophism, one further point is noteworthy. It cannot be inferred with certainty merely from the presence of chlorophyll that an organism is photoautotrophic. For example, a number of chlorophyllous algae like *Euglena* and species of *Chlorococcum* and *Eremosphaera* require vitamins which they are unable to synthesize, while one species of *Ochromonas* (p. 98) requires both vitamins and organic carbon sources.

The vast majority of bacteria and fungi are heterotrophic (as are animals). The energy they use in building their protoplasm is derived not from the sun or from the oxidation of inorganic compounds but from breaking down complex organic substances produced by other organisms. Heterotrophic species which are associated with living organisms are known as **parasites** (Gr. *parasitos,* eating at another's table); those that utilize either non-living organisms or the products of living organisms are known as **saprophytes** (Gr. *sapros,* rotten + Gr. *phyton,* plant). In the account of the fungi, a number of examples of both parasitic and saprophytic organisms will be described. Among the bacteria, some of the species present in human and animal bodies are parasitic; saprophytic species are more widely distributed. Certain fungi other than bacteria which ingest or engulf particles of organic matter are said to have **holozoic** (Gr. *holos,* whole + Gr. *zoion,* animal), or **phagotrophic** (Gr. *phagein,* to eat + Gr. *trophe,* nourishment), nutrition. This, of course, is characteristic of most animals and of certain primitive flagellates.

Microorganisms frequently serve as the point of departure for discussions concerning the ultimate origin of life and the nature of primitive life on this earth. In such speculations, knowledge of the types of nutrition is an important prerequisite. Some have postulated that chemoautotrophic organisms represent the most primitive living organisms, inasmuch as they could have existed in darkness and in the purely inorganic environment of the cooling earth's crust. According to this view, as the atmosphere cleared sufficiently for the penetration of light rays, photosynthetic organisms, also requiring purely inorganic substances, would have been able to exist. In the final stage, it is postulated that heterotrophic organisms arose as degenerate forms which secondarily lost the ability to chemosynthesize or photosynthesize and grew dependent upon other organisms or their products.

These conjectures have been questioned by those who believe that the evolution of nutritional and energy relations has proceeded in exactly the opposite direction. Their basic assumption is that "organic" substances were present on the earth before the appearance of living organisms. Therefore, they argue, the most primitive organisms would be those which could use organic substances to build their protoplasm, much as certain of our heterotrophic bacteria and fungi do at present. Furthermore, such organisms would require less complex enzyme systems than do chemosynthetic and photosynthetic organisms, which may start their synthetic chain with substances as simple as water and carbon dioxide. Evolution, beginning with the primitive heterotrophic organisms, proceeded in the direction of increasing capacity for effecting complex biosyntheses from decreasingly complex environmental substances. It culminated in the type of nutrition exhibited by chemosynthetic bacteria, which are able to synthesize their protoplasm and its building units from entirely inorganic substances, utilizing chemical energy. The final step, according to this hypothesis, was the appearance of photosynthetic organisms which developed a capacity for a similar synthesis, using the energy of the sun.

Thus the course of evolution of nutrition

and metabolism, like that of many morphological attributes, is interpreted by different scholars as having proceeded in opposite directions. However, the metabolism of microorganisms remains of fundamental importance in all discussions regarding the origin of life.

Division Schizomycota

The discussion of the Schizomycota (Gr. *schizo*, cleave + Gr. *mykes*, fungus), the bacteria, in a volume treating of the morphology of plants, is necessarily brief for several reasons. First, none of the several groups of plants approaches the bacteria in *apparent* simplicity of structure, although there is recent evidence of a higher degree of organization than hitherto had been suspected. Second, the relative simplicity of their morphology has stimulated and necessitated study of the physiology of bacteria, with the result that their classification is based in large measure on their extremely diverse physiological activities. As a result, the study of bacteria, originally initiated by botanists, has now come to be recognized as a separate field of biology, namely, bacteriology. Nevertheless, in a treatment of representatives of the plant kingdom and their possible relationships, the bacteria must be reckoned with, particularly in discussing such fundamental concepts as the nature of primitive life on earth. Furthermore, there are certain cytological aspects of bacteria which seem to parallel those of the Cyanophycophyta. These are considered by

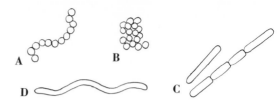

FIG. 9-1. Some representative genera of bacteria. A. *Streptococcus.* B. *Staphylococcus.* C. *Bacillus.* D. *Spirillum.* X 2000.

some authorities to be sufficiently significant to warrant classification of the two groups in a single division, the Schizophyta or, alternatively, Akaryota or Prokaryota. Approximately 122 genera of bacteria have been described. According to the 1953 edition of *Bergey's Manual*, 1630 species of bacteria were known in that year. It is debatable, however, whether bacterial species correspond precisely in scope to those of other plants.

Although bacteria were known to Leeuwenhoek as early as 1683, detailed knowledge of their structure and nutrition goes back only to the last decades of the nineteenth century. Bacteria sometimes are considered to be unicellular fungi which reproduce only by simple fission. A number of genera, however, consist of multicellular chains or filaments, or sporangiate aggregations suggestive of those of certain slime molds to be discussed in the following chapter. In general, bacteria are the smallest living organisms visible with the ordinary light microsope; they frequently have dimensions which range between 0.5 and 2.0 μ in width and 1.0 and 8.0 μ in length. As to cell form, many bacteria fall into three groups (Figs. 9-1, 9-2): those with spherical

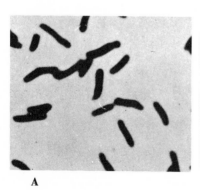
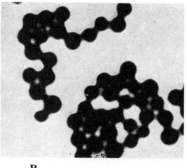
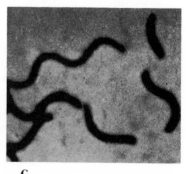

A   B   C

FIG. 9-2. Photomicrographs of three common forms of bacterial cell. A. Coccus. B. Bacillus. C. Spirillum. X 2000. (*After J. Novak.*)

MORPHOLOGY OF PLANTS

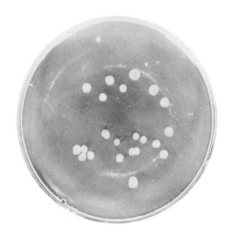

FIG. 9-3. Petri dish agar culture with colonies of *Escherichia coli.* X 1/2.

cells, the **cocci** (Gr. *kokkos*, berry) ; those whose cells are short rods or cylinders, the **bacilli** (L. *bacillus*, little stick) ; and those with their cells curved and twisted, the **spirilla** (Gr. *speira*, coil). Because many bacteria are similar in cellular form, it became apparent early that additional criteria must be employed to recognize bacterial genera and their species; these criteria are largely physiological. Many bacteria grow readily on a variety of organic culture media solidified with agar (Fig. 9-3) a colloidal derivative of seaweeds. The growth habit varies considerably among different species.

The individual bacterial cell is delimited from its environment by a cell wall and contains cytoplasmic and nuclear material (Fig. 9-4). The existence of a cell wall has been demonstrated by plasmolysis, by microdissection, and by electron microscopy. The chemical nature of the wall is by no means well known for all bacteria and seems to vary in different species. The wall appears to be composed of a complex carbohydrate of unknown nature and is sometimes referred to as hemicellulose. It is often impregnated with other substances, some of which contain nitrogen. As in the blue-green algae, diaminopimelic, muramic, and certain amino acids occur in some bacteria. The cell wall is surrounded, in turn, by a layer of slimy material of variable thickness, which may be present

as a recognizable **capsule** (Figs. 9-4, 9-5). The cytoplasm of bacteria devoid of insoluble metabolites appears optically homogeneous. It is bounded externally by a cytoplasmic membrane. Various granules involved in metabolism frequently are present in the cytoplasm.

The question of the organization of the nuclear material is one of the most controversial aspects of the morphology of the bacterial cell. Inasmuch as bacteria maintain certain specific, inheritable attributes through countless series of cell generations, our knowledge of other organisms would indicate that the bacteria possess some physical mechanism of inheritance—in other words, a nuclear mechanism. As a result of the study of a number of bacteria by special microchemical methods for the detection of deoxyribonucleic acid, which seems to be present universally in the nuclei of higher plants and animals, it was demonstrated that this substance is also present in bacterial cells (Figs. 9-4, 9-6). It may take the form of a somewhat dumbbell-shaped mass which lies parallel to the transverse axis of the cell (Fig. 9-4) or it may be more dispersed. This chromosomelike body divides

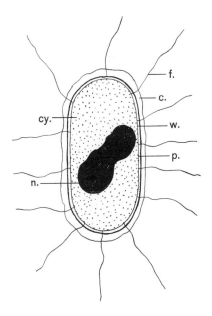

FIG. 9-4. Cellular organization in bacteria, schematized; c., capsule; cy., cytoplasm; f., flagellum; n., nuclear material; p., plasma membrane; w., wall. (*Modified from Clifton.*)

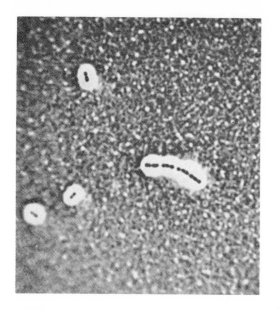

longitudinally prior to cell division; it thus has one of the attributes of chromosomes of higher organisms. It will be recalled that in certain Cyanophycophyta, similar rodlike bodies have been demonstrated in the central region of the cell. The nuclear material is often in the form of extremely delicate threads of DNA. There is apparently a certain precocity in the division of the chromosomal element of some bacteria. In these species, recently divided chromosomes may become separated by partition of the cytoplasm, while actual secretion of the dividing septum may be delayed. Thus a single cell, during active growth, may have its protoplast divided into a number of segments, in some of which the chromosomal element is dividing in prepara-

FIG. 9-5. Photomicrograph of stained streptococci showing capsules. X 1000. (*Courtesy of Dr. W. D. Frost.*)

FIG. 9-6. *Micrococcus radiodurans*, electron micrograph; c., cytoplasm; c. w., cell wall; n., nuclear material. X 65,000. (*Courtesy of Dr. R. G. E. Murray.*)

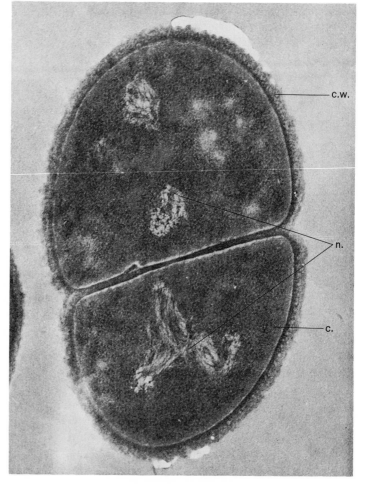

MORPHOLOGY OF PLANTS

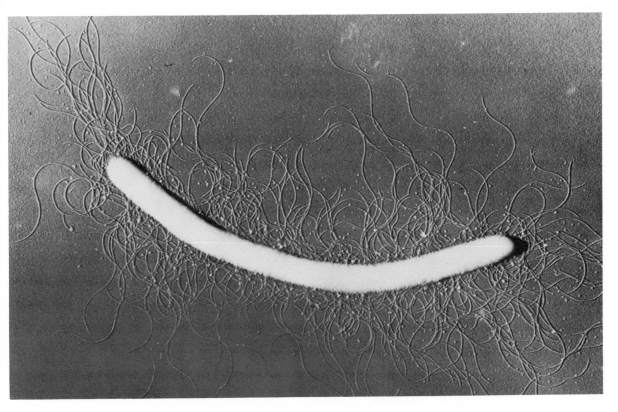

FIG. 9-7. *Proteus vulgaris.* Electron micrograph shadowed with chromium; note flagella. (*S.A.B. photograph LS-258, after Houwink and van Iterson.*)

tion for an ensuing cytokinesis, while formation of the transverse walls may lag behind karyokinesis and cytokinesis. Actual separation of daughter protoplasts occurs only after they have secreted these walls. It should be noted that bacterial cells, like those of blue-green algae (p. 13), lack mitochondria, Golgi bodies, and endoplasmic reticulum, which characterize the cells (Fig. 3-2E) of most other living organisms.

Some bacteria are nonmotile, but others are actively motile by means of flagella; their presence can be confirmed only by special illumination or methods of staining. A single flagellum or group of flagella may be present at one pole of the cell or the cells may be covered uniformly with flagella (Fig. 9-7). Various arrangements have been described.

Many of the rod-shaped bacteria have the capacity of forming **endospores** (Fig. 9-8A). There is some evidence that these are produced as a result of depletion of the nutrients in the surrounding medium and that they represent

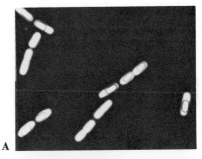

A

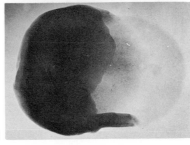

B

FIG. 9-8. A. *Bacillus cereus*, spore formation. X 3200. B. *Bacillus mycoides*, spore germination, electron micrograph. X 4400. (A. *Courtesy of Dr. G. J. Hageage.* B. *S.A.B. photograph 203, after Knaysi, Baker, and Hillier.*)

condensations of the protoplast within the cell wall. Each spore contains nuclear material and cytoplasm and at maturity is covered by an impermeable wall. Spores are extremely resistant to such unfavorable environmental conditions as high temperatures and desiccation. Upon germination (Fig. 9-8B), each spore produces a single vegetative cell. Spore formation in bacteria, therefore, usually is not a means of increasing the number of individuals, but rather a mechanism for survival in adverse environmental conditions.

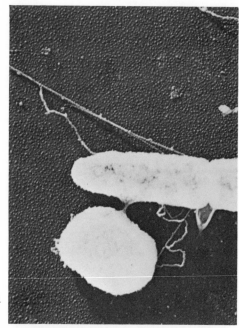
A
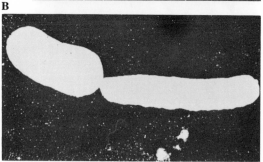
B

FIG. 9-9. Cytological evidence of gene exchange in *Escherichia coli*, electron micrographs. A. Two morphologically unlike (different strains) individuals laterally connected. B. The same in terminal connection. (*Courtesy of Dr. Thomas F. Anderson.*)

Sexuality

Mechanisms for gene interchange, or sexual phenomena, were unknown in bacteria until about 20 years ago. As compared with sexual phenomena in other organisms, those of bacteria are subtle and, for the most part, not obvious cytologically. Furthermore, all of the mechanisms for genic interchange which occurs in bacteria differ from those in other organisms in that complete union of two nuclei does not occur; hence zygotes are not produced, but only DNA-modified (genetically) cells known as **merozygotes** (partial zygotes).

The sexual process of *Escherichia coli* most closely approaches that in nonbacterial organisms. It involves the temporary (up to 2 hours) union of two cells by a tube which arises from a donor ("male") cell which attaches to a recipient ("female") cell (Fig. 9-9). Depending on the duration of the union, varying amounts of donor DNA are injected into the recipient cell where they may replace allelomorphic genes present therein. Thus, the genetic constitution of the donor cell becomes modified by incorporation of new genes and its progeny are accordingly changed.

Two other types of transfer of genetic materials occur in bacteria, namely, **transformation** and **transduction.** In the former, DNA from nonliving bacteria of a given species is taken up by living bacteria of the same species with modification of their genetic constitution. Thus, streptomycin resistance can be incorporated into some individuals of a non-streptomycin-resistant population by growing the latter in a culture medium containing streptomycin-resistant DNA.

In transduction, viruses enter a bacterial cell and DNA from their preceding host is carried and may replace in part that of the new host, which, accordingly, becomes modified.

In summary, it should again be emphasized that conjugation, transformation, and transduction in bacteria produce only incomplete zygotes, or merozygotes, in which a few genes are substituted for their alleles. In contrast to this, sexuality involving nuclear union, as it does in other plants and animals, results in the association of two complete sets of parental genes in the zygote.

The Actinomycetes

The organisms described in the preceding paragraphs are representative of the "true" bacteria, usually classified together in a single order distinct from several orders of "higher" bacteria which are morphologically more complex. One group of the latter, commonly called the **actinomycetes,** is of special interest in several respects. In the first place, the organisms are sometimes classified with the fungi because their plant bodies are filamentous in organization (Fig. 9-10), like those of many fungi. Furthermore, they produce chains of minute, dustlike spores, **conidia** (Fig. 9-10), which are similar to those of many fungi. However, the cytological organization of actinomycetes is similar to that of bacteria rather than to that of the fungi. The filaments of actinomycetes, which rarely exceed 1 μ in diameter, form radiating colonies in agar cultures. They are distributed widely in soil and many strains have been isolated into pure cultures. Three of them, among others—*Streptomyces*

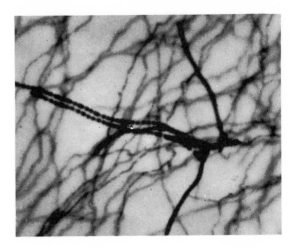

FIG. 9-10. *Streptomyces antibioticus* (Waksman and Woodruff) Waksman and Henrici; hyphae in background, chains of conidia in focus. X 1500. (*Courtesy of Dr. S. A. Waksman.*)

griseus (Krainsky) Waksman and Henrici, *S. aureofaciens* Duggar, and *S. rimosus* Routien —yield respectively, the antibiotics streptomycin, aureomycin, and terramycin. More than eighty other antibiotic substances have been obtained from species of the genus *Streptomyces*. There is every reason to believe that actinomycetes play an important role in the biology of soil.

DISCUSSION QUESTIONS

1. What attributes are possessed in common by bacteria and Cyanophycophyta? How do they differ?

2. Define or explain the terms autotrophic, heterotrophic, chemoautotrophic, photoautotrophic, chemosynthetic, photosynthetic, parasite, saprophyte, phagotrophic.

3. Discuss sexual reproduction in bacteria.

4. Are bacteria the smallest living organisms? Explain.

5. Can most bacteria be identified specifically by microscopic examination alone? Explain.

6. How would you prove that bacterial cells have walls?

7. What types of nutrition occur in bacteria?

8. What type of nutrition do you consider to be the most primitive? Give reasons for your answer.

9. Obligate parasites are those which cannot be cultivated except in a living host. Can you suggest an explanation for this?

10. In what respects are bacterial spores different from those of Cyanophycophyta?

11. List some harmful and some beneficial activities of bacteria.

REFERENCE WORKS ON BACTERIA

Breed, R. S., Murray, E. G. D., and Smith, H. R. *et al. Bergey's Manual of Determinative Bacteriology*, 7th ed., Williams and Wilkins Co., Baltimore, Md., 1957.

De Kruif, P., *Microbe Hunters*, Harcourt, Brace & World, New York, 1926.

Gunslaus, I. C., and Stanier, R. Y., *The Bacteria, A Treatise on Structure and Function*, vols. I–V, Academic Press, New York, 1960–1964.

Jacobs, F., and Wollman, E., *Sexuality and Genetics of Bacteria*, Academic Press, New York, 1961.

Oparin, A. I., *The Origin of Life*, 2nd ed., Macmillan Co., New York, 1953.

Pelczar, M. J., Jr., and Reid, R. D., *Microbiology*, 2nd ed., McGraw-Hill Co., New York, 1965.

Salle, A. J., *Fundamental Principles of Bacteriology*, 5th ed., McGraw-Hill Co., New York, 1961.

Stanier, R. Y., Doudoroff, M., and Adelberg, E. A., *The Microbial World*, 2nd ed., Prentice-Hall, Inc., Englewood Cliffs, N. J., 1963.

Thimann, K., *The Life of Bacteria: Their Growth, Metabolism, and Relationships*, Macmillan Co., New York, 1963.

Waksman, S. A., and Lechavalier, H. A., *Actinomycetes and Their Antibiotics*, Williams and Wilkins Co., Baltimore, Md., 1953.

CHAPTER 10

Division Myxomycota

Introduction

As treated here, the division Myxomycota (Gr. *myxa,* mucus + Gr. *mykes,* fungus) contains two classes, the **Myxomycetes** and **Acrasiomycetes.**

MYXOMYCETES

The Myxomycetes or **plasmodial slime molds** are characterized especially by their vegetative phase, which is quite unique in respect to nutrition and morphology. Slime molds are relatively inconspicuous elements of the vegetation, but they are objects of great beauty in miniature during the periods when they produce their reproductive structures.[1] The vegetative phase of these organisms is known as the **plasmodium** (Figs. 10-1, 10-2). It occurs on grass, decaying leaves, wood, and soil in moist, dark situ-

ations. Inasmuch as most of the vegetative period is spent within or beneath the organic substratum, the plasmodial stage is frequently overlooked. However, if one collects decaying leaves or wood and stores them in moist chambers on damp paper, the plasmodia may often be induced to leave their original substratum and may be maintained for considerable periods in the laboratory.

Illustrative Genera

The following account deals especially with *Physarum polycephalum* Schw. because it is a species readily observable in all stages in the laboratory. The plasmodium (Figs. 10-1, 10-2) is a yellow, macroscopically visible mass of multinucleate protoplasm normally in a more or less active state of flowing movement. The protoplasm ingests various organic particles and spores, pollen grains, and microorganisms during its migration; its nutrition is holozoic or phagotrophic. The ingested foods lie in vacuoles where they are digested by enzymes secreted by the plasmodial protoplasm. There

---

[1] For particularly beautiful illustrations of these organisms, see W. Crowder, 1926, "Marvels of Mycetozoa," *National Geographic Magazine,* 49:421–443.

FIG. 10-1. *Physarum polycephalum* Schw. Plasmodium on agar in Petri dish. X 1/2.

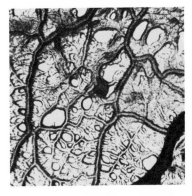

FIG. 10-2. *Physarum polycephalum.* Photomicrograph of portion of a plasmodium. X 12.5.

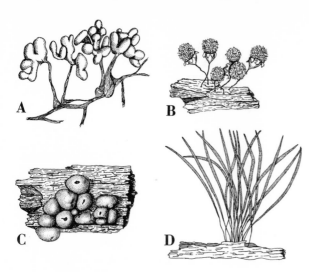

FIG. 10-3. Spore-bearing organs of various Myxomycetes. A. *Physarum polycephalum.* X 10. B. *Hemitrichia* sp. X 4. C. *Lycogala epidendrum* (L.) Fr. X 1. D. *Stemonitis* sp. X 2.

can be little doubt that soluble organic matter is also absorbed, so that nutrition is in part saprophytic as well as phagotrophic. The rate and direction of movement are influenced markedly by external stimuli. Hence plasmodia afford an excellent opportunity for the study of various tactic responses. Motility itself may be observed both macroscopically and microscopically. It consists of a rather regular rhythmic movement in one direction, followed by a short pause and reversal of direction. The prolonged movement, absence of a cellulose cell wall, and capacity for phagotrophic nutrition have suggested to some biologists that the Myxomycota have affinities with the Protozoa; they are sometimes classified with the latter and referred to as Mycetozoa. Their reproductive phases, however, are strikingly plantlike. Movement of the plasmodium may be as rapid as a rate of 3 cm. per hour in *Physarum.* Plasmodia which have not yet formed reproductive bodies may become concentrated into dormant **sclerotia** when moisture and/or temperature fall below a certain level. The sclerotia of *Physarum polycephalum* vary in color from yellow-orange to dark brown. They are composed of multinucleate segments called **spherules.** They may give rise to plasmodia again when adequate moisture becomes available.

After a relatively prolonged vegetative phase, which may be lengthened by maintain-

ing high levels of moisture and nutriment, the plasmodium enters the reproductive phase and produces **sporangia** (Fig. 10-3A). This may be hastened by withholding food. Yellow plasmodia, among various species of slime molds, require light to form sporangia. Blue light, 4360A, is especially efficacious in inducing sporangium production in *P. polycephalum.* The plasmodium begins to undergo concentration at one or more localized points, usually those more highly illuminated and drier. As the process continues, the fruiting body characteristic of the genus is produced (Figs. 10-3, 10-4). This may be irregular in form, not markedly different from that of the plasmodium, or it may consist of several or many individual sessile or stalked sporangia. In *Physarum polycephalum* the sporangia are dichotomously lobed, grey-green[2] at maturity, and supported on stalks (Fig. 10-3A). During sporangial development, the plasmodium usually discards much detritus at the base of the sporangia, forming a **hypothallus;** the remainder is used to produce a rather firm outer stratum, the **peridium** (Gr. *peridion,* small leather bag), over the sporogenous region.

When the protoplasm aggregates, the young fruiting bodies consist of vacuolate masses of protoplasm with numerous minute nuclei. As development proceeds, the nuclei increase in number by mitosis, and progressive cleavage is initiated both from the plasma membrane adjacent to the peridium and from the surface membranes of numerous vacuoles; hence a

---

[2] This color is due, in part, to the presence of lime on the sporangial surface. In laboratory cultures the lime may not be deposited, with the result that the sporangia are blackish.

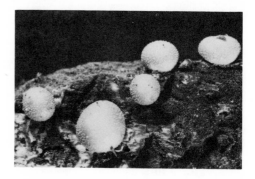

FIG. 10-4. *Lycogala epidendrum* sporangia. X 2.5.

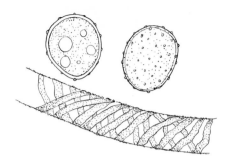

FIG. 10-5. *Hemitrichia vesparium* (Batch.) Macbr. Spores and segment of capillitium; the spore to the left in optical section, the one to the right in surface view. X 1500.

large number of spores is ultimately produced. In the meantime, depending on the species, nonliving material may be deposited in and on the surfaces of canallike vacuoles. When the sporangium is thoroughly mature and dry, the former vacuoles persist as a system of threads (Fig. 10-5), the **capillitium** (L. *capillitium*, hair).

The sporangial peridium is ruptured at maturity and the liberated spores are carried away by air currents. Furthermore, recent studies have demonstrated that slime molds are abundant in air-borne dusts. Those which settle on favorable substrata soon undergo germination, although they may retain their viability for a number of years. The spores of *P. polycephalum* have punctate walls and are uninucleate (Fig. 10-6A). The germinating spores usually give rise to but one or two motile cells. These are irregular in shape, and somewhat amoeboid; they develop two unequal flagella. Spore germination in *Fuligo*, another genus, is illustrated in Fig. 10-6B. These motile products of spore germination have been observed to ingest bacteria and other minute fragments of nutriment. It has been demonstrated in some genera of slime molds that these amoeboid or flagellate motile cells are potentially gametes which may unite in pairs to form amoeboid zygotes. This occurs in *P. polycephalum*. Some clones of Myxomycota are unisexual so that gametes of two different mating types must be present to form zygotes which initiate plasmodia. In each zygote, repeated mitotic nuclear division occurs without cytokinesis, so that a multinu-

cleate plasmodium is ultimately produced. The latter grows very rapidly; for example, a 1-cm.-square piece of plasmodium of *P. polycephalum* increased to 25 sq. cm. in area within 7 days when supplied with fungus mycelium for food.

Recent quantitative cytochemical studies[3] indicate that the plasmodial nuclei contain approximately twice as much DNA as do the nuclei of the mature spores. The site of meiosis in the life cycle of the Myxomycota has not been determined with certainty. Indeed, it is possible that meiosis does not occur in the same place in all species. Current information indicates that meiosis takes place either in the developing sporangium during cleavage or in the young spores after delimitation. In the latter event, all nuclei but one disintegrate. In either case, the spore, as it matures, is haploid.

A number of genera and species of slime molds other than *Physarum* are of common occurrence on substrata that are subject to prolonged periods of moisture. These include decaying wood and leaves, moist soil, and grass. *Stemonitis, Lycogala,* and *Hemitrichia* (Figs. 10-3B–D, 10-4) are genera which are widely distributed in such habitats.

[3] Therrien, C. D., 1965, "Microspectrophotometric analysis of nuclear deoxyribonucleic acid in some Myxomycetes." Ph.D. dissertation, University of Texas, Austin.

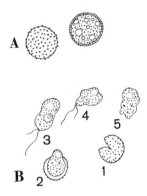

FIG. 10-6. A. *Physarum polycephalum;* spores. B. Spore germination in *Fuligo* sp.; 1. Empty spore wall. 2. Emergent protoplast. 3, 4. Flagellated stages. 5. Myxamoebae. X 770.

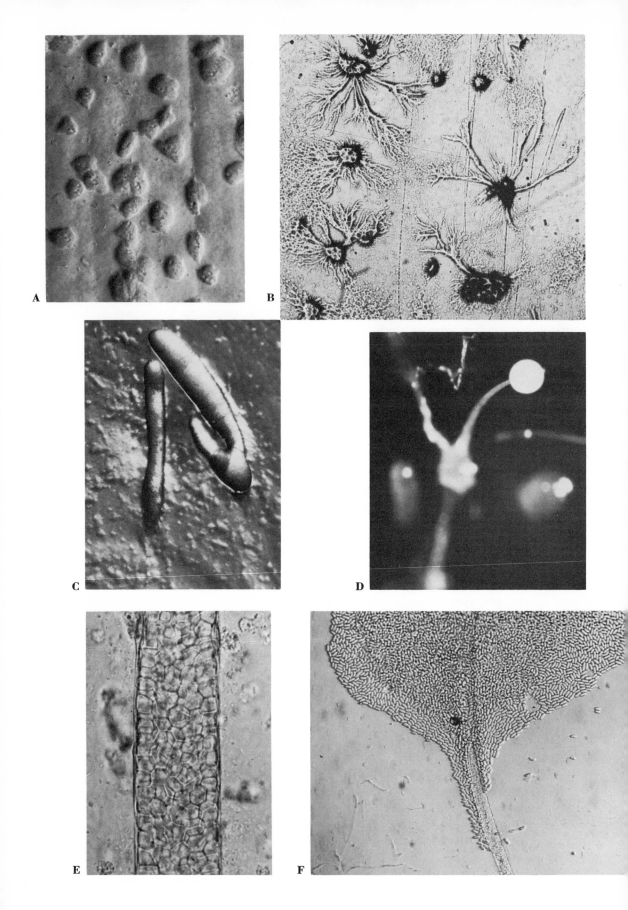

Summary and Classification

The Acrasiomycetes are **cellular slime molds.** Not clearly related to Myxomycota or other fungi, the cellular slime molds are organisms of uncertain affinity, included here because of their great biological significance. They differ from the Myxomycetes in that a true plasmodium is not produced; instead, the unit of organization is the individual amoeba (Fig. 10-7A).

Of the cellular slime molds, the life cycle of *Dictyostelium* is perhaps best known. The uninucleate amoebae emerge singly from within the cellulosic walls of germinating spores. The amoebae ingest food particles and bacteria as they move about the substrate, soon enlarge, and then undergo nuclear and cell division. When supplies of nutriment are adequate, a large population of amoebae arises rather rapidly.

After the population has become sufficiently dense, aggregation centers of amoebae develop (Fig. 10-7B) and they stop feeding. Aggregation has been shown to be a response to a secretion of **acrasin** by certain amoebae which chemotactically attract others. The aggregating amoebae soon form a colonial unit called a **pseudoplasmodium** because, unlike a true plasmodium, the component cells retain their individuality. The sluglike pseudoplasmodium (Fig. 10-7C) may migrate for some time but ultimately becomes transformed into a fruiting structure, the **sorocarp** (Fig. 10-7D). This consists of stalk cells (Fig. 10-7E) bearing amoebae at the apex which become transformed into thin-walled spores. The latter germinate to give rise to amoebae which may reinitiate the life cycle (Fig. 10-7F,G). Whether or not a sexual process occurs in the cellular slime molds remains unresolved.

In conclusion, it may be noted that the Myxomycota are of interest to the biologist because of the combination of plant- and animallike attributes they display. Their naked, plasmodial stages afford an excellent opportunity for the study of protoplasm, while the delicate beauty and design of the minute sporangia have attracted the attention of many students. As noted above, the slime molds are often classified by zoologists as members of the phylum Protozoa. When treated by botanists, they are generally considered to include at least three series which are accorded varying rank by different authors. The organisms discussed in this chapter may be classified as follows:

Division Myxomycota

    Class 1. Myxomycetes

        Order 1. Physarales

            Family 1. Physaraceae

                Genus: *Physarum*

        Order 2. Stemonitales

            Family 1. Stemonitaceae

                Genus: *Stemonitis*

        Order 3. Liceales

            Family 1. Reticulariaceae

                Genus: *Lycogala*

        Order 4. Trichiales

            Family 1. Trichiaceae

                Genus: *Trichia*

    Class 2. Acrasiomycetes

        Order 1. Acrasiales

            Family 1. Dictyosteliaceae

                Genus: *Dictyostelium*

DISCUSSION QUESTIONS

1. What characteristics distinguish the Myxomycetes from other fungi?

2. In what habitats would you look for slime molds?

3. How do the plasmodium and sporangiate stages of Myxomycetes differ in their tactic responses? Describe possible experiments to demonstrate such responses.

4. In what respect is the nutrition of Myxomycetes unlike that of other fungi?

5. Is the capillitium cellular? Explain, describing its origin.

FIG. 10-7. *Dictyostelium discoideum.* A. Myxamoebae. X 400. B. Convergence of myxamoebae at centers of aggregation. X 15. C. Migrating aggregation or slug. X 45. D. Sorocarp. X 30. E. Portion of sorocarp stalk enlarged; note component myxamoebae. X 525. F. Crushed sorocarp showing spores. X 230. (*Courtesy of Dr. A. C. Lonert and the General Biological Supply House.*)

6. Summarize the life cycle and reproduction of *Physarum polycephalum*.

7. List the animal- and plantlike attributes of slime molds.

8. If you were cultivating Myxomycetes in the laboratory, in what form could you supply the essential elements?

9. How does *Dictyostelium* differ from the Myxomycetes?

REFERENCE WORKS ON FUNGI[4]

Alexopoulos, C. J., *Introductory Mycology*, 2nd ed., John Wiley and Sons, Inc., New York, 1962.

Bessey, E. A., *Morphology and Taxonomy of Fungi*, The Blakiston Co., New York, 1950.

Bonner, J. T., *The Cellular Slime Molds*, Princeton Univ. Press, Princeton, N.J., 1959.

Buller, A. H., *Researches on the Fungi*, vols. 1–6, Longmans, Green and Co., vol. 7, University Press, Toronto, 1909–1950.

Christensen, C. M., *The Molds and Man*, 2nd ed., Univ. of Minnesota Press, Minneapolis, Minn., 1961.

Crowder, W., "Marvels of Mycetozoa," *National Geographic Magazine* 49:421–443, 1926.

---

[4] For use with Chapters 10–14.

Fitzpatrick, H. M., *The Lower Fungi. Phycomycetes*, McGraw Hill Book Co., Inc., New York, 1930.

Foster, J. W., *Chemical Activities of Fungi*, Academic Press, New York, 1949.

Gauman, E. A., and Wynd, F. L., *The Fungi*, Hafner Publishing Co., New York, 1952.

Gray, W. D., *The Relation of Fungi to Human Affairs*, Holt, Rinehart and Winston, New York, 1959.

Gwynne-Vaughan, H. C. I., and Barnes, B., *The Structure and Development of the Fungi*, Cambridge Univ. Press, London, 1937.

Krieger, L. C. C., "Common Mushrooms of the United States," *National Geographic Magazine* 37: 387–439, 1920.

Lindegren, C. C., *The Yeast Cell, Its Genetics and Cytology*, Educational Publishers, Inc., St. Louis, Mo., 1949.

Lister, A., *A Monograph of the Mycetozoa*, British Museum, London, 1925.

MacBride, T. H., and Martin, G. W., *The Myxomycetes*, The Macmillan Company, New York, 1934.

Ramsbottom, J., *Mushrooms and Toadstools*, William Collins Sons & Co., Ltd., New York, 1953.

Scagel, R. F. *et al.*, *An Evolutionary Survey of the Plant Kingdom*, Wadsworth Publishing Co., Inc., Belmont, Calif., 1965.

Smith, G. M., *Cryptogamic Botany*, vol. 1, McGraw-Hill Book Co., Inc., New York, 1955.

Sparrow, F. K., *Aquatic Phycomycetes*, 2nd ed., Univ. of Michigan Press, Ann Arbor, 1960.

Division Phycomycota

Introduction

The division Phycomycota (Gr. *phykos*, alga + Gr. *mykes*, fungus) contains a rather heterogeneous group of fungi, which may be distinguished from the Myxomycota by the absence of a plasmodial stage and from the Schizomycota by differences in cellular organization. The Phycomycota are readily distinguishable from the Ascomycota and Basidiomycota by the lack of spores characteristic of those division. The **mycelium,** the vegetative filamentous stage, also is distinctive in the Phycomycota, being either nonseptate or incompletely septate (Fig. 11-5B) and coenocytic. An individual branch of the mycelium is called a **hypha.** Both parasites and saprophytes occur among the Phycomycota. The name of the division reflects the opinion of those who see in its members evidences of relationship to the algae. The Phycomycota considered in this chapter represent five different groups of organisms. These are the chytrids, *Allomyces*, the water molds, *Albugo*, and bread mold.

Illustrative Types

CHYTRIDS

The chytrids are the simplest of the Phycomycota. They are often microscopic and may be unicellular. However, vegetative and reproductive portions may be separated by partitions as in siphonalean algae like *Bryopsis*, and as in *Vaucheria*. A division of labor is apparent in the vegetative phases of some genera, as indicated by the development of rhizoidal processes with tapering extremities (Fig. 11-1), somewhat like those of the alga *Botrydium*. In other genera, rhizoidal branches are absent.

Many parasitic species inhabit such hosts as algae, aquatic fungi, and the submerged portions of higher plants. Others, like *Synchytrium*, occur on terrestrial plants such as the hog-peanut, *Amphicarpa bracteata* (L.) Fern. Dormant reproductive bodies of chytrids are abundant in the soil and in submerged decaying vegetation. Accordingly, a number of species may be obtained readily for study by immersing various types of "bait," such as onion scale epidermis, untreated cellophane, pollen grains, chitinous substances, bleached leaves, algae, etc., in pond water and suspensions of soil and water.

Rhizophydium

Rhizophydium globosum (Braun) Rabenhorst represents one of the simpler chytrids (Fig. 11-1). It occurs on dead or moribund aquatic fresh-water vegetation. Infection is effected by a posteriorly uniflagellate zoospore, which settles on the surface of the host, withdraws its flagellum, and secretes absorptive

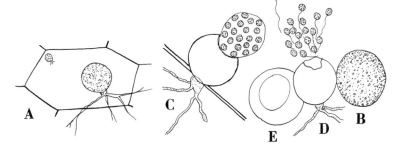

FIG. 11-1. *Rhizophydium globosum* (Braun) Rabenh. on leaf cells of *Elodea*, an aquatic angiosperm. A. Young and almost mature thalli on leaf cell. B. Vegetative thallus. C–E. Formation and discharge of zoospores. X 410.

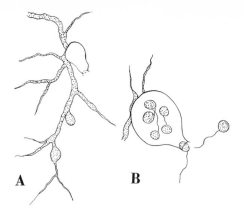

FIG. 11-2. *Polychytrium aggregatum* Ajello. A. Portion of fungus with developing zoosporangia. X 315. B. Discharge of zoospores. X 770.

FIG. 11-3. *Polyphagus starrii* Johns. A. Young thalli attached to colonies of the volvocacean alga *Eudorina*. X 450. B. Later stage in infection: prosporangium from which zoosporangium has emerged; note poor condition of host. X 625. C. Zoospores. X 1700. D. Cysts from zoospores; these can initiate new infections. X 1500. ps., prosprangium. (*Courtesy of Drs. Philip W. Cook, R. C. Starr, and the late R. M. Johns.*) ▶

▼

A

branches into a host cell (Fig. 11-1A). The fungus protoplast increases in size by absorbing nutriment from the host protoplasm (Fig. 11-1B) or its remains. After a period of vegetative development, during which increase in nuclear number occurs, the protoplast of the parasite undergoes cleavage to form a number of uniflagellate zoospores. These are liberated at maturity (Fig. 11-1C–E) through an apical orifice. The zoospores produce new infections.

Polychytrium

Polychytrium aggregatum Ajello is representative of the chytrids in which a branching system, the **rhizomycelium,** often is developed by the vegetative individual (Fig. 11-2A), which is saprophytic and present in decaying vegetation. Reproduction is accomplished by posteriorly uniflagellate spherical zoospores (Fig. 11-2B), which settle on the substratum and produce a branching penetration tube. The latter grows in length and diameter, producing a continuous branch system, the rhizomycelium, within and upon the surface of the substratum. At different loci on the rhizomycelium, terminal and intercalary swellings become delimited by septa and develop into zoosporangia (Fig. 11-2A). These are variously shaped, spherical to pyriform, and are either smooth or tuberculate. Both types of sporangia are uninucleate when first formed, but a period of mitotic nuclear division increases the nuclear number. Progressive cleavage of the zoosporangium protoplast into uninucleate zoospores follows.

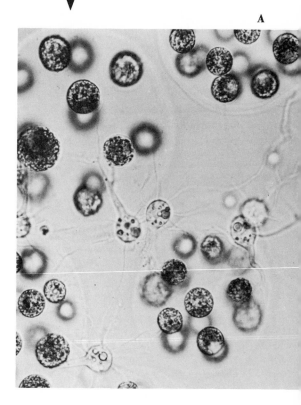

These are discharged from a short beak at the tip of the sporangium (Fig. 11-2B). The individual zoospores gradually become motile and swim away from the mass. Sporangial proliferation, in which a new sporangium is regenerated within the empty wall of a former one, is of common occurrence.

Polyphagus

Polyphagus starrii (Fig. 11-3), readily available in laboratory culture, has recently

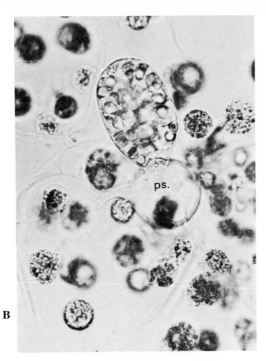

B

ps.

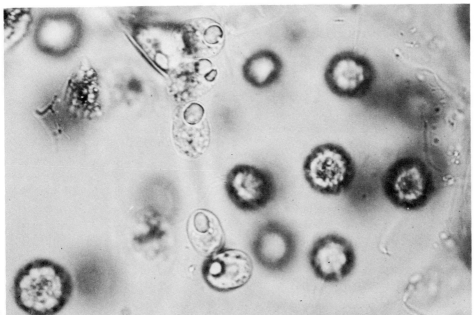

C

been described as a new chytrid species. It occurs in soil and ponds and is a destructive parasite of the algae of the chlorophycean order Volvocales (p. 58) which includes such genera as *Chlamydomonas, Pandorina, Eudorina* and *Volvox,* among others. Certain species of these genera can serve as hosts for *Polyphagus starrii.*

Infection is initiated by the radiating rhizoidal processes of recently quiescent zoospores which establish contact with the

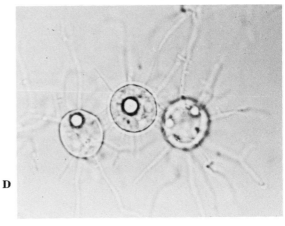

D

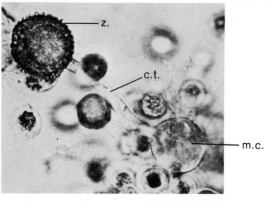

FIG. 11-4. *Polyphagus starrii.* Spiny-walled resting spore (zygote) from union of two thalli; z., zygote; c.t., connecting tube; m.c., male cell. X 770. (*After Johns.*)

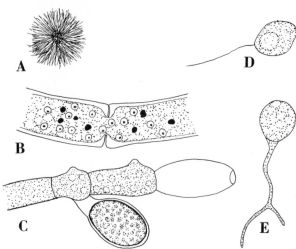

FIG. 11-5. *Allomyces macrogynus* Emerson. A. Habit of growth on submerged hemp seed. X 0.75. B. Median longitudinal section of hypha; note multinucleate condition and partial septum. C. Three seriate, thin-walled mitosporangia (the apical one empty) and a thick-walled, lateral meiosporangium. D. Zoospore. E. Zoospore germination. B, D, E. X 700. C. X 300.

flagella of host cells. From the latter, they withdraw nutriment and increase rapidly in size to form a **prosporangium** (Fig. 11-3A-B) from which a thin-walled **zoosporangium** (Fig. 11-3B) soon protrudes. The contents of this cleave into a number of posteriorly uniflagellate zoospores, each containing a single refractive globule (Fig. 11-3C). Upon quiescence, the cylindrical zoospores become spherical cysts which develop the infective rhizoidal protuberances (Fig. 11-3D).

In older cultures, as the hosts and the nutriment they provide become depleted, sexual reproduction of *Polyphagus* is initiated. Certain cells develop a conjugation tube which makes contact with a "female" cell; the cells which develop the conjugation tube are interpreted as male. The nucleus and protoplasm of the connected cells flow into the conjugation tube and a dormant, spiny-walled zygote is produced within the tube near the "female" or receptive cell (Fig. 11-4). Clones of *Polyphagus starrii* are bisexual. Germination of the zygote has not yet been observed. Experiments have demonstrated a marked host-parasite specificity in *P. starrii*, so that only certain strains or species are parasitized, and not others.

ALLOMYCES

Unlike the chytrids, which are either strictly unicellular or possess only rhizoidal processes, the plant body of *Allomyces* (Gr.

A

FIG. 11-6. *Allomyces* sp. A. Dichotomously branching vegetative hyphae. X 70. B. Meiosporangia. X 125. C. Mitosporangium. X 300. D. Release of mitospores. X 500. E. Meiosporangium. X 700. F. Sexual phase: male gametangia terminal, the female just below each. X 125. G. Male and female gametangia; note exit papillae. X 500.

allo, other + Gr. *mykes*) consists of a well-developed branching mycelium (Figs. 11-5A, 11-6A) anchored by rhizoidal absorptive branches which penetrate the substratum. The organism, which occurs in moist soil and aquatic habitats, grows readily in laboratory cultures on split hemp seeds or other organic substrata. Branching in *Allomyces* is typically dichotomous, and growth is apical. Superficially the mycelium appears to be septate, but careful scrutiny of the septations indicates that they are incomplete and that the protoplasm is continuous throughout the plant (Fig. 11-5B). The plant body with its many nuclei is **coenocytic.** The cell walls contain chitin and glucan.

After a period of vegetative growth, the mycelium enters the reproductive phase. In *A. macrogynus* Emerson, the terminal portions of the mycelium become delimited as zoo-sporangia (Figs. 11-5C, 11-6C). The portion of the hypha just below the sporangial septum may form a new branch; hence the originally terminal sporangial initial becomes secondarily lateral in position. As development proceeds, it becomes apparent that two types of sporangia may be produced. The first of these are thin-walled, ephemeral, and colorless **mitosporangia** (Figs. 11-5C, 11-6C) and are produced early in development. The second type, the **meiosporangium,** is thick-walled, persistent, and brown and occurs later (Figs. 11-5C, 11-6B,E). Both types of sporangia contain a number of nuclei at the time of their formation; this number is increased by division as the sporangia mature.

During development, the thin-walled sporangia undergo progressive cleavage to form a number of posteriorly uniflagellate zoospores. These are liberated at maturity through

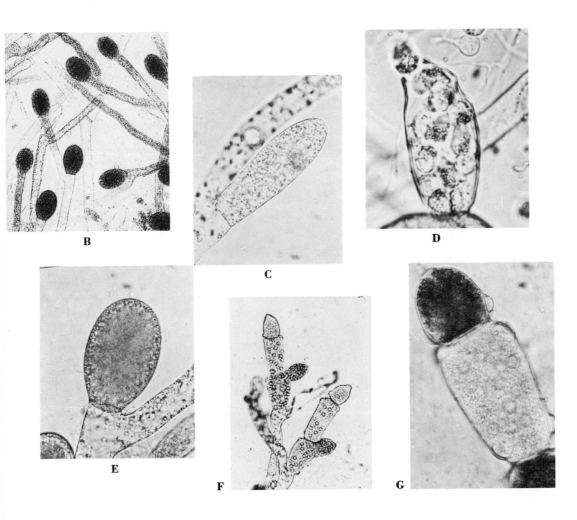

B

C

D

E

F

G

a pore in the sporangial wall (Fig. 11-6D). The zoospores[1] are attracted chemotactically by amino acids, a nutritional adaptation. The zoospores serve as agents for increasing the number of thalli (Fig. 11-5D,E), and under suitable conditions a large number of asexual generations is produced in this manner. Only 36 to 48 hours are required for a mature thallus to develop from a zoospore.

The thick-walled, resistant zoosporangia called meiosporangia (Figs. 11-5C, 11-6B,E) can withstand long periods of desiccation and temperatures up to 100° C. for short periods and still retain their viability. These sporangia also are multinucleate. It has recently been demonstrated that their nuclei persist for long periods in the prophase stages of meiosis, even when the sporangia have been dried. Transfer to water breaks their dormancy and stimulates further development. This consists in the completion of the nuclear divisions, which are meiotic, and the formation of approximately 48 uniflagellate zoospores. The haploid chromosome number in *A. macrogynus* is 14 or 28 (depending on the race); the haploid number in *A. arbuscula* Butler is 8 or 16. The zoospores from resistant sporangia settle on available substrata and develop into plants which form only gametangia, not zoosporangia.

The gametangia, as they first appear on the vegetative branches of a clonal culture, occur in pairs (Figs. 11-6F,G, 11-7A), but those produced subsequently may be borne in chain-like series. In their development the male gametangia produce an orange-red carotenoid pigment which is dissolved in droplets of oil in the gametes. The female gametangia remain colorless throughout their development. Both types of gametangia undergo progressive cleavage to form uninucleate gametes. The male gametangia contain more nuclei than the female, and as a result the male gametes are considerably smaller than the female (Fig. 11-7B). Both are liberated through pores and unite in pairs under suitable environmental conditions (Fig. 11-7B). *Allomyces macrogynus* is heterogamous and bisexual. The

---

[1] From both mito- and meiosporangia; also the motile zygotes.

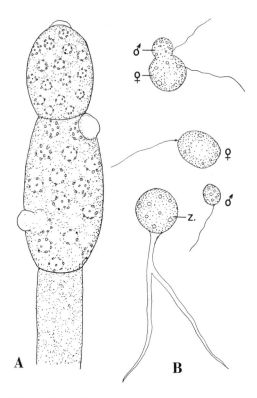

FIG. 11-7. *Allomyces macrogynus.* A. Male (upper) and female gametangia; clusters of granules (mitochondria?) indicate nuclear position; note exit papillae. X 700. B. Heterogametes, gamete union and germinating zygote (z). X 1500.

female gametes secrete a hormone called **sirenin** (Gr. *seirin*, siren) which attracts the male gametes chemotactically. Sirenin, which is now available in pure form, has been shown by its discoverer, Dr. Leonard Machlis and co-workers, to attract male gametes in concentrations as low as 10^{-10} M.

The zygote settles on an available substratum and develops (Fig. 11-7B) into a mycelium which develops only zoosporangia, not gametangia. Cultural and cytological studies have demonstrated the occurrence of isomorphic alternation of a diploid, asexual, zoospore-producing sporophyte with a haploid, sexual, gamete-producing gametophyte in *Allomyces macrogynus.* The life cycle of *Allomyces macrogynus* may be summarized as follows:

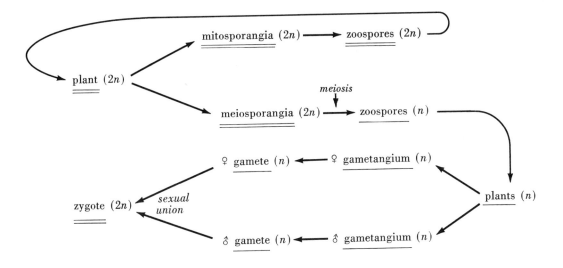

The life cycle here is similar to that of *Cladophora* and *Ectocarpus* Type D,h + d (pp. 48, 61). Deviations from this life cycle may occur in certain strains.

THE WATER MOLDS

The widespread genera *Saprolegnia* (Gr. *sapros*, rotten + Gr. *legnon*, border) and *Achlya* (Gr. *achlys*, mist) are representative of a considerable number of Phycomycota known as **water molds.** The great majority of the species is saprophytic, but a few parasitize fish and other aquatic animals. They are commonly observable as a cottony halo (Fig. 11-8) on the bodies of dead insects which have fallen into the water. These fungi can be readily obtained for laboratory study by using small pieces of coagulated egg albumen or boiled hemp seeds as bait in pond water and aqueous soil suspensions.

The plant body of the water molds differs from that of *Allomyces* in the absence of par-

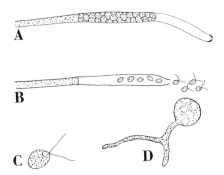

FIG. 11-9. *Saprolegnia* sp. A. Proliferative zoosporangium. X 75. B. Discharge of primary zoospores. X 75. C, D. Zoospore and its germination. X 760.

tial septa and in the lesser regularity of branching. Septa are formed only at the bases of the reproductive organs (Figs. 11-10A,B; 11-11C) or in response to injury. As in *Bryopsis* and *Vaucheria*, the tubular plant body is multinucleate, the minute nuclei lying in the thin peripheral cytoplasm which surrounds the central vacuole. Absorptive rhizoidal branches penetrate the substratum and serve the function of anchorage (Fig. 11-9D).

After a period of vegetative development, the reproductive phases, asexual at first, are initiated by the development of cylindrical zoosporangia (Figs. 11-9A,B; 11-10). These are elongate and terminal and undergo cleavage, forming a considerable number of biflagellate zoospores (Fig. 11-9C) which are liberated (Figs. 11-9B, 11-10B) through a

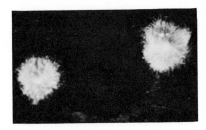

FIG. 11-8. *Achlya* sp. growing on submerged hemp seed. X 1.

terminal pore. The apex of the hypha just posterior to the zoosporangium may then protrude as a lateral branch or it may project up through the empty zoosporangium to form a second crop of zoospores; this is an example of **proliferation** (Fig. 11-9A). After a period of motility, the liberated pyriform zoospores withdraw their flagella, become spherical, and secrete walls, thus forming **aplanospores.** The latter germinate later to form biflagellate, reniform zoospores, one from each aplanospore; these also encyst after a period of motility. In germination to form a new plant, the cysts produce delicate hyphae known as **germ tubes** (Fig. 11-9D). The occurrence of two motile periods and two types of zoospores is termed **diplanetism.** *Achlya* may be distinguished from *Saprolegnia* in that its primary zoospores remain clustered and become aplanospores at the mouth of the zoosporangium. In *Saprolegnia*, in contrast, the primary zoospores are dispersed. Under some environmental conditions, probably mainly nutritional, segments of the coarse mycelium may become irregularly swollen and densely granular. These **gemmae** (L. *gemma*, bud) may germinate into new mycelia under favorable conditions.

Following a series of asexual generations, the mycelium initiates sexual reproduction. *Saprolegnia* and *Achlya* differ from *Allomyces* in that both male and female gametes are nonmotile. The male and female gametangia develop as lateral branches on the mycelium (Fig. 11-11). Some clones are bisexual and others unisexual. Careful study

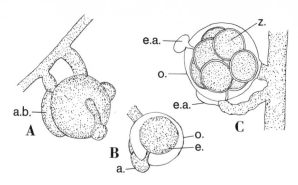

FIG. 11-11. *Achlya* sp. Sexual reproduction, bisexual species. A. Immature antheridial and oogonial branches. B. Oogonium with single egg, antheridium and fertilization tube. C. Oogonium containing dormant zygotes (oospores); a., antheridium; a.b., antheridial branch; e., egg; e.a., empty antheridium; o., oogonium; z., zygote. X 300.

of the development of the sex organs in *Achlya* has revealed a process of unsuspected complexity, involving the secretion of a number of complex chemicals which influence the course of development. It has been demonstrated that the formation and maturation of the sex organs in *Achlya* are controlled by a hormonal system which operates when potentially male and female hyphae of *Achlya anibisexualis* are in close proximity in an aquatic environment. This hormonal system is successively responsible for the proliferation of male vegetative hyphae to form antheridial branches; the stimulation of the potentially female hyphae to form oogonial branches; the attraction of the antheridial branches toward the oogonial branches; the delimitation of the antheridia from their subtending branches; and finally the septation of the oogonia from their stalks and the differentiation of the eggs.

The female gametangia, here known as oogonia, arise from lateral hyphae, the swollen apex of which is delimited by a septum (Figs. 11-11A, 11-12). The multinucleate protoplast of the oogonium undergoes cleavage into a number of multinucleate portions, each of which becomes a spherical, and ultimately uninucleate, egg (Fig. 11-12C) through the degeneration of all but one of the nuclei in each segment. The male gametangium, the antheridium (Figs. 11-11, 11-12B,C), forms at the tip of a slender, branching hypha which envelops the oogonium. It

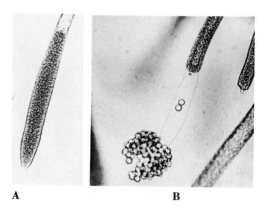

FIG. 11-10. *Achlya* sp. A. Mature zoosporangium. X 135. B. Release of primary zoospores. X 175.

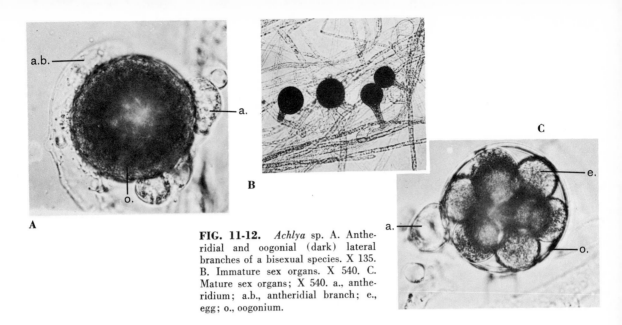

FIG. 11-12. *Achlya* sp. A. Antheridial and oogonial (dark) lateral branches of a bisexual species. X 135. B. Immature sex organs. X 540. C. Mature sex organs; X 540. a., antheridium; a.b., antheridial branch; e., egg; o., oogonium.

penetrates the oogonium and eggs by means of tubular protuberances called **fertilization tubes** (Fig. 11-11B,C). The antheridia are multinucleate, and contact and penetration of each egg by a fertilization tube make possible the union of male and female nuclei which follows. After fertilization, the zygotes rapidly develop thick walls which obscure their contents. The dormant zygote is known as the oospore; details of its germination are not well known, nor are the cytological features of the life cycle. Evidence regarding the site and time of occurrence of meiosis is at present inconclusive. It has been claimed both that meiosis is zygotic (so that the mycelium would be haploid) and gametic (which would signify a diploid mycelium).

ALBUGO

Except for *Polyphagus* (Figs. 11-3, 11-4) and a few species of *Saprolegnia*, the genera of Phycomycota so far described are all similar in that they are saprophytic in nutrition and aquatic in habitat. *Albugo* (L. *albus*, white), on the contrary, is a parasitic genus which occurs on a number of hosts. *Albugo candida* (Pers.) Kuntze grows on certain genera of mustards (Cruciferae). *Albugo ipomeae-panduranae* (Schwein.) Swing. is widespread on sweet potatoes and certain morning glories, and *A. blitii* (Bis.-Bern.) Kunze occurs on species of *Amaranthus*. Leaves of infected plants become covered with conspicuous mealy white spots or patches (Fig. 11-13A) which are caused by eruptions of large numbers of spores below the epidermis (Fig. 11-13B). Because of their lesions, infected plants are said to have **white rust**. *Albugo* is an obligate parasite, that is, it has never been grown in laboratory culture apart from a living host. The formation of the spores is preceded by the development of a vegetative mycelium which spreads through the host tissues from the site of the primary infection; the mycelium is entirely intercellular. The fungus obtains its metabolites by forming small, protuberant, papillate branches, **haustoria** (L. *haustor*, one who draws), which penetrate some of the host cells.

In sporangium formation, a number of multinucleate hyphal tips push out between the mesophyll cells and enlarge terminally (Figs. 11-13B, 11-14A). After several nuclei have migrated into the enlarged tip, the latter is delimited by an annular centripetal ingrowth of the wall. The tip of the hypha below the delimited sporangium now enlarges and is ultimately cut off like the first. The sporangia thus are produced in chains in basipetal succession, the oldest being farthest from the **sporangiophore**. The latter is the designation for the hypha which supports and produces sporangia. Continued sporangial production brings about a localized uplifting of the epidermis (Fig. 11-13B), which is finally ruptured, and the mature sporangia escape freely. The sporangia may function as zoosporangia, undergoing cleavage to form as

A

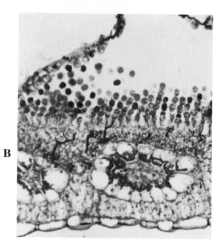

B

FIG. 11-13. *Albugo blitii* (Bis.-Bern.) Kunze. A. Portion of infected *Amaranthus* leaf. B. Transection of infected leaf showing ruptured epidermis, sporangiophores and sporangia. X 125.

many zoospores as there are nuclei present.

The mealy, dustlike sporangia are readily disseminated by air currents; and if they settle on moist surfaces of leaves of the host species, they germinate either by germ tubes or by producing zoospores. The biflagellate zoospores become spherical after a period of motility, encyst, and then develop delicate hyphal tubes which usually enter the host through a stoma. The infection is spread in this way.

Sexual reproduction may follow asexual later in the growing season. The sex organs are produced from the tips of hyphae among the mesophyll cells of the leaf and are suggestive of those of the water molds. After the hyphal tips have enlarged considerably, they are segregated from the remainder of the hyphae by cell walls. The antheridia are smaller than the oogonia, but both are multinucleate. As the oogonium matures, the protoplasm becomes rather densely aggregated in the center, leaving a more watery, vacuolate periplasm at the periphery. By the time of fertilization, all but one of the nuclei of the oogonium disintegrate in certain species, notably *A. candida;* the remaining nucleus functions as the egg nucleus. The egg is delimited from the peripheral cytoplasm by a delicate membrane. This type of cytokinesis in which a cell is delimited within another, leaving residual cytoplasm, is known as **free cell formation.** The antheridium, which is appressed to the oogonium, now produces a small hyphal protuberance that penetrates the

oogonial wall and grows through the periplasm, into the central dense cytoplasm containing the egg nucleus (Fig. 11-14B). After nuclear union, a multilayered wall is secreted by the zygote, the nucleus of which divides soon after fertilization, until about 32 nuclei are formed. In the spring, further nuclear division and, finally, cleavage occur. In this manner, the zygote gives rise to a large number of biflagellate zoospores which reinfect the leaves of the next season's plants. No convincing evidence of the time and site of occurrence of meiosis is available.

The sexual organs of *Albugo candida* are superficially similar to those of *Saprolegnia* and *Achlya.* The oogonia differ, however, in the production of a single egg which is delimited from the remaining cytoplasm (peri-

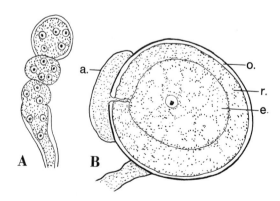

FIG. 11-14. *Albugo blitii.* A. Sporangiophore and seriate sporangia. B. Mature sex organs at fertilization; a., antheridium; e., egg; o., oogonium; r., residual cytoplasm. X 700.

plasm) by free cell formation. In *Saprolegnia* and *Achlya*, on the other hand, even in those cases when only one egg is developed, there is no residual cytoplasm.

RHIZOPUS STOLONIFER AND RELATED MOLDS

Perhaps the most familiar of all Phycomycota is *Rhizopus* (Gr. *rhiza*, root + Gr. *pous*, foot), one of a large group of phycomycetous molds. *Rhizopus stolonifer*, commonly known as black bread mold because of its occurrence on that substratum, frequently appears in damp, warm weather. *Rhizopus* and related genera may be present on all sorts of organic matter including dung, fruit, and fleshy fungi, when there is sufficient moisture to support growth. Its spores are almost always present in the atmosphere, as evidenced by the frequency with which it can be obtained when moistened bread and other organic substances are exposed to air currents and then maintained in a humid atmosphere. *Rhizopus oryzae* has been isolated from human beings with fatal cerebral disorders.

The mycelium is a cottony white mass during the vegetative phase but presents a sooty appearance at the time of sporulation. This is caused by the presence of large numbers of black-walled spores. Although the mycelium, as in most Phycomycota, is nonseptate and coenocytic, it exhibits considerable differentiation. Certain branches creep over the substratum much like stolons in higher plants (Fig. 11-15A). Also like stolons, the portions of the horizontal hyphae that make contact with the substratum produce rhizoidal branches (Fig. 11-15B), which serve as absorptive organs and secrete digestive enzymes. After a short period of vegetative development, groups of unbranched, elongate hyphae arise from the absorptive branches, forming erect hyphae whose tips become enlarged with nuclei and cytoplasm as increase in length ceases. These sporangiophores bear single sporangia (Fig. 11-15A).

The sporangia are formed in the following manner. As the enlarging tips of sporangiophores attain their characteristic size (Fig. 11-15C), the peripheral cytoplasm becomes dense and the central portion remains vacuo-

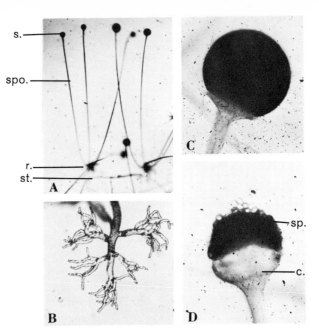

FIG. 11-15. *Rhizopus stolonifer.* A. Habit of growth. X 12.5. B. Rhizoidal hyphae. X 125. C. Mature sporangium. X 135. D. Sporangium after wall rupture showing columella and spores. X 135; c., columella; r., rhizoidal hyphae; s., sporangium; sp., spore; spo., sporangiophore; st., stolon.

late. The two regions are segregated from each other by the coalescence of a series of vacuoles which are present in a domelike arrangement. A wall finally is secreted between the two portions of the protoplasm (Fig. 11-16A). The central sterile portion is called the

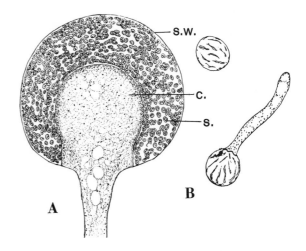

FIG. 11-16. *Rhizopus stolonifer.* A. Median longitudinal section of mature sporangium. X 260. B. Spore and its germination. X 380; c., columella; s., spores; s.w., sporangial wall.

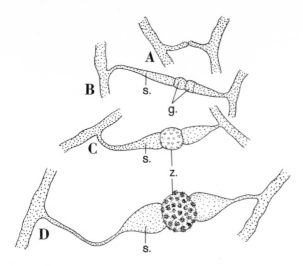

FIG. 11-17. *Rhizopus stolonifer.* A–D. Stages in sexual reproduction; g., multinucleate gametes; s., suspensor; z., zygote. X 65.

columella (L. *columella,* dim. of column); the peripheral portion is fertile and sporogenous. As the sporangium matures, the sporogenous protoplasm undergoes progressive cleavage, with the ultimate production of large numbers of minute spores (Fig. 11-16A), each of which contains several nuclei and develops a black wall. The outer sporangial wall is extremely delicate and readily torn. When this occurs, the exposed spores are quickly carried away by air currents; the naked columella remains (Fig. 11-15D). The spores germinate readily on moist substrata (Fig. 11-16B).

Clonal cultures of *Rhizopus stolonifer* are self-incompatible and considered to be isogamous in sexual reproduction. When spores of two sexually compatible strains are planted in reasonably close proximity in agar cultures, sexuality soon becomes manifest. Hyphae of the two strains which come in contact increase in size at their tips (Fig. 11-17A,B). Transverse septa are soon laid down, so that the multinucleate tip of each branch is delimited from the remainder of the hypha (Figs. 11-17B, 11-18A). The delimited portions are called **gametangia,** or considered to be multinucleate gametes, and the subtending hyphae are known as **suspensors.** The walls between the tips of contiguous gametangia dissolve, with the result that the cytoplasm and nuclei then lie free within a single lumen (Fig. 11-17C). During this period, the nuclei in

uniting gametangia increase in number; subsequently, many nuclei unite in pairs, but some supernumerary nuclei remain. A thick wall is secreted by the zygote (Figs. 11-17D, 11-18B). The supernumerary nuclei have been reported to disintegrate so that the dormant zygote contains only diploid nuclei.

Germination of the zygote has been observed infrequently, but there is some cytological evidence that the nuclear divisions which occur during germination are meiotic. This evidence is also supported by genetic studies of genera related to *Rhizopus.* The spores from such a sporangium are either all + or all −, or both + and − have been found. The cytological basis for this has not been elucidated.

It was proven more than 40 years ago (for the first time in fungi), that sexual reaction in *Rhizopus*-like molds is under chemical control, and subsequent research has been augmenting our knowledge. It is now clear that at least three sets of hormones are involved. (1) Both the + and − vegetative mycelia secrete **progamones** which in agar may diffuse up to 2–3 mm. beyond the mycelial apices. (2) If a + hypha invades the zone into which a − progamone has been secreted, secretion of a + gamone is stimulated. The respective **gamones** diffuse into the agar and evoke the formation of sexual organs 1–3 mm. posterior to the apex of the complementary strain. The sexual branches arise perpendicular to the substratum. (3) These + and − sexual

A

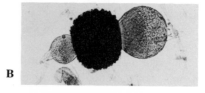

B

FIG. 11-18. *Rhizopus stolonifer.* Photomicrographs of sexual reproduction. A. Delimitation of gametes. B. Zygote and suspensors. X 125.

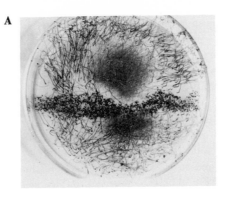

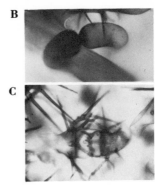

FIG. 11-19. *Phycomyces blakesleeanus.* Sexual reproduction. A. Petri dish inoculated with compatible mating types; note zone of dark zygotes. X 1/2. B. Early approach of sexually compatible hyphae. X 125. C. Delimitation of gametes and initiation of antler-like suspensor appendages. X 125.

branches become enveloped in a gaseous cloud of sex-specific hormone. The concentration of the latter decreases centrifugally through oxidation, so that a constant level of hormones is achieved. When a + hyphal tip enters a − hormone cloud (or vice versa) its apical growth is stimulated in the direction of the concentration gradient and contact, conjugation, and zygote formation follow. Thus, three sets of hormones, one of them volatile, are involved in the mating reaction, namely (1) + and − progamones, secreted by the vegetative mycelium; (2) + and − gamones secreted by the sexual branches after stimulation by the complementary progamones; and (3) + and − gaseous "contact-conjugation" gamones which effect contact, conjugation, and zygote formation.

A number of genera similar to *Rhizopus* are widespread on organic substrata. *Mucor* (L. *muceo*, be moldy) is similar to *Rhizopus* except that its sporangiophores arise from the main branches, rhizoids being absent at their bases.

Phycomyces (Fig. 11-19) produces sporangiophores which may attain a length of 4 inches. Its zygotes are made conspicuous by the development of dark, branching projections on the arched suspensors (Fig. 11-19).

The genus *Pilobolus* (Gr. *pilos,* ball + Gr. *bolos,* a throwing) is an interesting dung-inhabiting mold. Its resistant spores pass unharmed through the digestive tract of animals. Horse dung, if stored in a moist chamber, soon becomes covered with the positively phototropic sporangiophores of this organism (Fig. 11-20A). Each of them bears a terminal black sporangium (Figs. 11-20B, 11-21A,B).

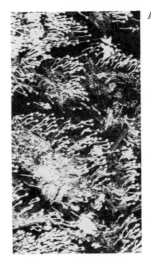

FIG. 11-20. *Pilobolus* sp. A. Habit of growth on horse dung; unilateral light was from the right during development. X 1.5. B. Enlarged view of maturing sporangium. X 315.

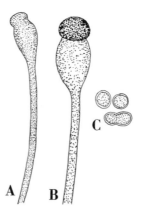

FIG. 11-21. *Pilobolus* sp. A, B. Stages in sporangium development. X 15. C. Spores. X 315.

Unlike that of *Rhizopus*, the sporangial wall of *Pilobolus* is firm and the sporangium is abscised as a unit. The sporangiophores originate in the afternoon from the mycelium just below the surface of the substratum. In early evening their tips enlarge to form sporangia. Shortly after midnight a subsporangial swelling appears (Fig. 11-21B) which explodes as a propulsive jet late the following morning because of excess turgor pressure. The sporangia and their spores (Fig. 11-21C) thus are forcibly ejected for distances as great as 6 feet[2] and at a rate of 16 m/sec.

Summary and Classification

The name Phycomycota reflects the views of those who speculate that these fungi have been derived from algal progenitors which have lost their chlorophyll and have entered upon either a saprophytic or a parasitic mode of life. This concept is based largely upon the similarity of the nonseptate mycelium of the Phycomycota to the tubular, nonseptate filaments of the siphonalean Chlorophyceae and such Xanthophyceae as *Vaucheria* and *Botrydium*. The superficial similarity of the oogamous reproduction of such genera as *Achlya*, *Saprolegnia*, and *Albugo* to that of oogamous algae like *Vaucheria*, and of the isogamous conjugation of *Rhizopus* to that of *Spirogyra* and the desmids, no doubt has served to make the hypothesis of algal origin an attractive one to some mycologists. Others look upon these supposed similarities as examples of parallel and independent evolution, pointing out that although colorless genera of algae are well known, they continue to store starch, a storage product which is absent in most fungi. Furthermore, because so many Phycomycota possess zoospores with one flagellum, a condition rarely encountered among algae, these same students are inclined to look upon the Phycomycota as a group with protozoan affinities.

As far as is known, the Phycomycota, with the exception of some species of *Allomyces*,[3]

are haplobiontic in their life cycle, with zygotic meiosis. Many types of sexuality occur, from the union of motile isogamous gametes in certain chytrids and the nonmotile isogametes of *Rhizopus*, through the heterogamous sexuality of *Allomyces*, to the advanced oogamy described above in *Saprolegnia*, *Achlya*, and *Albugo*. The last-named genus is of interest in that it offers a clue, in its alternate methods of sporangial germination, to the origin of the change in method of sporulation effected by the assumption of a terrestrial habitat by originally aquatic fungi.

The organisms representative of the Phycomycota which have been discussed in this chapter may be classified as follows:

Division Phycomycota
  Class 1. Phycomycetes
    Order 1. Chytridiales
      Family 1. Synchytriaceae
        Genus: *Synchytrium*
      Family 2. Phlyctidiaceae
        Genus: *Rhizophydium*
      Family 3. Cladochytriaceae
        Genus: *Polychytrium*
      Family 4. Rhizidiaceae
        Genus: *Polyphagus*
    Order 2. Blastocladiales
      Family 1. Blastocladiaceae
        Genus: *Allomyces*
    Order 3. Saprolegniales
      Family 1. Saprolegniaceae
        Genera: *Saprolegnia*, *Achlya*
    Order 4. Peronosporales
      Family 1. Albuginaceae
        Genus: *Albugo*
    Order 5. Mucorales
      Family 1. Mucoraceae
        Genera: *Mucor*, *Rhizopus*, and *Phycomyces*
      Family 2. Pilobolaceae
        Genus: *Pilobolus*

---

[2] For more detailed discussion of this and spore dispersal mechanisms in plants see: T. C. Ingold, *Spore Liberation*, Clarendon Press, Oxford, 1965.

[3] There is recent evidence that in the water molds the mycelium may be diploid and meiosis gametic.

DISCUSSION QUESTIONS

1. Which of the genera of Phycomycota discussed in this chapter do you consider to be the most primitive? Give the reasons for your answer.

2. Give a summary of the morphology and life cycle of each of the genera described in this chapter; include reference to nuclear condition.

3. What similarities can you see in comparing sexual reproduction in *Rhizopus* and *Spirogyra?* How does their reproduction differ?

4. In what respects is sexual reproduction in *Saprolegnia* and *Albugo* similar to that in *Vaucheria?* How does it differ?

5. Define the terms hypha, mycelium, haustorium, intercellular, host, sporangiophore, suspensor, sporangial proliferation, rhizomycelium, obligate parasite, saprophyte.

6. If the Phycomycota are algal in origin, to what alga might *Rhizophydium* be related?

7. To the life cycle of what algae does that of *Allomyces macrogynus* correspond?

8. How would you ascertain the nutritional requirements of a saprophytic fungus?

9. What attributes distinguish the Phycomycota from the Schizomycota and Myxomycota?

10. Give examples of the chemical regulation of sexual reproduction in Phycomycota.

CHAPTER 12

Division Ascomycota

Introduction

The Ascomycota (Gr. *askos*, sac + Gr. *mykes*, fungus) differ from most of the Phycomycota in that their mycelium is usually septate, even if incompletely so, the cells thus delimited being either uninucleate or multinucleate. The transverse hyphal walls have single, minute pores through which the protoplasm of adjacent cells is continuous. The hyphal walls contain a large proportion of chitin. Furthermore, as a result of sexual reproduction, a saclike hypha, the **ascus,** is developed in which typically eight (Figs. 12-10, 12-11), but sometimes more or fewer, ascospores are produced. The asci may be single and scattered or they may be aggregated into a specially differentiated fruiting body, the **ascocarp** (Gr. *askos* + Gr. *karpos*, fruit). The structure of the sex organs themselves varies considerably among the many genera of Ascomycota; therefore, it will be described separately in connection with each of the type genera selected. Finally, flagellate cells are absent in the Ascomycota, as they are in Rhodophycophyta. Four types of Ascomycota will be considered in the present chapter. These include the yeasts; the brown, green, and pink molds; the powdery mildews, and fleshy forms.

Illustrative Types

THE YEASTS

The yeasts are ascomycetous fungi in which an extensive mycelium is not produced; hence the plant body is unicellular. In some genera, however, rudimentary mycelium development may take place under certain conditions. Furthermore, the asci usually are produced singly and are free-floating in the medium, not protected by special sterile outgrowths, or borne in ascocarps.

Schizosaccharomyces

Schizosaccharomyces (Gr. *schizo*, cleave + Gr. *saccharon*, sugar + Gr. *mykes*) is a unicellular organism which occurs in nature on such fruits as grapes and figs. Certain species of *Schizosaccharomyces* are the agents of fermentation in tropical beers. The cells of *S. octosporus* Beijer. are spherical to ellipsoidal, vacuolate, and uninucleate (Fig. 12-1). Multiplication is effected by cell division which follows nuclear division (Fig. 12-1B). Recently divided cells may remain adherent or they may separate promptly. After several days' growth in laboratory cultures, sexuality occurs. In this process (Fig. 12-1C-G), two adjacent cells produce short protuberances which meet; the tips of the protuberances dissolve, and plasmogamy and karyogamy follow. The zygote nucleus soon undergoes three successive nuclear divisions resulting in the formation of eight nuclei (Fig. 12-1F). Each of these is the center around which an ascospore is delimited (Fig. 12-1G), leaving residual cytoplasm called **epiplasm.** This method of cytokinesis (which occurs also in

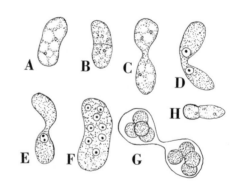

FIG. 12-1. *Schizosaccharomyces octosporus* Beijer. A. Vegetative cell. B. Cell division. C. Cell union (isogamy). D. Cell union, stained; note nuclei. E. Zygote with diploid fusion nucleus. F. Free nuclei of ascus. G. Ascus with eight ascospores. H. Ascospore germination. X 1400.

142

MORPHOLOGY OF PLANTS

egg formation in *Albugo*, p. 136) is known as **free-cell formation.** The zygote is transformed directly into a single ascus which liberates the ascospores ultimately; the latter contain abundant starch. They produce new generations of plants asexually by nuclear and cell division (Fig. 12-1H). It has been demonstrated recently that meiosis occurs in the ascus during the nuclear divisions which follow karyogamy.

Saccharomyces

Saccharomyces cerevisiae Hansen, a brewers' yeast (Figs. 12-2, 12-3), is representative of the budding yeasts which occur in nature on various fruits. The ovoidal cells of *Saccharomyces* (Gr. *saccharon*, sugar + Gr. *mykes*) contain a rather large vacuole and an excentric nucleus (Fig. 12-3).

Multiplication occurs by budding (Fig. 12-2A–C), during which nuclear division takes place. One of the daughter nuclei migrates into the bud, which subsequently enlarges and becomes segregated from the parent cell. Rapid budding may result in the formation of short chains of cells.

Under certain environmental conditions, ordinary vegetative cells may become transformed into asci, each of which usually produces four ascospores (Fig. 12-2D). It has been demonstrated that the ascospores from a single ascus, if isolated into individual culture vessels, will germinate to form spherical vegetative cells which will continue to reproduce by budding as long as the four cultures remain separated. However, when the cells of the four strains are brought together into one culture, union of the haploid cells in pairs

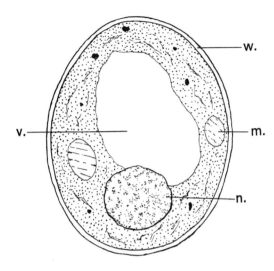

FIG. 12-3. *Saccharomyces cerevisiae.* Cellular organization based on electron microscopy; m., mitochondrion; n., nucleus; v., vacuole; w., wall. X 8500.

establishes a diploid population. Furthermore, two of the ascospores of a given ascus are of one mating type and two are of another. The diploid vegetative cells of *S. cerevisiae* function as asci under certain conditions. Therefore, there occurs an alternation between two distinct phases in the life cycle of *S. cerevisiae*, namely, between diploid cells (potential asci), which reproduce asexually by budding, and haploid cells, which also reproduce by budding. The latter are derived from the germinating ascospores.

The importance of various types of yeast to man, because of their biochemical activities, can scarcely be described adequately. They are used as agents of alcoholic fermentation in brewing and as an agent of leavening in baking, and for these reasons have been the subject of intensive cytological, genetic, and physiological investigations.

BROWN, GREEN, AND PINK MOLDS

The brown, green, and pink molds are here illustrated, respectively, by the genera *Aspergillus*[1] (L. *aspergo*, sprinkle), *Penicillium*[1]

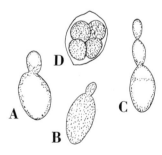

FIG. 12-2. *Saccharomyces cerevisiae* Hansen. A–C. Budding vegetative cells. D. Ascus with ascospores. X 1700.

[1] Strictly speaking, *Aspergillus* and *Penicillium* are imperfect fungi (see p. 170); however, the ascomycetous genera *Eurotium* and *Carpentelus* have *Aspergillus*-like and *Penicillium*-like stages in their life cycle.

(L. *penicillus*, pencil), *Neurospora* (Gr. *neuron*, nerve + Gr. *spora*), and *Sordaria* (L. *sordes*, filth or dirt). These four genera contain mostly saprophytic species that occur commonly on a wide variety of organic substrata, such as foods and fruits, on which they produce the phenomenon of moldiness. *Penicillium* and *Aspergillus* are frequent contaminants of laboratory cultures. The former is often the agent of the mildewing of leather and clothing. Many species of *Penicillium* are greenish when fruiting; those of *Aspergillus* are frequently yellowish or dark brown. The spores of these genera are ubiquitous in air and soil. *Neurospora*, on the other hand, is pink and is known as pink bakers' mold; *Sordaria* is brown.

These genera have a well-developed mycelium (Fig. 12-4) which is extensive and septate (Fig. 12-5). It absorbs food from

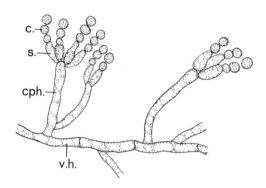

FIG. 12-5. *Penicillium notatum*; c., conidium; cph., conidiophore; s., sterigma; v.h., vegetative hypha. X 770.

the substratum by haustorial branches. The nuclear condition in the mycelium is variable; further cytological study is needed.

Aspergillus and Penicillium

In *Penicillium notatum* Westling, the apical hyphae are usually uninucleate, but older hyphae become multinucleate because of the absence of cytokinesis following mitosis. After some vegetative growth has occurred, the older portions of the mycelium produce asexual spores, **conidia.** In both *Penicillium* and *Aspergillus*, these are produced in specially differentiated fruiting heads (Figs. 12-4 to 12-7) called **conidiophores** (Gr. *konis*, dust + Gr. *phores*, bearer). The conidiophores of *Penicillium* are short-celled hyphae which are terminated by bottle-shaped cells called **sterigmata** (Gr. *sterigma*, support) (Fig. 12-5). Each of these produces a chain of conidia, the oldest conidium being farthest from the tip of the sterigma. The older spores are readily dislodged from the chains by air currents or other slight disturbances; hence it is sometimes difficult to obtain satisfactory microscopic preparations unless one uses relatively young fruiting branches. The color of the fungi during spore production is the result of the maturation of large numbers of conidia with pigmented walls. Conidia germinate readily into new mycelia (Fig. 12-7B).

In *Aspergillus* (Figs. 12-6A,B, 12-7), the fruiting head arises from a foot cell (Fig. 12-7A). The apex ultimately becomes spherical

A

B

FIG. 12-4. A. *Aspergillus niger* van Tiegh. B. *Penicillium notatum* Westling. Petri-dish cultures on agar. X ½.

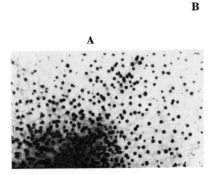

FIG. 12-6. Photomicrographs of conidiophores and conidia. A, B. *Aspergillus niger.* A. X 12. B. X 135. C. *Penicillium notatum.* X 135.

as growth in length ceases, and is covered with densely ranked sterigmata, sometimes in two series. The tip of the sterigma is a spore-producing tube, nuclei of which multiply. Each pair of division products migrates into the tube, the tip of which is delimited by cytoplasmic division. This tip enlarges to become a conidium (Figs. 12-6, 12-7). Repetition of this process results in the seriate arrangement of conidia on each sterigma, the oldest being farthest from the sterigma.

Our knowledge of the details of sexuality in *Aspergillus* (*Eurotium*) and *Penicillium* (*Carpentelus*) is incomplete, but in some species special female hyphae, the **ascogonia,** have been described (Fig. 12-7C). The cytological aspects of sexuality in these molds have not been satisfactorily elucidated. Differentiated antheridia are absent in many species, but nuclear pairing has been found to take place in the ascogonium, from which branching **ascogenous hyphae** then arise. These give rise to saclike cells, the asci (Fig. 12-7D). It has been demonstrated that in *Aspergillus fischeri* Westling the ascogonial cells are binucleate when they generate ascogenous hyphae. Each ascus typically produces eight ascospores by free-cell formation; the

FIG. 12-7. *Aspergillus niger.* A. Conidiophore on foot cell. X 315. B. Spores and spore germination. X 700. C. *Aspergillus chevalieri* Mangin; ascogonial coil. X 700. D. Ascus and ascospores. X 1500.

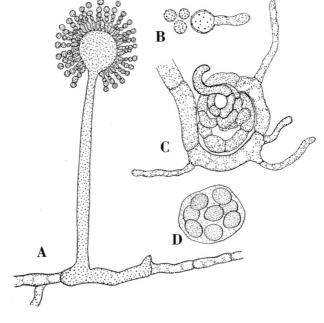

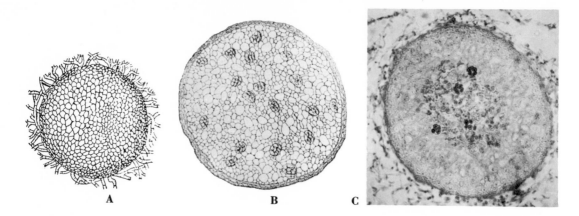

FIG. 12-8. A. *Penicillium crustaceum.* Cleistothecium, surface view. X 450. B. *Aspergillus nidulans.* Cleistothecium, in section; note asci and ascospores. X 600. C. *Penicillium* sp. Photomicrograph of section of cleistothecium; note asci and ascospores. X 450. D. *P. crustaceum,* asci and ascospores. X 1700. (A and D. *After Brefeld from Wolf and Wolf.* B. *After Eidam from Raper and Fennell.*)

spores are liberated by the breakdown of the ascus wall. While the ascogenous hyphae and asci are maturing, sterile interwoven hyphae form a loose protective layer about them. The whole structure is frequently globose, and inasmuch as it lacks an opening it is called a **cleistothecium** (Gr. *kleistos,* closed + Gr. *theke,* case). The cleistothecium (Fig. 12-8) is one of several types of ascocarp, the general term for ascomycetous fruiting bodies. The asci of *Penicillium,* like those of *Aspergillus,* are borne in cleistothecia. The ascospores, which are liberated by decay of the cleistothecial wall, germinate into conidium-forming mycelia.

A number of species of *Aspergillus* and *Penicillium* are notable for both harmful and beneficial activities. Among the former may be listed the propensity for spoilage and decay of foods, especially bread, fruits, and fruit products, and the destruction of leather and textiles in damp climates. Several species of *Aspergillus* and *Penicillium* are pathogenic in animals and man. Other species, however, are of great benefit to mankind in several connections. Certainly the most noteworthy of these is the antibiotic substance penicillin, secreted by *Penicillium chrysogenum* Thom and *P. notatum* Westling. *Penicillium roqueforti* Thom and *P. camemberti* Thom should be more widely appreciated than they seem

to be for their role in imparting distinctive flavors to Roquefort and Camembert cheese, respectively, during ripening.

Neurospora

In *Neurospora,* the conidiophores are not markedly differentiated from the vegetative hyphae (Fig. 12-9A). Some species of this genus produce minute, uninucleate **microconidia** in addition to those of ordinary size; the latter are multinucleate and are called **macroconidia.** The conidial walls are responsible for the pink color of the fungus. Our knowledge of the details of sexuality in *Neurospora* is still incomplete, a surprising fact in view of the intensive genetic studies of this fungus. In *N. sitophila* Shear and Dodge, the young ascogonium, a curved septate hypha with several nuclei in each cell, becomes covered with several layers of interwoven sterile hyphae. This structure has been called a **protoperithecium.** Certain cells of the ascogonium produce long, tenuous, trichogynelike branches which penetrate the sterile hyphal layers surrounding the ascogonium. It has been demonstrated that not only the macroconidia but also the microconidia and even vegetative hyphae and trichogynes of one strain may unite with the trichogynes and vegetative hyphae of another compatible strain. Fusion of compatible vegetative hyphae

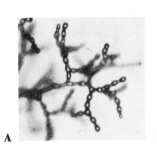

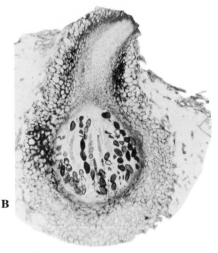

FIG. 12-9. *Neurospora sitophila* Shear and Dodge. A. Conidia. X 175. B. Median longitudinal section of perithecium. X 135.

A   B

is called **somatogamy.** Even though a clonal mycelium, derived from one ascospore, produces both ascogonia and microconidia (probably spermatia), these sex organs will not function to produce ascospores. Thus, although the mycelium is bisexual morphologically, it is physiologically self-incompatible. This condition is called **heterothallism** by many mycologists. In this way presumably, nuclei of the two strains are brought together into the same mycelium, and ultimately into the ascogonial coil. The latter now gives rise to ascogenous hyphae the tips of which enlarge to form elongate asci. Meanwhile, the sterile layer of the protoperithecium has increased in extent and organized itself into a flask-shaped structure (Fig. 12-9B), at the

apex of which a small aperture, the **ostiole,** develops. This type of ascocarp is known as a **perithecium** (Gr. *peri,* around + Gr. *theke*).

The young asci of *Neurospora* are binucleate. The two nuclei of each ascus represent descendants of nuclei of two compatible strains originally brought together in trichogynal or other types of plasmogamy. In further development, nuclear fusion takes place in each ascus. This is soon followed by three successive nuclear divisions during which meiosis is accomplished. The asci at this stage contain eight linearly arranged nuclei. These, with a portion of their surrounding cytoplasm, are finally segregated from the residual cytoplasm of the ascus by free-cell formation (Fig. 12-10). The mature asco-

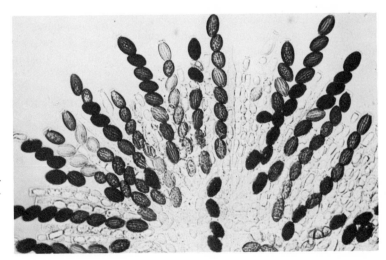

FIG. 12-10. *Neurospora sitophila.* Asci and ascospores. X 1000. (*After B. O. Dodge.*)

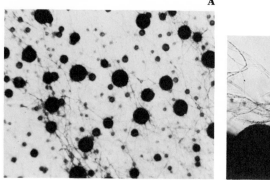
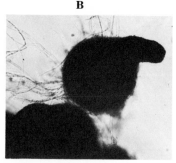

A

B

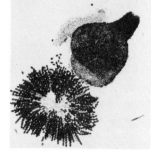
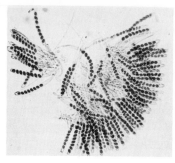

FIG. 12-11. *Sordaria fimicola* (Roberge) Cesati and Notaris. A. Perithecia and mycelium on agar. X 8. B. Single perithecium. X 60. C. Complex of asci crushed from perithecium. X 40. D. The same at higher magnification. X 125.

C

D

spores become binucleate as a result of mitosis within each spore. At maturity they are discharged from the perithecium through its ostiole. The mature spore walls are ribbed, an attribute which suggested the generic name.

The ascospores germinate, in laboratory cultures after suitable treatment,[2] giving rise to a mycelium which produces only protoperithecia and conidia, unless contact is made with a mycelium or conidia of a compatible strain. It has been shown experimentally that four of the eight ascospores of each ascus of *N. sitophila* give rise to one compatible strain, and that the other four are of the opposite type. Various species and races of *Neurospora* have provided the basis for important genetic and biochemical studies. It should be noted that the necessity for fusion between two strains of *N. sitophila* for maturation of the perithecia is analogous to the self-incompatibility found in certain types of flowers. As in certain flowers, both types of reproductive organs are present but fail to function; the controlling factor here apparently is physiological.

Sordaria

Sordaria, an organism closely related to *Neurospora*, differs from the latter, among other respects, in producing dark-brown ascospores. *Sordaria fimicola* (Fig. 12-11) does not produce conidia or microconidia,[3] but reproduces solely by ascospores. The latter are surrounded by a gelatinous sheath. The perithecial necks are positively phototropic. As asci mature within, one of them at a time enlarges and protrudes through the ostiole. Its ascospores are violently discharged, the ascus collapses and then, in turn, another protrudes to liberate its ascospores (Fig. 12-11C,D).

POWDERY MILDEWS

The powdery mildews are so called because they form a mealy, powdery-white stratum on the surfaces of leaves in a number of plants. Their mycelium is obligately parasitic on a specific host. All attempts to grow them for prolonged periods in artificial culture have

---

[2] With heat or furfural.

[3] Accordingly, it is less of a threat as a laboratory contaminant.

thus failed. Examples of powdery mildews which infect well-known plants are the following: *Microsphaera alni* (DC.) Wint. on lilacs (Fig. 12-12), *Erysiphe cichoracearum* DC. on garden plantain, *Sphaerotheca pannosa* (Wallr.) Lev. on roses, and *Erysiphe graminis* DC. on cereal grains. The mycelium spreads over the leaf from the original point of infection (Fig. 12-12A) and obtains nourishment by means of haustoria which penetrate into the epidermal cells (Fig. 12-12C). The hyphal cells of most species are uninucleate. After a period of vegetative growth, certain hyphae produce erect branches which form conidia in chains (Fig. 12-12B). These are blown about by air currents and germinate, initiating new infections, especially under humid conditions. This cycle, frequently repeated, rapidly spreads the fungus.

Sexual reproduction and ascocarp formation occur later in the growing season. The sex organs, which precede the cleistothecium, are not highly differentiated but consist of short hyphae that curve around each other.

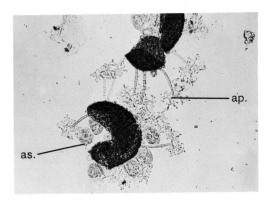

FIG. 12-13. *Microsphaera alni*; crushed cleistothecia; ap., appendage; as., ascus. X 285.

One has been identified as an antheridium and the other as the ascogonium. The walls between these dissolve at one point of contact, and the antheridial nucleus is reported to migrate into the ascogonium. Nuclear union is probably delayed, as in other Ascomycota. Descendants of the sexual nuclei are distributed among the cells of the ascogenous hyphae. The latter, depending on the genus, give rise to one or more asci. Soon after the sex organs have developed, vegetative hyphae at their base form a sterile protective layer which becomes the wall of the cleistothecium. Three successive nuclear divisions occur in each ascus, so eight potential ascospore nuclei are developed. In some species each of these is delimited to form an ascospore by free-cell formation. In others, fewer ascospores are produced, and the supernumerary nuclei disintegrate in the epiplasm. The cleistothecia (Figs. 12-12A,C, 12-13) usually remain on the leaves when the latter are shed, and dissemination of the ascospores does not occur until the following growing season. Ascospores which come to rest on the leaves of the proper host plant are capable of initiating a new conidial cycle.

CUP FUNGI

The final group of Ascomycota to be considered in this chapter is known as the cup fungi, because their fleshy, often brightly colored, conspicuous ascocarps are usually cup-, urn-, or saucer-shaped (Figs. 12-14, 12-15). Such an ascocarp is called an **apothe-**

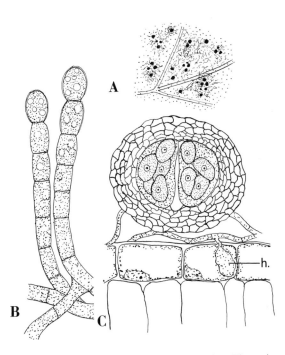

FIG. 12-12. *Microsphaera alni* (DC.) Wint. A. Mycelium and cleistothecia on lower surface of lilac leaf. X 3. B. Conidiophore with seriate conidia. X 275. C. Stained section of cleistothecium on upper surface of lilac leaf. X 400; h., haustorium in epidermal cell.

FIG. **12-14.** *Humaria axillaris* (Nees) Seaver, a cup fungus (among plants of the moss, *Funaria*). X 6.

A

FIG. **12-15.** A. *Sarcoscypha coccinea* Sacc. apothecium. X 2. B, C. *Pyronema domesticum*. B. Apothecia on soil. X 8. C. Section of apothecium; note hymenial layer with asci. X 60. (A. *After Alexopoulos.*)

B

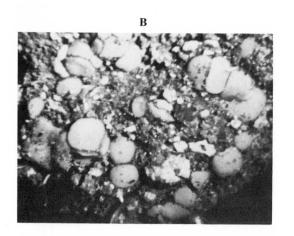

C

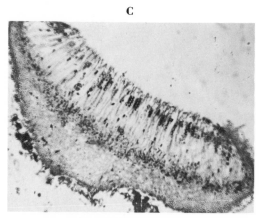

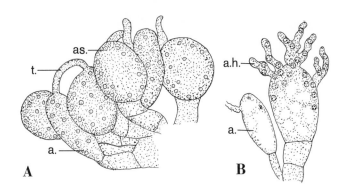

FIG. 12-16. *Pyronema domesticum* (Sow.) Sacc. Sexual reproduction. A. Sex organs at fertilization. B. Postfertilization; a., antheridium; a.h., ascogenous hyphae; as., ascogonium; t., trichogyne. X 400. (*After Gwynne-Vaughan and Williamson.*)

A   B

cium. The cup fungi are for the most part saprophytes that occur on a wide variety of organic substrata such as rich soil, decaying wood, dung, burlap, and fallen fruit. Several genera, among them *Pyronema* (Fig. 12-15B), are inhabitants of burned-over or sterilized soil. The apothecia vary from a millimeter in diameter up to the size of small tea cups. In some genera the apothecia are stalked.

Although the fruiting body is somewhat ephemeral, its formation is in all cases preceded by an extended period of vegetative activity on the part of the mycelium, which ramifies in the substratum, absorbing nutriment. In a few genera the vegetative mycelium reproduces itself asexually by conidia, but these are entirely absent in others. There is good reason to believe that the apothecium arises as a result of sexuality; but the latter has been clearly demonstrated only in a few species, and even in these there is a difference of opinion regarding the cytological details of the process. *Pyronema* (Gr. *pyr*, fire + Gr. *nema*, thread) has been investigated frequently regarding its cytological and sexual features. In this genus well-differentiated antheridia and ascogonia are developed (Fig. 12-16).

In *Pyronema domesticum*, an inhabitant of burned-over ground, the multinucleate antheridia and ascogonia (Fig. 12-16) arise in clusters from the tips of lateral hyphae. Each sex organ contains between 100 and 200 nuclei. The apex of the ascogonium is prolonged into a trichogynelike tube at maturity. The trichogyne at first is separated from the ascogonium by a septation. As development proceeds, the tip of the trichogyne establishes contact with an antheridium, and dissolution of the walls takes place at the point of contact (Fig. 12-16A). Trichogynes of several ascogonia may establish contact with the same antheridium, and several antheridia and ascogonia may be involved in the formation of a single apothecium. Antheridial nuclei migrate into the multinucleate ascogonium through the trichogyne, the basal septum of which is dissolved at this stage but develops again after the nuclear migration. The male and female nuclei become associated in pairs. During the earliest stages of this process, sterile hyphae grow around and envelop the functioning sex organs, ultimately forming the apothecial wall and paraphyses.

Following nuclear association, slender ascogenous hyphae protrude from the surface of the ascogonium (Fig. 12-16B). A number of nuclei migrate into these and multiply there by mitosis. Ultimately, the ascogenous hyphae are divided into binucleate cells which give rise to the asci by a process known as **crozier formation** (Fig. 12-17). Although this process is probably involved in the formation of the asci of a majority of Ascomycota, the cup fungi are especially favorable for demonstrating it. The tip cell of a branch of an ascogenous hypha becomes recurved (Fig. 12-17A) like a crozier, and its two nuclei undergo mitosis, with their spindles oriented in such a manner that at the completion of nuclear division two nuclei (one descendant of each of the original sexual nuclei, presumably) lie in the apical bend of the crozier; one nucleus lies at the apex of the recurved hypha, and one at the proximal portion of the ascogenous hypha. Cytokinesis follows, pro-

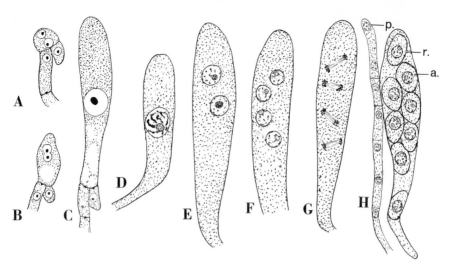

FIG. 12-17. *Pyronema domesticum.* Ascus and ascospore development. A–C. Origin of the ascus by crozier formation. D–G. Successive nuclear divisions in the ascus. H. Paraphysis and ascus; a., ascospore; p., paraphysis; r., residual cytoplasm.

ducing a uninucleate terminal ("ultimate") cell, a binucleate intermediate ("penultimate") cell, and a uninucleate basal ("antepenultimate") cell (Fig. 12-17A,B). The binucleate penultimate cell enlarges to form the ascus. In certain species, the ultimate cell may reunite with the antepenultimate cell and again undergo crozier formation. The yellow-orange pigment of the paraphyses and other sterile hyphae of the *Pyronema* apothecium is responsible for its color.

Nuclear union follows in each ascus (Fig. 12-17B,C). Three successive nuclear divisions (Fig. 12-17D-H) occur, resulting in the formation of eight haploid nuclei. These are incorporated into ascospores by free-cell formation (Fig. 12-17H). The ascospores germinate, producing a multinucleate mycelium in which the sexual cycle is repeated; a given clone of *Pyronema domesticum* is bisexual and self-compatible.

The inner surface of the apothecium in cup fungi, the **hymenium,** is composed of intermingled columnar asci and sterile paraphyses (Fig. 12-18). The remainder of the apothecium is made up of sterile interwoven hyphae which form pseudoparenchyma, as viewed in section. Spore discharge is explosive in many species, and large numbers of spores may be disseminated simultaneously in visible puffs.

Although *Pyronema* has been chosen here as the type genus to illustrate reproduction in the cup fungi, its apothecia are relatively small and inconspicuous, and plane or almost convex. The apothecia of *Peziza*, *Patella*, *Urnula*, and *Sarcosoma* are widely distributed, larger, and more conspicuous than those of *Pyronema*; they are flat or concave. Unfortunately, however, their life cycles have not

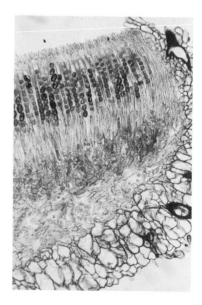

FIG. 12-18. *Peziza* sp. Segment of vertical section of apothecium; note hymenial layer composed of asci and paraphyses. X 320.

been worked out as completely as that of *Pyronema*.

Summary and Classification

Of the representative genera of Ascomycota described above, all are saprophytic with the exception of the powdery mildews, which are obligate parasites. Except for the unicellular yeasts, the vegetative phase regularly consists of a branching, septate mycelium, which may be composed of uninucleate (powdery mildews) or multinucleate hyphae. Some yeasts may develop short, myceliumlike stages under certain conditions. For this reason, they often have been interpreted as organisms reduced from higher, strictly mycelial genera.

The life cycle of most Ascomycota consists of an asexual phase in which conidia are produced, and a sexual phase in which the zygote, either directly as in the yeasts, or indirectly as in other genera, produces asci. Indirect ascus formation involves the production of ascogenous hyphae. The vegetative cells of *Saccharomyces* are diploid; they become transformed directly into single asci. In most other Ascomycota, there is an interval between plasmogamy and karyogamy; the fusion cell produces ascogenous hyphae which give rise to asci in which karyogamy occurs. In *Saccharomyces*, as a result of one sexual union and budding of the diploid cells, many agents of propagation (in this case, ascospores) are produced. Further examples of the same phenomenon among the algae and other groups of plants will occur to the reader.

Both the conidial and the ascogenous (ascus-forming) stages may be well developed, as in the powdery mildews, *Neurospora*, and certain species of *Aspergillus* (*Eurotium*) and *Penicillium* (*Carpentelus*), or one or the other phase may be absent from the life cycle. Thus, for many species of *Aspergillus* and *Penicillium*, no ascogenous stages have been discovered, and such species are classified with the Deuteromycota. In many cup fungi, on the other hand, no conidial stages have been observed.

The Ascomycota exhibit considerable range of variation with reference to the production of differentiated sex organs. Among the yeasts, the haploid vegetative cells function directly as gametes, as in the alga *Chlamydomonas*. In other genera, markedly differentiated sex organs may be present, as in *Pyronema*. Among the powdery mildews, the so-called antheridia and ascogonia are scarcely distinguishable from each other or from vegetative hyphae. Ascogonia have been observed in a number of ascogenous forms of *Aspergillus* and *Penicillium*, but differentiated male organs are rarely present. In *Neurospora*, the number of alternate mechanisms by which approximation of sexually compatible nuclei can be effected suggests that the original male sex organs may have been lost.

As to the origin of the Ascomycota, several hypotheses have been presented. According to one, they have been derived from the Rhodophycophyta. Evidence listed in support of this view is absence of flagellated cells in both groups, the similarities between the ascocarp (especially cleistothecia and perithecia) and the cystocarp of Rhodophycophyta, the occurrence in some Ascomycota of nonmotile spermatia and trichogynes, and the resemblance between diploid gonimoblasts of certain Rhodophycophyta and the ascogenous hyphae of the Ascomycota. At first glance, the marked physiological differences between the Rhodophycophyta and Ascomycota would seem to present an insurmountable barrier to relationship. It has been pointed out, however, that several species of extant Rhodophycophyta have lost their pigments and are parasitic on other Rhodophycophyta. In opposition to the theory of rhodophycophytan origin of the Ascomycota, there has developed a theory of origin from the Phycomycota. According to this view, the Ascomycota in which the zygote directly forms ascospores (as in certain yeasts) are considered primitive and derived from Phycomycota. Genera with highly differentiated sex organs and ascogenous hyphae are considered to have evolved from yeastlike ancestors. Supposed homologies between sex organs, gonimoblasts, and ascogenous hyphae and cystocarps and ascocarps of Ascomycetes and Rhodophycophyta are interpreted by proponents of the theory of phycomycetous origin of the Ascomycota as examples of parallel development. A satisfactory solution to these questions is not available in the present state of our knowledge.

The genera of Ascomycota discussed in this chapter may be classified as follows:

Division Ascomycota
  Class 1. Ascomycetes
    Order 1. Endomycetales
      Family 1. Endomycetaceae
        Genera: *Schizosaccharomyces,*
            Saccharomyces
    Order 2. Eurotiales
      Family 1. Eurotiaceae
        Genera: *Eurotium* (= *Aspergillus*),
            Carpentelus (= *Penicillium*)
    Order 3. Sphaeriales
      Family 1. Sordariaceae
        Genera: *Neurospora, Sordaria*
    Order 4. Erysiphales
      Family 1. Erysiphaceae
        Genera: *Erysiphe, Microsphaera,*
            Sphaerotheca
    Order 5. Pezizales
      Family 1. Pezizaceae
        Genera: *Pyronema, Peziza, Ascobolus,*
            Humaria, Patella, Urnula,
            Sarcosoma, Sarcoscypha

DISCUSSION QUESTIONS

1. What characteristics distinguish the Ascomycota, as a group, from the Phycomycota?

2. Of what economic importance are such Ascomycota as *Aspergillus, Penicillium, Neurospora, Saccharomyces*, and the powdery mildews?

3. What aspects of the life cycle of Ascomycota require further investigation, in your opinion?

4. How do you explain the fact that a given race of *Neurospora* which produces ascogonia, trichogynes, macroconidia, and microconidia on the same mycelium still requires "mating" with another race to produce ascospores?

5. How does the production of ascospores from the zygote of *Schizosaccharomyces* differ from the production of zoospores from the zygote of *Chlamydomonas?*

6. Define or explain the following terms in comparative fashion: ascocarp, apothecium, perithecium, cleistothecium.

7. How would you determine whether or not a certain ascomycetous fungus is homothallic or heterothallic?

8. Where does segregation of genes take place in Ascomycota?

9. What genus of Ascomycota has been most extensively employed in genetic investigations?

10. Why are such organisms especially favorable for correlating genetic and cytological data?

11. Define free-cell formation. How does it differ from progressive cleavage and repeated bipartition?

12. Where would you search for cup fungi in nature?

13. Where and when would you attempt to collect powdery mildews in the perithecial stage?

14. Describe a possible procedure to determine whether or not the powdery mildews are heterothallic.

15. Outline the methods and procedures you would use to investigate the life cycle and reproduction of an unknown cup fungus.

16. Do the terms homothallism and heterothallism refer to morphological or physiological attributes? Explain variations in usage of these terms.

CHAPTER 13

Division Basidiomycota

Introduction

The **basidium** (Gr. *basis*, di.-pedestal) is as characteristic of Basidiomycota (Gr. *basis* + Gr. *mykes*) as the ascus is of Ascomycota. Like the ascus, the young basidium or its immediate precursor (either a hypha or a spore and its germ tube) contains two nuclei which unite to form a fusion nucleus, which in two ensuing divisions undergoes the meiotic process. The mycelium of the Basidiomycota is always septate; its cells may be either uninucleate or binucleate. The basidia, each of which typically produces **basidiospores,** either are borne directly at the tips of vegetative hyphae or may arise as outgrowths of germinating spores. The basidia may or may not be aggregated in fruiting bodies called **basidiocarps.** The Basidiomycota include two groups. To the first belong organisms, like the rusts and smuts, the basidia of which are produced as a result of the germination of a thick-walled spore (Fig. 13-12). The second group includes the mushrooms, puffballs, and jelly fungi, in which the basidia are specialized hyphal tips (Fig. 13-17A) that do not arise from spores. In this text, four series representative of these two groups will be considered—the rusts, the smuts, the mushrooms, and a group of miscellaneous organisms.

Illustrative Types

RUSTS

The rusts are a very large assemblage of fungi (perhaps 7,000 species) which are obligate parasites on vascular plants. Recently, however, the mycelium of one species has been maintained in artificial culture. Their common name was suggested by the rust-colored, streaked, or linear lesions that infections produce on various parts of host plants. The genera and species of rusts exhibit considerable complexity in their life cycles, in the types of spores they produce, and in their physiological relationships to one or more hosts. They are of tremendous economic importance because their presence markedly reduces the yield in infected plants, particularly of fruits and cereal grains.

Puccinia

One of the most widely distributed and best-known rust species is *Puccinia graminis* Pers. (after *T. Puccini*, Italian anatomist), the numerous races of which parasitize various cereal grains, among them wheat, oats, barley, rye, and species of wild grasses. Distinct strains or races infect each of these hosts. The leaves and stems of infected plants bear small, rust-colored, usually linear streaks or lesions which are manifestations of the presence of the fungus (Fig. 13-1A). A magnified view of a section through one of these (Fig. 13-1B) reveals that the epidermis of the infected organ has been lifted up by the formation of a **uredinium** (L. *uredo*, blight), a group of rust-colored spores, each of which is stalked. During the growing season of the host plant the infection spreads through the agency of these spores, the **urediniospores**[1] (Fig. 13-3A). These are blown about by air currents after they have been liberated from the uredinium; and if they chance to reach other leaves or stems of the host species, they can germinate

---

[1] The terminology used follows that of J. C. Arthur, *The Plant Rusts (Uredinales)*, John Wiley and Sons, 1929. There are a number of synonyms for the terms used to describe reproductive structures in the rusts. These may be summarized as follows:

uredinium: uredosorus	**basidiospore:** sporidium
urediniospore: uredio-spore, uredospore	**spermagonium:** pycnium
telium: teleutosorus	**spermatium:** sperm cell, pycniospore
teliospore: teleutospore	**aeciospore:** aecidiospore
basidium: promycelium	

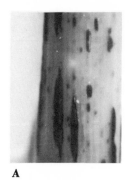

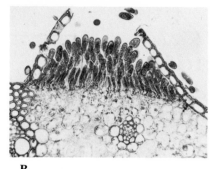

FIG. 13-1. *Puccinia graminis* Pers. A. Uredinial lesions on wheat stem. X 6. B. Section of uredinium on wheat leaf; note ruptured epidermis and urediniospores. X 135.

A   **B**

under suitable conditions. A delicate hyphal tube emerges from one of several pores in the urediniospore wall, grows over the surface of the leaf, and enters it through a stoma. Once inside the leaf, the primary hypha branches and spreads through the intercellular spaces. The mycelium thus formed grows at the expense of the host protoplasm, from which it obtains nutriment by means of intracellular haustorial branches. After seven or eight days, certain branches of the mycelium aggregate at localized points between the mesophyll and epidermal cells of the leaves and just below the epidermis of the stems, where they produce a new generation of urediniospores (Fig. 13-1). It has been estimated that the mycelium arising from the germination of a single urediniospore may produce several thousand urediniospores; hence the spread of the fungus through a field of grain is very rapid, especially when the relative humidity is high. The urediniospore cycle may be repeated many times during the growing season of the host.

As the latter approaches maturity, the rust-

colored lesions are gradually replaced by some of darker color, the **telia** (Gr. *telos*, end). Microscopic study reveals that these darker sori contain another type of spore, a two-celled[2] one, the walls of which are deeply pigmented at maturity. These **teliospores** (Figs. 13-2, 13-3B,C), so called because they are produced at the end of the growing season of the host, are borne on a mycelium that arises from a germinating urediniospore; they may occur either in a separate sori or mixed with urediniospores. The thick wall of each of the teliospore cells is homogeneous except for a single germination pore.

---

[2] In *P. graminis*; not all teliospores are two-celled.

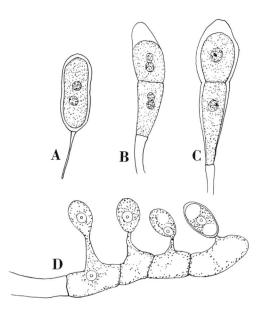

FIG. 13-3. *Puccinia graminis.* A. Single urediniospore. B. Immature teliospore, before nuclear fusion. C. Mature two-celled teliospore, each cell with a diploid nucleus. D. *Gymnosporangium* sp. Tip of basidium with four basidiospores. X 700.

FIG. 13-2. *Puccinia graminis.* Section of telial infection on wheat leaf. X 135.

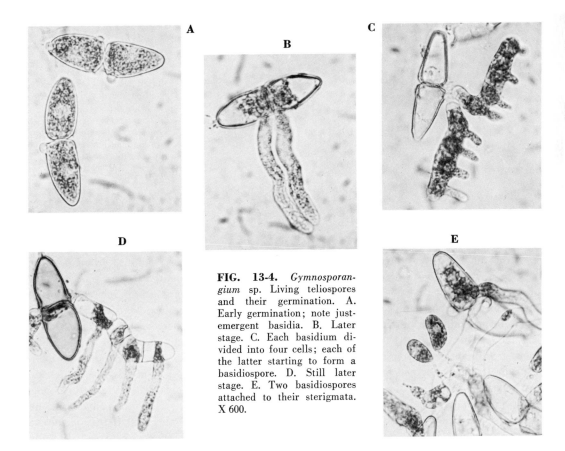

FIG. 13-4. *Gymnosporangium* sp. Living teliospores and their germination. A. Early germination; note just-emergent basidia. B. Later stage. C. Each basidium divided into four cells; each of the latter starting to form a basidiospore. D. Still later stage. E. Two basidiospores attached to their sterigmata. X 600.

The teliospores of *Puccinia graminis* apparently require a period of dormancy and low temperature before they develop further. Some are shed from the telia on the host plants before or during harvesting and fall to the ground; others remain in the telia on the stubble. The germination of the teliospores of another rust, *Gymnosporangium*, is illustrated in Figs. 13-3D and 13-4. After a suitable period of dormancy, each cell of the teliospore germinates by producing a slender, colorless hypha, the apical portion of which soon divides into four cells (Fig. 13-4A-D). Each of these develops a minute sterigma on which a single, thin-walled basidiospore (Fig. 13-4E) is produced. The slender septate hypha which produces the basidiospores is called the basidium.[3] Germination of the teliospores, formation of the basidium and basidiospores, and discharge of the latter are very rapid

processes which may take only a few hours. The basidiospores are violently discharged from their sterigmata and caught up by air currents; they may be carried great distances.

The thin-walled basidiospores of *Puccinia graminis* are capable of forming a mycelium only if they chance to fall upon the leaves or young stems of several species of barberry, among them *Berberis vulgaris* L. The germination hypha from the basidiospore penetrates the cuticle of the leaf and enters an epidermal cell, where it absorbs metabolites, begins to branch, and forms a mycelium which is mostly intercellular, nutriment being obtained by haustoria.

Certain mycelial branches aggregate at localized spots between the upper mesophyll cells and epidermis; within 6 days after the original infection by the basidiospore, they form flask-shaped organs, the **spermagonia** (Fig. 13-5A,B). Spermagonia may also be produced on the lower surface of the leaf. The apex of the spermagonium ruptures the leaf

---

[3] Strictly speaking, both the teliospore and the four-celled germ tube constitute the basidial apparatus.

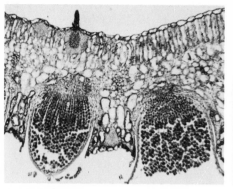
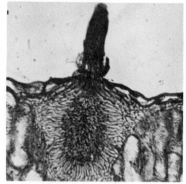

A   B

FIG. 13-5. *Puccinia grami-nis.* A. Transection of infected barberry leaf; spermagonium above, two aecial cups with aeciospores below. X 75. B. Spermagonium in median longitudinal section; note projecting periphyses and wall lined with columnar hyphae bearing spermatia (see 13–6B). X 250.

epidermis at maturity; through its ostiole there project slender, curved hyphae, the **periphyses.** The central portion of the spermagonium is composed of columnar hyphae which form chains of minute, conidiumlike cells, the **spermatia** (Figs. 13-5B, 13-6B). The latter are discharged through the ostiole in a syrupy liquid and spread over the leaf surface near the orifice of the spermagonium. Meanwhile, other branches of the mycelium from the original basidiospore infection have grown through the leaf in all directions. Usually there are produced near the lower surface of the leaf a number of densely interwoven masses of hyphae which appear yellow-orange to the naked eye. As development continues, each of these hyphal masses grows into a somewhat bell-shaped cup the outer surface of which projects through the ruptured lower epidermis of the leaf (Figs. 13-6A, 13-7). A few of these structures may also be borne on the upper epidermis. The basal cells within each of these cup-shaped **aecia** (Gr. *aikia,* in-

jury) give rise to chains of orange-colored spores, the **aeciospores,** which are usually separated by compressed intercalary cells (Figs. 13-5A, 13-6C). As the latter disintegrate, the mature aeciospores are violently discharged from their cups, often to a distance as great as 8 mm. It is thought that the intercalary cells play a role in this violent dissemination of the spores. The latter, which may number as many as 11,000 in a single cup, are caught up by air currents. If they chance to fall upon young stems or leaves of grain plants, they germinate and produce an intercellular mycelium by which the urediniospore cycle is again initiated. The aecial cups occur in groups (Figs. 13-6A, 13-7), each of which may include between four and thirty-five cups. By calculating the number of spores in a cup, the number of cups in a group, the number of groups on a leaf, and the total number of leaves, it has been estimated that a single barberry bush might produce 64,512,000,000 aeciospores!

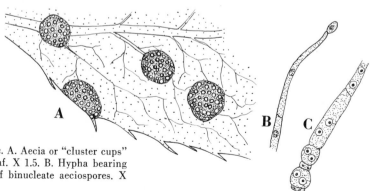

A   B   C

FIG. 13-6. *Puccinia graminis.* A. Aecia or "cluster cups" on lower surface of barberry leaf. X 1.5. B. Hypha bearing spermatium. X 600. C. Chain of binucleate aeciospores. X 600.

A   B

FIG. 13-7. *Puccinia graminis.* Photograph of aecial cups at successively higher magnification. A. X 1.5. B. X 15.

From this account of the life cycle of *Puccinia graminis,* two facts, among others, are especially noteworthy. In the first place, the fungus produces five distinct types of reproductive cells, namely, urediniospores, teliospores, basidiospores, spermatia, and aeciospores. Second, two hosts, a cereal grain and barberry, are usually required for the completion of its cycle. The latter attribute is characteristic of **heteroecious** (Gr. *heteros,* other + Gr. *oikos,* house) rusts.

Special attention must now be given the question of nuclear condition in *Puccinia graminis,* as it is correlated with the life cycle and successive appearance of the various spore types. Stained preparations of urediniospores and the mycelium which produces them reveal that both are binucleate, as is also the mycelium which gives rise to teliospores. Each cell of the teliospore likewise is binucleate at the time of its formation. The two nuclei in each cell unite during the maturation of the teliospore, so that each now contains a diploid nucleus. Cytological evidence in another species of *Puccinia, P. malvacearum* Bert., and in *Gymnosporangium* indicates that the two diploid nuclei of the teliospore undergo meiosis during germination, the four nuclei of the septate basidium resulting from this process. Genetic evidence proves that meiosis occurs at the same point in the life cycle of *P. graminis.* In the latter, the chromosome number is approximately $n = 5$. The basidiospores, therefore, contain haploid nuclei, as does the primary mycelium which they produce within the barberry plant. The spermagonia and spermatia also apparently contain haploid nuclei, as well as the hyphae which aggregate to form the rudimentary aecium. The aeciospores themselves, however, are regularly binucleate; the origin of this condition has been under investigation for many years.

There is now considerable evidence that the binucleate hyphae in the aecial stages of *P. graminis* and other rusts may arise in a variety of ways. Soon after infection of the leaf by the basidiospore, and during the production and exudation of spermatia, haploid receptive hyphae may protrude through the stomata and between the epidermal cells of the leaf much like trichogynes among the Ascomycota and Rhodophycophyta. These may unite with spermatia, the nuclei of which migrate into the trichogynelike hyphae, multiply, and migrate further, thus transforming the originally haploid mycelium into one with cells containing two genetically different haploid nuclei. It has also been reported that spermatia may unite with periphyses of the spermagonia themselves, that certain cells of the young aecium may send to the leaf surface trichogynous branches which receive spermatial nuclei, and finally, that hyphal fusions (somatogamy) between different haploid basidiosporal infections may take place within the tissues of the leaf. The conjugate $n + n$ (dikaryotic) nuclear condition apparently can be initiated by several mechanisms; but unless it is initiated, the aecia usually remain sterile and fail to mature their aeciospores.

It has been demonstrated experimentally that in some rusts—*P. graminis,* for example —the mycelium derived from a single basidiospore is unisexual.[4] Infections of the barberry leaf arising from the germination of a single basidiospore may produce spermagonia and rudimentary aecia; but fertile, spore-producing aecia do not develop as a result of such infections. Furthermore, in such rusts, two of the four basidiospores produced by a basidium are "plus" and two are "minus" as to com-

---

[4] Or physiologically self-incompatible, this condition is often referred to as **heterothallism** in *P. graminis, Rhizopus stolonifer* and *Neurospora sitophila* in contrast to the self-compatibility or **homothallism** of *Pyronema.*

patibility, as a result of segregation during meiosis. Unless compatible nuclei are brought together into the aecial rudiment by one of the several methods listed above, the aecium fails to mature. In other rusts, infection by a single basidiospore is sufficient to produce fertile aecia; such species are regarded as bisexual or self-compatible. There is good evidence that insects play an important role in carrying plus and/or minus spermatia to compatible receptive hyphae. The life cycle of *Puccinia graminis* may be summarized as follows:

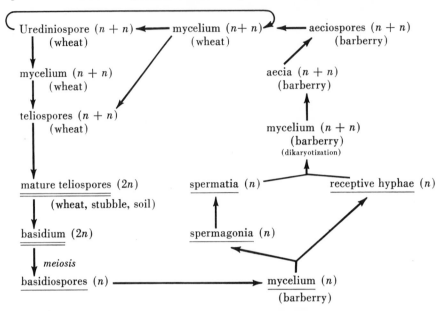

Rusts like *Puccinia graminis* which produce binucleate spores—in this case aeciospores and urediniospores—in addition to teliospores, are said to be **macrocyclic.** Those in which the teliospore is the only binucleate spore are said to be **microcyclic.**

Puccinia malvacearum, the widespread rust of hollyhocks and related plants, is chosen here to represent the life cycle of a microcyclic and **autoecious** rust (Figs. 13-8, 13-9).

In the life cycle of *P. malvacearum*, only two types of spores, teliospores and basidiospores, are produced. Reinfection is accomplished by thin-walled basidiospores which are binucleate as a result of a mitosis that takes place shortly after their formation. The basidiosporal germ tube enters the hollyhock epidermal cell and forms a short primary mycelium of uninu-

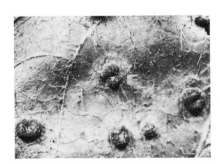

FIG. 13-8. *Puccinia malvacearum* Bert. Photograph of lesions on lower surface of hollyhock leaf. X 3.

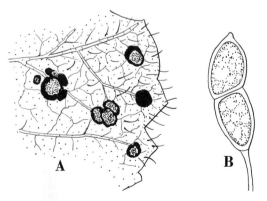

FIG. 13-9. *Puccinia malvacearum.* A. Telial lesions on hollyhock leaf. X 3. B. Teliospore from same. X 600.

cleate hyphae. These give rise to a more permanent mycelium which spreads through the leaf in both intercellular and intracellular fashion. Where hyphae from two different basidiosporal infections meet in the leaf, abundant anastomoses occur which involve nuclear migrations as well. This is sometimes interpreted as evidence that *P. malvacearum* is self-incompatible. It is thought that this process initiates the binucleate mycelium which becomes aggregated at certain loci near both leaf surfaces. A new generation of teliospores is produced on these hyphae which soon rupture the leaf epidermis. The two nuclei in each teliospore cell unite during maturation of the spore. Meiosis and formation of a basidium and basidiospores occur during teliospore germination. The teliospores of *P. malvacearum* do not require a period of dormancy before germination.

Puccinia graminis and *P. malvacearum* represent two extremes in type of life cycle among rusts. The former is heteroecious, requiring two hosts, and macrocyclic. It produces five types of reproductive cells. *P. malvacearum* is autoecious, confined to one host, and produces only teliospores and basidiospores. A number of other rust species fall between these two extremes with respect to degree of complexity of life cycle.

SMUT FUNGI

Although the smut fungi are parasitic Basidiomycota, some of them have been induced to complete their life cycles in laboratory cultures. The smuts which parasitize cereal grains are of tremendous economic importance. In epidemic years they have caused the loss of millions of bushels of grain. Their presence on the host is usually strikingly manifest by the sooty-black malformations on the fruiting spikes and vegetative portions of the plant.

Ustilago

Ustilago zeae (Beckm.) Unger, the corn smut, occurs in most spectacular fashion in the ears and tassels of the plant, where it causes immense enlarged growths (Fig. 13-10). These tumorlike galls of *Ustilago* (L. *ustus*, burned) are black at maturity. The

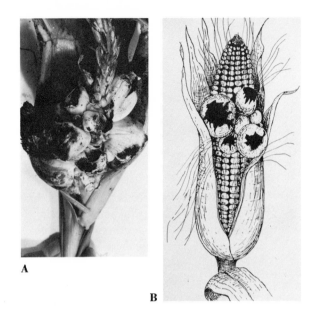

FIG. 13-10. *Ustilago zeae* (Beckm.) Unger. A. Infection on emergent staminate inflorescence. X ½. B. Infected ear of golden bantam corn. X ⅓.

color results from the transformation of the mycelium in the swollen host tissue into a mass of countless dark-walled teliospores (Fig. 13-11) which are binucleate. The two nuclei in the young teliospore undergo union as the spore wall thickens.

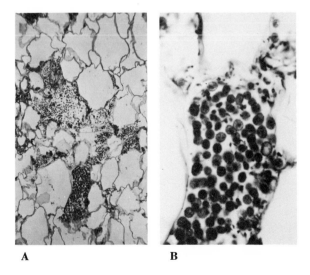

FIG. 13-11. *Ustilago zeae.* Hypertrophied corn cells containing smut spores. A. X 60. B. X 770.

FIG. 13-12. *Ustilago zeae.* Germinating teliospore with septate basidium and basidiospores. X 770.

The epidermis of the host, which at first covers the growing galllike enlargement, is finally ruptured. The interior of the mass is composed of large numbers of teliospores, intermingled with the remains of sterile hyphae and host cells. The spores are readily disseminated by air currents and can germinate immediately, or they may undergo dormancy until the next growing season of the host. Upon germination, the thick spore wall is ruptured by the protrusion of a delicate basidial hypha which becomes divided into four linearly arranged cells (Fig. 13-12), each containing a single haploid nucleus. The nucleus in each cell of the basidium divides mitotically to form two nuclei, one of which migrates into a thin-walled basidiospore that is budded off each basidial segment. Each of the latter may continue to produce additional basidiospores. It has been demonstrated, by the technique of single spore isolation and culture, that meiosis occurs during the division

of the primary basidial nucleus, i.e., the fusion nucleus of the teliospore. Therefore, the basidiospores are usually of two kinds in their sexual potentialities. Host plants inoculated with a single basidiospore fail to develop typical smut galls.

The basidiospores which chance to fall on the meristematic epidermis of young host tissues form delicate germination tubes which penetrate it and develop an intercellular mycelium, nourished by intracellular haustorial branches. The cells of this mycelium are uninucleate. The binucleate mycelium which produces the gall-like growth is initiated by somatogamy from different basidiosporal infections that chance to be in close proximity within the host. The infected region of the plant undergoes cell enlargement as a result of the presence of the fungus, and a new gall is ultimately produced. Other species of *Ustilago* cause smut diseases in different cereal grains. *U. tritici* Körn causes "loose smut" of wheat, and *U. avenae* (Pers.) Jens. causes a similar disease of oats. In addition to the origin of the binucleate (dikaryotic) mycelium by somatogamy described above, other mechanisms occur among smuts to effect the same result. For example, the dikaryotic mycelium is initiated in some smuts by conjugation of compatible basidiospores, often called **sporidia.** Once initiated, the binucleate condition of the mycelium of many smuts and other Basidiomycota is maintained by the formation of clamp connections, a phenomenon illustrated in Fig. 13-13 and described in its legend.

MUSHROOMS

The mushroom or toadstool (Figs. 13-14, 13-15) represents the fruiting body or basidiocarp of the fungus. Aggregation of the basidia into basidiocarps does not occur among the rusts and smuts. In the mushrooms, countless basidia and basidiospores are produced on the surface of the gills. The mushroom itself appears after a long period of vegetative development by a saprophytic mycelium which permeates the substratum, usually rich soil, decaying leaves or wood, or other organic debris. The mycelial branches

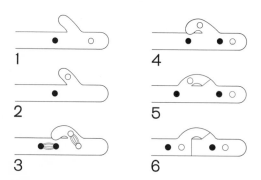

FIG. 13-13. Stages in cell division and clamp connection formation in the mycelium of Basidiomycota, schematized; black nuclei represent one type and white nuclei, another type of compatible nuclei. Successive stages show mechanism by which the dikaryotic condition is maintained. (*Modified from Dr. C. J. Alexopoulos.*)

MORPHOLOGY OF PLANTS

FIG. 13-14. A wild mushroom, *Lepiota molydites.* X 0.5. (*Courtesy of Dr. L. R. Hesler.*)

are often twisted together in ropelike strands called **rhizomorphs.** By the time the mycelium has matured sufficiently to produce basidiocarps, its cells are binucleate.

Among laymen, the term "mushroom" usually is employed to designate edible basidiocarps, whereas "toadstool," used as the antonym, signifies inedible or deleterious species. Morphologically, both mushrooms and toadstools are basidiocarps. As a matter of fact, very few forms are poisonous, although a number are unpalatable or otherwise unpleasant. In spite of many popular "rules" for distinguishing edible and poisonous mushrooms, "the only certain test is eating. . . . To know whether a fungus is safe to eat, we must be able to recognize it and know its proved reputation."[5] The most poisonous species are members of the genus *Amanita,* the toxicity of which varies with the species.

The mushroom originates as a minute ball of interwoven hyphae which increases in size and soon develops the familiar "button" stage. In sectional views, the closely interwoven cells give the appearance of parenchyma tissue, but their origin, from interweaving hyphae, indicates that they are merely pseudoparenchymatous. The immature, button stages may be produced in large numbers within the substratum, from which they emerge very rapidly following a rainfall. The word "mushroom" is commonly used metaphorically to exemplify the epitome of rapid growth. The latter is effected by the absorption of large quantities of water by the hyphae, which become extremely turgid and enormously stretched. In some genera, like *Coprinus* (Gr. *kopros,* dung), the basidiocarp is raised by elongation of the stipe early in the morning; all its spores are shed by afternoon, after which it deliquesces.

The basidiocarp of the mushroom (Figs. 13-14, 13-15), as it appears above the substratum, consists of an expanded, frequently disclike portion, the **pileus** (L. *pileum,* cap), which is subtended by the stalk or **stipe** (L. *stipes,* branch). The entire basidiocarp may be covered during early development by a membranous tissue which ruptures as the mushroom enlarges. Its remnants are visible in some genera as scales on the upper surface of the pileus and as a cup, the **volva,** at the base of the stipe. The ventral surface of the pileus consists of radiating plates of hyphae,

---

[5] Ramsbottom, *Mushrooms and Toadstools,* Collins, 1953, p. 35.

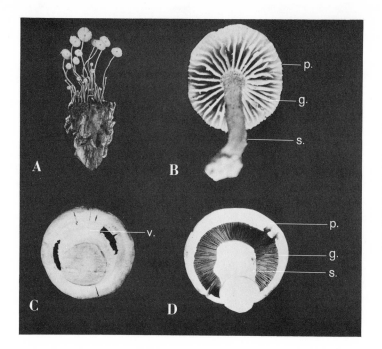

FIG. 13-15. Mushrooms. A. A wood-inhabiting species, *Marasmius rotula* (Scop.) Fr. X ½. B. Single basidiocarp of *Marasmius*: ventral view of pileus and gills. X 2. C, D. *Agaricus bisporus*. Stages in development of the basidiocarp; note partially ruptured velum in C. X ¼; g., gills; p., pileus; s., stipe; v., velum.

the **gills** (Fig. 13-15B,D), the arrangement, color, and structure of which are of taxonomic value in distinguishing various genera. The ventral surface of the pileus is often covered during its development by a membrane, the **velum** (Fig. 13-15C); its remnants may persist as an annulus on the stipe.

The gills (Fig. 13-16) comprise the fertile region of the basidiocarp. They are composed of a series of interwoven hyphae with enlarged terminal cells which protrude from the gill

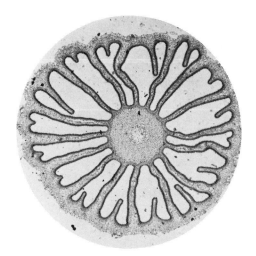

FIG. 13-16. *Coprinus* sp. Transection of pileus and gills; the dark margins of the latter comprise the hymenium; note central stipe. X 40.

surface and function as basidia. Unlike the rusts and smuts, the basidia here arise from vegetative hyphae, not from teliospores. A section of a mushroom gill, prepared at the proper point in development, shows a series of stages in the production of basidia and basidiospores (Fig. 13-17). The surfaces of the gills are covered by a fertile layer of basidia in various phases of development, and of paraphyses or sterile cells. Specialized cells, the **cystidia,** the function of which is not entirely clear, are intermingled with the basidia of certain species. The surface layer of the gill is called the **hymenium.** The basidia and paraphyses are borne on hyphae which form a subhymenial layer, and the central portion of the gill is composed of elongate hyphae which form a **trama.** The young basidia, as well as the sterile hyphae of the basidiocarp, are binucleate, but the two nuclei of the former unite early in development (Fig. 13-17A). The enlarged diploid nucleus then undergoes two nuclear divisions (Fig. 13-17B), during which meiosis occurs. It has been reported that the chromosome number in *Agaricus bisporus* (Gr. *agarikon,* mushroom), the commercially cultivated mushroom of the United States, is $n = 9$. Following meiosis, each of the four haploid nuclei migrates into a sterigma, which enlarges at the

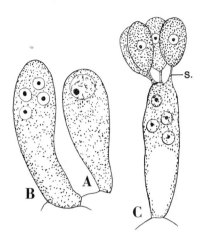

FIG. 13-17. *Coprinus* sp. Successive stages in the development of basidium and basidiospores. A. Young basidium with diploid nucleus. B. Postmeiotic nuclei. C. Basidiospores maturing; note supernumerary nuclei remaining in basidium; s., sterigma. X 1700.

tip to form a basidiospore (Fig. 13-17C). These are produced gradually by all the basidia, so that tremendous numbers of spores are shed from each pileus. One may gain some idea of their enormous numbers by placing a pileus, ventral surface down, on a suitable piece of paper, covering it with a bell jar, and examining the spore print which appears. It has been estimated that a single basidiocarp of *Agaricus campestris*, 4 inches in diameter, produces about 16 billion spores during the 5–6 days of spore discharge. Two-spored races occur in a number of mushrooms. In these, each basidiospore receives two of the four haploid basidial nuclei. Cultivated races of *Agaricus* are usually two-spored.

The liberated basidiospores germinate promptly, if they chance to fall upon a suitable substratum. Each produces a primary mycelium with uninucleate cells. Many species have been grown in artificial culture. It has been demonstrated that some genera of mushrooms are homothallic and others are heterothallic. In self-compatible (homothallic) species, mycelium from a single basidiospore will ultimately produce a basidiocarp. In self-incompatible (heterothallic) species, on the other hand, the haploid mycelium remains sterile unless it undergoes dikaryotization by a suitable compatible strain. This results in a mycelium with binucleate cells, a dikaryotic condition. Dikaryotization may be accomplished by somatogamy or by union of hyphal segments, **oidia.** The nuclei which unite in the young basidia are the descendants of the original pair or pairs of compatible nuclei brought together at the time of initial dikaryotization. It has been shown experimentally in self-incompatible species that two of the four spores contain nuclei of one sexual type and that two have nuclei of the other. Spores of self-compatible species apparently contain both sexual potentialities in their nuclei.

Cultivation of the field mushroom, *Agaricus bisporus*, has become an important commercial enterprise. Mushroom cultivation was practiced in France early in the seventeenth century. Mushroom mycelia are inoculated into specially prepared beds, containing a mixture of soil, leaves, and manure called compost; these beds are kept moist and at a suitable temperature. Blocks of such compressed soil mixture containing the mycelium are often spoken of as mushroom "seed" or "spawn."

OTHER BASIDIOMYCOTA

In addition to the rusts, smuts, and mushrooms, several other representatives of the Basidiomycota are of widespread occurrence. These will be treated briefly in the following account.

Jelly Fungi

Fruits of *Tremella* (L. *tremo*, tremble) and *Auricularia auricularis* (S. F. Gray) Martin are saprophytes on decaying logs in damp situations. They are most conspicuous after periods of prolonged rainfall. The basidiocarp of *Tremella* (Fig. 13-18A) is usually yellow, markedly convoluted, and of gelatinous consistency. *Auricularia* (Fig. 13-18B), the "ear fungus," is brown and, although gelatinous, is somewhat firmer. The saprophytic vegetative mycelium ramifies through the substratum, producing basidiocarps after a period of vegetative development. The mycelial cells are binucleate at the time the fruiting bodies are developed, but the exact origin of this condition is not known with

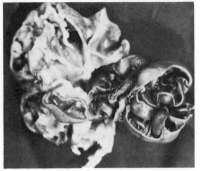

FIG. 13-18. A. *Tremella* sp., a jelly fungus; basidiocarps on decaying wood. X ½. B. *Auricularia auricularis* (S. F. Gray) Martin, the ear fungus; basidiocarp. X ½.

certainty. It presumably results from somatogamy of uninucleate primary mycelia.

The basidia and basidiospores of these genera are of interest to students of the phylogeny of fungi because they exhibit similarities both to the basidia of mushrooms and to those of rusts. In *Tremella*, the basidia occur all over the surface of the basidiocarp and are bathed in a gelatinous exudate secreted by the mycelium. This arrangement recalls the vegetative structure of such Rhodophycophyta as *Nemalion* and *Batrachospermum*. It has been demonstrated that nuclear union, followed by meiosis, takes place in each basidium as it develops. Cytokinesis follows the formation of four nuclei in such a manner that the basidium is divided into four cruciately arranged cells. Each of these produces an elongated sterigmalike protuberance which gives rise to a basidiospore on the surface of the gelatinous basidiocarp.

In *Auricularia*, the entire undersurface of the basidiocarp also is fertile. Nuclear union is followed by meiosis and production of four nuclei in the developing basidium. Here, however, cytokinesis divides the basidium into a chain of four cells very similar to the arrangement in the rusts. Each cell of the four-celled basidium now develops an elongate, sterigmalike hypha which grows to the surface of the basidiocarp and produces a basidiospore. The latter are violently discharged from the sterigmata.

Pore Fungi

The pore fungi comprise the Basidiomycota in which the hymenial layer is developed as a layer over the surface of pores or tubes

in the basidiocarp. The pores are often visible to the unaided eye. The basidiocarp is often a shelflike or bracketlike outgrowth on living trees and timber, as in the genus *Polyporus* (Gr. *polys*, many + Gr. *poros*, pore) (Fig. 13-19A). The basidiocarp of bracket fungi may be soft in texture or woody or leathery; it may be annual or perennial. The appearance of the basidiocarp is preceded by an extensive

A

B

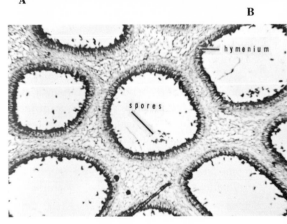

FIG. 13-19. A. *Polyporus* sp.; basidiocarps on wood. X ⅓. B. Transection of pores of *Boletus*; note that pores are lined with a basidiospore-producing hymenial layer. X 60.

MORPHOLOGY OF PLANTS

A

B

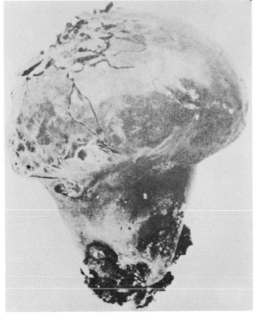

C

FIG. 13-20. A. *Scleroderma cepa* (Vaill.) Pers.; a puffball. X ½. B. *Geastrum* sp.; an earth star. X 1. C. *Calvatia* sp., a puffball X ½.

sterigmata. Little information is available as to the details of the life cycle in these pore fungi; the nuclear conditions and reproductive phases are unknown for a majority of genera. The pore fungi are of great economic importance as the cause of the rotting of standing and stored timber; they are probably largely saprophytic, although some attack sapwood which contains living cells.

Puffballs

In concluding this short treatment of the Basidiomycota, brief mention must be made of the puffball type (Fig. 13-20). The basidiocarp in these organisms always remains closed until after the basidia have matured their basidiospores. Indeed, in some genera, the basidiocarp never opens, the spores being disseminated only after the decay of the wall. In others, like *Lycoperdon* (Gr. *lykos*, wolf + Gr. *perdomai*, break wind), *Calvatia* (L. *calvus*, bald), *Scleroderma* (Gr. *scleros*, hard + Gr. *dermo*, to skin), and *Geastrum* (Gr. *ge*, earth + Gr. *aster*, star) (Fig. 13-20A,B), one or more small ostioles develop on the surface of the basidiocarp; the basidiospores are emitted in puffs through these when the basidiocarps are subjected to pressure. Our knowl-

development of vegetative mycelium within the substratum. The vegetative mycelium is dikaryotic at the time the fruiting body makes its appearance. There is evidence that somatogamy occurs in several species. In perennial types, countless basidiospores are shed from the basidiocarp during its existence. Figure 13-19B shows a portion of a section through the fruiting body of another pore fungus. The wall of each pore is covered with a layer of hymenium, much like that in mushrooms. Each basidium forms four basidiospores which are explosively discharged from their edge of cytological and reproductive features of the puffballs is scanty.

Summary and Classification

The representative genera of Basidiomycota described in the preceding sections of this chapter comprise a rather heterogeneous assemblage of fungi which, however, possess in common the attribute of producing a structure called the basidium. The basidium itself is not uniform in structure or time of occurrence in the life cycle. In the mushrooms, jelly fungi, pore fungi, and puffballs, the basidia appear directly on the mycelium as enlarged terminal hyphal tips (Fig. 13-17A). In the rusts and smuts, on the other hand, the basidium always develops as the result of the germination of a thick-walled spore, the teliospore (Fig. 13-12). As to the structure of the basidium itself, the genera described exhibit variation. In the mushrooms and pore fungi, the basidium is nonseptate, and the post-meiotic nuclei migrate directly into the basidiospores as they are formed. In the rusts, certain jelly fungi, and *Ustilago zeae*, the post-meiotic nuclei are segregated as the basidium becomes septate, each ultimately occupying a separate cell of the basidium.

Obvious manifestations of sexuality, such as specially differentiated gametes and gametangia, are usually absent in the Basidiomycota (the rusts excepted), and somatogamy prevails. For these reasons, sexuality is often said to be *reduced* in this assemblage of fungi. On the other hand, in many other organisms in which sexuality is considered to be highly developed—as in isogamous species of *Chlamydomonas*, *Spirogyra*, and *Rhizopus*, for example—highly differentiated gametangia and gametes are also lacking. The primary manifestations of sexuality, the union of cells and nuclei and the association of chromosomal and gene complements, are obviously present in the Basidiomycota, in spite of the absence of such secondary criteria as specialized gametes and gametangia. It is quite true that plasmogamy and karyogamy may be separated in time for an exceptionally long interval (*Puccinia graminis*), but descendants of the original pairs of nuclei of opposite sex potentiality, brought together at plasmogamy, are maintained by conjugate nuclear division, and one or more pairs of these descendant nuclei ultimately unite in the teliospore, chlamydospore, or basidium. Clamp connections are associated with the maintenance of the dikaryotic condition in many Basidiomycota.

The Basidiomycota are frequently divided into two groups on the basis of basidium structure. The illustrative genera discussed in this chapter may be classified as follows:

Division Basidiomycota

Class 1. Heterobasidiomycetes (basidium septate or consisting of a thick-walled teliospore or chlamydospore and its germ tube)
  Order 1. Uredinales (Rusts)
    Family 1. Pucciniaceae
      Genera: *Puccinia, Gymnosporangium*
  Order 2. Ustilaginales (Smuts)
    Family 1. Ustilaginaceae
      Genus: *Ustilago*
  Order 3. Tremellales (Jelly fungi)
    Family 1. Tremellaceae
      Genus: *Tremella*
  Order 4. Auriculariales (Jelly fungi)
    Family 1. Auriculariaceae
      Genus: *Auricularia*

Class 2. Homobasidiomycetes (basidium nonseptate, one-celled, a hyphal tip)
  Subclass 1. Hymenomycetes (basidia exposed to air, discharging their basidiospores freely at maturity)
  Order 1. Agaricales (Gilled fungi)
    Family 1. Agaricaceae
      Genera: *Agaricus, Coprinus, Marasmius, Amanita*
  Order 2. Polyporales (Pore fungi)
    Family 1. Polyporaceae
      Genus: *Polyporus*
  Subclass 2. Gasteromycetes (basidia and basidiospores permanently enclosed in basidiocarp, or enclosed until basidiospores have matured)
  Order 1. Lycoperdales (Puffballs)
    Family 1. Lycoperdaceae
      Genera: *Lycoperdon, Calvatia, Scleroderma*
    Family 2. Geastraceae
      Genus: *Geastrum*

DISCUSSION QUESTIONS

1. In outline form, summarize the life cycle of *Puccinia graminis.* How does it differ from that of *P. malvacearum?* Distinguish between macrocyclic and microcyclic rusts. Give an account of the nuclear cycle in *P. graminis.*

2. Can you suggest any *a priori* reasons why mycologists have failed, with few exceptions, to cultivate rusts independently of their specifically required host plant? How would you proceed in attempting to do so?

3. Why has the eradication of barberry bushes not caused the disappearance of the wheat rust?

4. Sexual reproduction in rusts has been compared with that in the Rhodophycophyta. What evidences of parallelism can you cite?

5. How do you account for the frequent occurrence of mushrooms in circles or "fairy rings"?

6. How do you explain the rapid appearance of mushrooms after a rain?

7. Define the terms basidium, basidiocarp, basidiospore, conjugate nuclear division, hymenium, diploidize, somatogamy, dikaryotic.

8. How would you determine whether or not a given rust fungus is self-incompatible or not? A mushroom? A smut?

9. Is it always necessary to count the chromosome number to establish the occurrence of meiosis?

10. How do rusts and smuts reduce the yield of cereal grains?

11. The introduction of nuclei of one strain into the mycelium of another in Ascomycota and Basidiomycota, has been called "diploidization." Does this involve the production of diploid nuclei? Explain.

12. In view of the tremendous number of spores produced by such organs as the mushroom basidiocarp and the aecium of the rusts, why is the world not overrun with mushrooms and rusts?

13. Male and female sex organs are absent in most Basidiomycota. Is sexual reproduction present in your opinion? Give the reasons for your answer.

14. Consult one or more of the references listed at the end of Chapter 10 for an account of the life cycle of rusts other than *Puccinia.* On the basis of your reading, cite variations from the *Puccinia* type.

CHAPTER 14

Deuteromycota; Predaceous Fungi; Lichens; Recapitulation of the Fungi

Deuteromycota

In concluding the several chapters dealing with fungi, brief mention must be made of a great group of organisms known as Fungi Imperfecti or Deuteromycota (Gr. *deuteros*, second + Gr. *mykes*). These organisms, which include both parasitic and saprophytic species, produce only asexual reproductive cells, namely, conidia or chlamydospores, at maturity. The spores may be borne directly on the mycelium (Fig. 14-1), or on conidiophores which develop within or upon special fruiting structures (Fig. 14-2) composed of densely interwoven hyphae. When cultivated under controlled environmental conditions properly manipulated, a number of fungi once included in this alliance have been in-

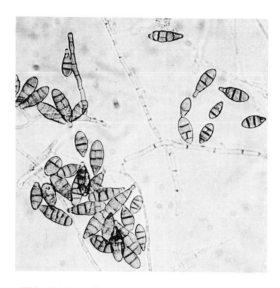

FIG. 14-1. *Alternaria* sp., an imperfect fungus with septate chlamydospores. X 540.

duced to undergo sexual reproduction and thus complete their life cycles. The spores produced as a result of sexual reproduction have been ascospores in a majority of species, but basidia and basidiospores have developed in a few. When the ascosporic or basidiosporic phase is known, the fungus can also be classified in the appropriate genus of Ascomycota or Basidiomycota. Although ascospores and basidiospores are unknown for many Deuteromycota, many of them have a mechanism for genetic interchange known as **parasexuality.** In this a given mycelium may be made heterokaryotic (genetically inhomogeneous) by fusion of two hyphae containing nuclei which differ genetically. It seems evident that the species of Fungi Imperfecti represent alternate stages of Ascomycota and Basidiomycota in which the characteristic asci and ascospores or basidia and basidiospores are produced rarely, if ever.

It is probable that some Deuteromycota never produce sexual stages, ascospores, or basidiospores. They are classified in an artificial system which emphasizes the location of the conidiophores and the color and structure of the conidia. Further consideration of this group is beyond the scope of the present volume. Two representatives are illustrated in Figs. 14-1 and 14-2.

Predaceous Fungi

No account of the fungi, however necessarily abbreviated, should fail to present at least a brief discussion of a remarkable and miscellaneous group of organisms, nutrition of which, at least facultatively, is based on

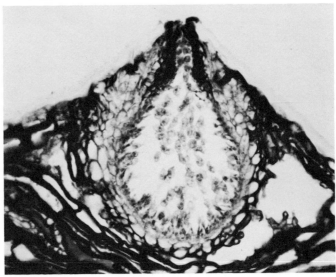

FIG. 14-2. *Guignardia bidwellii* (Ell.) Viala and Ravaz. A. Pycnidia on grape leaf. X 5. B. Median longisection of pycnidium showing spores. X 125. (*Courtesy of Dr. C. J. Alexopoulos.*)

capture and digestion of minute animals. The latter include amoebae, rotifers, nematodes, and springtails. The fungi involved are members of the Phycomycota, Basidiomycota, and Deuteromycota.

Of especial interest are some nematode-destroying organisms. Nematodes are minute (0.1–1.0 mm. long) wormlike animals many of which live in soil and are important enemies to horticultural and crop plants. More than 50 species of nematode-destroying fungi are known. The mechanisms used by the fungi to trap the nematode are various and remarkable. In some species, undifferentiated hyphae adhere to the animals, but in others special networks of adherent branches (Fig. 14-3A,B), stalked adhesive knobs (Fig. 14-3C,D), nonconstricting and constricting rings occur (Fig. 14-3E).

The last are especially interesting, consisting of three curved cells in the form of a closed ring (Fig. 14-3F) at the end of a short stalk. As the nematode enters the ring, the ring cells rapidly increase to three times their original size, thus constricting and holding the organism. This may occur in 0.1 second. After capture, hyphae of the fungus penetrate the animal and digest and absorb its substance. It is possible that the fungus produces a toxin.

In writing of these organisms, Duddington[1] has remarked succinctly:

It must be remembered that nematodes are, for their size, powerful and enormously active; they

[1] Duddington, C. L., *The Friendly Fungi*, Faber & Faber, London, 1957.

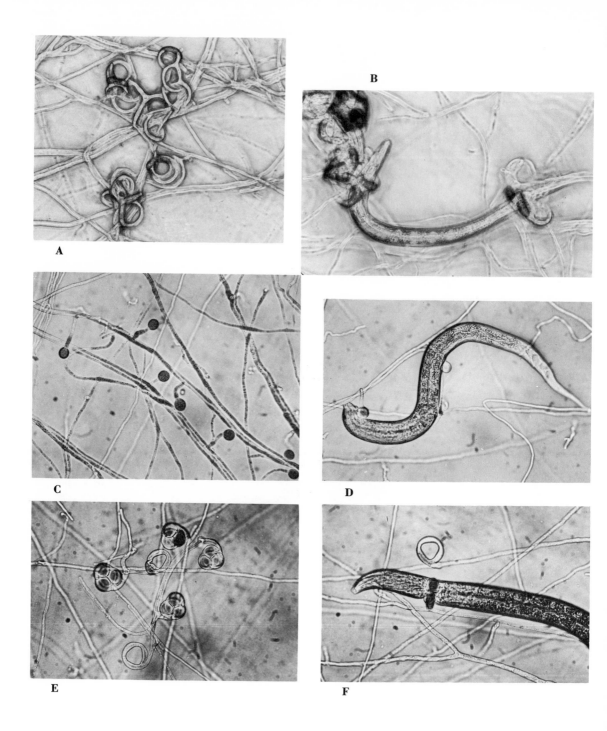

FIG. 14-3. Nematode-trapping fungi. A. *Arthrobotrys connoides*; note hyphal loops, the latter coated with a mucilaginous layer. B. Capture of a nematode. C. *Dactyella dreschsleri*; note short-stalked, adhesive knobs which capture nematodes upon contact, as in D, E. *Arthrobotrys dactyloides*; note constricting rings and their role in capturing a nematode, in F. X 300. (*Courtesy of Dr. David Pramer.*)

move from place to place by means of a rapid thrashing of their bodies, so that a vigorous specimen will cross the vision field of a microscope with the ferocious speed of a conger eel on the deck of a trawler. To capture such an animal is no mean task for a fungus that is itself composed of threads so delicate that the finest gossamer would by comparison be as a steel hawser is to a piece of string, and the means by which this is accomplished by the predaceous fungi are as extraordinary as they are efficient.

Lichens

The organisms known as lichens, of which there are approximately 15,000 species, might be classified as a separate division of the plant kingdom, were it not for the marked artificiality of such a grouping. Such a hypothetical division might be named the Mycophycophyta (Gr. *mykes*, fungus + Gr. *phykos*, alga + Gr. *phyton*, plant), a name which emphasizes that these organisms are dual in nature, consisting of an algal and a fungal component that grow together to form a plant body of consistently recognizable structure and appearance. Because the component organisms are members of other divisions— the Cyanophycophyta, Chlorophycophyta, Ascomycota, Basidiomycota, and Deuteromycota—the lichens usually are not classified as a separate division but instead are often grouped with the fungi. This probably stems from the circumstance that in a majority of lichens the fungus grows more rapidly than the alga, its mycelium forming a sort of framework within which the algal cells develop.

Lichens (Figs. 14-4, 14-5) are ubiquitous plants. They occur in a great variety of habitats, ranging from the bare surfaces of exposed rocks to the frozen substrata of arctic regions. A few are submerged aquatics periodically exposed to the air. Many of them flourish on decaying wood and undisturbed soil in organic debris. Tree bark supports an extensive flora of lichens. Some species are able to survive long periods of desiccation, and others thrive in extremely moist habitats. A number grow as epiphytes on the bark and branches of trees. Rock-inhabiting lichens are important agents in initiating soil formation. Their secretions etch the rock which is then readily broken down by ice and other physical agents to form a primitive type of soil. As organic remains from lichen vegetation become incorporated among the rock particles, higher forms of vegetation are established. A few marine lichens are known.

The exact relationship between the organisms, called the **phycobiont** and **mycobiont,** comprising a lichen thallus is only now beginning to be understood. Some look upon a lichen as a fungus parasitizing an alga, while, at the same time, the former is connected with the substratum. Support for this view is afforded by the lichens in which the fungus hyphae are connected to the algal cells by means of **appressoria** or haustoria (Fig. 14-8). On the other hand, the fungus component of a number of lichens has been grown successfully in artificial culture media, so the supposed parasitism is not obligate or highly specialized. Furthermore, in spite of the inferred parasitism, the algal cells grow and multiply for long periods within the lichen thallus without apparent injurious effects from the fungus.

Other investigators interpret lichens as manifestations of a type of **symbiosis** (Gr. *syn*, together + Gr. *bios*, life), with benefit accruing to each partner. The alga is surrounded and mechanically protected by the meshwork of fungus hyphae which absorb and adsorb water, mineral salts, and organic materials from the substratum. The fungus, presumably by means of appressoria or haustoria, diffusion from the algal cells, or autolysis of the latter, is supplied with a source of carbohydrate, organic nitrogen compounds, and vitamins. Our knowledge of the physiological relations between fungi and algae in lichens has in the past been colored to some extent by teleological considerations and speculation. While it is obvious that the algal component of lichens occupying xeric habitats like bare rocks could not and does not exist alone in the same environment,[2] it is more difficult to be convinced that the algal component of lichens growing in moist habitats is benefited by association with a fungus. In fact, it seems probable that the fungus hyphae surrounding the algae may reduce their rate of photosynthesis by shading. However, again considering the case of the xerophytic lichen on a bare rock surface, it is reasonable to suppose

---

[2] The author has recently found and has been studying nonlichenized blue-green and green algae which discolor stone buildings in exactly such a habitat!

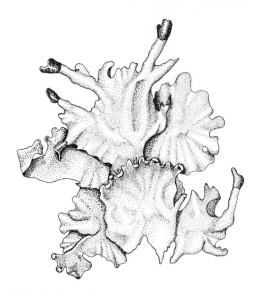

FIG. 14-4. *Peltigera rufescens* (Neck.) Hoffm. Portion of plant with fertile (ascospore-bearing) lobes. X ⅔. (*After Ahmadjian.*)

the case of lichens of moist soil and bark habitats, it seems probable that the substratum itself can supply a great part of the organic materials required by the fungus, so that association with an alga would seem to be superfluous. Furthermore, it is well known that algae can utilize available organic matter to supplement their nutritional requirements. In summary, it is difficult to generalize with assurance concerning the physiological relations between the component organisms of lichens. Further investigations of these questions are now being carried on intensively by Dr. Vernon Ahmadjian of Clark University.[3] These investigations are based on pure culture studies of the organisms grown separately and together, as well as on growth in the laboratory of lichens collected in the field.

The great majority of lichens have mycobionts which are ascomycetous, probably re-

that the fungal component could not exist in such a habitat, devoid of organic metabolites, unless it were supplied by the alga. Again, in

[3] For summary of relatively current knowledge of lichen component relationships see the articles by Ahmadjian cited on p. 182.

FIG. 14-5. Various lichens. A. *Parmelia* sp.; note apothecia. B. *Allectoria* sp. C, D. Two different species of *Usnea*. X 0.5.

lated to the cup fungi or to perithecium-forming genera. In a few lichens, the fungus is one of the Basidiomycota often one of the mushrooms. Their phycobionts are alternatively myxophycean genera like *Gloeocapsa*, *Nostoc*, and *Stigonema*, or chlorophycean genera like *Trebouxia* (a *Chlorococcum*-like genus) (Fig. 14-8).

The plant body of the lichen may be leaflike or foliose (*Peltigera* [Figs. 14-4, 14-5A,B, 14-6B], *Parmelia*, *Umbilicaria*), crustlike or crustose (Fig. 14-6A), or branching and cylindrical or fruticose (*Cladonia*, *Usnea*) (Figs. 14-5C,D, 14-6C). In most lichens, the fungus forms a general network around the algal cells. It often looks pseudoparenchymatous because of the dense interweaving of its hyphae. The growth pattern of the fungus determines the form of the lichen. It is of interest, however, that when the fungus is

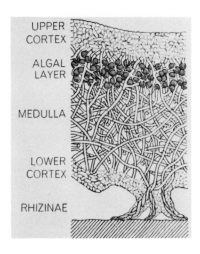

FIG. 14-7. Organization of a lichen, diagrammatic. (*After Ahmadjian.*)

grown free from the alga in laboratory culture, its growth pattern is usually different from that assumed when it is growing with the alga. Thus the latter seems to play a morphogenetic role.

Considerable internal differentiation may be present in the lichen thallus (Fig. 14-7). The surface hyphae may assume an epidermislike configuration, which may have a colloidal, water-holding sheath. The hyphae below the epidermal layer form the upper cortex. The algal cells lie immediately beneath this (Fig. 14-7), among loosely woven fungus hyphae. The central portion of the thallus, the **medulla,** is also composed of a loose network of hyphae below which a dense lower cortex may be present. The medullary hyphae are longitudinal in orientation in *Peltigera* and function in conduction. Special absorbing hyphae, the **rhizines** or rhizinae, enter the substratum from the lower surface of the thallus. Rhizines are complex bundles of hyphae which have anastomosed by fusion of young hyphal tips. They conduct water rapidly in the capillary spaces among the component hyphae and also in their lumina, as demonstrated by experiments with water-soluble dyes.

Multiplication of the usually slowly growing lichen thallus is effected by fragmentation as the older portions of the plant body die and leave the growing regions isolated. A number of lichens produce special bodies, the **soredia**

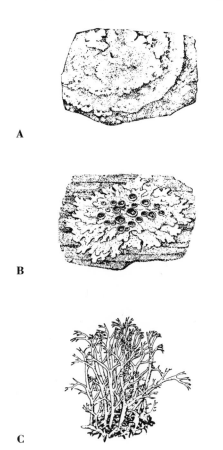

FIG. 14-6. Growth habits of lichens, diagrammatic. A. Crustose. B. Foliose. C. Fruticose. (*After Ahmadjian.*)

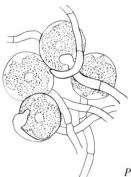

FIG. 14-8.
Parmelia sp. Soredium.
X 315.

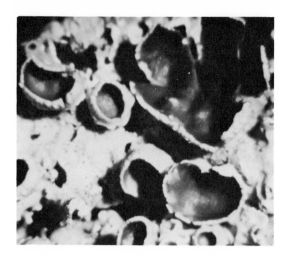

FIG. 14-9. *Parmelia* sp. Apothecia. X 10.

(Gr. *soros*, heap), for propagation (Fig. 14-8). These are small fragments of the thallus consisting of one or more algal cells surrounded by fungus hyphae. The soredia are readily detached from the thallus and, when borne to suitable environments by air currents, may develop into new plants. In *Cladonia chlorophaea* (Flk.) Spreng, the soredia are borne in gobletlike structures. It is probable that fragments containing both algal and fungal components are the primary agents of lichen multiplication and colonization.

In addition to multiplication of the lichen as a unit, the component organisms also reproduce independently. Under conditions of abundant moisture, the algal member may undergo rapid growth and cell division, thus outstripping the enveloping fungus; groups of algal cells are thus set free into the substratum. In many lichens, the fungus regularly produces ascocarps and asci (Figs. 14-5A,D, 14-6B); the ascocarp may be a perithecium or an apothecium (Figs. 14-5A, 14-6B, 14-9 to 11), or have some other form (Fig. 14-4). The picturesque red tips of certain ascending branches of *Cladonia cristatella*, for example, are aggregations of asci. It has been demonstrated in a number of genera that the formation of the ascocarp is preceded by the development of a coiled ascogonium, often with a trichogyne, which is probably fertilized by a spermatium. Cytological details are unknown in most cases.

The mature ascocarp may be elevated on a stipe above the thallus or it may be sessile or even sunken. The ascocarps are apparently perennial. The hymenial layer of the apothe-

cium is composed of densely intermingled asci and paraphyses (Figs. 14-9, 14-10, 14-11); the wall of the ascocarp may be composed only of fungus hyphae, or it may be overgrown by an alga-containing layer of the thallus. The ascospores vary among the various genera in form and number of component cells. They are discharged explosively from the apothecia and usually germinate readily if they fall upon a favorable substratum.

It is clear that both the algal component and the spores of the fungus, once separated from the parent thallus, initiate an independent existence. The synthesis of a new lichen thallus

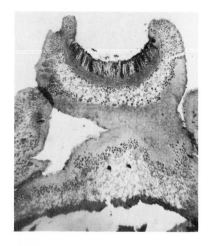

FIG. 14-10. *Physcia* sp. Section of apothecium; note hymenial layer. X 60.

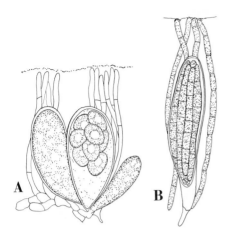

FIG. 14-11. A. *Parmelia* sp. Asci and paraphyses. B. *Peltigera* sp. Ascus with septate ascospores and paraphyses. X 600.

depends upon the fortuitous proximity of a germinating fungal spore and algal cells of the species with which the fungus has been associated in the parent lichen thallus. For this reason it is questionable whether ascospores play an important role in the multiplication of lichens, as such. It is probable that fragmentation and soredium production are more efficacious in this connection.

The researches of Dr. Ahmadjian have demonstrated clearly that assumption of the lichen relationship by an alga and a fungus depends on the existence of minimal nutrition for both organisms. Attempts to induce or initiate a lichen synthesis in culture media rich in nutrients are consistently failures. However, in low-nutrient, minimal culture media, lichen synthesis has been successfully evoked.

Until recently, lichens have been neglected by most botanists, except for a few who have occupied themselves almost exclusively with the taxonomy of these interesting plants. Careful physiological studies of the components, grown separately and together in laboratory culture under controlled conditions, would probably augment our understanding of these organisms.

It is difficult to assign lichens a natural position in any plan of classification of the plant kingdom. If they were classified with the group of ascomycetous or basidiomycetous fungi to which their fungus component is related, as is usually done, the importance of the algal component would be minimized. The opposite objection might be raised were they to be classified on the basis of their algal components. In the present volume, therefore, they have been assigned no formal position in the classification of the plant kingdom but are treated in the present chapter that concludes the discussion of the algae and fungi.

Fossil Fungi

Among the fungi, *sensu lato*, fossil bacteria (Fig. 14-12), approximately 2 billion years old, have been identified in such ancient strata as the Precambrian (Table 32-1) iron ores of northern Michigan, and in strata of northern Minnesota. Very recently, evidence of the existence of bacteria in still earlier Precambrian strata (ca. 3.1 billion years old) has been reported.[4] Other bacteria, assumed to have been parasitic, have been identified within the sporangia of certain Carboniferous (Table 32-1) plants.

Fossilized fungal remains are not as abundant as those of algae. Fungal hyphae have been reported in Precambrian cherts (along with blue-green algae), an indication that mycelial fungi also are an ancient group.

In the stems and associated remains in an ancient bog at Rhynie, Scotland, which is of Lower Devonian (Table 32-1) age, very well-preserved fossil fungi (Fig. 14-14A) are present. Mycorrhizal[5] fungi were functioning in the superficial root cells of certain Carboniferous gymnosperms (Fig. 14-13).

As stated in the discussion of fossil algae, the fossil record of fungi, in part because of its paucity and fragmentary nature, has shed little light on fungal evolution. The ancient fungi seem to have been very similar to extant forms, so that the fungi, like the algae, are a long-lived race which have been little modified through the ages.

---

[4] Barghoorn, E. S., and J. W. Schopf, 1966. "Microorganisms Three Billion Years Old from the Precambrian of South Africa," *Science*, 152: 758–763.

[5] Fungi associated with roots.

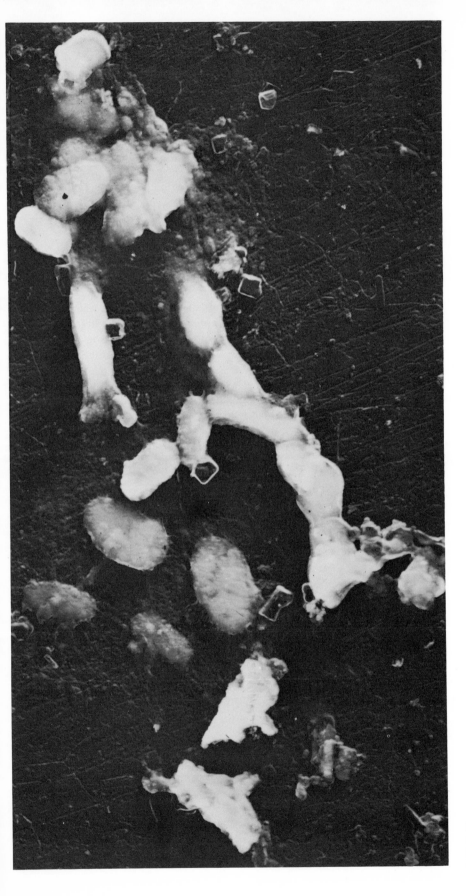

FIG. 14-12. Fossil bacteria from the Gunflint Iron Formation. X 10,500. (*After Schopf et al.*)

MORPHOLOGY OF PLANTS

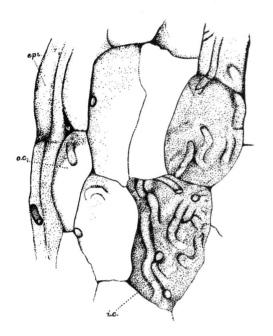

FIG. 14-13. Fungus in rootlet of *Amyelon radicans* Will. Mississippian; epi., epidermis; i.c., inner cortex; o.c., outer cortex. X 200. (*After Osborn.*)

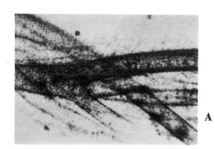

A

B

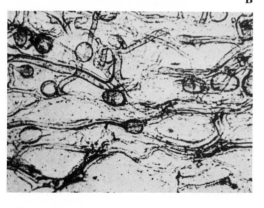

FIG. 14-14. Devonian fungi. A. Mycelium in decayed stem of *Asteroxylon*. X 250. B. *Palaeomyces asteroxyli* (Kidston and Lang). Hyphae and vesicles in the cortex of *Asteroxylon*. X 125. (*After Kidston and Lang.*)

Recapitulation of the Fungi

Chapters 9 through 13 contain a brief survey of organisms known as fungi in the broad sense of the term, as exemplified by descriptions of the structure and reproduction of certain selected genera and species. It was stated in Chapter 1 that in older systems of classification the algae and fungi were grouped together in a single division, Thallophyta, within which the fungi comprised a class coordinate with the algae. It became clear long ago that the bacteria and slime molds represent series fundamentally distinct from the remainder of the fungi. The characteristic cell structure of the bacteria, with respect to wall structure, nuclear organization, flagellation, lack of Golgi apparatus and mitochondria, and their endospore formation, mark them as a group apart. It seems quite logical, therefore, to consider them as a phyletic unit or division, although future investigation may reveal that the assemblage is a heterogeneous one. Their affinities are, perhaps, with the Cyanophycophyta with which they are sometimes classified in the taxon Prokaryota.

The slime molds differ from the bacteria in their nuclear organization, and from the bacteria and other fungi in their possession of naked amoeboid stages (the plasmodium and pseudoplasmodium), as well as in their phagotrophic manner of nutrition. In spite of the stationary sporangial stages of slime molds, a number of distinguished mycologists are of the opinion that they are more closely related to protozoa than to fungi. For these reasons, the slime molds, like the bacteria, are usually considered to represent a distinct phyletic group and have in this book been accorded divisional rank.

The three remaining groups of fungi, treated in this volume as separate divisions—namely, the Phycomycota, Ascomycota, and Basidiomycota—are assigned class rank and combined into a single division, Eumycophyta, by most mycologists. Approximately 3,585 genera and 80,000 species are included in this alliance. If the division is indeed the expression of phyletic unity, such a grouping would indicate close kinship among phycomycetous, ascomycetous, and basidiomycetous fungi. When one reviews the attributes which these several classes of fungi have in common, attributes which might serve as evidences of kinship, the results are not convincing, if speculation is distinguished from data. These organisms do possess the negative attribute of nonphotosynthetic nutrition, but they share this with the great majority of Schizomycota and Myxomycota. Their most striking common characteristic, perhaps, is the structure of their plant bodies, which, for the most part, are composed of branching filaments, the mycelium. It should be noted, however, that the occurrence of branching filamentous plant bodies in the Chlorophycophyta, Phaeophycophyta, Rhodophycophyta, and Cyanophycophyta is considered evidence of parallel development rather than of relationship among these algae. It should be interpreted in similar fashion in the fungi. The Phycomycota, Ascomycota, and Basidiomycota certainly are distinct enough from each other, with respect to their reproduction, to warrant our considering them as separate phyletic groups of divisional rank.

There are two important, divergent points of view, among others, regarding the relationship of these three groups of fungi. According to one hypothesis, the fungi are probably derivatives of algae which have lost their photosynthetic capacity. This view is based upon similarities between the structure of the siphonalean Chlorophycophyta and the mycelium of the Phycomycota, on the occurrence of flagellate motile cells in the lower Phycomycota and Chlorophycophyta, and on the similarity between the reproductive phases of the Ascomycota and the Rhodophycophyta. On the other hand, the flagellate motile cells of the lower Phycomycota and the absence of chlorophyll have suggested a protozoan origin to other mycologists.

There is no unanimity of opinion regarding the relation of the Phycomycota to the other two groups of fungi. According to some mycologists, the ascus is the homologue of the zygote of the Phycomycota, and the formation of ascospores by free-cell formation is interpreted by them as a derived condition. If this is granted, the unicellular yeasts, in some of

which the zygotes produce ascospores directly, are probably the simplest Ascomycota. The genera with indirect ascus formation from ascogenous hyphae are considered to be derived types in this hypothesis. On the basis of similarities in reproduction reviewed in Chapter 12, other mycologists have suggested that the Ascomycota have been derived from a rhodophycean ancestry. To them, the yeasts are secondarily simplified or reduced organisms which originated from more complex mycelial ancestors. Most students of the fungi are of the opinion that the Basidiomycota have originated from an ascomycetous ancestry, and they interpret the basidium as the homologue of the ascus. They support this theory by emphasizing that nuclear union and meiosis occur in both basidium and ascus, that the special mechanisms involved in maintaining the dikaryotic condition which precedes the ascus and basidium (crozier formation and clamp connections, respectively) are similar, and that both organs form spores, albeit those of the ascus are endogenous and those of the basidium exogenous. On the basis of these considerations, it should be clear to the reader that so-called evidence of relationship among the several groups of fungi is largely founded on speculation and hypothesis. As such, it should not be accepted as final. In the writer's opinion, the available evidence is inadequate to indicate common origin for the Phycomycota, Ascomycota, and Basidiomycota, and accordingly they have been classified as separate divisions in this book.

As compared with the range of complexity of types of plant body in the algae, the fungi are more homogeneous, for the vegetative phases are either unicellular or composed of amorphous masses of mycelia. In complexity, however, the spore-bearing bodies of the Ascomycota and Basidiomycota surpass the fertile tracts of algae.

Both asexual and sexual reproduction are involved in the life cycles of a majority of the fungi. Zoospores and gemmae of the aquatic genera and air-borne spores of a number of genera of Phycomycota, the conidia of the Ascomycota, and the urediniospores and aeciospores of the Basidiomycota are all clearly asexual reproductive bodies in the sense that they can continue development without union with other cells. Such spore types as ascospores and basidiospores, while asexual in the sense that they can continue development into a mycelium without sexual union, nevertheless are closely associated with sexual phenomena which precede their formation. The absence of differentiated sex organs in many Ascomycota and Basidiomycota, together with alternate paths of effecting association and ultimate union of compatible nuclei, emphasizes, once again, as is clear in the algae, that highly differentiated sex organs and differentiated gametes are not indispensable prerequisites for sexual reproduction.

When one attempts to interpret life cycles among the fungi in the light of their range in the algae, difficulties soon arise. It is quite clear that with respect to life cycle, such genera as *Saprolegnia*, *Achlya*, and *Rhizopus* are similar to *Chlamydomonas*, *Spirogyra*, and *Nemalion*, that is, haplobiontic with haploid plant bodies. The life cycles of *Allomyces macrogynus* and *Saccharomyces cerevisiae*, with their isomorphic alternation of generations, are similar in all fundamental respects to those of *Cladophora*, *Ulva*, and *Ectocarpus*. Difficulties present themselves, however, in comparing life cycles of other Ascomycota and

Basidiomycota with those of algae. While it is tempting to homologize ascogenous hyphae, basidioferous hyphae, and diploid rhodophycean filaments producing carpospores, it must be remembered that the latter are diploid, not dikaryotic, and that normally dikaryotic cells are unknown among algae.

In conclusion, brief mention must be made of the relation and importance of fungi to mankind. Although most people are painfully aware of their harmful or inconvenient and unpleasant activities—among them production of a number of diseases of plants, animals, and human beings; decay of foods, textiles, and building materials; and such aesthetic offenses as mildews—the countless useful activities of these organisms are usually not appreciated sufficiently. One has but to mention such processes as acetic and lactic acid fermentations by bacteria and the role of the latter in the nitrogen cycle; the relation of the yeasts to the alcohol, baking, and brewing industries; the important antibiotics, which, like penicillin, streptomycin, aureomycin, terramycin and chloromycetin, are of fungal origin; and finally the relation of molds to the ripening of highly prized cheeses, to be reminded of some of the beneficial activities in which fungi have a stellar role.

DISCUSSION QUESTIONS

1. Explain the nature of the organisms in the Deuteromycota.

2. Discuss the nutritive relations between the phycobionts and mycobionts in lichens.

3. What types of algae occur in lichens?

4. What types of fungi are present in lichens?

5. How do lichens reproduce?

6. How would you go about isolating and growing the components of a given lichen?

7. How would you go about resynthesizing the lichen?

8. Why are lichens sometimes called "soil builders"?

9. List the distinctive attributes of the divisions of fungi.

10. What evidence is usually cited in support of the practice of grouping the Phycomycota, Ascomycota, and Basidiomycota in a single division?

11. Do nonphotosynthetic organisms occur only in the animal kingdom and among the fungi? Explain.

12. Assume that all fungi (including bacteria and slime molds) were to disappear from the earth tomorrow. What immediate and what ultimate results would you predict, if this occurred?

REFERENCE WORKS ON LICHENS

Ahmadjian, V., "The Fungi of Lichens," *Scientific American* 208:122–131, 1963.

Ahmadjian, V., "Lichens," *Ann. Rev. Microbiology* 19:1–20, 1965.

Ahmadjian, V., "Lichens," *Symbiosis*, vol. 1, Academic Press, New York, 1966.

Fink, B., *The Lichen Flora of the United States*, Univ. of Michigan Press, Ann Arbor, Mich., 1949.

Hale, M., *Lichen Handbook*, Smithsonian Institution, Washington, D.C., 1961.

Lamb, I. M., "Lichens," *Scientific American*, October, 1959.

CHAPTER 15

Introduction to the Land Plants; Division Hepatophyta

Introduction to the Land Plants

Chapters 2 through 14 included a discussion of the algae and fungi, both of which were formerly classified together in the single division, Thallophyta (Table 32-2, p. 516). It will be recalled that the algae differ from the fungi in that algae are chlorophyllous and photoautotrophic,[1] whereas the fungi, with the exception of a few types of bacteria, are achlorophyllous heterotrophic organisms. With the rarest exceptions, the plants to be described in the present and succeeding chapters are, like the algae, also photoautotrophic. Although the algae are largely aquatic organisms, with relatively few terrestrial representatives,[2] the remaining groups of photosynthetic plants are primarily land dwellers. However, almost every division provides examples of genera which probably have become secondarily adapted to the water from an originally terrestrial habitat, although a few may be primitively aquatic.

When one compares the organization of the aquatic algae with that of terrestrial plants, it becomes evident that most of the complexities of the latter are manifestations of adaptation to existence in a drying atmosphere. As compared with its postulated algal ancestors, the land plant is a pioneer in a harsh and unfavorable environment. Aquatic plants are immersed continuously in a solution containing the inorganic materials which are used in the synthesis of their protoplasm. On the contrary, large portions of the body surface of terrestrial plants are not in direct contact with

water and dissolved nutrients, and, furthermore, may lose a large percentage of the water that has been absorbed. Study of the structure of land plants reveals a variety of both morphological and physiological adaptations to a terrestrial life. The degree and efficiency of these adaptations are undoubtedly correlated with the habitats of land plants in relation to moisture and with the very survival of the plants themselves.

Division Hepatophyta

The Hepatophyta (Gr. *hepar,* liver) or liverworts,[3] containing about 300 genera and between 8,000 and 10,000 species, are certainly among the most primitive extant land plants. The earliest fossil liverworts are Devonian (Table 32-1, p. 512; Fig. 15-64). Several of the genera included in this group are aquatic organisms; the remainder, with few exceptions, are restricted to moist habitats. In some of them, like *Sphaerocarpos, Pellia* and *Takakia,* the plant body is scarcely more complex, internally and externally, than that of such algae as *Ulva.* The liverworts are considered by many botanists to be "allies" of the mosses with which they are usually grouped in a single division, Bryophyta. In this text, for reasons that will be cited later (p. 245), the liverworts and mosses are classified in separate divisions. The division Hepatophyta here is considered to include two distinct classes: (1) The Hepatopsida or liverworts; and (2) the Anthocerotopsida or hornworts.

---

[1] At least a majority of those investigated seem to be photoautotrophic.

[2] In spite of the ubiquity of soil algae.

[3] The name "liverwort" was first applied to the genus *Conocephalum* because of an imagined resemblance of its lobes to the lobes of the liver.

Class 1. Hepatopsida

Introduction

The gametophyte is the dominant phase in the heteromorphic alternation of the liverworts. This class contains approximately 225 genera and 8,500 species, which are grouped into orders and families on the basis of differences in the structure of their gametophytic and sporophytic phases. If one attempts to list first in the class the most primitive organisms exhibiting the greatest simplicity, he is at a loss to make a decision, for low and/or high degree of complexity in both sporophyte and gametophyte do not coincide in the same organism. Furthermore, attributes which some morphologists interpret as simple may have been interpreted as either primitive or reduced by others. Thus, for example, on the basis of structure of the sporophyte alone, if simplicity is the criterion, *Ricciocarpus* and *Riccia* deserve first place, but their internally differentiated gameto-

phytes are more complex than those of genera like *Pellia, Pallavicinia,* and *Sphaerocarpos.*

The Hepatopsida may be divided into five orders as follows: Takakiales, Calobryales, Marchantiales, Sphaerocarpales, and Jungermanniales. Representative types of the Marchantiales, Sphaerocarpales, and Jungermanniales will be emphasized in the following account, with briefer treatment of the Takakiales and Calobryales.

Order 1. Marchantiales

The order Marchantiales includes thallose or bladelike, flat, dorsiventral organisms with some degree of internal differentiation of tissues. Representatives of two families of Marchantiales are considered intensively in the following discussion.

FAMILY 1. RICCIACEAE

Ricciocarpus and Riccia

Habitat and vegetative morphology

Ricciocarpus natans (L.) Corda (Fig. 15-1) and *Riccia fluitans* L. (Fig. 15-2) are amphibious. Both, however, usually grow only vegetatively[4] when stranded or when cultivated on damp soil (Fig. 15-1B). Other species of *Riccia* are terrestrial, forming rosettes on moist soils.

---

[4] That is, without forming reproductive structures.

FIG. 15-1. *Ricciocarpus natans.* A. Floating plants. X 0.75. B. Plants on soil. X 0.37. (A. *Courtesy of Dr. William C. Steere.*)

B

A

FIG. 15-2. *Riccia fluitans.* Culture on agar; note dichotomous branching. X 1.

Vegetative morphology

The individual plants of *Ricciocarpus* (Fig. 15-1) taper posteriorly from a broad, dichotomously lobed anterior growing region. The posterior portion of the plant is continually sloughing off as growth occurs at the tip. Increase in number of individuals occurs when branches become separated or when death and decay extend to the region of a dichotomy. Plants which contain mature sporophytes may attain a length of 2.5 cm. Four or more rows of **ventral scales** are present on the lower surface of each plant. The scales, which are a single cell layer thick, are often purple because of the presence of a pigment dissolved in the cell sap. Unicellular protuberances, or **rhizoids,** emerge from the cells of the lower surface of terrestrial plants and penetrate the substratum.

The apparent midrib in *Ricciocarpus* is in reality a furrow that extends deeply into the plant body from the dorsal surface. Observed in transverse section (Fig. 15-3A), this furrow is approximately in the form of an inverted Y. The lower portion of the plant is composed of rather compact parenchyma cells which contain few chloroplasts and function as storage cells; these are covered above by several tiers of air chambers. The latter are responsible for the spongy appearance of the plants when they are viewed in dorsal aspect under low magnifications (Fig. 15-3B). The walls of the air chambers are built up of photosynthetic parenchyma (chlorenchyma) cells rich in chloroplasts. The cells of the upper surface contain only a few poorly developed plastids and function as an epidermis. That their outer walls are cutinized at least delicately is suggested by the occurrence of apertures, one corresponding to each air chamber, on the upper surface of the plant body (Fig. 15-4). The epidermal cells surrounding the aperture are modified in structure.

Growth of the plant body of *Ricciocarpus* and *Riccia,* and of almost all land plants, is localized at the apex, where one or more prominent meristematic cells, the **apical cells,** and the cells derived from them undergo orderly divisions which augment the tissues of the plant. A median sagittal section through

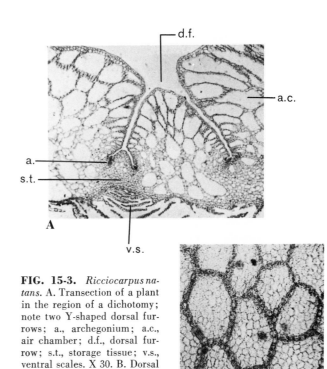

FIG. 15-3. *Ricciocarpus natans.* A. Transection of a plant in the region of a dichotomy; note two Y-shaped dorsal furrows; a., archegonium; a.c., air chamber; d.f., dorsal furrow; s.t., storage tissue; v.s., ventral scales. X 30. B. Dorsal surface of plant showing air chambers. X 60.

the plant body demonstrates its ontogeny (Fig. 15-5). Dorsal derivatives of the apical cell form chlorophyllous tissue while the ventral derivatives give rise to the storage tissue, ventral scales, and rhizoids.

Reproduction: the gametophyte

Other than vegetative reproduction by fragmentation, increase in number of individuals in *Ricciocarpus* and *Riccia* is the ultimate result of sexuality. The reproductive organs are sunken in chambers on the floor and walls of the dorsal furrow by the time that they are mature (Figs. 15-5, 15-6). They arise from

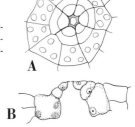

FIG. 15-4. *Ricciocarpus natans.* A. Surface view. B. Sectional view of a pore and surrounding cells. X 410.

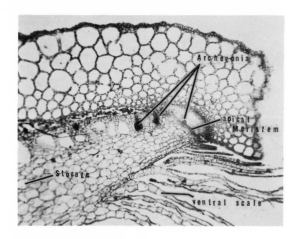

FIG. 15-5. *Ricciocarpus natans.* Median longitudinal (sagittal) section of plant apex cut parallel to the dorsal furrow; note air chambers above. X 30.

said to be **protandrous** (Gr. *proteros,* prior + Gr. *ander,* male), those in which archegonia are produced are said to be **protogynous** (Gr. *proteros* + Gr. *gyne,* female). Sex organs usually appear only in floating plants of *Ricciocarpus,* but they may develop in occasional terrestrial individuals. Floating plants which bear only antheridia are young individuals in which archegonia have not yet developed. Plants bearing only archegonia are older ones in which the antheridia have been lost through decay of the posterior portion of the individual. It should be noted that the floating plants are usually abundant if not actually contiguous.

The antheridia and archegonia are arranged in three or more rows in the dorsal furrow (Figs. 15-3, 15-6). They differ from the gametangia of the algae, with the exception of the plurilocular gametangia of the Phaeophycophyta, the antheridia and oogonia of the Charophyta, and those of certain fungi, in their multicellular construction. Furthermore, unlike the plurilocular gametangia of the Phaeophycophyta, the sex organs are composed, in part, of sterile cells.[5] The antheridium (Figs. 15-6, 15-7A) consists of a short

single cells and at first protrude from the surface of the furrow (Fig. 15-5); they become secondarily sunken in chambers because of the upgrowth of the surrounding cells. The liverwort plant body is gametophytic. *Ricciocarpus* is bisexual, for the male and female sex organs arise on one and the same plants. Some species of *Riccia* have bisexual individuals and others unisexual ones.

The antheridia appear first in young plants and are followed by the **archegonia,** the term applied to the female reproductive organs in the land plants. Inasmuch as both types of sex organs are from dorsal derivatives of the apical cells (Fig. 15-5), the earlier-formed antheridia are posterior in the furrow to the later-formed archegonia in bisexual species. Plants like *Ricciocarpus,* in which the male sex organs develop before the female, are

[5] Some students of phylogeny, who postulate an algal ancestry for the land plants, have been impressed by an apparent similarity between the sex organs of the latter and the plurilocular gametangia of Phaeophycophyta. The current view that the Phaeophycophyta and Chlorophycophyta are parallel, rather than closely related, groups offers scant encouragement to such speculations.

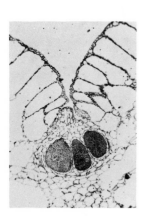

FIG. 15-6. *Ricciocarpus natans.* Transection of plant with almost-mature antheridia. X 60.

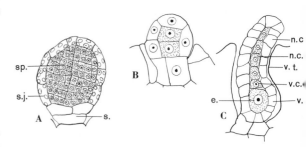

FIG. 15-7. *Ricciocarpus natans.* Sex organs in median longitudinal section. A. Immature antheridium. B, C. Stages in development of archegonium; e., egg; n.c., neck cell; n.c.c., neck canal cell; s., stalk; s.j., sterile jacket; sp., spermatogenous tissue; v., venter; v.c.c., ventral canal cell; v.t., ventral tissue of plant body. X 546.

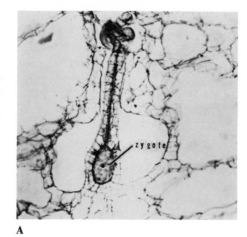
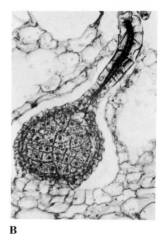

FIG. 15-8. *Ricciocarpus natans.* A. Median longitudinal section of archegonium with zygote; note opened apex of archegonium. X 200. B. Archegonium containing young sporophyte at about the stage shown in 15-9B. X 250.

zygote

A   B

stalk and a single layer of surface cells, the **sterile jacket,** which encases the small, cubical **spermatogenous cells** in which the sperms are organized. The archegonium (Figs. 15-7B,C, 15-8) is flasklike, consisting of an axial row of cells, including the **egg, ventral canal cell,** and **neck canal cells,** surrounded by a jacket of six rows of sterile cells that form the slender **neck** and **venter,**[6] the latter, the enlarged basal portion of the archegonium. As the latter matures, the neck canal cells and ventral canal cell disintegrate and are extruded as slime, thus leaving a moist canal through which the sperm swims to the egg, probably through chemotactic attraction (Fig. 15-8A).

Because of the marked protandry, it is possible that sperms from other plants often fertilize the later-maturing archegonia, a process of cross-fertilization. Sexual reproduction in *Ricciocarpus* and all land plants is oogamous.

Reproduction: the sporophyte

Shortly after its formation, the zygote of *Ricciocarpus* (Fig. 15-8A) undergoes a series of nuclear and cell divisions which produce a

[6] The ventral canal cell and neck canal cells are considered by some to represent vestigial female gametes which have become sterile, a view which is fraught with mechanical difficulties, unless one postulates that at the time they were still functional all the female gametes were shed into the water; otherwise, only the most distal (represented by the first neck canal cell near the neck orifice) could have been reached by a sperm.

spherical mass of tissue within the venter of the archegonium (Figs. 15-8B, 15-9). As in such algae as *Cladophora, Ulva, Ectocarpus, Laminaria, Griffithsia,* and *Polysiphonia,* the divisions of the zygote nucleus are mitotic, rather than meiotic, so that diploid tissue is formed. The venter of the archegonium becomes two-layered by **periclinal** (Gr. *peri,* around + Gr. *klino,* bend) divisions which occur immediately after fertilization (Fig. 15-9A); and by continuous **anticlinal** (Gr. *anti,* against + Gr. *klino*) divisions, the archegonial venter keeps pace with the growth of the diploid tissues within it (Figs. 15-9B). A differentiation of the latter occurs during development as a result of periclinal divisions in the outermost layer of cells, which

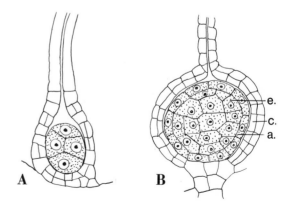

A   B

e.
c.
a.

FIG. 15-9. *Ricciocarpus natans.* Development of the sporophyte. A. Four-celled stage. B. Later stage; a., amphithecium; c., calyptra; e., endothecium. X 250.

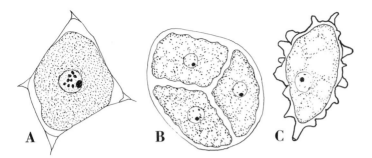

FIG. 15-10. *Ricciocarpus natans.* Sporogenesis. A. Sporocyte in prophase of meiosis. B. Spore tetrad. C. Section of mature spore. X 500.

segregate a peripheral layer, the **amphithecium** (Gr. *amphi,* around + Gr. *theke,* case), from the central mass of tissue, the **endothecium** (Gr. *endon,* within + Gr. *theke*) (Fig. 15-9B). When the endothecium has increased to about 400 cells, enlargement of the endothecial cells of the diploid tissue occurs, and the cells separate and become suspended in the liquid within the amphithecial wall. Traces of a green pigment, presumably chlorophyll, in the form of dispersed or aggregated droplets appear in both the amphithecial and endothecial cells during their development.

The endothecial cells now undergo two successive divisions during which the chromosome number of the diploid tissue ($2n = 8$) is reduced ($n = 4$) (Fig. 15-10). Each of the cells now contains four haploid nuclei, tetrahedrally arranged. Cytokinesis follows, and the original floating cells are transformed into groups of four coherent haploid cells, i.e., into spore tetrads (Figs. 15-10B, 15-11A). Each member of the tetrad later becomes invested with a thick, black wall (Fig. 15-10C).

The inner layer of the archegonial venter disintegrates at about this stage, with the result that the spore tetrads are surrounded by the diploid amphithecium and the outermost layer of the archegonial venter; these usually cohere. The augmented archegonium which surrounds the developing diploid tissue in *Ricciocarpus* and in many land plants is known as the **calyptra** (Gr. *kalyptra,* veil).

Meiosis in *Ricciocarpus* and in all land plants is sporic rather than zygotic or gametic. The cells which undergo meiosis and form spore tetrads are usually called **spore mother cells** or **sporocytes** in the land plants. The four products of meiosis and cell division of each sporocyte become the spores.

The spherical mass of diploid tissue within the enlarged archegonial venter is called the **sporophyte.** One unfamiliar with life cycles in the algae, on the one hand, and with those in the vascular land plants, on the other, would be at a loss to understand this designation, literally "spore plant," because the slightly chlorophyllous, spherical mass of tissue scarcely would pass muster as a "plant." However, comparison of its attributes with those of the free-living sporophytes of certain algae and of vascular plants provides evidence that it possesses the attributes of diploidy and spore production generally associated with free-living sporophytes. Furthermore, it is similar in origin and in ultimate function, so

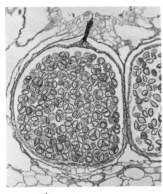

A

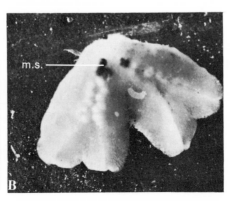

FIG. 15-11. *Ricciocarpus natans.* Sporophytes. A. Median section of a sporophyte with spore tetrads; note archegonial neck above; remains of amphithecium and calyptra united. X 60. B. Plant with sporophytes; m.s., mature sporophyte. X 2.

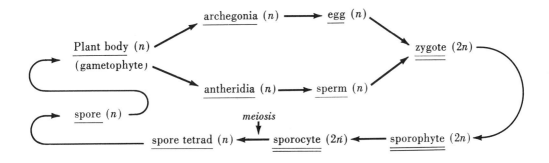

archegonia (n) → egg (n)

Plant body (n)
(gametophyte)

antheridia (n) → sperm (n)

zygote $(2n)$

spore (n)

meiosis

spore tetrad (n) ← sporocyte $(2n)$ ← sporophyte $(2n)$

that on grounds of **homology** (Gr. *homo,* same + Gr. *lego,* speak), application of the designation "sporophyte" seems to be justified.

No special mechanism for dissemination of the spores is present in *Ricciocarpus* and *Riccia.* The older, posterior sporophytes mature first (Fig. 15-11B), as evidenced by their blacker color, which results from the thickening deposited on the spore walls. As the thallus grows apically and decays in the older portions, the spores are liberated.

The germination of the spores (Fig. 15-12) of *Ricciocarpus* occurs in the southern United States late in the summer or in autumn on damp soil on the margins of ponds as the water level recedes. The young plants remain terrestrial until they become submerged by the rise in the water level which accompanies autumn and winter rains and spring thaws.

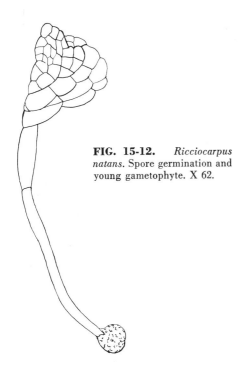

FIG. 15-12. *Ricciocarpus natans.* Spore germination and young gametophyte. X 62.

The germinating spores give rise to plants like the original gametophytes. When submerged by the rising water level, the apices, which are not anchored by rhizoids, become detached and float to the surface where they initiate large colonies of floating plants which multiply early in the spring by fragmentation. A typical hepatophytan life cycle may be summarized as above.[7]

FAMILY 2. MARCHANTIACEAE

Marchantia

Habitat and vegetative morphology

The manifestations of internal differentiation and specialization already noted in *Riccia* and *Ricciocarpus* are still more pronounced in *Marchantia* (after *N. Marchant,* a French botanist), a genus semiaquatic or terrestrial in habitat. *Marchantia polymorpha* L. (Fig. 15-13), perhaps the most widespread species, often grows on moist soil on which the vegetation has been burned; *M. paleacea* Bertol. grows on moist limestone rocks, and *M.*

---

[7] Note that haploid phases are underlined once, diploid phases twice.

FIG. 15-13. *Marchantia polymorpha.* Note gemma cups. X 0.33. (*Courtesy of Dr. F. R. Trainor.*)

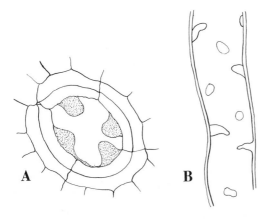

FIG. 15-14. A. *Marchantia domingensis.* Lobe of plant enlarged; note pores and gemma cup. X 7. B. *Marchantia polymorpha.* Ventral surface of plant showing scales. X 5.

domingensis Lehm. and Lindenb. (Fig. 15-14) lives on moist clay banks as well as upon calcareous rocks. The last two species are southern in distribution in the United States, while *M. polymorpha* is more northern.

The plant body of *Marchantia polymorpha* is larger than that of *Ricciocarpus* and *Riccia;* under favorable conditions of moisture and nutrition, it may exceed 4 inches in length. It also is dichotomously lobed and branched, exhibiting the apical growth and posterior decay common to most Hepatophyta. The upper surface of the plant is conspicuously divided into polygonal air chambers, each with a central pore (Figs. 15-13 to 15-16). Numerous rhizoids emerge from the ventral surface of the thallus; both smooth-walled and tuberculate ("pegged") rhizoids are produced (Fig. 15-15B). The smooth-walled rhizoids penetrate the soil, while the pegged type run along the plant undersurface like wicks. The ventral scales of *M. polymorpha* (Fig. 15-14B) are arranged in six or eight rows. The tuberculate rhizoids originate from the portions of the ventral surface under the scales or near them. The smooth-walled rhizoids develop near the mid-portion of the ventral surface. Bundles of tuberculate rhizoids from below the scales converge toward the midrib. It has been shown that the scales and bundles of rhizoids are involved in the rapid conduction of water by capillarity over the ventral surface.

It is apparent from sections (Figs. 15-16, 15-17) that the upper portion of the plant is composed of a single layer of air chambers, and that the remainder is made up of densely arranged parenchymatous cells which contain few chloroplasts and probably serve as storage cells. The cells forming the walls and floor of the air chamber, on the other hand, are filled with chloroplasts. Although the photosynthetic

FIG. 15-15. *Marchantia polymorpha.* A. Surface view of pore. X 410. B. Segment of tuberculate ("pegged") rhizoid in median longitudinal section. X 770.

A

B

FIG. 15-19. *Marchantia polymorpha.* Sexual branches. A. Plants with antheridiophores.
B. Plants with archegoniophores. X 1.3. (*Courtesy of Dr. A. R. Grove.*)

FIG. 15-20. *Marchantia polymorpha.* A. Transection of stalk of archegoniophore; note dorsiventrality. X 125. B. Median longisection of antheridiophore before elongation of its stalk; note younger antheridia at the margins. X 60. C. Hemi-longisection of antheridiophore; note air chambers above storage tissues and ventral scales. X 100. (A. *Courtesy of Dr. Madeline Wang Wu;* C. *From a Kny chart.*)

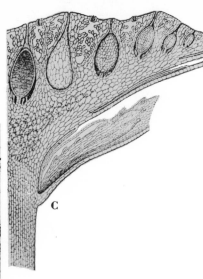

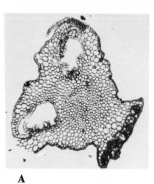

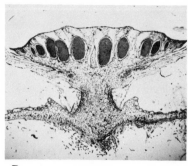

A

B

C

(Fig. 15-21). Here again, there are six rows of neck cells. The rows of archegonia, with the last-formed in each group nearest the stalk of the archegoniophore, are separated by fringed involucral membranes. The antheridia and archegonia of *Marchantia* are quite similar to those of *Riccia* and *Ricciocarpus* but somewhat larger.

Fertilization of the first-formed archegonia occurs before the elongation of the archegoni-

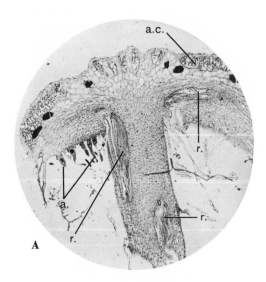

a.c.

r.

a.

r.

A

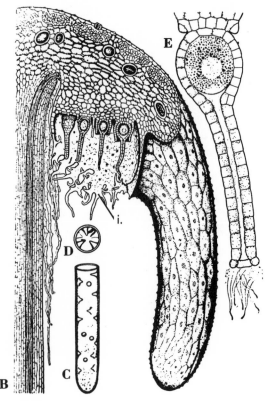

E

i.

D

C

B

FIG. 15-21. *Marchantia polymorpha.* A. Median longisection of an archegoniophore. X 30. B. Hemi-longisection, diagrammatic. X 100. C, D. Longi- and transections of tuberculate rhizoid. X 350. E. Median longisection of archegonium at fertilization. X 1000; a., archegonia; a.c., air chamber; i., involucre; r., rhizoids. (B–E. *From a Kny chart.*)

MORPHOLOGY OF PLANTS

ophore stalk, and because of the differing degrees of maturity of the antheridia in a single antheridiophore, discharge of the sperms, effected by flooding, probably continues over a considerable period. Fertilization of the later-formed archegonia probably takes place after their elevation above the plant body. This indicates either that the sperms remain viable for long periods or that they reach the archegonia through splashing or by swimming through the surface films of water on the surface of and in the canals of the stalks of archegoniophores. Raindrops falling on antheridiophores have been observed to splash the sperms for distances up to 60 cm. That the elongation of the archegoniophore stalk is not dependent upon fertilization is evidenced by its occurrence even in segregated female plants in which fertilization has not taken place.

Reproduction: the sporophyte

Although the eggs of many archegonia on an archegoniophore may be fertilized, not all of the zygotes develop into mature sporophytes, possibly because of crowding and insufficient nutrients. The more mature sporophytes usually occur near the periphery of each radiating group, corresponding in position to that of the first mature archegonia. Successive transverse and longitudinal divisions of the zygote result in the formation of a spherical mass of diploid tissue enclosed in the venter (Fig. 15-22A) as in *Ricciocarpus* and *Riccia*. The latter undergoes cell divisions, increases in size, and remains as a covering layer, the calyptra, as in *Ricciocarpus*. During these stages, a collarlike layer, the **pseudoperianth,** grows down from the receptacle enclosing each archegonium (Fig. 15-22A).

Further development of the sporophyte results in differentiation and specialization not present in the sporophyte of *Ricciocarpus* and *Riccia*. Certain cells of the young spherical sporophyte now grow through the base of the venter into the compact storage tissue of the archegoniophore, forming an anchoring and absorptive organ, the **foot.** Enlargement of the opposite pole also occurs, so the sporophyte is differentiated ultimately into three regions (Fig. 15-22B): an enlarged **foot;** an intermediate short cylindrical region, the **seta** or stalk; and a fertile region, the **capsule** or sporangium. In the capsule the differentiation of the tissues into amphithecium and endothecium, observed in *Ricciocarpus*, also takes place (Fig. 15-22C). At first, all the cells in the endothecial portion of the capsule are similar, but differentiation into rows of spherical cells and elongate cells follows (Figs. 15-23A, 15-24A). The rows of spherical cells function as sporocytes (Figs. 15-23A, 15-24A,B), and, as in *Ricciocarpus*, undergo two successive nuclear and cell divisions during

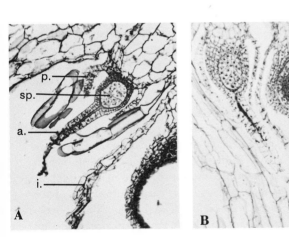
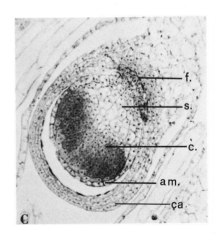

FIG. 15-22. *Marchantia polymorpha.* A, B, C. Stages in the development of the sporophyte; a., archegonium; am., amphithecium; c., capsule region; ca., calyptra; f., foot; i., involucre; p., pseudoperianth; s., seta region; sp., sporophyte. A, B. X 125. C. X 175.

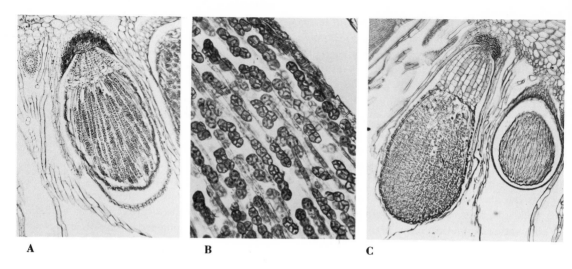

A   B   C

FIG. 15-23. *Marchantia polymorpha*. Late stages in sporophyte ontogeny in median longi-section. A. At the spore-tetrad stage; note alternating strips of tetrads and elaters, enlarged at B. C. Maturing sporophyte; note foot, elongating seta, and capsule with mature spores and elaters. A, C. X 30. B. X 400.

which meiosis is accomplished (Fig. 15-23B). The individual spores thicken their walls (Fig. 15-24C), and the tetrad finally dissociates (Fig. 15-24C). The remaining cells of the endothecium, which have elongated, secrete spirally arranged thickenings on the inner surfaces of their walls, after which their protoplasts disintegrate (Figs. 15-23C, 15-24C). These pointed, elongated cells are called **elaters** (Gr. *elater*, driver) and are sensitive at maturity to slight changes in atmospheric moisture. They seem to have a role in effecting gradual, rather than simultaneous, spore dispersal.

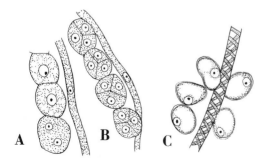

A   B   C

FIG. 15-24. *Marchantia polymorpha*. Sporogenesis and elater development. A. Sporocytes and elater precursor. B. Tetrads with elater precursor. C. Mature spores and elater. X 700.

Examination of sections of living sporophytes during their development reveals that they contain abundant chloroplasts, often with enclosed starch grains, an indication that photosynthesis occurs actively. While there can be little doubt that organic substances as well as water and dissolved salts are absorbed from the parent gametophyte through the foot and transported through the seta into the capsule, it is also quite evident that the sporophyte of *Marchantia* (and that of all Hepatophyta) is photoautotrophic to some degree. When one compares the independent, photoautotrophic sporophytes of such Chlorophycophyta as *Cladophora*, which have no physical connection with the gametophyte, with those of *Ricciocarpus* and *Marchantia*, he may interpret the paucity of chlorophyll and photosynthetic activity in *Ricciocarpus* and their abundance in *Marchantia* in one of two ways: either the paucity is primitive and the presence of the chlorophyll incipient, or these are manifestations of reduction in *Ricciocarpus*. It seems to the writer that in the light of comparison with the carposporophytes of the algae, especially those of the Rhodophycophyta, it is probable that permanent retention of the sporophyte of the Hepatophyta (and Bryophyta) upon the gametophyte has been accompanied by degeneration of green tissue

196

and adoption of a facultative heterotrophic form of nutrition by the sporophyte.

Up to the time sporogenesis has been completed, the sporophytes are surrounded by several protective layers which seem to function in preventing premature drying, namely, the calyptra, the pseudoperianth, and, in addition, the two involucral membranes. When the spores have matured, elongation of the seta pushes the capsule of the sporophyte out through calyptra, pseudoperianth, and the involucres (Fig. 15-25). As elongation ceases, the capsule dehisces into a number of petallike segments from within which the elaters and spores form a protuberant mass. The spores are carried away by air currents; those that

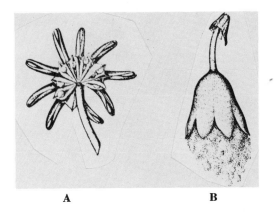

A   **B**

FIG. 15-25. *Marchantia polymorpha.* A. Ventral surface of archegoniophore with maturing sporophytes visible between involucres. X 3. B. Dehiscent sporophyte. X 12. (*From a Kny chart.*)

A

B

FIG. 15-26. *Reboulia hemisphaerica.* A. Habit of growth on limestone cliff. X 0.165. B. Portion of colony enlarged. X 0.5. C. *Lunularia* sp.; note characteristic gemma cups. X 15.

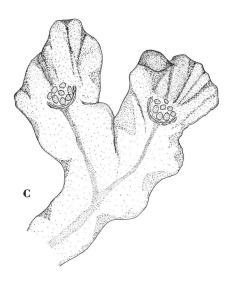

C

FIG. 15-27. *Conocephalum conicum.* X 0.5.

fall on favorable substrata germinate and ultimately form new gametophytes. Two of the spores of each tetrad presumably grow into male and two into female gametophytes. Similarly, the gemmae from potentially male plants and those from potentially female plants always grow into male and female plants, respectively.

Other Marchantiaceae

A number of genera related to *Marchantia* occur commonly in moist habitats in North America. Among them may be mentioned *Reboulia* (Fig. 15-26A,B), *Asterella, Lunularia* (Fig. 15-26C), and *Conocephalum* (Fig. 15-27), the last-named of special interest because cell divisions take place within the spores while they are still enclosed in the capsule. This endosporic germination is similar to the primary germination which occurs in *Selaginella* (p. 294) and other vascular plants.

Reboulia and *Conocephalum* are common on moist, calcareous rocks. *Lunularia* and *Asterella* usually occur on soil.

Order 2. *Sphaerocarpales*

Members of the very small order Sphaerocarpales have the simplest gametophytes which occur among the Hepatophyta. The plant consists of a single sheet of cells except at the midrib region where it may be several cell layers thick. Externally, the plant body is a simple foliose thallus. Two families, the Sphaerocarpaceae and Riellaceae comprise the Sphaerocarpales.

FAMILY 1. SPHAEROCARPACEAE

Sphaerocarpos

Habitat and vegetative morphology

Sphaerocarpos texanus Aust. is widely distributed in the southern United States where it occurs on bare soil in undisturbed fields and on the alluvial deposits of streams. It is a fall-winter-spring annual and disappears as the soil dries. It grows readily on inorganic culture media. Another species, *S. michelii* Bellardi has a similar distribution.

The thalli of *Sphaerocarpos* (Gr. *sphaira,* sphere + Gr. *karpon,* fruit) are bilaterally symmetrical (Figs. 15-28, 15-29), consisting of a midportion several cells thick and monostromatic wings. They are not unlike certain fern gametophytes in gross appearance. Ventral scales and cuticle are absent, and the plants bear only simple, nontuberculate rhizoids. There is no internal differentiation. Growth originates from a transverse row of apical cells. All cells but the rhizoids are rich in chloroplasts.

Plants of *Sphaerocarpos* often become lobed. The lobes are readily detached and being regenerative, grow rapidly into new plants.

Spores of *Sphaerocarpos* present in the soil germinate after the soil becomes thoroughly moist in the autumn, and they rapidly pass through a vegetative phase to sexual maturity.

Reproduction

Sphaerocarpos is strictly unisexual and sexually dimorphic, the male plants being markedly smaller than the female and often purplish. Both the antheridia and archegonia protrude from the dorsal surface and both are surrounded by involucres (Figs. 15-28, 15-29). The archegonial involucre is inflated

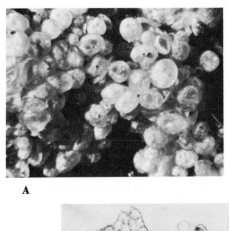

A

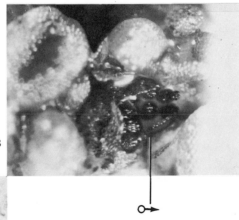

B

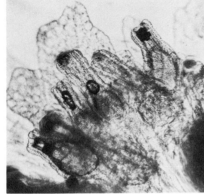

C

FIG. 15-28. *Sphaerocarpos texanus.* A. Female plants. X 5. B. Male plants (arrow). X 10. C. Enlarged view of male plants; note antheridia within flask-shaped involucres. X 60.

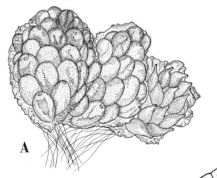

A

FIG. 15-29. A. *Sphaerocarpos texanus.* Two female and one male plant (at the right). X 15. B–E. *Sphaerocarpos* sp. Ontogeny of sex organs. B, C. Archegonia. B. X 485. C. X 325. D, E. Antheridia. X 325. (B–E. *After G. M. Smith.*)

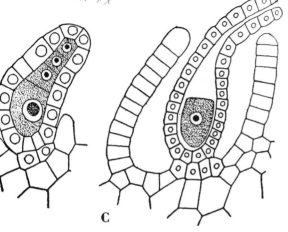

C

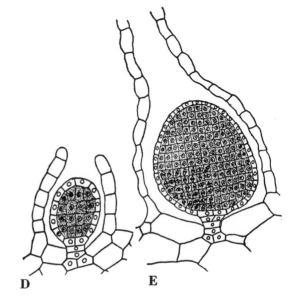

D   E

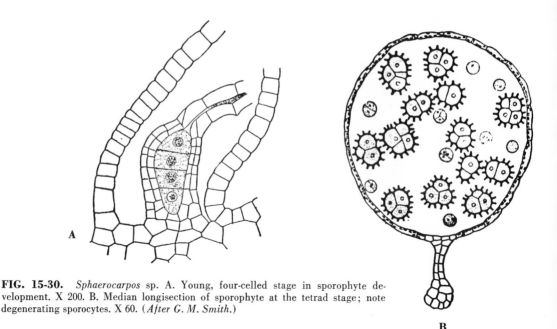

FIG. 15-30. *Sphaerocarpos* sp. A. Young, four-celled stage in sporophyte development. X 200. B. Median longisection of sporophyte at the tetrad stage; note degenerating sporocytes. X 60. (*After G. M. Smith.*)

B

and cylindrical with an apical ostiole (Fig. 15-28A). Surprisingly, the involucre surrounding each antheridium (Fig.-28B,C) is flask-shaped and smaller than the archegonial involucre.

The archegonial necks are composed of six rows of cells as in the Marchantiales. The archegonia (Fig. 15-29B,C) mature and fertilization occurs before their involucres have grown as tall as the archegonia. The antheridia (Fig. 15-29D,E) are almost globose and borne on stalks which are partially embedded in the thallus.

Fertilization stimulates increase in size and inflation of the archegonial involucre but they enlarge whether or not fertilization occurs. The zygote undergoes mitotic nuclear division and cytokineses to form a chain of four cells (Fig. 15-30A). During these divisions the venter becomes two-layered. In each of the four cells of the young sporophyte, two perpendicular vertical divisions occur to make a 16-celled sporophyte. Additional cell divisions in the most basal tier form a small foot, while the next upper tier above a rudimentary seta is formed. The upper two tiers divide rapidly to form a globose capsular region which is early differentiated into an endothecium and single-layered amphithe-

cium, the latter rich in chloroplasts and photosynthetic.

In the endothecium, the cells separate, become spherical, and float in fluid. Some of them function as sporocytes which undergo meiosis, forming tetrads of black, spiny-walled spores. Others, which contain chloroplasts, fail to undergo meiosis but are gradually absorbed, thus contributing to the nutrition of the developing spores. Figure 15-30B shows a median section of an immature sporophyte.

The amphithecium is persistent and indehiscent, and the spores are set free only upon disintegration of the plants.

In *Sphaerocarpos texanus* the spores remain coherent in tetrads. Thus, upon germination, male and female gametophytes are in close proximity, since two spores develop into male and two into female gametophytes.

Sphaerocarpos has been the object of numerous genetic and cytological studies which have revealed that the unisexual gametophytes differ in their chromosome constitution. The nuclei of the female plants contain a special X or female-determining chromosome, and those of the male plants contain a Y or male-determining chromosome. *Sphaerocarpos* was the first *plant* in which sex chromosomes were discovered. Thus, in meiotic divisions during sporogenesis, the descendants of the parental sex chromosomes, brought together at fertilization, are segregated, so that two of the spores of the tetrad are male-producing and two are female-producing. While this type of chromosome mechanism in relation to sex suggests that which is present in such insects as *Drosophila*, the fruit fly, it should be noted that sex in the gametophyte of *Sphaerocarpos* is manifested only after the sex chromosomes have been *segregated*, whereas in the diploid insect body it is expressed only when they become *associated* in the same nuclei.

FAMILY 2. RIELLACEAE

Riella

The single genus *Riella*, with two species, *R. americana* Howe and Underw. and *R. affinis* Howe and Underwood, occurs in the United States (Texas, South Dakota, and California) but is localized in distribution. However, the plants grow luxuriantly in laboratory cultures.

Riella (Fig. 15-31) is a submerged aquatic in which the plant body is asymmetrical and the life cycle is completed under water. The plant is composed of an erect, sparingly branched axis from one side of which an *Ulva*-like wing, one cell thick, emerges. A few simple rhizoids at the base of the axis anchor the plant to the substratum. Delicate ventral (one row) and lateral scales (two rows) occur on the axis and along its junction with the blade. Growth is strictly apical.

Vegetative propagation occurs by gemmae (Fig. 15-32C,D) borne among the scales; the gemmae grow into adult gametophytes.

Riella americana is unisexual, while *R. affinis* is bisexual. The antheridia occur in groups along the margin of the blade (Fig. 15-32A). The archegonia are produced singly at the juncture of the wing and axis. Development, organization, and nutrition of the sporophyte (Fig. 15-32B) parallel those of *Sphaerocarpos*. Here too, the spores are liberated upon disintegration of the thallus.

Order 3. *Jungermanniales*

The order Jungermanniales, the largest among the Hepatophyta (190 genera and 8,000 species), as presently constituted includes both thallose genera and those having branching axes with leaves, as well as some intermediate types. All lack the internal histological complexity of the Marchantiales and differ in other attributes both from them and the Sphaerocarpales.

It is convenient here to distinguish two suborders, (1) the Metzgerineae (Anacrogynae) and (2) the Jungermannineae (Acro-

FIG. 15-31. *Riella affinis.* A. Living plants. X 3. B. Portion of same, enlarged. X 30.

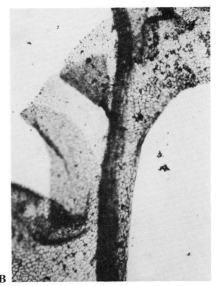

A   B

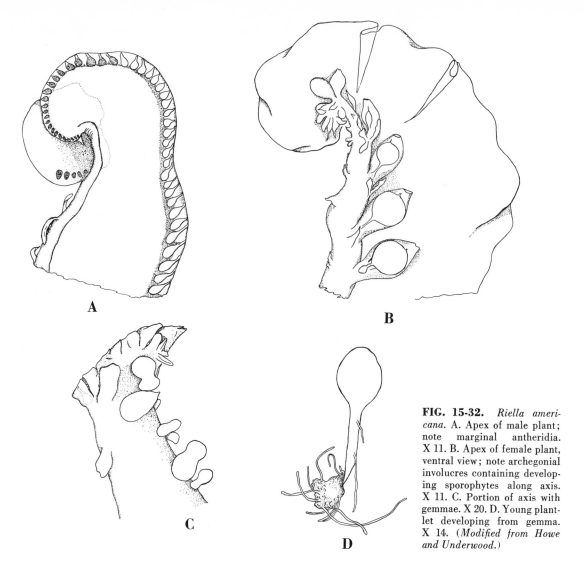

A

B

C

D

FIG. 15-32. *Riella americana*. A. Apex of male plant; note marginal antheridia. X 11. B. Apex of female plant, ventral view; note archegonial involucres containing developing sporophytes along axis. X 11. C. Portion of axis with gemmae. X 20. D. Young plantlet developing from gemma. X 14. (*Modified from Howe and Underwood.*)

gynae). The former includes the thallose and lobed genera which are **anacrogynous.** This term refers to the condition in which the apical cell of a thallus branch does not itself give rise directly to an archegonium, so that the female branches or lobes are of indeterminate growth. To the suborder Jungermannineae belong the leafy genera in which the apical cell itself becomes "used up" in forming an archegonium. This is the **acrogynous** condition.

Suborder 1. *Metzgerineae*

FAMILY 1. METZGERIACEAE

In marked contrast to the progressively more elaborate internal differentiation ob-

servable in the plant bodies of *Riccia, Ricciocarpus,* and *Marchantia,* the thallose genera of the Anacrogynae, as for example, *Pellia* (after *Leopoldi Pelli-Fabroni* a Florentine lawyer) and *Pallavicinia* (after *L. Pallavicini,* Archbishop of Genoa), and *Metzgeria* (after *Johannes Metzger* of Staufen, Germany) exhibit marked internal simplicity. In *Pallavicinia* and *Metzgeria,* for example, the greater portion of the plant body consists of a narrow, several-layered midrib and two wings composed of a single layer of chlorenchymatous cells on each side, quite similar to those of such membranous algae as *Ulva,* the sea lettuce, of the Chlorophycophyta. Because of their wider distribution, availability, and larger size, *Pellia* and *Pallavicinia* will be emphasized in the following account.

Pellia

Habitat and vegetative morphology

Pellia (Fig. 15-33) is encountered frequently on moist sandstone rocks and on stream banks in shady woods where the soil is neutral or acid in reaction. It may be submerged during high water. The irregularly dichotomously branching plant body of *Pellia* is smaller, smoother in appearance, and usually a brighter green than those of *Marchantia polymorpha*. The smooth appearance of the plants is due to the absence of pores and air chambers on their upper surface. Numerous nontuberculate rhizoids arise from the ventral surface of each branch along the thickened central portion. Ventral scales are absent, but mucilage-secreting, glandular hairs occur in the region of the growing points (Fig. 15-33B). The latter has a dome-shaped apical cell at its apex. The margins of the plants may be slightly lobed and ruffled. As in many other Hepatophyta, anterior growth and branching and posterior decay of the plant body result in vegetative multiplication by fragmentation; gemmae are absent in *Pellia*.

Growth is strictly apical and may be traced to the division of a single, dome-shaped apical cell with a curved base (Fig. 15-33B). This cell undergoes mitoses and cytokineses; and the derived cells, cut off in a direction parallel to the curved basal wall, add to the tissues of the plant body by subsequent divisions. Transverse sections of a branch reveal the absence of any considerable internal differentiation, as compared with *Marchantia*, although the cells near the center may have thickened bands in their walls. There is a gradual diminution in thickness of the branches from the center toward each margin so that the latter are monostromatic. All the cells of the plant body contain chloroplasts. The superficial layers are not noticeably differentiated as epidermal cells.

Reproduction

Pellia epiphylla (L.) Corda, a species widely distributed in the United States, is bisexual and strongly protandrous. However, the antheridia are slow in maturing and still contain viable sperms when the archegonia have matured. In habitats where the plants have overwintered, the old dark thalli produce light-green branches early in the spring. After a period of vegetative development, these attain sexual maturity, some of the dorsal derivatives of the apical cell differentiating as antheridia (Fig. 15-34). These occur scattered on the dorsal surface of the plant in the central portion of each branch. Each globose antheridium is protected by a moundlike layer of cells with a circular pore. Somewhat later in the season the same plants produce archegonia at their apices (Fig. 15-34A,B). The archegonia arise on a mound of tissue formed from derivatives of the apical cell. The entire group, composed of fifteen or more archegonia, is covered by a protuberant involucral flap (Fig. 15-34A,B). The archegonia of

FIG. 15-33. *Pellia epiphylla.* A. Mat of living plants from a cranberry bog, Cape Cod. X 0.5. B. Sagittal section of apex; note homogeneous tissue, apical cell, and the mucilage glands near the latter. X 175.

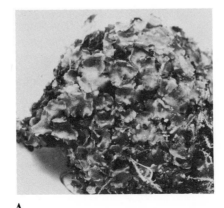

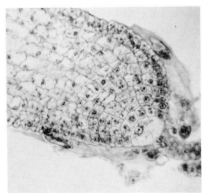

A

B

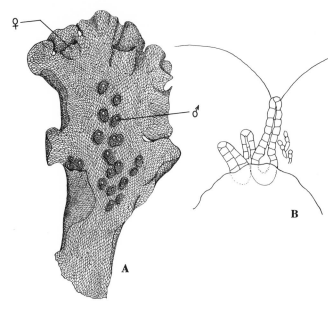

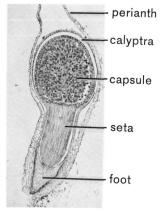

FIG. 15-34. *Pellia epiphylla.* A. Lobe of thallus showing male and female involucres. X 7. B. Apex of lobe, as seen from above, showing archegonia (diagrammatic). X 125.

Pellia differ from those of the Marchantiales and Sphaerocarpales in that they have short stalks and the necks are composed of only five vertical rows of neck cells.

It has been demonstrated that rapid movement of films of capillary water takes place on both surfaces of the *Pellia* plant. There is little doubt that such films of water, as well as heavy rains and dew, accumulate in the space between the antheridial wall and the antheridial chamber and aid in the dehiscence of the antheridia and liberation of the sperms. The latter are among the largest in the Hepato-

phyta and Bryophyta, attaining a length of 70 μ. They are released by rupture of the antheridial wall and emerge in gelatinous spheres from which their movements ultimately liberate them. The close proximity of the thallus branches and of the antheridia and archegonia on a single thallus ensure abundant fertilizations. Although the eggs of several of the archegonia on one receptacle may be fertilized, normally only one develops into a mature sporophyte (Fig. 15-35A). The other eggs and zygotes abort but remain recognizable during the early stages of development of the functional sporophytes.

A transverse division of the zygote initiates the development of the sporophyte which is later differentiated into foot, seta, and capsule regions. Growth of the sporophyte of *P. epiphylla* in the eastern United States progresses as far as the sporocyte stage before midwinter; development is then arrested until the following spring. The dormant sporophytes are covered by the basal portion of the receptacles by their calyptras, and also by the involucral flap (Fig. 15-35B). As in *Marchantia*, the cells of all the regions of the sporophyte contain abundant starch-filled chloroplasts, which indicates active occurrence of photosynthesis during ontogeny. The capsule wall in the immature sporophyte is amphithecial in origin and consists of several layers of cells in contrast to the single-layered amphithecium of the Marchantiales and Sphaerocarpales. The interior of the capsule becomes differentiated into lobed sporocytes and elongate cells, the latter maturing as

A

B

perianth

calyptra

capsule

seta

foot

FIG. 15-35. *Pellia epiphylla.* A. Archegonial complex; the two enlarged archegonia contain sporophytes. X 60. B. Median longisection of sporophyte. X 12.5.

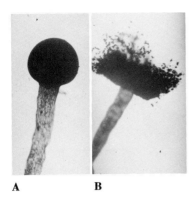

FIG. 15-36. *Pellia epiphylla*. A. Capsule at distal portion of seta. B. The same capsule at dehiscence. X 12.5.

elaters. Some of the latter are oriented with one end, in each case, at the base of the capsule, thus forming an **elaterophore.** Following meiosis in the four-lobed sporocytes, the members of the spore tetrads separate and, as in *Conocephalum*, each spore undergoes a limited number of nuclear and cell divisions within the spore wall, so that by the time of their dissemination the spores have already begun development. As the sporophyte matures, its outermost layer of cells of the capsule becomes thickened and brown, except for four vertical rows of cells which remain thin-walled; the latter foreshadow the lines of dehiscence of the capsule. When the spores are multicellular and the capsule mature, the seta lengthens and raises the capsule above the gametophyte (Fig. 15-36A). Elongation of the seta is very rapid; it may increase in length within 3 or 4 days

from 1 to 80 mm. Setae 110 mm. long are common on plants in shady ravines. The spherical capsule dries when elongation has been completed; it dehisces violently (Fig. 15-36B) when contraction ruptures the four rows of thin-walled cells, and many of the spores are simultaneously disseminated. Others remain in the meshes of the twisted elaters which are attached at the base of the opened capsule. Spores that are carried by air currents and which settle in proper habitats continue their development into new *Pellia* thalli (Fig. 15-37).

Pallavicinia

Habitat and vegetative morphology

Pallavicinia occurs on moist or boggy, nonalkaline soils. The plants are densely overlapping in mats.

Pallavicinia (Fig. 15-38) is similar to *Pellia* in a great many respects. Its elongate, rather sparingly branched, ribbonlike thalli, approximately 4 mm. wide, occur on moist, humusrich soil. The plants can withstand periodic submersion. Branching is largely monopodial in *P. lyellii* (Hook.) S. F. Gray, the only North American species. The branches originate from the ventral side of the thallus near the prominent midrib. Numerous smoothwalled rhizoids develop along the midrib region ·and penetrate the substratum. The plant body is clearly differentiated into midrib and lateral wings; the latter are one cell layer thick and somewhat undulating. Growth of each branch is localized in the region of the prominent apical cell which is slightly sunken

FIG. 15-37. *Pellia epiphylla*. A. Spore germination, 48 hours after spores had been planted on agar. X 400. B. Young plants, 45 days later. X 30.

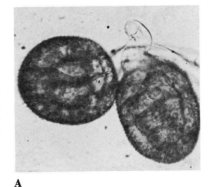

A

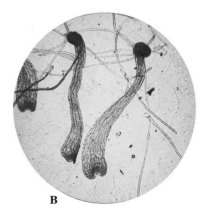

B

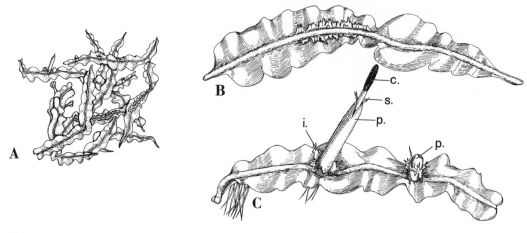

FIG. 15-38. *Pallavicinia lyellii* (Hook.) S. F. Gray. A. Male and female plants in mat. X 1. B. Male plant enlarged. X 3. C. Enlarged view of female plant with emergent sporophyte. X3; c., capsule; i., involucre; p., perianth; s., seta.

in a notch because of the more rapid growth of the wings at that point. The central portion of the midrib (Fig. 15-39) is occupied by a strand of elongate, pitted-walled cells without nuclei or cytoplasm at maturity, which have been shown experimentally to function in the conduction of water. Although these cells are strikingly like tracheids (p. 256) in structure and function, their walls, unlike those of tracheids, are not lignified. However, some of the pits lack closing membranes so that vessellike organization (p. 256) is approached.

The wings of the thallus are composed of photosynthetic parenchyma cells rich in chloroplasts.

Reproduction

Plants of *Pallavicinia lyellii* are unisexual. The male plants are slightly smaller than the female, with which they are usually intermingled in dense colonies (Fig. 15-38A). The antheridia are produced on the dorsal surface of the thallus in linear order on both sides of the midrib (Fig. 15-38B). Each antheridium is short-stalked and is covered during development by a scalelike involucre (Fig. 15-39A). The fringed involucres of several antheridia may become more or less confluent (Fig. 15-38B). The archegonia, which are also produced above the midrib, are borne in groups on receptacles (Fig. 15-39B). As is obvious from the figure, formation of archegonia does not

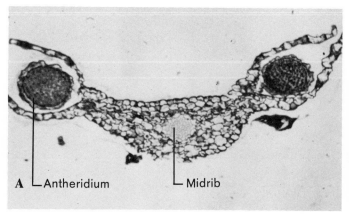

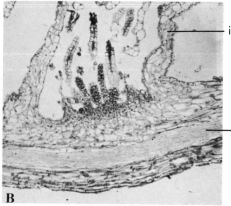

FIG. 15-39. *Pallavicinia lyellii*. A. Transection of male plant. X 20. B. Portion of sagittal section of female plant. X 30; i., involucre; m., midrib.

limit elongation of the branch as it does in *Pellia; Pallavicinia,* therefore, is anacrogynous. The archegonia of a given group, between eighteen and thirty in number, mature at different rates. As in *Pellia,* the archegonia are stalked, with elongate necks composed of five vertical rows of neck cells. Each archegonial group is surrounded by an involucre which becomes fringed (Figs. 15-38C, 15-39B). As the first archegonia mature, a ringlike layer, the **perianth,** appears at their base. Immediately after fertilization, the perianth grows rapidly, forming a prominent cylindrical structure from within the involucre (Fig. 15-38C).

Development of the sporophyte follows much the same pattern as that described for *Pellia,* the first division of the zygote being transverse. Here too, usually only one sporophyte matures on one receptacle (Fig. 15-38C). The calyptra attains a thickness of four or five cells and increases in size with the developing sporophyte (Fig. 15-40A), which is surrounded by three protective sheaths of gametophytic origin, namely, the calyptra, perianth, and involucre. Meiosis of the lobed sporocytes (Fig. 15-41A) reduces the chromosome number from $2n = 16$ to $n = 8$. Following elongation of the seta, the spores (Fig. 15-40B) are shed by the longitudinal divisions of the capsule wall along predetermined dehiscence lines into four segments (Fig. 15-41B) called valves. In most individuals, these valves remain united at the apex so that the capsule opens by four longitudinal slits. The germi-

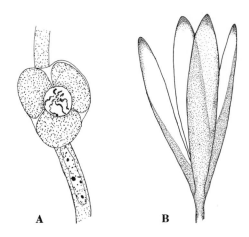

FIG. 15-41. *Pallavicinia lyellii.* A. Lobed sporocyte with elater precursor. X 770. B. Dehiscent capsule. X 25. (B. *Courtesy of Dr. H. W. Bischoff.*)

nating spores grow into a new generation of ribbonlike *Pallavicinia* plants.

Fossombronia

Fossombronia (Fig. 15-42) is a thallose genus in which the various species exhibit degrees of lobing and incision of the wings which suggest an approach to the leafy organization characteristic of the Jungermannineae. It grows readily in laboratory culture and forms sex organs under a 12-hour photoperiod.

Suborder 2. *Jungermannineae*

FAMILY 1. JUNGERMANNIACEAE

The Jungermannineae comprise the so-called "leafy liverworts" in which the plants are dorsiventral, composed of axes with two rows of delicate leaves and often a third row of ventral leaves; or, more rarely, the plants are erect and more or less radially symmetrical. In the Jungermannineae histological simplicity is combined with complex external form. Leafy liverworts are abundant in regions of heavy rainfall and high humidity, where they are ubiquitous on tree bark, fallen logs, soil, stones and, in tropical habitats, on the leaves of vascular plants. A few, like *Frullania,* may be xerophytic. Several, like *Porella pinnata* L., are periodically submerged aquatics. The large group is here typified by the widespread genus *Porella,* of which two species, *P. pinnata*

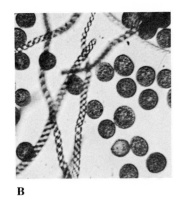

A   B

FIG. 15-40. *Pallavicinia lyellii.* A. Immature living sporophyte within calyptra; note aborted archegonia at base. X 12.5. B. Spores and elaters. X 250.

FIG. 15-42. *Fossombronia.*
A. Plants with sporophytes.
X 8. B. Dehiscent sporophyte.
X 30.

A B

and *P. platyphylloidea* (L.) Lindb., are common.

Porella

Vegetative morphology

Porella (Fig. 15-43) and other leafy liverworts superficially resemble certain mosses. Their leaves are unequally bilobed, folded, and only one cell layer thick. The plant body is composed of rather flattened, branching leafy axes from the undersurfaces of which emerge scattered rhizoids that penetrate the substratum. The relative paucity of rhizoids indicates that they play a minor role in water absorption. In many cases their major role

seems to be anchorage. Inasmuch as the leaves and stems lack a cuticle, absorption in many leafy liverworts occurs directly through the leaf and stem cells which, except at their growing tips, are closely appressed to the moist substratum. Moreover, the dense colonial habit of most genera, coupled with the partial overlapping of their leaves as well as the folded lobing of the leaves in some genera, provides extensive appressed surfaces between which water may be held by capillarity. Furthermore, the plants grow in densely interwoven mats which contribute to their water-holding capacity.

The plants are approximately 3 mm. in

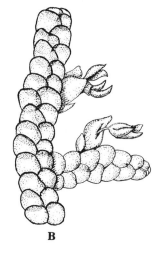

FIG. 15-43. *Porella platyphylloidea* (L.) Lindb. A. Portion of ♀ plant. X 4. B. The same with dehiscent sporophytes. X 5.

A B

width and rather abundantly branched in monopodial fashion. The branch originates from the ventral half of a lateral derivative of the apical cell and replaces the ventral lobe of a leaf at the site of branch origin.

The plant body develops from an apical cell with three cutting faces (two lateral and one ventral), from which derivatives are successively cut off in three directions (Fig. 15-44A). These derivatives, by further orderly cell divisions, contribute to the stem and to the formation of new leaves and underleaves which are arranged in three regular rows along the axes, but only two rows are visible in dorsal aspect (Fig. 15-43). The plants are strongly dorsiventral, and the under row of leaves, called **amphigastria**, is visible only ventrally (Fig. 15-44B,C). When rhizoids are present, they arise from the basal portions of the amphigastria. In ventral aspect, plants of *Porella* seem to possess five rows of leaves (Fig. 15-44B,C), but in reality only three are present. The impression that there are five rows is due to the occurrence of ventral lobes on each of the dorsal leaves; the former are more or less

closely pressed against the dorsal portions of the leaves. The leaves themselves consist of a single layer of rather uniform chlorenchymatous cells. The stems show little internal differentiation. *Porella* and many other leafy Hepatopsida are remarkable in their tolerance of prolonged and periodic drying. The osmotic properties and water relations of the component cells have not been fully investigated, but there is every indication that they must differ from those of other plants which seemingly also lack cuticles but which are unable to withstand desiccation.

Reproduction

Plants of *Porella platyphylloidea* are strictly unisexual, the male plants being slightly narrower than the female, a condition suggestive of *Pallavicinia* and certain macrandrous species of *Oedogonium*. The antheridia are borne singly in the axils of densely overlapping bractlike leaves on projecting conelike branches (Fig. 15-44C). Each globose antheridium, which is attached to the leaf axil by a rather long stalk two cells in width, bears

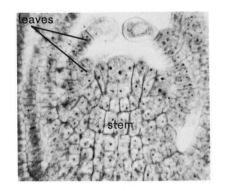

A

B

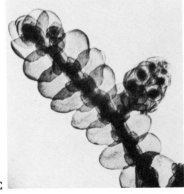

C

FIG. 15-44. *Porella platyphylloidea.* A. Median longisection of the apex; note apical cell. X 250. B. Ventral view of plant near apex. X 12. C. Ventral view of male plant; note two lateral, antheridium-bearing branches. X 4; a., amphigastrium; v.l., ventral lobe.

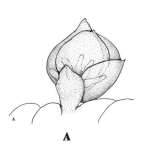

A

FIG. 15-45. *Porella platy-phylloidea.* A. Female lateral branch with archegonia. X 25. B. Living archegonia. X 125.

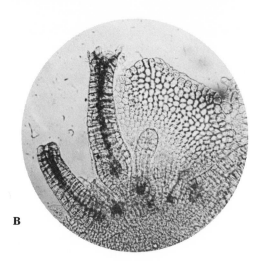

B

numerous sperms. At maturity, if sufficiently moist conditions prevail, the upper jacket cells of the antheridium separate from each other at its apex, curve back, and liberate the sperms. The archegonia are produced on short, lateral branches (Fig. 15-45A) of the female plants. The archegonial branches are scarcely different from young vegetative branches until later in their development and, therefore, are difficult to recognize. Development is acrogynous, so that elongation of archegonial branches is stopped. After fertilization, the development of an inflated perianth surrounding the group of terminal archegonia adds to the prominence of the archegonial branch. Eight to ten archegonia occur in each group. The archegonium is stipitate, with a scarcely swollen venter and five rows of neck cells (Fig. 15–45B).

The abundance of maturing sporophytes, which may be observed in female plants of *Porella* collected early in the spring, indicates that numerous fertilizations have occurred the preceding autumn. Little information is available regarding the mechanism by which the sperms reach maturing archegonia; but the fact that male and female plants often grow intermingled in dense mats, as well as the extensive, continuous capillary spaces that exist between the plants, the substratum, and the overlapping leaf surfaces, suggest that a convenient avenue is available for the dissemination of the motile sperms.

Although the eggs of several archegonia in each branch may be fertilized, only one of the zygotes usually develops into a sporophyte (Fig. 15–46). The others abort but often persist at the base of the calyptra of the

A

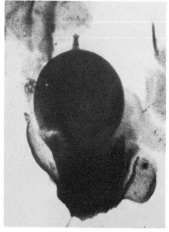

B

FIG. 15-46. *Porella platy-phylloidea.* A. Female plant with immature sporophyte at f. X 7. B. Living sporophyte within calyptra. X 45.

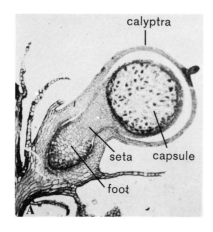

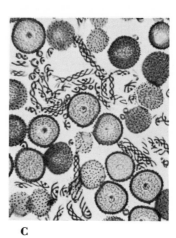

calyptra

seta   capsule

foot

B

C

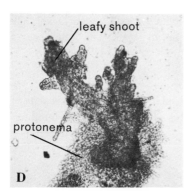

leafy shoot

protonema

D

FIG. 15-47. *Porella platyphylloidea.* A. Median longisection of female lateral branch with sporophyte. X 30. B. Later stage; seta elongation, rupture of calyptra. X 20. C. Spores and elaters. X 300. D. Young leafy shoot on protonema. X 60.

fertile archegonium. The cells of the sporophyte contain abundant chlorophyll during the later stages of their development and are undoubtedly photoautotrophic to some degree. The sporophyte is finally embedded, in part, in the enlarged stem tip and is surrounded by the enlarging calyptra, by the common archegonial envelope, the perianth, which is somewhat trihedral in form, and by the basal female bracts and bracteole of the archegonial branch. The sporophyte is differentiated ultimately into a capsule, a seta, and a rather poorly developed foot (Fig. 15–47). The sporocytes are lobed like those of *Pallavicinia,* and the capsule wall is two to four layers in thickness. After sporogenesis and maturation

FIG. 15-48. *Frullania* sp. A. Ventral view of portion of male plant; note sac-like ventral lobes and antheridial branch. X 60. B. Frontal view of dehiscent capsule; note four valves with attached elaters; v.l., ventral lobe. X 60.

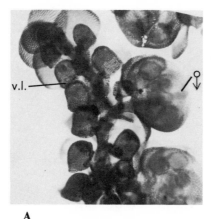

v.l.

A

B

of the spores and elaters (Fig. 15–47C), the seta cells elongate, thrusting the capsule out from its protective envelopes (Fig. 15–47B), and dehiscence of the latter then takes place along four vertical rows of thin-walled cells, the four dehiscence lines.

The rather large spores of *Porella* usually undergo precocious and endogenous divisions before they are shed from the capsule, as in *Pellia* and *Conocephalum*. They develop into an amorphous structure, sometimes called a **protonema,** which gives rise to one or more leafy axes (Fig. 15–47D).

Frullania

In many species of *Frullania*, another genus with complicate-bilobed leaves, the ventral lobes (lobules) form water sacs (Fig. 15-48A). These have been shown to serve as water reservoirs, but their efficiency in storing water is not markedly greater than that of other portions of the plant body. In this genus, tufts of elaters remain attached to each of the

four valves of the dehiscent capsule (Fig. 15-48B).

Order 4. Calobryales

FAMILY 1. CALOBRYACEAE

Calobryum

Calobryum (Gr. *kalos*, beautiful + Gr. *bryo*, moss) is an important morphological type with certain mosslike attributes. *Calobryum mnioides* (Lind.) Stephani (Fig. 15-49), native to Japan, is an erect plant, the branches of which are about 3–5 cm. tall. These develop from a subterranean, branched, rhizomelike axis which lacks rhizoids, as do the aerial stems. The latter bear their leaves in three rows. The leaves of one row may be slightly smaller than those of the other two.

Plants of *Calobryum* are unisexual. The male plants terminate in a rosette of prominent leaves (Fig. 15-49A) surrounding a flattened receptacle on which the stalked, pseudoglobose

FIG. 15-49. *Calobryum mucoides* from Japan. A. Male plant. B. Female plants. C. Female plant with maturing sporophyte. X 5. (*Courtesy of Drs. Zennoske Iwatsuki and A. J. Sharp.*)

antheridia are borne. The apices of the female shoots also end in a rosette of leaves surrounding a flat receptacle on which approximately six to seven archegonia are borne. The archegonial necks are unusual in being very long and twisted like those of mosses, but unlike either mosses or other liverworts, they are composed of four vertical rows of neck cells.

A single sporophyte (Fig. 15–49C) usually develops from the group of archegonia. The capsule is elongate-cylindrical and its wall is a single layer thick except at the apex. Dehiscence by four valves liberates the spores and elaters. There is no perianth as such but the rather thick covering of the sporophyte is a shoot-calyptra (composed of the stem and archegonial venter) with many (often) deformed, unfertilized archegonia over the surface.

The absence of rhizoids, erect shoots with leaves almost equal in size, the pseudoglobose antheridium and unusual archegonia distinguish *Calobryum* from other Hepatophyta.

Order 5. Takakiales

FAMILY 1. TAKAKIACEAE

Takakia

The monotypic genus *Takakia*[8] (in honor of Dr. K. Takaki), although first collected at high altitudes in Japan in 1951, was not described until 1958. The genus has also been found in the offshore islands of British Columbia and in the mountains of Borneo. *Takakia lepidozioides* Hattori and Inoue is an extremely simple plant (Fig. 15-50A) which superficially might be confused with the leafy liverworts (Jungermanniaceae). The plant consists of erect, delicate branching axes, up to 1 cm. tall, which lack rhizoids although an associated fungus is thought to function in absorption. The smaller cylindrical branches have been called **phyllids** (Fig. 15-50B). Archegonia are known but antheridia and sporophytes have not yet been found.

Takakia is currently thought by some to be an extremely primitive plant, perhaps similar to the ancestors of modern Hepatophyta and Bryophyta. It may also be a reduced, aberrant

---

[8] Monotypic genera have only a single species.

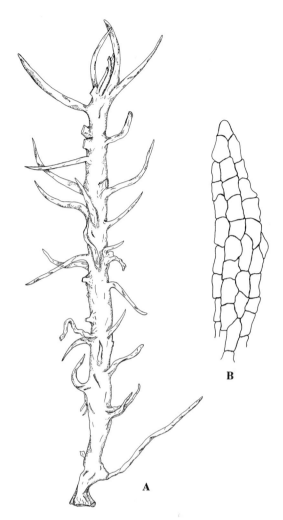

FIG. 15-50. *Takakia lepidozioides.* A. Portion of axis. X 13. B. A single appendage or phyllid. X 300. (*Modified from Hattori and Mizutani.*)

leafy liverwort. Its chromosome number is $n = 4$.

Class 2. Anthocerotopsida

Introduction

The Anthocerotopsida, or hornworts, are given ordinal rank and included in the Hepatopsida by some authorities. However, while in a number of respects suggestive of certain thallose Hepatopsida, the members of the Anthocerotopsida differ in numerous important characters, and their segregation into a separate class appears to be warranted. The features in which they differ from members of the Hepatopsida are both gametophytic and sporophytic. The Anthocerotopsida include five to six genera and approximately 320 species.

Order 1. Anthocerotales

FAMILY 1. ANTHOCEROTACEAE

Anthoceros

Habitat and vegetative morphology

Anthoceros[9] (Gr. *anthos*, flower + Gr. *keras*, horn) (Fig. 15-51) is widely distributed over the world. Some species of *Anthoceros*, like *Sphaerocarpos*, grow as winter annuals in the southern United States, often developing on moist roadside cuts, eroded areas, and in unplowed fields; they occur later in the season northward. The gametophytes appear on the soil in the late autumn, produce sex organs during the winter, and mature their sporophytes during April and May, after which the plants disappear. Other species of *Anthoceros*, *A. laevis* L., for example, are perennial, occurring in permanently moist areas.

In uncrowded conditions in the field, the thallus of *A. carolinianus* Michx. develops an orbicular form. The dark-green plants have a rather dull, greasy appearance and are somewhat fleshy and brittle in texture. In the vege-

_____

[9] The yellow-spored species, on the basis of spore color and other attributes, are sometimes segregated from *Anthoceros* as the genus *Phaeoceros*.

FIG. 15-51. *Anthoceros carolinianus* Michx. Group of plants with sporophytes. X 0.66.

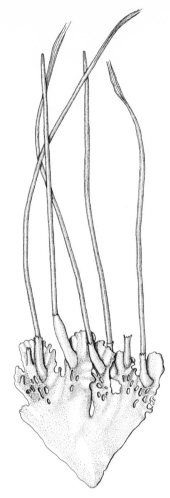

FIG. 15-52. *Anthoceros carolinianus.* Marginal lobes; note (empty) antheridial craters and sporophytes. X 2.

tative condition they suggest such thallose genera as *Pellia* and related forms; however, they can be distinguished readily by features to be described below.

The orbicular shape of the thallus reflects frequently repeated dichotomies during the early phases of growth; somewhat laciniate lobes may project from the margins of the plants (Fig. 15-52). The gametophytes are anchored to the soil by nontuberculate rhizoids which arise from the ventral surface. The lower surfaces of the plants of *A. carolinianus* are interrupted by minute fissures which communicate with chambers which frequently contain colonies of the cyanophycophytan alga *Nostoc* which has been reported to fix free nitrogen. With the exceptions of the ventral chambers, the plants lack internal differentiation (Fig. 15-54B). The component cells are chlorenchymatous and differ from those of the Hepatopsida in containing single massive chloroplasts (Fig. 15-53) in which are embedded a number of proteinaceous segments

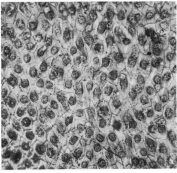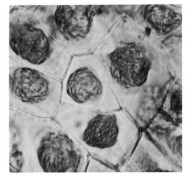

FIG. 15-53. *Anthoceros* sp. A, B. Plant surface at increasingly higher magnification; note the single, massive chloroplast in each cell. A. X 75. B. X 500.

A   **B**

that have been designated pyrenoid bodies because of their position and suggested role in condensing glucose units into starch. Vegetative reproduction occurs by the separation of marginal lobes from the parent thallus and, in some species of *Anthoceros*, by the formation of tuberlike bodies which penetrate the soil and later regenerate new gametophytes.

Reproduction: the gametophyte

Careful studies of laboratory cultures of a number of species of *Anthoceros* have revealed that some have unisexual plants, whereas others (*A. carolinianus*) bear antheridia and archegonia on the same gametophyte. The sex organs arise in rows from dorsal derivatives of the marginal apical cells with two cutting faces from which derivative cells are formed. *Anthoceros carolinianus* is markedly protandrous, so that its antheridia lie back from the apices on each rosette (Fig. 15-52); however, antheridia and archegonia may be borne in alternating zones. Although the sex organs are derived from superficial dorsal cells, they are sunken within the gametophyte at maturity because of their method of development.

The antheridium arises from a superficial cell recently derived from the apical cell. This undergoes periclinal division to form an inner and outer cell. The antheridium arises entirely from the innermost cell which early becomes separated from the outer cell along the common periclinal wall. This space enlarges to form the cavity in which the antheridia lie. The outer cell divides anticlinally and periclinally to form the roof of the chamber as the antheridia enlarge. From one to more than twenty-five antheridia may develop in a single cavity (Fig. 15-54A). Cavities containing mature antheridia are recognizable to the unaided eye as small, orange-yellow pustules. The color results from the transformation of the chloroplasts in the antheridial jacket cells into chromoplasts. When the antheridia are

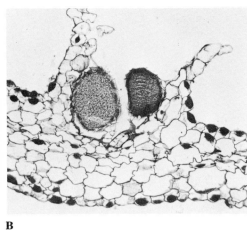

FIG. 15-54. *Anthoceros* sp. A. Antheridia, surface view, living. X 10. B. Transverse section of plant with antheridia; note tissue homogeneity. X 125.

A   **B**

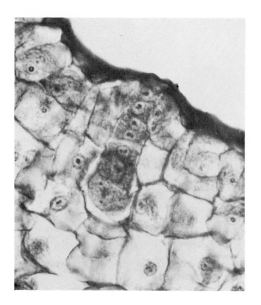

FIG. 15-55. *Anthoceros* sp. Embedded archegonium, immature; in median longisection. X 600.

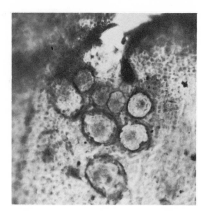

FIG. 15-56. *Anthoceros* sp. Surface view of plant with archegonia; the circles represent transparent, colloidal globules over each archegonium. X 45.

mature, the superficial cells of the antheridial cavity break down, permitting water to come in contact with the antheridia. These dehisce at their apices and liberate large numbers of extremely minute biflagellate sperms.

The archegonia are also completely sunken within the dorsal surface (Figs. 15-55, 15-56). The apex of the archegonial neck is surmounted by four cover cells, and the neck itself is composed of six vertical rows of neck cells. The latter are difficult to recognize, because they are so closely associated with the surrounding cells of the gametophyte, but they are evident in a surface view of the thallus,

after the cover cells have disintegrated. The axial row of cells of the archegonium is composed of the egg, ventral canal cell, and four or five neck canal cells. As the archegonium matures, the tip of its neck becomes covered with a mound of mucilage as the disintegrating ventral canal and neck canal cells are extruded, after the cover cells have separated.

Reproduction: the sporophyte

After fertilization in *Anthoceros*, numerous zygotes scattered over the plant complete their development into sporophytes. The latter are elongate, green, cylindrical, needlelike structures which project from the upper surface of the thallus (Figs. 15-51, 15-52). In its ontogeny, the zygote undergoes a longitudinal division followed by two additional

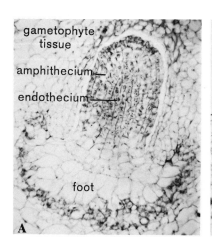

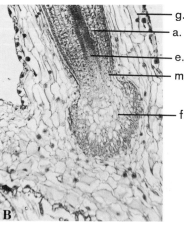

FIG. 15-57. *Anthoceros carolinianus*. A. Median longisection of young sporophyte before emergence from the gametophyte. X 125. B. Median longisection of basal region of an older sporophyte; a., amphithecium; e., endothecium; f., foot; g., gametophyte; m., meristematic zone. X 90.

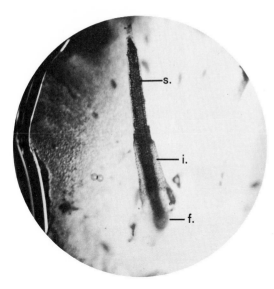

divisions which form eight cells, in two tiers, within the archegonial venter. The lowermost tier of the octant, by further multiplication, gives rise to the sterile bulbous foot of the sporophyte (Fig. 15-57). The upper tier undergoes a series of transverse divisions that form a columnar structure which becomes differentiated, by periclinal divisions, into an outer, amphithecial layer and an inner, endothecial zone. The amphithecial layer, by further periclinal divisions, ultimately becomes about four cells deep (Fig. 15-57).

In *Anthoceros,* very early in the development of the sporophyte, the region that corresponds to the seta of the liverwort sporophyte becomes actively meristematic and functions as an intercalary meristem much like that in *Laminaria,* so that the sporophyte increases in length by growth near its base. As a result, the cylindrical sporophyte emerges from the gametophyte, lifting up or pushing aside a portion of the latter (Fig. 15-58). The elongation of the sporophyte by intercalary growth may continue for several months. Sporogenesis and spore dissemination are continuous and progressive in *Anthoceros,* not simultaneous as they are in the sporophytes of the Hepatopsida.

Considerable histological differentiation is

present in the more mature regions of the sporophyte (Figs. 15-59, 15-60). The entire endothecium remains sterile and is called the **columella** (Fig. 15-59). It is composed of elongate, thin-walled cells which function in conduction. The surface layer of the amphithecium is cutinized; it serves as an epidermis and develops **stomata,** the guard cells of which are thickened along the stomatal aperture (Fig. 15-60C). The wall layers are also photosynthetic and play an important role in the nutrition of the sporophyte. The innermost layers of the amphithecium develop into sporogenous tissue, many cells of which, in older regions of the developing sporophyte, separate, become spherical, and function as sporo-

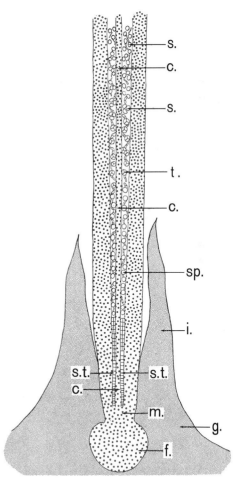

FIG. 15-59. *Anthoceros* sp. Median longisection of sporophyte; diagrammatic; c., columella; f., foot; g., gametophyte; i., involucre; m., meristematic zone; s., spore; sp., sporocyte; s.t., sporogenous tract; t., spore tetrad.

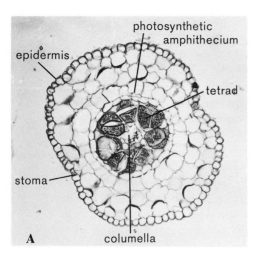

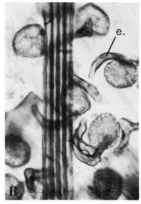

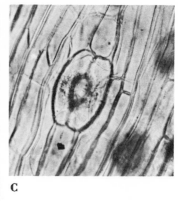

FIG. 15-60. *Anthoceros* sp. A. Transection of sporophyte at tetrad level. X 250. B. Columella, spores and elaters. X 300. C. Epidermis and stoma of sporophyte; e., elater. X 250.

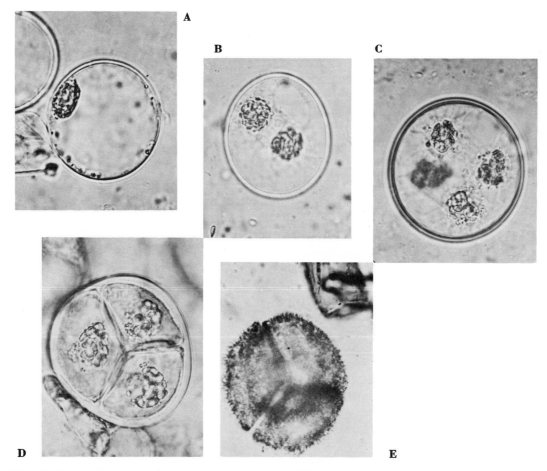

FIG. 15-61. *Anthoceros* sp. Sporogenesis (photomicrographs of living material). A. Young sporocyte with single chloroplast which masks the nucleus. B. End of first division of chloroplast; sporocyte nucleus between plastids. C. Sporocyte with four plastids and central nucleus. D. Spore tetrad within sporocyte. E. More mature spore tetrad; sporocyte wall has disappeared; spore walls have thickened. X 770.

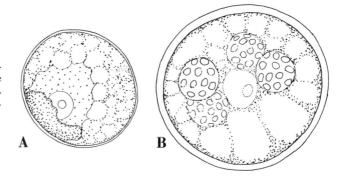

FIG. 15-62. *Anthoceros* sp. Sporocytes. A. With single laminate chloroplast and nucleus. X 770. B. After chloroplast division. X 1000.

cytes (Figs. 15-61, 15-62), each giving rise to a tetrad of spores as a result of the meiotic process. It is worthy of note that one of the earliest accounts of the origins of cells by division, published about 145 years ago, was based on a study of living sporocytes of *Anthoceros*. Certain groups of potentially sporogenous cells remain sterile but divide and elongate slightly (Fig. 15-60B). Because of their multicellular condition and lack of spiral thickening, they are sometimes referred to as **"pseudoelaters."** As the spores near the apical portion of the sporophyte mature, the surrounding tissues lose their chlorophyll and become dry and brown. During ontogeny, the walls of the epidermal cells of the more mature portions of the sporophyte thicken, the common walls between the vertical rows of cells in one or two shallow grooves on the surface of the sporophyte remaining thin-walled. Dehiscence of the sporophyte valves begins near the apex of the sporophyte and extends toward the base as development proceeds. The two or more valves and the pseudoelaters ex-

hibit twisting, hygroscopic movements which have a role in the dissemination of the spores. The valve apices may remain adherent at the apex and twist about each other, or they may separate (Figs. 15-51, 15-52). The columella persists and appears as a dark thread between the open valves.

Stages in spore germination and the development of young gametophytes are illustrated in Fig. 15-63. It has been reported that sex chromosomes are present in certain species of *Anthoceros*.

Fossil Hepatophyta

The fossil record of liverworts, like that of other nonvascular plants, is relatively sparse and fragmentary. A recent summary lists 7 liverworts from the Paleozoic; 14 liverworts from the Mesozoic; and 35 liverworts from the Tertiary (Table 32-1, p. 512). The liverworts and mosses are separate lines as far back as the fossil record is available. Until recently,

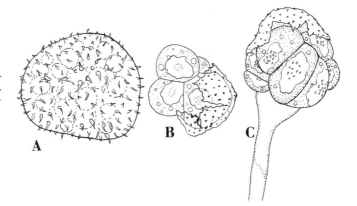

FIG. 15-63. *Anthoceros carolinianus*. A. Mature spore, surface view. X 770. B, C. Stages in spore germination. X 315.

FIG. 15-64. *Hepaticites kidstonii* Walton. A fossil liverwort from the Carboniferous. X 30. (*After Walton.*)

Hepatophyta were not known earlier than the Carboniferous (Table 32-1), (Fig. 15-64). However, a well-authenticated liverwort, *Hepaticites devonicus*, has now been described from the Devonian (Table 32-1) of New York state. A leafy liverwort, *Naiadita*, with axial archegonia, gemma cups, and globose sporophytes, is known from the Upper Triassic (Table 32-1); genera from later strata, such as *Jungermannites* and *Marchantites*, are increasingly like extant liverworts. The fossil liverworts provide evidence that the group is an ancient one and that diversification into marchantialean and jungermannialean types had already occurred by the Carboniferous.

Summary and Classification

In summarizing this account of the representatives of the Hepatophyta discussed in this chapter, attention will be devoted first to the question of their classification, now that the basic facts of their morphology have been presented. As noted in the introductory section, the liverworts and mosses are classified together in a single division, Bryophyta, almost universally. The reasons for placing these groups in separate divisions, Hepatophyta and Bryophyta, as is done in this text, will be

enumerated at the conclusion of the following chapter. A comprehensive survey of the complete classification of these organisms presupposes familiarity with a wider range of genera than has here been described. However, the criteria which are used to delimit the higher categories among the liverworts and hornworts should be sufficiently familiar at this stage to permit some fruitful discussion.

No single scheme of classification of the Hepatophyta has met with univeral approval. Some authorities consider that the liverworts and the hornworts are sufficiently different morphologically to warrant their separation into separate classes (Hepatopsida and Anthocerotopsida) of coordinate rank, as has been done in this text. Others reduce the Anthocerotopsida to ordinal rank and include them in the liverwort class. The following classification includes the representative genera discussed in this chapter:

Division Hepatophyta

    Class 1. Hepatopsida (Liverworts)

        Order 1. Marchantiales

            Family 1. Ricciaceae

                Genera: *Ricciocarpus, Riccia*

            Family 2. Marchantiaceae

                Genera: *Marchantia, Conocephalum, Lunularia*

        Order 2. Sphaerocarpales

            Family 1. Sphaerocarpaceae

                Genus: *Sphaerocarpos*

            Family 2. Riellaceae

                Genus: *Riella*

        Order 3. Jungermanniales

            Suborder 1. Metzgerineae

            Family 1. Metzgeriaceae

                Genera: *Pellia, Pallavicinia, Metzgeria*

            Suborder 2. Jungermannineae

            Family 1. Jungermanniaceae

                Genera: *Porella, Frullania*

        Order 4. Calobryales

            Family 1. Calobryaceae

                Genus: *Calobryum*

        Order 5. Takakiales

            Family 1. Takakiaceae

                Genus: *Takakia*

    Class 2. Anthocerotopsida (Hornworts)

        Order 1. Anthocerotales

            Family 1. Anthocerotaceae

                Genus: *Anthoceros*

In discussing a classification such as this, a question at once arises regarding the criteria that were considered in grouping or segregating the several categories. Whether they be considered in relation to a class or an ordinal rank, the attributes which distinguish the liverworts and horned liverworts are fairly striking and numerous. Among them may be cited such features of the gametophytic phase of *Anthoceros* as its single[10] massive chloroplasts (containing pyrenoid bodies) in each cell and the endogenous development of antheridia and archegonia. As contrasted with those of Hepatopsida, the sporophytes of the Anthocerotopsida, as exemplified by *Anthoceros*, are elongate cylindrical structures with marked internal complexity and long-continued development. The latter is effected by a basal intercalary meristematic zone which adds continuously to the sporophytic tissues. These include a cutinized epidermis with functional stomata, a zone of photosynthetic parenchyma cells, a fertile sporogenous layer, and a central sterile columella composed of elongate cells which function in conduction. Furthermore, unlike those of the Hepatopsida, the sporophytes of *Anthoceros* have a sterile endothecium and are dehiscent into two (or more) valves. These characters, among others, are interpreted as manifestations of fundamental dissimilarity from the members of the Hepatopsida.

Within the class Hepatopsida, the characteristics which distinguish the Marchantiales, Sphaerocarpales, and Jungermanniales are also both gametophytic and sporophytic. The gametophytes of the Marchantiales, unlike those of the Jungermanniales, always have some degree of internal differentiation into photosynthetic and storage regions. A specially differentiated epidermis with air pores may be present (*Marchantia*), as well as ventral scales. Both tuberculate and nontuberculate rhizoids occur in the Marchantiales, while only nontuberculate rhizoids are present in the Sphaerocarpales and Jungermanniales, both of which also lack ventral scales. The Takakiales and Calobryales lack scales and rhizoids and in both of these the gametophyte is erect and radially symmetrical.

[10] Some species have been reported to have two.

The sporophytes of the Marchantiales are either undifferentiated spheres and indehiscent, or, if differentiated into foot, seta, and capsule regions, they are irregularly dehiscent. The capsule wall is but a single cell layer thick.

On the other hand, the gametophytes of the Sphaerocarpales and thallose Jungermanniales show little internal differentiation, their tissues being largely chlorenchymatous. Their archegonia have five rows of neck cells in contrast to the six rows of the Marchantiales. In the Sphaerocarpales and Metzgerineae, the plant bodies are thallose or ribbonlike, with smooth or undulate margins. In the Jungermannineae, the plants are leafy, with leaves in two lateral rows and, frequently, a third, ventral row is present. In the Jungermanniales, spore dissemination is usually preceded by splitting of the capsule into four valves. Furthermore, the capsule wall is always more than one cell layer thick.

The arrangement of classes and orders presented above is based on the view that evolution in the Hepatophyta has been in the direction of increasing complexity in both sporophyte and gametophyte. That such an arrangement is not always feasible is demonstrated by the fact that the Ricciaceae, which have the simplest sporophytes among those in the land plants, are listed before the Sphaerocarpales and Metzgerineae, which have gametophytes simpler than those of the Ricciaceae.

According to some authorities, the history of the sporophyte generation in the Hepatophyta has been one of increasing complexity through sterilization of potentially sporogenous tissue. Thus, according to this view, the foot, seta, capsule, and elaters are interpreted as manifestations of progressive sterilization. This tendency is said to culminate in the sporophyte of *Anthoceros*, which is perhaps the most complex in this division. Other students of the liverworts read the series in quite the opposite direction. According to them, the leafy Jungermanniales represent the primitive stock, from which both the Marchantiales and the Anthocerotopsida have been derived by secondary simplifications known as reductions. As evidence of leafy ancestry, the ventral scales of the Marchantiales and the involucres of the Metzgeriaceae are often cited.

It has also been suggested that the Anthocerotopsida represented reduced forms derived from the vascular cryptogams (Chapters 18–24), possibly the Psilophyta (Chapter 18). This hypothesis is based on comparison of the sporophytes. There is evidence that the columella of the *Anthoceros* sporophyte can conduct solutions; its organization is looked upon as a possible reduction from the psilophytan protostele. The presence of incomplete spiral thickenings of the outer columella cells and innermost sterile amphithecial layer in *Dendroceros crispus*, a member of the Anthocerotopsida, is cited in support of this viewpoint.

As a matter of fact, an increasing number of liverworts with erect, radially symmetrical, leafy axes have been described. In many of these, the leaves of the three rows are similar (isophyllous) as in erect mosses. Most of these genera are known only from the southern hemisphere. These radially symmetrical forms are modifying an early concept of the Hepatophyta as exclusively dorsiventral plants.

The Calobryales and imperfectly known Takakiales differ significantly from other liverworts. Their erect habit of growth and the three rows of leaves of the former suggest the mosses (Chapter 16); the erect habit itself, and the attribute of having but one type of leaf, are considered to represent the primitive condition among leafy liverworts.

In discussing the phylogeny of a group,[11] the most important evidence is frequently found in the fossil record. However, the few fossil representatives of the Hepatophyta which have been discovered do not differ markedly from living genera and they shed little light on the origin or relationship of the extant types. What little fossil evidence there is, both Devonian and Carboniferous, indicates that the Metzgeriaceae, practically in

their present form, are ancient; furthermore, the origin of the liverworts from algal stock, from which they are universally considered to have arisen, is likewise unsupported by evidence other than speculative, although the fossil record is undoubtedly incomplete.

Finally, the Hepatophyta, which are often considered to represent the most primitive land plants, afford an excellent opportunity to examine the relationship between the gametophytic and sporophytic phases of the life cycle of primitive plants. If the ancestors of the Hepatophyta are algalike, the relationship of the sporophyte and gametophyte in the latter is relevant to the discussion of the same phenomenon in the liverworts. It will be recalled that in all the Chlorophycophyta discussed in Chapter 3, the zygote is free or is set free from the parent plant after its formation, so that further development is independent of the gametophyte. In the Rhodophycophyta, which retain zygotes on the parent plant, the subsequent development of the zygote seems to have been modified as a result, especially in regard to nutrition. In the land plants, the retention of the zygote within the archegonium and parent gametophyte is permanent. Although retention and intimate association with the parent gametophyte may have resulted in marked morphological variations in the structure developed from the zygote, its capacity for photoautotrophic nutrition seems to have been deeply rooted, for evidence of its persistence is available in the widespread occurrence of photosynthetic tissues in the sporophyte generation of Hepatophyta and Bryophyta (Chapter 16). It is doubtful, however, whether in any member of these divisions the sporophyte leads an entirely autotrophic existence while enclosed in gametophytic tissues, inasmuch as the foods elaborated by the gametophyte are available to the developing sporophyte through diffusion. But this should appear no more remarkable than the repeatedly demonstrated fact that in all groups of photoautotrophic green plants, individuals can lead a facultatively heterotrophic existence when suitable organic compounds are supplied.

That photosynthesis and other vegetative functions were attributes of the sporophyte

---

[11] For an up-to-date discussion of these and related topics see:

Fulford, Margaret. 1964. "Contemporary Thought in Plant Morphology: Hepaticae and Anthocerotae," *Phytomorphology*, 14: 103:119.

Fulford, Margaret. 1965. "Evolutionary Trends and Convergence in the Hepaticae," *Bryologist*, 68: 1–31.

generation, as it is observed among the algae, seems also to be true of the sporophytic phase of the Hepatophyta, for only in *Ricciocarpus* (and probably also in *Riccia*) are chloroplasts absent from the sporophytic tissues, as far as this can be ascertained with light microscope alone. Instead of interpreting the presence of chlorophyll in the liverwort sporophyte as evidence of its secondary assumption of vegetative functions by sterilization of originally sporogenous tissues, one is equally justified in citing the same phenomenon as a vestigial attribute of the sporophyte of free-living algal ancestors.

This second interpretation supports the **homologous theory** of the origin and nature of the alternating generations, according to which sporophytes are considered to be modified gametophytes and not fundamentally different from them in organization. The alternate hypothesis, that spore production is the primary function of the sporophyte and that vegetative functions were assumed secondarily as a result of the sterilization of potentially sporogenous tissue, is corollary to the **antithetic theory** of alternation of generations. This interprets the two alternating generations as fundamentally different and looks upon the sporophyte as an entirely new phase secondarily interpolated into the life cycle. The bearing of evidence from other groups of plants on these theoretical aspects of the life cycle will be presented again where relevant in later chapters.[12]

---

[12] For a stimulating discussion of the phenomenon of alternation of generations consult: Wahl, H. A. 1965. "Alternation of Generations—Again," *Turtox News*, 43: 206–209; 248–251.

DISCUSSION QUESTIONS

1. With reference to the structure of the gametophytic phase, which genera of the Hepatophyta do you consider most simple? Which most complex? Give the reasons for your answers.

2. With reference to the sporophytic phase, which of the Hepatophyta do you consider most simple? Which most complex? Give the reasons for your answers.

3. What phenomenon among Chlorophycophyta can you cite as similar to gemma formation?

4. To what type of algal life cycle is that of the Hepatophyta most similar? How does it differ?

5. What attributes distinguish sporophytes and gametophytes? Do these alternate phases occur among algae? Explain.

6. Can the terms "haplobiontic" and "diplobiontic" be applied appropriately to the Hepatophyta? Explain.

7. What factors seem to be involved in effecting the distribution of liverworts?

8. Can you suggest a mechanism, and explain its operation, for the occurrence of unisexual plants in *Sphaerocarpos?* In *Marchantia?* How, then, can you explain bisexuality in genera like *Ricciocarpus?*

9. Can you suggest any biological advantages, with respect to survival of the organism, which may accrue from the fact that in Heptophyta meiosis is delayed until sporogenesis?

10. What significance do you attach to the occurrence of chlorophyll in the sporophytes of the Hepatophyta? What is the source of the inorganic salts, carbon dioxide, and oxygen used by the sporophyte?

11. In what respects do rhizoids differ from roots and rhizomes?

12. How do the sex organs of Hepatophyta differ from those of algae? Are there exceptions?

13. According to some morphologists, the sporophytes of Hepatophyta afford evidence that there has occurred a progressive sterilization of potentially sporogenous tissue to form vegetative or somatic tissues. Cite evidence in support of this statement.

14. In the same connection, it has been postulated that *all* vegetative tissue of the sporophyte has arisen by sterilization of sporogenous tissue. What evidence do the algae provide in this connection?

15. Define or explain sporophyte, gametophyte, homology, apical growth, complicate-bilobed, amphigastrium, foot, elater, sporocyte, tetrad, calyptra protandrous, periclinal, anticlinal.

16. In your opinion, to the gametophytes of which of the Hepatopsida is that of *Anthoceros* most similar? How does it differ?

17. On what grounds is one justified in segregating *Anthoceros* from other liverworts?

18. What innovations are present in the sporophyte of *Anthoceros* as compared with those of the Hepatopsida?

19. How could one distinguish a vegetative gametophyte of *Anthoceros* from that of *Pellia?*

20. What is the origin of the elaters of *Anthoceros?*

21. How would you plan an experiment to clarify the role of the endophytic *Nostoc* which occurs in *Anthoceros?*

22. Each young sporocyte of *Anthoceros* contains one chloroplast. Each young spore also contains one. Explain. Why do the cells of the sporophyte not contain two chloroplasts since they are diploid?

23. What significance do you attribute to the occurrence of stomata on the *Anthoceros* sporophyte?

24. Describe an experiment you could design to, ascertain the degree of autotrophism of the *Anthoceros* sporophyte.

25. Describe an experiment which might prove whether or not the columella functions in conduction.

26. How could you prove whether or not the gametophyte of *Anthoceros* is photoautotrophic?

27. Give the classification of the Hepatophyta as presented in this chapter; cite distinguishing attributes and illustrative genera.

REFERENCE WORKS ON HEPATOPHYTA AND BRYOPHYTA[13]

Bower, F. O., *Primitive Land Plants*, Macmillan & Company, Ltd., London, 1935.

Campbell, D. H., *The Structure and Development of Mosses and Ferns*, The Macmillan Company, New York, 1928.

Campbell, D. H., *The Evolution of the Land Plants (Embryophyta)*, Stanford Univ. Press, Stanford, Calif., 1940.

Conard, H. S., *How to Know the Mosses and Liverworts*, Wm. C. Brown Co., Dubuque, Iowa, 1956.

Frye, T. C., and Clark, L., *Hepaticae of North America*, Parts I–V, Univ. of Washington Press, Seattle, Wash., 1937–1947.

Goebel, K., *Organography of Plants, Especially of the Archegoniatae and Spermatophyta*, Part 2, (English ed., transl. I. B. Balfour), Oxford University Press, London, 1905.

Grout, A. J., *Mosses with a Hand-Lens and Microscope*, published by the author, 1903.

Grout, A. J., *Mosses with a Hand-Lens*, published by the author, 1924.

Grout, A. J., *Moss Flora of North America North of Mexico*, vols. 1–3, published by the author, 1928, 1940.

Haupt, A. W., *Plant Morphology*, McGraw-Hill Book Co., Inc., New York, 1953.

Parihar, N. S., *An Introduction to Embryophyta*, vol. I, *Bryophyta*, 4th rev. ed., Central Book Depot, Allahabad, 1961.

Scagel, R. F. *et al.*, *An Evolutionary Survey of the Plant Kingdom*, Wadsworth Publishing Co., Inc., Belmont, Calif., 1965.

Smith, G. M., *Cryptogamic Botany*, vol. II, *Bryophytes and Pteridophytes*, Mc-Graw-Hill Book Co., Inc., New York, 1955.

Verdoorn, F., *Manual of Bryology*, Martinus Nijhoff, The Hague, Netherlands, 1932.

Wardlaw, C. W., *Embryogenesis in Plants*, John Wiley and Sons, Inc., New York, 1955.

Watson, E. V., *The Structure and Life of Bryophytes*, Hutchinson and Co., Ltd., London, 1964.

---

[13] For use with Chapters 15 and 16.

CHAPTER 16

Division Bryophyta

Introduction

As noted at the beginning of the preceding chapter, the division Bryophyta, as conceived by most taxonomists, includes the liverworts, hornworts, and the mosses. In the present text, on the other hand, the liverworts and hornworts have been classified together in a separate division, the Hepatophyta; hence the division Bryophyta, as here constituted, has narrower limits, since it includes only the mosses. Some 600 genera and 14,000 species are included in the Bryophyta. It generally is agreed that there are three basically different morphological types among mosses. This occasions the division of the group into three classes as follows: Class 1. Sphagnopsida, the peat mosses; Class 2. Mnionopsida, the "true" mosses; and Class 3. Andreaeopsida. Because of their rather restricted occurrence and few members, the Andreaeopsida will be treated only briefly in the concluding section of this chapter, although, they are, in some respects intermediate in structure and organization between the other two classes.

Class 1. Sphagnopsida

Order 1. Sphagnales

FAMILY 1. SPHAGNACEAE

Sphagnum

Habitat and vegetative morphology

The class Sphagnopsida includes only a single genus, *Sphagnum* (Gr. *sphagnos*, kind of moss) with many species. The spongy, pale-green mats and mounds of *Sphagnum* (Fig. 16-1) are familiar to all who have frequented the out-of-doors, especially in those regions where the soil is not markedly alkaline. *Sphagnum* typically is an inhabitant of pools, bogs, and swamps and often occurs abundantly around the shores of ponds and lakes. Its rapid growth under such conditions, and its

FIG. 16-1. *Sphagnum* sp. A. Mat of plants *in situ*. X 0.33. B. Plants separated to show branching. X 0.5.

A

B

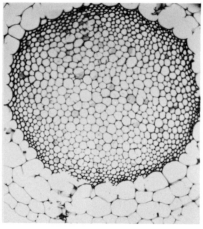

A   **B**

FIG. 16-2. *Sphagnum* sp. A. Median longisection of stem apex; note apical cell and stages in leaf development. X 300. B. Portion of transection of main stem (slightly torn); note central cells surrounded by water-storage cells of cortex. X 130.

great water-holding capacity, frequently combine to "fill in" completely fairly large bodies of water. At one stage in this process, that in which the plants form a dense surface mat over the water below, so-called quaking bogs are formed. In certain parts of the world—Ireland, for example—the plant is gathered, dried, compressed, and used as fuel. Its antiseptic and highly absorptive qualities have been responsible for its use in a number of circumstances. Among these may be cited its use as dressings for wounds, especially during wars, as packing material about the roots of living plants in transit, and as colloidal material for increasing the water-holding capacity of soils, as well as acidifying them; it has also been used as wicks in lamps. Various species of *Sphagnum* have been shown, when tested, to hold as much as 16–26 times as much water as their dry weight.

The individual plants are closely matted together, but careful study reveals that each terminates in a dense series of apical branches. In addition, the stem bears other branches of two kinds. The ascendant branches are more or less horizontal in position and project outward from the main axes; the other branches are pendulous and usually twisted about the axes (Fig. 16-1B). The densely intertwined condition of the individual plants, the wicklike action of their pendulous branches, the overlapping leaves, and finally, the special cellular modifications of the latter all increase the water-holding capacity of the *Sphagnum*

plant. Mature plants lack rhizoids and all absorption takes place through the leaf and stem surfaces.

The development of the individual plant may be traced to a single apical cell at the tip of the stem (Fig. 16-2A). This cell is triangular in transverse section, and three rows of derivative cells are regularly produced. By further cell divisions these give rise to the young leaves and tissues of the stem. The three-ranked origin of the leaves becomes obscured in older parts of the branches.

The stem of the main axes is composed of a central region surrounded by a cortex of hyaline cells; the cortex of the branches also is similar but less extensive (Fig. 16-2B). The cortical cells are primarily water-storage cells. It is doubtful whether the cells of the central strand function efficiently in conduction. Instead, fluids are conducted by the wicklike branches and the numerous capillary surfaces in the densely interwoven plants.

The **leaf primordium** (L. *primordium*, beginning or origin) develops into a mature leaf through the activity of an apical cell, the derivatives of which arise as a result of cell division in two directions. The cells of young leaves are at first uniform in size and shape; but as development proceeds, cell division occurs in such a pattern that the mature leaf is composed of large, barrel-shaped, colorless cells between which there are smaller, photosynthetic cells (Fig. 16-3). The colorless cells are nonliving at maturity, are often thickened

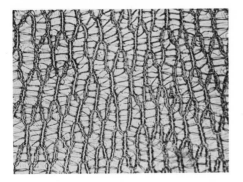

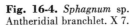

Fig. 16-4. *Sphagnum* sp.
Antheridial branchlet. X 7.

FIG. 16-3. *Sphagnum* sp. Leaf cell dimorphism;
note large, colorless water-storage cells and interspersed photosynthetic cells. X 125.

with annular-spiral[1] markings, and frequently
perforated by circular pores. They store large
quantities of water. The smaller size of the
photosynthetic cells and the abundance of the
colorless water-storage cells account for the
pale-green color of the mature plants.

Reproduction

The leafy *Sphagnum* plant sometimes is
called the **leafy gametophore** (Gr. *gamos*,
marriage + Gr. *phora*, bearer), inasmuch as
it bears the sex organs when mature. Some
species have unisexual and others bisexual
plants. The antheridia occur in short lateral
branches (Fig. 16-4) near the apex of a main
axis and are reddish or light purple. The leaves
of the branch are closely overlapping and suggest the antheridial branches of the leafy

liverworts. Each leaf bears a single antheridium in its axil (Fig. 16-5A). The antheridium
is rather long-stalked, as in *Porella*, but differs from the antheridium of the Hepatopsida in that its development involves the divisions of an apical cell. The sperms of *Sphagnum* are biflagellate.

The archegonia (usually three) (Fig. 16-
5B) are also borne on very short lateral
branches clustered near the apex of the main
axis. The apical cells of these branches, as in
acrogynous liverworts, ultimately give rise to
an archegonium, so that increase in length of
the branch ceases and ontogeny of this (terminal) archegonium involves an apical cell. The
two lateral archegonia do not have apical cells
in their ontogeny. Mature archegonia are massive and stalked. Their necks are elongate and
curved and are composed of five or six rows
of neck cells. The eight or nine neck canal
cells become disorganized as the archegonium
matures.

Fertilization has been infrequently observed
in *Sphagnum* but seems to occur in the late

---

[1] Usually incompletely spiral.

FIG. 16-5. A. *Sphagnum* sp.
Longisection of antheridial
branch; note stalked antheridia
in leaf axils. X 30. B. *Sphagnum
palustre*. Enlarging, terminal
archegonium containing sporophyte (note large foot of the latter) and two infertile archegonia.
X 30.

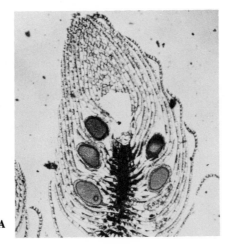

A

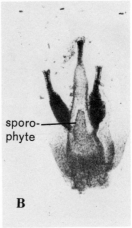

sporo-
phyte

B

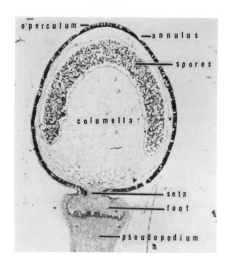

FIG. 16-6. *Sphagnum* sp. Median longisection of sporophyte. X 25.

autumn and winter in the eastern portion of the United States. At Highlands, N.C., for example, at an altitude of 4000 feet, the young sporophytes of *S. palustre* are already in the sporocyte stage early in May, but dehiscence of the capsule and dissemination of the spores do not occur until late June or early July.

A   B

FIG. 16-7. *Sphagnum squarrosum* Pers. Sporophytes. A, B. Before dehiscence. C. After spore dispersal. Note annulus and operculum in B. A. X 3. B, C. X 4.

C

Sphagnum squarrosum Perc. and other species have mature sporophytes in July in northern Michigan. The zygote of only one of the archegonia usually develops into a sporophyte; the other two archegonia may persist for some time in association with the fertile one (Fig. 16-5B). The first division of the zygote is transverse, and further divisions in the same direction result in the formation of a short chain of diploid cells. Approximately the upper half of this chain continues nuclear and cell division to form the capsule region of the sporophyte; an extremely short seta and haustorial foot develop from the lower cells. In the early stages of development, the foot and seta regions of the sporophyte exceed the precursor of the fertile region in size. The cells of the sporophyte contain actively photosynthetic chloroplasts throughout their development. The sporophyte remains covered by the calyptra and leaves of the gametophore until just before spore dissemination. An endothecium and amphithecium are differentiated early in the development of the sporophyte, in its upper portion. The sporogenous tissue arises from the innermost layer of the amphithecium and becomes four layers deep; it occupies a domelike position within the capsule (Fig. 16-6). The central sterile tissue, which arises from the endothecium, is called the columella, as in *Anthoceros*. The sterile cells of the amphithecium are covered by an epidermis in which pairs of apparently nonfunctional guard cells develop. The basal portion of the sporophyte consists of a short seta region and an enlarged foot (Fig. 16-6).

All the potentially sporogenous cells undergo sporogenesis and form tetrads of spores. Meiosis is accomplished during these divisions, so the spores are haploid. No elaters or other sterile cells, such as those observed in many Hepatophyta, occur in the Bryophyta.

As the spores mature, they secrete a brown, sculptured wall, and the sterile tissues within the capsule become dehydrated. Meanwhile, the walls of the cells composing the outer part of the capsule thicken and also become brown. A circular layer of cells, the **annulus** (Fig. 16-7B), near the apex of the capsule, remains thin-walled and is torn when the upper portion of the capsule, the **operculum,** and spores

FIG. 16-8. *Sphagnum palustre.* Protonema with young leafy gametophore. X 12.5.

are explosively shed (Fig. 16-7C). Just before this, the stem of the lateral branch which bears the sporophyte elongates rapidly (Fig. 16-7A), thus raising the entire sporophyte above the gametophore. This elongated stalk is called the **pseudopodium.** Its function is similar to that of the seta of the Hepatophyta and Bryophyta other than *Sphagnum.* The explosive discharge of the spores is audible, and the spores may be ejected for distances as great as 10 cm.

The spores of *Sphagnum* can germinate immediately after being shed from the capsule. If they do so in crowded cultures, they form algalike filaments which ultimately develop flattened, spatulate apices one layer of cells thick. A spore that is well separated from others forms a minute thallose structure, the **protonema** (Gr. *protos*, first + Gr. *neme*, thread) (Fig. 16-8), very early in its development. The posterior marginal cells of this structure produce multicellular rhizoids which anchor it to the substratum. Each protonema ultimately gives rise to a single leafy shoot or gametophore (Fig. 16-8) which develops from one basal, marginal protonematal cell. The first few leaves of the young gametophore lack the cellular dimorphism characteristic of *Sphagnum* leaves; the latter attribute appears gradually, beginning with the fourth or fifth leaf. The multicellular rhizoidal branches of the protonema frequently give rise to secondary protonemata from their apical cells.

Summary

In summarizing the morphology and life cycle of the peat moss, *Sphagnum,* a number of noteworthy features may be emphasized. Although the mature plants (leafy gametophores) lack rhizoids and specialized conducting tissue, they attain a stature which exceeds that of most Hepatophyta and rivals that of the largest mosses which have well-developed rhizoids and supporting and conducting tissues. This probably is effected by their growth in dense mats in boggy soil or water, where the individual plants are able to furnish each other with mutual mechanical support. The numerous adaptations for storage and conduction of water are significant. Among them may be cited the matted growth of the leafy gametophores, the overlapping of the leaves and branches, the presence and wicklike action of the pendulous branches, and the occurrence of special water-storage cells in the leaves and cortex of the stems.

The stalked antheridia suggest those of leafy liverworts; the long-necked stalked archegonia are more massive than those of other Bryophyta. The activity of an apical cell in the formation of the antheridia and one[2] of the archegonia is characteristic of the Bryophyta and absent in the Hepatophyta, except in such acrogynous forms as *Porella.*

The structure and dehiscence of the sporophytic capsule are strikingly different from those of the Hepatophyta. It should be noted that relatively less sporogenous tissue develops in the capsule of *Sphagnum* than in that of the Hepatophyta, and that sporogenesis is simultaneous, unlike that in *Anthoceros.* As in the latter, however, the central region of the capsule is occupied by a sterile columella which involves the entire endothecium, the sporogenous tissue of *Sphagnum* also arising from the innermost layer of the amphithecium.

Class 2. Mnionopsida

Habitat and vegetative morphology

The Mnionopsida, the so-called "true mosses," include approximately 600 genera,

---

[2] In *Sphagnum.*

the largest number among the Bryophyta. In spite of their abundance, they display a remarkable uniformity in structure and life cycle. While a number of representative genera have been selected to illustrate certain aspects of the Mnionopsida, *Funaria* and *Polytrichum* will be emphasized in the following account.

Although *Sphagnum* is relatively limited in distribution, being confined to markedly acidic, aquatic, or boggy habitats, representatives of the Mnionopsida may be collected from xeric, mesic, and hydric environments. The great majority, however, live under moderately moist conditions rather than in extremely wet habitats. *Fissidens, Amblystegium,* and *Fontinalis* are often submerged in small streams. *Mnium* and certain species of *Bryum* are mosses of very moist substrata but are not submerged. *Orthotrichum* and *Grimmia,* on the other hand, are examples of the numerous xerophytic mosses. Terrestrial species grow on various substrata such as rock, tree bark, wood, and on moist soil. Members of the group are often pioneers on freshly exposed, bare soil surfaces, where they rapidly carpet the substratum with their filamentous, branching protonemata. In this connection, they are no doubt of considerable importance in preventing incipient erosion. Most mosses are perennial, forming increasingly dense mats each year on a given substratum. A few are annuals which frequently develop in the fall or winter.

As in the genus *Sphagnum,* the gametophyte generation of the Mnionopsida is represented in the life cycle by two phases, the protonema and the leafy gametophore. In most genera the protonema is a uniseriate, branching filament (Fig. 16-10A), in contrast to the spatulate protonema of *Sphagnum.* This protonema ultimately produces a number of leafy shoots which often are known as leafy gametophores because they produce sex organs at maturity. In a few mosses, like *Buxbaumia* and one species of *Pogonatum,* the protonematal stage is long-lived and persistent; the leafy gametophoric phase in such genera is reduced and consists of as few leaves as one borne on the protonema (*Buxbaumia,* male plants). The zygote develops into a sporophyte borne on the female gametophores (leafy stem). The complexity of the sporophyte in most genera in the Mnionopsida is unparalleled among Hepatophyta and other Bryophyta.

Because of the large number of genera available which furnish suitable material for the study of the moss life cycle, a number of them will be referred to in the following account. Moss spores shed from the capsule of a mature sporophyte germinate promptly if they are carried to a suitable environment. Their germination and subsequent development may be followed readily in laboratory cultures in which the spores have been sown on agar that contains inorganic salts. In *Funaria hygrometrica* (L.) Schreb., the cord moss, each spore is covered with a brown outer wall which ruptures (Fig. 16-9) as a result of the swelling of the spore protoplast and inner spore wall. The spores of many strains of *Funaria* (Lat. *funarius,* pertaining to a cord or rope) will not germinate unless they are illuminated. How-

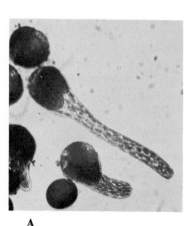

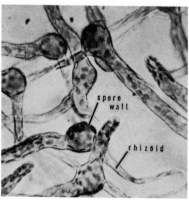

FIG. 16-9. *Funaria hygrometrica.* Spore germination. A. 48 hours after spores were planted. X 80. B. At 96 hours. X 60.

A   B

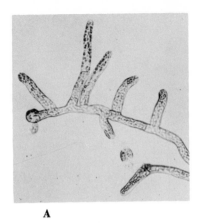

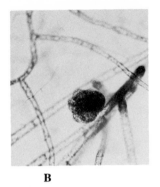

B

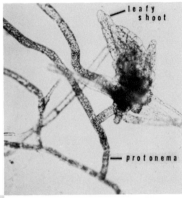

leafy shoot

protonema

C

FIG. 16-10. *Funaria hygro-metrica.* A. Early protonema. X 60. B. Bud which will form leafy shoot. X 60. C. Young leafy shoot. X 60. D. Erect leafy shoot —about 40 days after spores were planted. X 30.

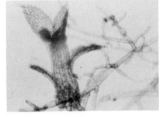

D

ever, they will germinate in darkness if provided with glucose, but under such conditions the protonema is almost colorless. Electron microscopy and cytochemical tests reveal that in germination, even before the spore wall cracks, active metabolic processes are in progress.

At germination, the spore protoplast may protrude at both poles of the spore. The germ tube enlarges rapidly and soon gives rise to a branching filamentous system (Fig. 16-10A) as a result of repeated nuclear and cell division.

Growth of the protonema is apical, that is, localized in the terminal cells of the branching filaments. Its cells are rich in lens-shaped chloroplasts. The protonema may be readily distinguished from terrestrial green algae by the discrete, lenslike plastids, together with the oblique position of the end wall of some of its component cells. The protonema from a single spore of *Funaria hygrometrica* has been shown to cover an area 16 inches in diameter within several months. Some branches of the protonema are superficial, whereas others penetrate the substratum, often developing brown walls. Transitional types between subterranean and surface-growing protonematal branches are common. After a period of growth and vegetative activity, certain cells of the *Funaria* protonema undergo nuclear and cell divisions in which an apical cell is differentiated which gives rise to three series of derivative cells. These apical cells and their derivatives, which may occur on both surface and subterranean branches of the protonema, soon are organized as minute buds (Fig. 16-10B). With the continued activity of the apical cell, each may form a young leafy gametophore (Fig. 16-10C,D, 16-11). In laboratory cultures at 22° C., on inorganic salt-agar media illuminated at 150 foot-candles intensity, gametophore formation is usually initiated within 30 days after spore germination. A protonema arising from a single spore can produce a large number of leafy gametophores rather than one, as in *Sphagnum;* this accounts for the densely colonial growth of young moss plants. The protonematal branches function as absorbing organs for the very young gametophores. As

FIG. 16-11. *Funaria hygrometrica.* A. Group of leafy shoots on protonema. X 20. B. Single older leafy shoot attached to protonema. X 12.5; l., leaf; p., protonema; r., rhizoid.

the latter increase in age and stature, slender rhizoids, which are much like subterranean protonematal branches, arise from the bases of the stems (Fig. 16-11B).

Continued development of the gametophore is effected by the activity of the apical cell with three cutting faces and the derivatives therefrom. In a majority of mosses, the leaves in young plants are arranged in three rows, the result of the order in which the derivatives are cut off from the apical cell of the stem. In older plants, the three-ranked leaf arrangement is usually disturbed. In a few mosses—*Fissidens,* for example—the occurrence of leaves in two ranks is correlated with the presence of an apical cell from which only two rows of derivatives are produced.

Stems of many mosses (Fig. 16-12) are differentiated into three regions: a superficial epidermal layer, a thick cortex, and a central strand. The latter may be composed of both thick-walled and thin-walled cells, as in *Polytrichum* (Gr. *polytrichos,* very hairy). Living cells of many moss stems are actively photosynthetic. In genera like *Pogonatum,* increase in stem length may be very limited, whereas in others, like *Polytrichum,* the stem may attain a length of 6 or more inches.

Development of the leaves in the Mnionopsida may be traced to the activity of an apical cell which gives rise to cells from two of its surfaces. The young leaf is composed of only a single layer of cells, but in most genera the central region becomes thicker, forming a midrib. This is composed of layers of elongate cells, some of which are thickened and function in support. *Funaria* is typical of the mosses in which leaf structure is relatively simple (Fig. 16-13A), but *Polytrichum* and *Atrichum* leaves exhibit considerable com-

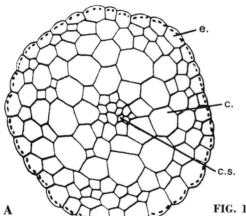

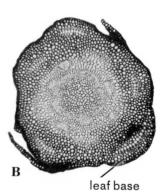

leaf base

FIG. 16-12. A. Transection of stem of *Funaria* sp. X 60. B. Transection of stem of *Polytrichum* sp. X 130; c., cortex; c.s., central strand; e., epidermis. (A. *After Parihar.*)

232

FIG. 16-13. A. Transection of young leaf of *Funaria* sp. X 250. B. Transection of leaf of *Polytrichum*. X 125; m., midrib. (A. *After Parihar*.)

m.

A

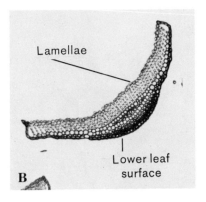

Lamellae

Lower leaf surface

B

plexity (Fig. 16-13B). In these, the many-layered midrib is considerably expanded and sclerotic. From its upper surface arise a number of parallel lamellae of thin-walled photosynthetic cells which are separated from each other by narrow fissures. These are capillary spaces in which water is stored after rains. The photosynthetic cells are protected from desiccation by inrolling of the sclerotic leaf margins.

The mature leafy plants of most Mnionopsida are anchored to the substratum by systems of multicellular rhizoids with oblique terminal walls. As noted above, the rhizoidal system of the young plant is composed largely of protonematal branches. Secondary rhizoids may arise from the superficial cells of the stems and leaf bases. In some genera (*Polytrichum*) they become twisted into ropelike masses. Older rhizoids are usually brown-walled and contain few chloroplasts. It has been demonstrated in many mosses that such environmental stimuli as wounding may evoke the production of protonematal branches from almost any portion of the plant body, including the stem, leaves, and even parts of the sporophyte. The rhizoids may give rise to secondary protonemata and ultimately to young gametophores (see p. 248).

With respect to the water translocation in mosses, experimental evidence indicates there is little internal movement of water through the tissues of the stem, so that the thin-walled cells of the central strand are not efficient conducting cells. On the contrary, available evidence indicates that most water moves over and is absorbed by the external surfaces of moss plants. The prime source of water used

by mosses is rain, which is held with great avidity by the densely matted plants and in small capillary spaces between leaves and stem, and within rolled leaves. Experimental analyses make it doubtful that absorption of water vapor is adequate to keep mosses turgid under mesophytic conditions.

Reproduction: the gametophyte

Vegetative reproduction, that is, propagation of the individual from fragments of leaves, stems, and segments of protonema, is widespread in mosses. The regenerative potentialities of mosses are phenomenal, so that fragments of various organs, including paraphyses and the sterile portions of the sex organs themselves (see p. 248), give rise to protonemata and, ultimately, to leafy gametophores, when conditions are favorable. In addition, some species produce special agents of propagation, **gemmae,** which replicate the gametophytic phase.

The leafy plants of most mosses have been observed to produce sex organs at maturity. These may be borne either at the apex of the main axis, as in *Polytrichum* and *Atrichum*, or terminal on special lateral branches in other genera (species of *Mnium*, for example). The distribution of sex organs varies among the several genera. In *Polytrichum* and *Atrichum*, the gametophores are clearly unisexual, as manifested by the dimorphism of the male and female plants (Fig. 16-14C,D). Plants of *Funaria*, although bisexual, produce antheridia and archegonia in separate branches of the same plant (Fig. 16-14A,B). *Funaria* is protandrous and the male branch at first overshadows the female, which is a lateral branch

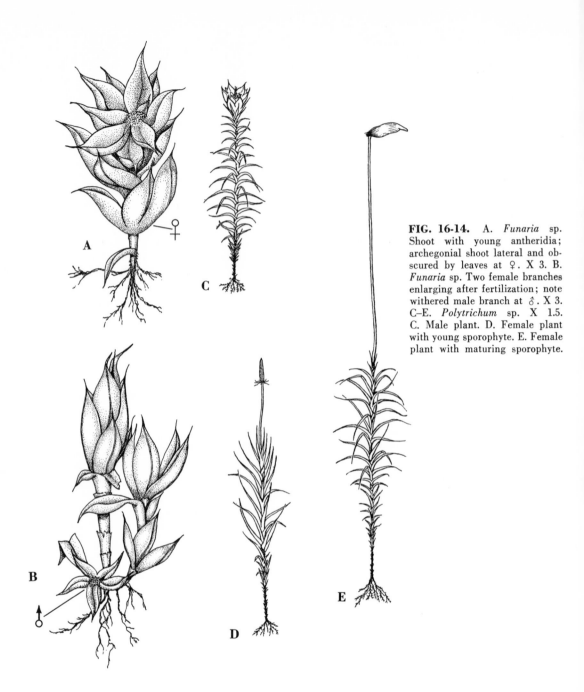

FIG. 16-14. A. *Funaria* sp. Shoot with young antheridia; archegonial shoot lateral and obscured by leaves at ♀. X 3. B. *Funaria* sp. Two female branches enlarging after fertilization; note withered male branch at ♂. X 3. C–E. *Polytrichum* sp. X 1.5. C. Male plant. D. Female plant with young sporophyte. E. Female plant with maturing sporophyte.

of it (Figs. 16-14A,B; 16-15A). In bacteria-free laboratory cultures of *Funaria*, initiation of sex organs in experimental laboratory cultures occurred at temperatures of 10° C. or below, when the cultures were illuminated between 6 and 20 hours daily. It has been reported that *Polytrichum*, on the other hand, while also not strongly affected by photoperiod, forms gametangia best at 21° C.

In certain species of *Mnium*, antheridia and archegonia occur in the same group at the stem apex. Sexual, as distinct from vegetative, apices in mosses may often be recognized by the occurrence of somewhat modified leaves about the sex organs. The apices of male individuals (Figs. 16-14A,C; 16-15) appear to be cuplike because of their closely packed leaves which may be red or purple. Certain identification of branches bearing archegonia is more difficult; it is best made by periodic study of

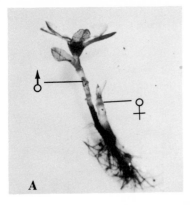

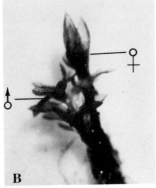

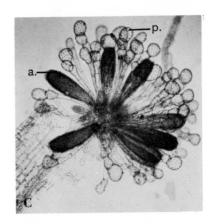

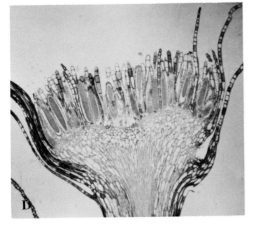

FIG. 16-15. *Funaria hygrometrica*. A. Leafy shoot before fertilization; female branch dwarfed by male. X 6. B. Leafy shoot after fertilization; the female branch growing beyond the male. X 12. C. Complex of living antheridia (a.) and paraphyses (p.). X 60. D. *Mnium* sp. Median longisection of apex of male plant; note antheridia and paraphyses. X 30.

apparently vegetative apices of a given species at a time when some individuals of the same species bear antheridia. Periods when sex organs are present differ in various moss species, in different seasons, and in different latitudes. After they have produced sex organs and sporophytes, new vegetative shoots may proliferate through the old sexual apices, or new branches may arise below the apices that have borne sporophytes.

Development of both the antheridia and archegonia in the Mnionopsida involves the activity of apical cells. Sterile hairlike or bulbous filaments and modified leaves, all called **paraphyses**, occur among the sex organs of the Mnionopsida (Fig. 16-15C,D). It has been suggested that the paraphyses function in preventing drying of the sex organs by increasing the surface on which capillary water may be held. The antheridia (Fig. 16-15C,D) and archegonia (Fig. 16-16) are massive, visible to the unaided eye in many cases, and always considerably larger than those of the Hepatophyta. Both types of sex organs are stalked. The archegonia have extremely long, often twisted, necks composed of six vertical rows of neck cells which enclose a correspondingly long series of neck canal cells. These and the ventral canal cell disintegrate when the archegonium is mature, thus providing an unobstructed passageway to the egg.

In many mosses the chloroplasts of the antheridial jacket cells are transformed into chromoplasts when the antheridia are mature; hence, ripe antheridia may be recognized by their red color. The spermatogenous cells within the jacket layer divide repeatedly, forming a columnar mass of rather minute cubical cells. At the conclusion of these divisions, the protoplast of each minute cell becomes organized as a biflagellate sperm. Mature antheridia undergo dehiscence if they are submerged in water. This is accomplished by the absorption of water by the jacket cells; their increased turgidity causes expansion of the spermatogenous cells in a vertical direction, with the result that one or more specially modified cells of the apex of the antheridium

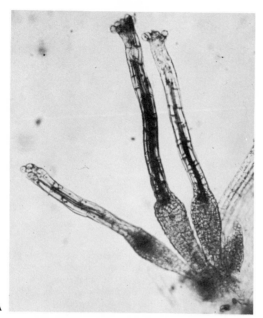

A

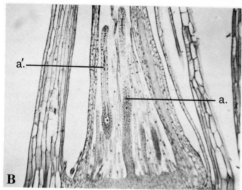

a'.

a.

B

FIG. 16-16. A. *Funaria hygrometrica.* Three mature archegonia just after fertilization. X 120. B. *Mnium* sp. Longisection of apex of female plant showing archegonia (a., a'.) and paraphyses. X 60.

are ruptured. The sperms ooze out slowly from the opened antheridium (Fig. 16-17A) and at first are surrounded by cell walls (Fig. 16-18A). The sperms at the surface of the mass become motile and are shed from the cells which produced them, in a hyaline, vacuolate vesicle of cytoplasm bounded by the plasma membrane (Figs. 16-17B, 16-18B). The flagella, which are attached to the spirally coiled nucleus, project through and are attached partially to the surface of the plasma membrane on which they undergo undulating movements which causes the vesicle to turn in the water. Ultimately, the vesicle disappears

A   B

FIG. 16-17. *Funaria* sp. A. Antheridium shedding sperm. X 60. B. Living sperm. X 800.

and the sperm swims rapidly and freely in the water (Fig. 16-18C).

The way in which sperms reach the archegonial necks of bisexual moss plants can be readily understood. Probably the moisture of a heavy dew filling the capillary spaces between the apical leaves and sex organs is sufficient to effect antheridial dehiscence and suffices for the sperms to swim to the necks of the proximate archegonia. In the case of species in which the colonies of male and female gametophores frequently are separated by considerable distances, it is more difficult to explain the *apparent* frequency of fertilization as evidenced by the production of abundant sporophytes on the female plants. It is well known, however, that splashing raindrops probably account for the distribution of the sperms. In view of the paucity of cytological investigations of mosses, the possibility of **parthenogenetic** (Gr. *parthenos*, virgin + Gr. *genesis*, origin) development of

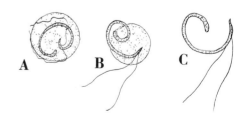

A   B   C

FIG. 16-18. *Funaria hygrometrica.* Final stages in development of motile sperm. A. Sperm with vesicle; note partially free flagella. B. Flagella entirely free. C. Free-swimming sperm. X 1200.

A

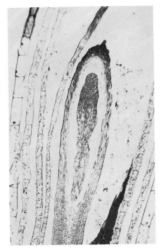

B

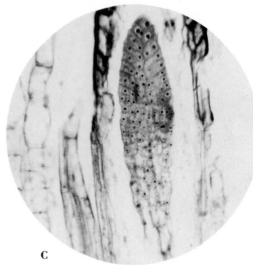

C

FIG. 16-19. *Funaria* sp. Early development of the sporophyte. A. Early, biapical sporophyte. X 600. B. Older embryonic sporophyte within enlarging calyptra. X 125. C. Enlarged view of sporophyte of B; note apical cell above. X 250. (A. *After Campbell*.)

the egg in some cases cannot be excluded, but has not yet been demonstrated.

Reproduction: the sporophyte

The ontogeny of the sporophyte from the zygote has been investigated more thoroughly in *Funaria* than in any other moss, and the following account emphasizes development in that genus. After fertilization, the male branch withers, while the female branch enlarges and overgrows it (Fig. 16-15B). The first division of the zygote is transverse. An apical cell with two cutting faces is differentiated early by divisions in both hemispheres (Fig. 16-19A). Subsequent development of the sporophyte is traceable to the activity of these two apical cells and their derivatives. The apical growth of the sporophyte of the Mnionopsida is a departure from that in the Hepatophyta and from the transient activity of the apical cell in the young sporophyte of *Sphagnum*.

The bi-apical development of the sporophyte of *Funaria* is prolonged and results in the formation of a spindlelike structure, the **embryo,** within the old archegonium (Fig. 16-19B,C). The lower apical cell and its derivatives form the lower portion of the sporophyte, the base of which digests its way through the archegonial pedicel into the stem tissue of the gametophore, functioning as a foot. The upper apical cell and its derivatives

are even more active and develop the major portion of the sporophyte, including most of the seta and the capsule.

Serial transverse sections, beginning at the apex of the cylindrical sporophyte, reveal that the derivatives of the apical cell divide so as to form an endothecium which is at first composed of four quadrately arranged cells surrounded by eight primary amphithecial cells. By continued periclinal and anticlinal divisions the amphithecium and endothecium increase in thickness and circumference.

The cells near the junction of the archegonial venter and its stalk undergo rapid divisions, and form an inflated **calyptra** (Fig. 16-20) so that the young sporophyte is enclosed for a time; but the rapid and inexorable enlargement of the sporophyte soon causes the calyptra to rupture at its base. In this manner, the archegonial neck and upper portion of the calyptra are raised above the leaves of the gametophore. The distal portion of the archegonium, which surmounts the apex of the sporophyte, is also called the calyptra (Figs. 16-20, 16-21, 16-22). In *Polytrichum* (Fig. 16-23), the major portion of the calyptra is composed of thick-walled protonemalike branches which arise from the venter soon after fertilization and expand during development of the sporophyte.

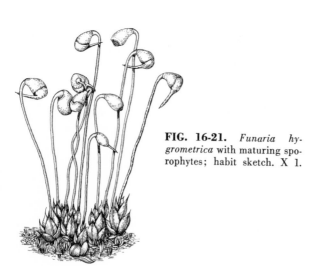

FIG. 16-20. *Funaria* sp. Photographs of successively later phases in sporophyte development. A, B. Early stages; note aborted archegonium in A. X 30. C. Female branch with sporophyte (within calyptra) at apex; note male branch at left. X 3. D. Apex of C, dissected and enlarged. X 8. E. Rupture of inflated calyptra by sporophyte elongation. X 6. F. Similar stage, showing foot. X 8. G, H. Stages in seta elongation; note elevation of calyptra. X 3.

Although the moss sporophyte is chlorophyllous throughout development, there can be little question that elaborated foods as well as water and inorganic salts from the gametophore are transferred to the young sporophyte through the foot.

FIG. 16-21. *Funaria hygrometrica* with maturing sporophytes; habit sketch. X 1.

It has been shown[3] that the pigments of the moss sporophyte are chlorophylls *a* and *b*, *a*- and *β*-carotene, lutein, violaxanthin, and zeaxanthin, and that these coincide with the pigments of the gametophyte. Quantitative studies of the relative rates of photosynthesis and respiration in moss sporophytes and gametophytes and of their chlorophyll *a* and *b* content have recently been made. The ratio of chlorophyll *a* to *b* is approximately 2.5 : 1 in both sporophyte and gametophyte, but the total chlorophyll content of the gametophyte was greater than that of the sporophyte. The ratio of photosynthesis to respiration in the sporophyte did not exceed 1.6 : 1, while in the gametophyte it varied between 2.8–6.3 : 1. It was concluded that the sporophyte was not totally self-sufficient (insofar as photosynthate is involved) but that its nutriment was augmented by the gametophyte.

[3] Rastorfer, J. R. 1962, "Photosynthesis and Respiration in Moss Sporophytes and Gametophytes," *Phyton*, 19:169–177.

A   B

FIG. 16-22. *Funaria hygrometrica.* A. Photograph of living plants with sporophytes. X 0.75. B. Capsules and calyptras. X 4.

The sporophyte of most Mnionopsida exceeds in stature and complexity that of any Hepatophyta or other Bryophyta. In duration of development, it is surpassed only by the sporophyte of *Anthoceros.* The sporophytes of *Funaria* (Figs. 16-21, 16-22) may exceed 2 inches in length, and those of species of *Polytrichum* (Figs. 16-14E, 16-23) may attain a length of 6 inches.

The sporophyte remains a needlelike, cylindrical structure until the distal apical elongation has ceased (Fig. 16-20). At that time the distal portion of the sporophyte becomes much enlarged and differentiated into the **capsule** (Figs. 16-21–16-23). The major portion of the sporophyte below the capsule functions as a **seta;** the short **foot** is embedded in the gametophore. The central cells of the seta are thin-walled and probably function in conduction. As the sporophyte matures, profound changes occur in the capsule region; it becomes a rather complicated, highly differentiated structure, the organization of which is illustrated in Fig. 16-24. In *Funaria* and certain other mosses, the basal portion of the capsule remains sterile, enlarges somewhat, and is actively photosynthetic; this region is known as the **apophysis.** Its epidermis includes guard cells and functional stomata (Fig. 16-24B). The upper portion of the capsule contains both sterile and fertile cells. The latter (Fig. 16-24A,B), ultimately two layers in extent, arise from the outermost layers of

the endothecium and are arranged in the form of a barrel or urn, with the distal portion wider than the proximal. The cells within the region of sporogenous tissue in the central portion of the capsule form a columella which represents the whole endothecium, except the sporogenous tissue. The cells external to the sporogenous tissue remain sterile and form photosynthetic tissue and the capsule wall (Fig. 16-24A,B). Relatively late in development, the sporogenous cells function as sporocytes, each undergoing meiosis to form a tetrad of spores (Fig. 16-25). As in *Sphagnum,*

FIG. 16-23. *Polytrichum* sp. Female plants with maturing sporophytes. X 0.5.

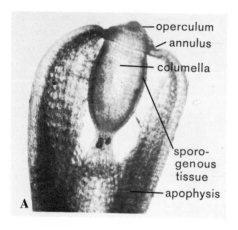

A

operculum
annulus
columella
sporo-
genous
tissue
apophysis

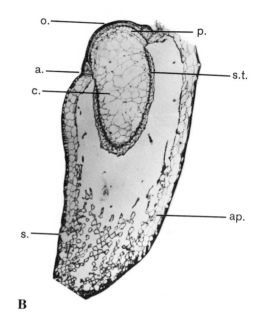

B

o.
p.
a.
c.
s.t.
s.
ap.

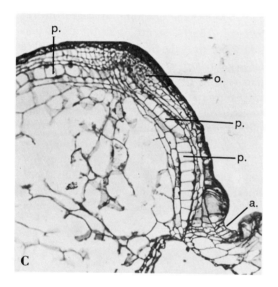

C

p.
o.
p.
p.
a.

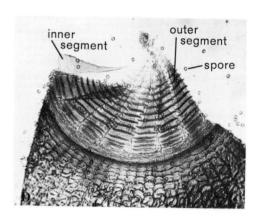

inner segment
outer segment
spore
D

FIG. 16-24. *Funaria* sp. Morphology of the capsule. A. Free-hand dissection of living capsule. X 30. B. Microtome section of immature capsule. X 30. C. Section of capsule apex. X 125. D. Portion of peristome of mature capsule of *F. hygrometrica.* X 125; a., annulus; ap., apophysis; c., columella; o., operculum; p., peristome; s., stoma; s.t., sporogenous tissue.

elaters are absent in the Mnionopsida. The apical portion of the capsule is entirely sterile and undergoes considerable differentiation. The outer layers thicken and are shed ultimately as a caplike **operculum** which is loosened as the thin-walled cells below the rimlike **annulus** at its base dry.

In *Funaria,* walls of the fourth to sixth layer of cells from the surface layer of the operculum become differentially thickened and at maturity dry, forming a ring of toothlike segments, the **peristome** (Gr. *peri,* around + Gr. *stoma,* mouth) (Figs. 16-24C,D; 16-26A). This thickening also extends for a short distance centripetally from the tangential walls along the horizontal walls. As a matter of fact, inasmuch as the thickening of the tangential walls occurs also on the cell layers adjacent to the fifth (the fourth and sixth), three cell layers are actually involved in peristome formation in *Funaria.* The vertical, radial walls of the fifth layer remain unthickened. As these

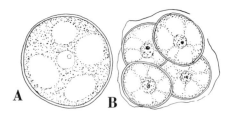

FIG. 16-25. *Funaria hygrometrica.* A. Sporocyte. B. Spore tetrad. X 700.

cells dry, they split along the thin radial walls, thus freeing the outer tangential walls and the inner tangential walls. In *Funaria hygrometrica* the peristome is double, consisting of sixteen teeth and sixteen inner, more delicate segments (Fig. 16-24D); *Funaria flavicans* has but a single peristome composed of sixteen teeth (Fig. 16-26A). The peristome is attached to a ring of thick-walled cells which form the rim of the capsule.

Meanwhile, the thin-walled cells within the capsule dry, and it ultimately contains a powdery mass of cellular debris intermingled with spores. The peristome teeth are hygroscopic, responding to slight changes in humidity by expansion and resultant curving. As they dry, they become somewhat arched and lift the operculum from the capsule apex. The teeth remain arched and separated from each other (Fig. 16-26A) during periods of

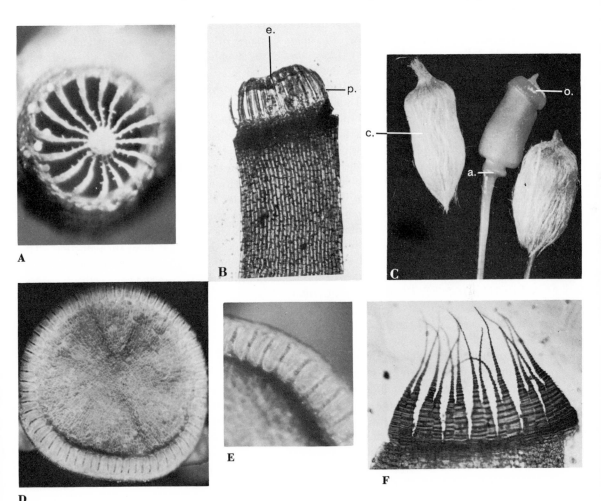

FIG. 16-26. A. *Funaria flavicans.* Frontal view of (single) peristome; note spore. X 12. B. *Atrichum undulatum.* Apex of capsule showing peristome (p.) and epiphragm (e.). X 30. C. *Polytrichum* sp. Organization of the capsule. X 4. D. *Polytrichum* sp. Frontal view of peristome and epiphragm. X 16. E. Same as D, enlarged. X 45. F. *Fissidens*, portion of peristome showing bifid teeth. X 90; a., apophysis; c., calyptra; o., operculum.

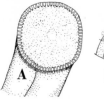

FIG. 16-27. *Polytrichum* sp. A. Capsule apex, showing peristome and epiphragm. X 10. B. Enlarged segment of preceding. X 25.

low humidity, but in dampness or rain they expand longitudinally and laterally and thus cover the mouth of the capsule. Because of such mechanisms, spore dissemination in the Mnionopsida is almost always a gradual process.

The variation in structure and mechanism of the peristome of mosses is a fascinating subject which can be studied readily in the field at low magnification, with the aid of only a hand lens. In some genera, like *Atrichum* (Fig. 16-26B) and *Polytrichum* (Figs. 16-26C–E; 16-27) and their relatives, the short peristome teeth are cellular instead of being composed only of portions of cell walls, as in *Funaria*. Furthermore, in these plants, the teeth are short and are attached to a' membranous layer, the **epiphragm,** which covers the mouth of the capsule. A number of other widely distributed mosses have double, acellular peristomes like those of *Funaria*. Among these may be cited *Aulocomnium, Mnium,* and *Bryum*. In other genera with acellular peristomes, a single ring of teeth is formed because only the inner tangential walls of the peristome-forming cells become thickened. *Fissidens* (Fig. 16-26F), *Dicranum,* and *Ceratodon* are mosses with single peristomes. Among commonly encountered genera, *Physcomitrium* is an example of a moss in which a peristome is altogether lacking. Finally, there is evidence that dryness does not always effect the opening of the capsule mouth and spore dissemination. In species of *Leucodon, Neckera,* and *Forsstroemia*, for example, the wet peristome is reported to open the mouth of the capsule and thus to enhance egress of the spores.

Summary

In summary, a number of features in the morphology and reproduction of the Mnionopsida are worthy of note. The gametophyte includes two separate phases, the protonema, with few exceptions a branching filament (in contrast to the spatulate protonema of *Sphagnum*), and a leafy gametophore which is produced from buds on the protonema. The gametophores develop sex organs at maturity. The sex organs are large and stalked and develop through the activity of apical cells. The zygote gives rise to the embryonic sporophyte, development of which is bi-apical. The mature sporophyte is composed of foot, seta, and capsule, the last more complex than that of the Sphagnopsida and Hepatophyta; the capsule is elevated by gradual elongation of the seta. Apical cells are involved in its development, in contrast to that of the Hepatophyta. Except for the foot cells, the sporophyte is actively photosynthetic from the earliest stages of development, and particularly so in the apophysis of the capsule, where stomata and guard cells are present in many genera. The sporogenous tissue is restricted in amount and arises as a double-layered, hollow cylinder from the outermost cells of the endothecium; unlike that of the Sphagnopsida, it does not overarch the columella. A complicated mechanism, the peristome, related to spore dissemination, is organized at the mouth of the capsules in most Mnionopsida; this becomes operative after the operculum has been shed. In mosses which lack a peristome, it is thought to have been lost through reduction. The sporophyte in this class exceeds that of other Bryophyta in stature and complexity.

Class 3. Andreaeopsida

Order 1. *Andreaeales*

FAMILY 1. ANDREAEACEAE

This class of mosses contains but a single order and family and only two genera, of which one (*Neuroloma*) is monotypic. The other, *Andreaea* (Fig. 16-28A), contains more than 100 species which are known as "granite mosses." These plants are abundant in cold regions and occur in the temperate zone only at high altitudes on exposed siliceous rocks.

The plants are blackish-green, sympodially branched, and anchored to the substrate by rhizoids. Growth is apical and the crowded leaves are borne in three rows.

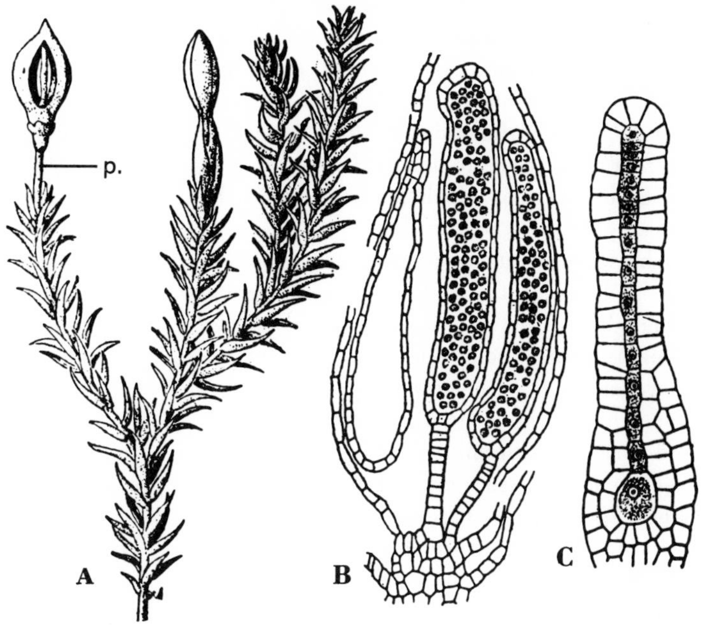

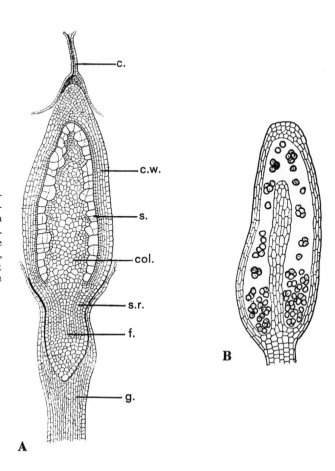

FIG. 16-28. *Andreaea rupestris* Hedw. A. Plant with maturing sporophytes. X 3. B. Antheridia. X 215. C. Median longisection of an almost-mature archegonium. X 430; p., pseudopodium. (*After G. M. Smith.*)

p.

A   B   C

FIG. 16-29. *Andreaea* sp. A. Median longisection of immature sporophyte. X 100. B. *A. rupestris*. Median longisection of maturing capsule. X 105; c., calyptra; c.w., capsule wall; col., columella; f., foot; g., gametophore; s., sporogenous tract; s.r., seta region. (A. *After Kühn from Bower.* B. *After G. M. Smith.*)

c.

c.w.

s.

col.

s.r.

f.

g.

A

B

Most species have bisexual gametophores, but, as in *Funaria,* the archegonia and antheridia (Fig. 16-28B,C) are borne at the tips of separate branches. The digitate antheridia are long-stalked and the archegonia massive.

An apical cell functions in development of the seta and capsule region of the sporophyte. An absorbing foot which penetrates into the gametophore also is formed.

The sporogenous tissue arises from the outermost layer of the endothecium, while the remainder of the structure forms a sterile, elongate, central columella (Fig. 16-29); the sporogenous tissue overarches the columella. The amphithecium is four or more layers thick and forms the capsule wall. Until late in development, the tissues are rich in chloroplasts. When sporogenesis has been completed, the surface cells of the capsule develop thick walls except for four vertical strips of cells, the dehiscence lines, which, however, do not extend to the apex of the capsule. Accordingly, at maturity, the capsule opens with four clefts (Fig. 16-28A). The seta is rudimentary in *Andreaea* and the capsule is elevated by elongation of the gametophore axis as a pseudopodium.

The spores of *Andreaea* develop into branching straplike or platelike protonemata. A number of buds which initiate gametophores are formed on this.

Summary

Andreaea has attributes suggestive of both the Sphagnopsida and Mnionopsida. Among the former may be cited the flattened protonema, the elevation of the capsule on a pseudopodium, the absence of a peristome, the long-stalked antheridia, and the overarching of the columella by the sporogenous tissues. Attributes which suggest the Mnionopsida are the gross morphology and the origin of the sporogenous tract from the endothecium. The dehiscence of the capsule by four clefts is unique among the Bryophyta[4] and unknown in the Sphagnopsida and Mnionopsida.

----
[4] As herein treated.

The Relationship of Liverworts and Mosses

The division Bryophyta is often considered to include mosses and their "allies," namely, the liverworts and hornworts. This concept of the scope of the division dates back to the late eighteenth century. Now that representatives of these groups have been described, it may be profitable to review the morphological attributes they possess in common and those in which they differ, with the purpose of reaching some conclusion regarding their origin and relationship and the bearing of these attributes on their classification.

It will be recalled (see Chapter 15) that in the Division Hepatophyta, the class Hepatopsida was considered to include five orders, the three major ones being (1) Marchantiales, in which external simplicity of body form is combined with internal differentiation; (2) Sphaerocarpales, in which both internal and external simplicity coincide; (3) Jungermanniales containing a simple (externally and histologically) thallose series and a leafy series, the latter simple histologically but complex in gross morphology.

The class Anthocerotopsida in this text[5] is represented largely by the classic hornwort, *Anthoceros,* morphological attributes of which were summarized also in the preceding chapter.

Representatives of three classes of the division Bryophyta (Sphagnopsida, Mnionopsida, and Andreaeopsida) have been discussed in the present chapter.

When one reviews the structure and reproduction of the members of the several groups, the diversities among them appear more striking than the resemblances. Why, then, are mosses and liverworts so often grouped together, inasmuch as such grouping implies, at the very least, morphological parallelism, or, to some people, real relationship and common origin? In the writer's judgment, there is only a single unique major attribute characteristic of both liverworts and mosses:

----
[5] There are several other genera of Anthocerotopsida including *Notothylas, Dendroceros,* and *Phaeoceros.*

all these plants are similar in life cycle which involves the regular alternation of a free-living gametophyte and an epiphytic sporophyte. The gametophyte of the liverworts, the hornworts, and mosses is clearly the dominant, longer-lived phase, although the sporophyte in the Mnionopsida perhaps rivals the gametophyte in complexity but is at least partially dependent on the latter. While such characteristics as biflagellate sperms, multicellular sex organs, sporic meiosis, aerial spore dissemination, and the terrestrial habitat may seem significant as important common attributes, one or more of them are also found in the algae or in the vascular plants. In the final analysis, it is largely the life cycle and the relative balance between the alternating generations upon which the usual concept of the division Bryophyta is based. Finally, the fossil record, as far as it is known, shows clearly that liverworts and mosses, if, indeed, they are related, diverged very early in their evolutionary development.

It has been emphasized recently, however, that both liverworts and mosses have certain cytological features in common, including some small "m" chromosomes and a heteromorphic bivalent chromosome. These cytological attributes, it is reported, do not occur elsewhere in the plant kingdom. Whether these common attributes, namely, life cycle and cytological organization, provide sufficiently compelling evidence for inferring phylogenetic unity is, of course, a matter of opinion.

Fossil Bryophyta

The fossil record of mosses is perhaps more satisfactory than that of Hepatophyta. A recent summary[6] listed nine mosses from the Paleozoic (Table 32-1, p. 512), three from the Mesozoic, and 134 species from the Tertiary. *Muscites*, having two species, is a well-authenticated Carboniferous and Triassic (Table 32-1) moss somewhat like *Polytrichum*. About a

FIG. 16-30. *Palaeohypnum arnoldianum* Steere, a Miocene moss. X 1.25. (*Courtesy of Drs. W. C. Steere and C. A. Arnold.*)

dozen mosses, some related to *Sphagnum* and some to Mnionopsida, have been reported from the Permian. A *Hypnum*-like species, *Palaeohypnum arnoldianum* (Fig. 16-30) has been described from Miocene (Table 32-1) strata.

A fossil *Sphagnum*-like moss, *Protosphagnum*, with leaf cells permanently arranged much like those in the immature leaves of *Sphagnum*, has recently been described. Unlike modern *Sphagnum*, the leaves of *Protosphagnum* appeared to have had a midrib with branches.

The available fossil remains of Bryophyta are largely like modern genera and have shed no light on the origin of the groups or on their possible relationship. As is true of algae and fungi, the fossil record indicates that our extant mosses are little modified from their ancient fossilized relatives.

Phylogenetic Considerations

The great German morphologist Goebel[7] wrote more than sixty years ago: "Between Hepaticae (liverworts) and Musci (mosses) there are no transition-forms; as there are none between Bryophyta and Pteridophyta, and as there never were such transitions their absence is not caused by their having died out." No evidence has been educed in the interim to contradict these views. The liverworts and mosses, therefore, have been considered as separate phyletic lines and placed

[6] For a modern summary see: Savicz-Ljubitzkaja, L. I., and I. I. Abraniov. 1959, "The Geological Annals of Bryophyta," *Rev. Bryol. and Lichnol.*, 28: 330–342.

[7] Goebel, K., *Organography of Plants*, Part 2, p. 7, Oxford University Press, London, 1905.

in separate divisions (Hepatophyta and Bryophyta) in this text.[8]

With reference to the origin of the Hepatophyta and Bryophyta, there are two divergent theoretical hypotheses. According to one, their origin should be sought among algal ancestors. If one recalls the various algal divisions described in earlier chapters—the Cyanophycophyta, Chlorophycophyta, Phaeophycophyta, Rhodophycophyta, and miscellaneous additional groups—certain suggestive parallelisms become apparent. In the first place, in photosynthate and pigmentation the Hepatophyta and Bryophyta (and all the vascular plants) are fundamentally similar to the Chlorophycophyta,[9] but they differ in these respects from the remaining groups of algae. It is quite possible, however, that the variation in pigmentation and photosynthate among the several groups of algae may represent biochemical divergences from an original common type, so that morphological parallelisms between Hepatophyta and Bryophyta, on the one hand, and groups of algae other than Chlorophycophyta, on the other hand, perhaps should not be excluded from discussion.

Certain ecological and morphological attributes also are common to Chlorophycophyta, liverworts, and mosses. Among these may be cited the occurrence of parenchymatous plant bodies, apical growth, terrestrial or amphibious existence, morphological alternation of generations, biflagellate motile reproductive cells (with apical insertion of the flagella), algalike protonematal stages, and the development of anchoring and absorptive organs. Examples of green algae with one or more of these attributes will occur to the reader.

On the other hand, multicellular sex organs having sterile jackets, like the antheridia and archegonia of Hepatophyta and Bryophyta, are absent among Chlorophycophyta. Furthermore, morphological alternation of generations with the balance and nutritive relations characteristic of the Hepatophyta and Bryophyta is lacking in the Chlorophycophyta. The Charophyta furnish a possible exception to these statements, insofar as multicellular sex organs are concerned.

An alternate hypothesis is that the liverworts and mosses, or at least some of them, represent reduced plants which have evolved from vascular plants, perhaps like some of those in the division Psilophyta (Chapter 18). In these discussions, comparison between the leafless axes of Psilophyta and the cylindrical sporophytes of *Anthoceros* is prominently featured. The columella and elaters of *Anthoceros*, it has been suggested, are the remnants of a vascular tract which are surrounded by a photosynthetic cortex and cutinized epidermis with stomata. The recent discovery of partially developed spiral thickenings on the outermost cells of *Dendroceros crispus*, a member of the *Anthocerotopsida*, is of special interest in relation to the "reduction" hypothesis of the origin of liverworts and mosses.

Classification of Bryophyta

Finally, there remains the problem of classification of the Bryophyta, with special reference to the illustrative genera described in this chapter. Each of two classes of the division Bryophyta, the Sphagnopsida and Andreaeopsida, are usually considered to contain but a single order and family. The class Mnionopsida, however, is the largest of the Bryophyta and is composed of a number of diverse types which have occasioned the creation of a number of orders (seven to thirteen) and numerous families. These have been delimited on the basis of varying combinations of sporophytic and gametophytic attributes, among them number of rows of leaves, growth habit of the gametophores (erect or prostrate), longevity of the gametophores (annual, biennial, or perennial), and position and structure of the sporophyte and capsule, especially the peristome. Inasmuch as approximately 14,000 species of Mnionopsida have been described, detailed consideration of their classification is outside the scope of this book. The more important illustrative genera described in this chapter may be grouped as follows.

---

[8] For a different viewpoint from that given here see: Steere, W. C. 1958, "Evolution and Speciation in Mosses," *Am. Naturalist*, 92: 5–20.

[9] And Charophyta.

Division Bryophyta

  Class 1. Sphagnopsida (Peat mosses)
    Order 1. Sphagnales
      Family 1. Sphagnaceae
        Genus: *Sphagnum*

  Class 2. Andreaeopsida (Granite mosses)[10]
    Order 1. Andreaeales
      Family 1. Andreaeaceae
        Genus: *Andreaea*

  Class 3. Mnionopsida (True mosses)[11]
    Order. Funariales
      Family. Funariaceae
        Genus: *Funaria*
    Order. Eubryales
      Family. Mniaceae
        Genus: *Mnium*
    Order. Polytrichales
      Family: Polytrichaceae
        Genera: *Atrichum, Polytrichum*

Review of these classes, as illustrated by their representative genera, will reveal the morphological differences on the basis of which the three classes are separated. The Sphagnopsida are distinguished from the Mnionopsida by the unique structure of their gametophores; by their thallose protonema, which produces but a single gametophore; by the lack of apical growth except in the early development of their sporophytes; by the formation of the sporogenous tissue from the amphithecium and its domelike position over the columella; and, finally, by the possession of a pseudopodium rather than an active sporophytic seta. Furthermore, all the genera of Mnionopsida discussed in this chapter differ from *Sphagnum* in having a peristome. The Andreaeopsida have certain features in common with both the Sphagnopsida and Mnionopsida, such as origin of sporogenous tissue from the endothecium and a pseudopodium which elevates the capsule.

The three orders of Mnionopsida, representatives of which have been emphasized in this chapter, differ as follows: The gametophores of the Funariales are usually annual or biennial[12] inhabitants of soil and are small in stature. The peristome, if present, may be single or double and is composed of sixteen portions; the operculum is not beaked. The gametophores of the Eubryales usually form perennial cushions or mats and their stems bear many rows of spirally arranged leaves. The sporophyte is terminal on the main axis or on a lateral branch of the gametophore and its capsule is usually bent or pendulous. The Polytrichales are distinguished by their angular capsules which have thirty-two to sixty-four cellular teeth attached to an epiphragm that closes the capsule orifice. A more complete discussion of the classification of mosses will be found in certain of the reference works listed at the conclusion of Chapter 15.

Theoretical Aspects of Alternation of Generations

The question of the origin of the alternating generations[13] and of their relation to each other has always played a prominent role in discussions of the phylogeny of land plants and has already been discussed in part (p. 57). Two somewhat different interpretations of the nature, relation, and origin of the alternating generations have developed since the time when the life cycle of land plants was clarified by Hofmeister in the middle of the nineteenth century. These interpretations are known as the **homologous** and **antithetic theories of alternation of generations.** According to the antithetic theory, which was developed in large part before the complexity and range of algal life cycles were fully appreciated, the gametophyte generation is the primitive one, and the sporophyte is of secondary origin. Furthermore, according to this theory, the sporophyte is not merely a modified gametophyte but an entirely different phase of the life cycle which has been interpolated between successive gametophyte generations because of a delay in meiosis. Proponents of this "interpolation" theory view the

---

[10] Here placed between the Sphagnopsida and Mnionopsida because of attributes which suggest both these classes.

[11] Representatives of the other orders of Mnionopsida have not received detailed treatment in this text.

[12] *Funaria* seems to be perennial in the vicinity of Austin, Texas.

[13] For another viewpoint see: Wahl, H. A. 1965, "Alternation of Generations—Again," *Turtox News*, 43:206–209; 248–251.

gametophyte of the simpler land plants as having had an algal origin, but they are inclined to the assumption that the first appearance of the sporophyte in the land plants coincided with the inception of the terrestrial habitat. Assuming that the sporophyte appeared as a result of delay in meiosis, with the result that many diploid cells (rather than one) ultimately produce tetrads of spores, they interpret the primary function of the sporophyte as spore production. With the production of increasingly large numbers of spores, it is postulated that the sporophyte gradually took upon itself nutritional and other vegetative functions by sterilization of some of the sporogenous tissue. According to this theory, the vegetative tissues of the sporophytes of the land plants all have had their origin in the sterilization of potentially sporogenous tissue. Furthermore, it is strongly implied that alternation of generations in the land plants arose independently of that in aquatic algae. Alternation in algae and in land plants is interpreted as an example of parallel evolution or homoplasy.

In contrast to the proponents of the antithetic or interpolation theory of the alternation of generations, those who hold the homologous theory, while agreeing that the gametophyte generation is the more primitive, view the sporophyte as a modified gametophyte. The range of variation in the life cycles described for the various genera of algae in earlier chapters furnishes evidence in support of the homologous theory. Especially strong support is available in the genera in which the alternating generations are almost indistinguishable morphologically, as in *Ulva*, *Cladophora*, *Ectocarpus*, and possibly *Polysiphonia* and *Griffithsia*. In these life cycles, the diploid, spore-producing sporophytes are strikingly similar to their corresponding gametophytes. Furthermore, it should be noted that like the gametophytes, they are photosynthetic throughout their development. There is no evidence that their photosynthetic tissues arose by sterilization of potentially sporogenous tissues. Even in haplobiontic algae like *Chlamydomonas* and *Spirogyra*, the homologue of the sporophyte, namely, the unicellular zygote, is photosynthetic.

Further evidence for the homologous theory of alternation of generations is available in the deviations from the normal life cycle observable in certain mosses and vascular plants. In such cases, either naturally or as a result of artificial stimulation, portions of the sporophyte can give rise to gametophytes, or gametophytes may give rise directly to sporophytes in the absence of a sexual process. These phenomena are known as **apospory** and **apogamy,** respectively. This is certainly an indication that sporophyte and gametophyte generations are not as fundamentally different as postulated by the interpolation theory.

Hepatophyta and Bryophyta have remarkable powers of regeneration. Small fragments (even single cells, in some cases) of both liverworts and mosses can regenerate to form new plants. It was demonstrated long ago that fragments of sporophytic setae could regenerate diploid protonemata, an example of direct transition of the sporophyte to the gametophytic phase and evidence which favors the homologous theory of alternation of generations. From such protonemata, diploid gametophores matured and gave rise to tetraploid sporophytes.

With respect to regeneration, not only leaves, stems, rhizoids, and setae but also paraphyses, archegonial neck and venter cells, and antheridial stalk and jacket cells develop protonemata in culture; these ultimately produce leafy shoots. However, all attempts[14] to achieve regeneration from the egg and spermatogenous tissue have so far met with failure.

While it may be possible to assume that alternation of gametophyte and sporophyte originated independently in the land plants at a time when their supposed algal ancestors took up a terrestrial habitat, and to attempt to reconcile the divergence between their sporophytes and gametophytes by this device, quite another view is possible. The algae exhibit types of alternation in which the sporophyte and gametophyte are as markedly heteromorphic (*Laminaria*) as those of the land plants, yet both develop in an aquatic habitat.

[14] By Dr. James H. Monroe, in the writer's laboratory.

It seems quite possible that the stimulus which so profoundly modified the sporophyte generation in so many land plants was retention of the zygote and the sporophyte within the nourishing tissues of the gametophyte. The carpospore-bearing generation of such Rhodophycophyta as *Griffithsia* and *Polysiphonia* may well indicate the result of such retention among the algae.

It is impossible, of course, to decide which of these two theories regarding alternating generations is correct, for much of the "evidence" on which both are based is speculative rather than verifiable by observations or experiment. Nevertheless, these views have been presented for the consideration of the student to guide him toward a synthesis of his own views on the phylogeny of plants.

DISCUSSION QUESTIONS

1. What attributes distinguish the Bryophyta from the Hepatophyta?

2. What attributes do the Hepatophyta and Bryophyta share in common?

3. Which of the Bryophyta, in your opinion, have the most highly developed gametophyte, with reference to size and/or tissue differentiation? Which has the most highly developed sporophyte? In each case, give the reasons for your answer.

4. On what grounds can you support separation of the Sphagnopsida from the Mnionopsida?

5. What evidence can you cite in support of an algal origin for Hepatophyta and Bryophyta? What alternate hypothesis is there and on what evidence is it based?

6. Can you suggest an explanation for the scarcity of liverwort and moss fossils?

7. Describe the modifications related to water absorption in *Sphagnum*.

8. How does *Polytrichum* withstand drought?

9. Of what theoretical significance is the observed fact that wounded moss setae produce protonemata? What mechanism is involved?

10. Can you suggest a procedure for obtaining diploid moss gametophytes? Triploid moss sporophytes?

11. Review your knowledge of the structure and nutritional arrangements in the sporophytes of algae, Hepatophyta, and Bryophyta. Then state whether or not you are of the opinion that the evidence supports the interpolation (antithetic) theory of alternation of generations, especially its doctrine of progressive sterilization. Give the reasons for your answer.

12. Can you suggest an experimental approach for obtaining evidence which might support the homologous theory of alternation of generations?

13. With the aid of labeled diagrams, describe the structure and reproduction of *Sphagnum* and one of the Mnionopsida.

14. Observe mosses in the field and examine various species for the presence of sex organs and sporophytes.

15. How do the Andreaeopsida differ from the Sphagnopsida? From Mnionopsida?

16. What seems to be the primary source of water for Mnionopsida?

17. *Funaria*, although bisexual, produces antheridia and archegonia on separate branches of the same plant. If leaves, stem, archegonia, antheridia and paraphyses were to regenerate, would the resulting plants be, in each case, male, female, or both? Discuss.

CHAPTER 17

Introduction to Vascular Plants

It is generally agreed that life arose and then developed during more than 3 billion years in an aquatic environment. Terrestrial life, both plant and animal, is relatively recent in geologic time (Table 32-1).

In the plant kingdom, **vascular plants** (having the conducting tissues, **xylem** and **phloem**) evolved, colonized, and have come to dominate terrestrial habitats, so much so, that they are sometimes spoken of as "the land plants," a designation that quite overlooks many algae, fungi, liverworts, and mosses that share this same habitat.

Although the fossil record does not clarify for us the *origin* of vascular plants, it does reveal clearly that by Devonian (Table 32-1) times considerable evolutionary diversification of these plants had already occurred, so that representatives or precursors of four[1] great lines of vascular plants are represented in the Devonian floras. Their origin may have been monophyletic or polyphyletic (multiple or separate); in either case, a long prior period (evidence for which is not yet available in paleobotanical data), during which diversification occurred, must have preceded the Devonian floras. The four evolutionary lines present in the Devonian floras are representatives of the divisions Psilophyta, Microphyllophyta, Arthrophyta, and Pterophyta; these will be discussed in the six chapters which follow. Before beginning that discussion, some features of the classification and organization of vascular plants will be reviewed in the remainder of the present chapter.

I. Classification of Vascular Plants

Consideration of the modern period of plant classification may begin appropriately with that of Linnaeus published in 1753 in his *"Species Plantarum"* and in 1767 in his *"Systema Naturae."* In Linnaeus' summary, the vascular plants are dominant, since all but one of the twenty-four major categories of classification included vascular plants only. The twenty-fourth category, the Cryptogamia (Gr. *kryptos*, hidden + Gr. *gammos*, marriage), Linnaeus characterized as plants having "flowers" scarcely visible to the naked eye, their sexual reproduction concealed. In contrast, the remaining twenty-three divisions, often called "Phanerogams" (Gr. *phaneros*, apparent + *gamos*, marriage) have flowers plainly visible and sexual reproduction (as manifested by stamens and pistils, according to Linnaeus) obvious or apparent. In the period since Linnaeus, his group Cryptogamia (which included ferns and fernlike plants, mosses, liverworts, algae and fungi) has been dismembered into a number of separate categories (Table 32-2). Furthermore, it has become clear that their sexual reproduction is not concealed or obscure.

The terms "Cryptogamia" used by Linnaeus and "Phanerogamae"[2] of earlier plant taxonomists are no longer used as formal taxa in classification, nor do we use them in their original, literal, etymological sense. Cryptogamic plants do *not* have "hidden" gametangia nor, conversely, are those of phanerogams exposed or obvious. In fact, quite the opposite is

---

[1] There is recent evidence that a fifth line, the progymnosperms of upper Devonian, were contemporaneous with these four lines. Probably other groups were present in addition.

[2] The formal taxon "Phanerogamae" was established by Eichler in 1883.

the case.[3] The term **cryptogam** in current usage designates a plant lacking seeds. All **phanerogams** are seed-bearing and vascular; however, both nonvascular (algae, fungi, liverworts, and mosses) and vascular (Psilophyta, Microphyllophyta, Arthrophyta, and Pterophyta) cryptogams are known.

At present, there is a diversity of opinion regarding classification of vascular plants. According to one viewpoint, they are monophyletic, and vascular tissue—postulated to have evolved just once—is the manifestation of their common origin. Proponents of this doctrine, accordingly, group all vascular plants in a single division, Tracheophyta (Table 32-2). However, that vascular tissue, i.e., phloem, evolved more than once is certainly evident from its presence in certain kelps (p. 65).

Another group of botanists, impressed by (1) the evidence of the fossil record which clearly indicates that there were at least four distinct lines of vascular plants at the time (Devonian, Table 32-1) they became prominent in the earth's land flora; and (2) by the fundamental diversities among the extant and extinct members of these lines (and later series), refuse to accept the unidivisional Tracheophyta concept. Alternatively, they have provisionally assigned divisional rank to the several classes of Tracheophyta (Table 32-2) until such time as more compelling evidence of their relationship should become available.

This second alternative has been followed in classifying the vascular plants in the present text. Examination of Table 32-2 will reveal that, for the most part, the divisions of vascular plants as herein conceived correspond to classes and subclasses usually included under the single division Tracheophyta.

II. Organization of the Vascular Plant Body

The vascular plants are composed of well-differentiated organs, both vegetative and reproductive. The former comprise the stem,

---

[3] Stamens and pistils are spore-bearing organs (p. 469).

root, and leaf; the latter include spore-bearing organs, seeds, and fruits.

A. The Stem

(1) ONTOGENY OF THE PRIMARY STEM

An individual vascular plant may originate either sexually, as a zygote, or asexually by growth of a fragment of the plant body. The fragment may be a totipotent single cell,[4] a group of cells (such as a callus or tissue culture), or a stem, leaf, or root cutting.

In the first alternative, the zygote develops initially into a seemingly undifferentiated[5] mass of cells which subsequently differentiates both externally into organs (leaves, stems, roots) and internally with respect to component tissues. These diverse tissues arise from localized groups of embryonic or meristematic cells which are replicating themselves frequently. Such meristematic cells occur at the stem and root tips and in the young leaves.

In a sense, the stem and root apices of vascular plants recapitulate continually the embryogenic development from the zygote, since these apical groups of undifferentiated cells continue to reproduce themselves throughout the life of the plant, while some of their progeny differentiate. It is most convenient to study development or ontogeny of the individual by means of serial transverse and longitudinal sections of the plant body.

The **axis** or **stem** is apparently the fundamental organ in many vascular plants.[6]

A majority of vascular plants, however, have axes with both leaves and roots. Leafy axes are often called **shoots** as distinct from roots.

Stems may be both subterranean and aerial. Horizontal stems which are often, but not

---

[4] Prof. F. C. Steward first accomplished this experimentally for a vascular plant, using carrot phloem tissue cultures. See Steward, F. C., et al., 1964, "Growth and Development of Cultured Plant Cells," *Science*, 143:20–27.

[5] Undifferentiated in the sense that all the cells are meristematic. In some taxa, certain cells of the young embryo *are* differentiated in that they have very fixed patterns of division which anticipate the later organization of distinct meristematic apices.

[6] Although this has been challenged in the case of certain ferns (p. 327), a number of primitive vascular plants (the Psilophyta) both living and extinct, consist solely of leafless and rootless axes (Figs. 18-1, 18-13, 18-17).

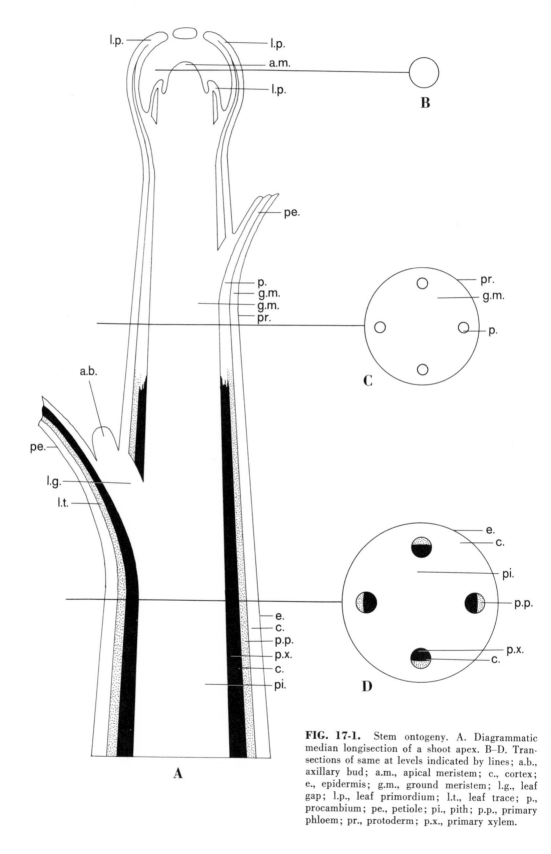

FIG. 17-1. Stem ontogeny. A. Diagrammatic median longisection of a shoot apex. B–D. Transections of same at levels indicated by lines; a.b., axillary bud; a.m., apical meristem; c., cortex; e., epidermis; g.m., ground meristem; l.g., leaf gap; l.p., leaf primordium; l.t., leaf trace; p., procambium; pe., petiole; pi., pith; p.p., primary phloem; pr., protoderm; p.x., primary xylem.

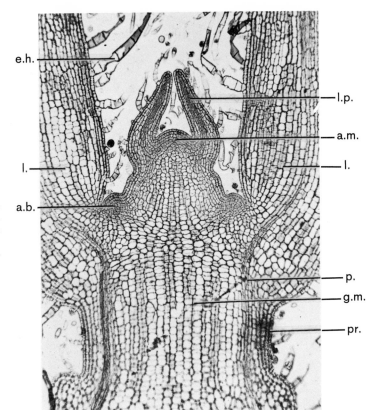

FIG. 17-2. *Coleus blumei.* Median longisection of stem apex; a.b., axillary bud; a.m., apical meristem; e.h., epidermal hair; g.m., ground meristem; l., leaf; l.p., leaf primordium; p., procambium; pr., protoderm. X 60. (*After Bold.*)

always fleshy, are known as **rhizomes.** Aerial stems are always photosynthetic, at least early in their development.

Figure 17-1 represents diagrammatically a median longitudinal section and increasingly older transections of a developing shoot; Fig. 17-2 is a photomicrograph of a median longitudinal section of such a stem. The apex is usually covered by overlapping leaves to form a **terminal bud.** Leaves in an orderly sequence arise by localized cell division at various points on the stem surface. Each immature leaf is called a **leaf primordium,** and in its axil a small group of meristematic cells repre-

sents an **axillary bud,** the precursor of a branch. The convex stem apex is composed of actively dividing cells, accordingly said to be **meristematic** or embryonic. This region of the stem is designated the **apical meristem,** or, sometimes, the **promeristem.** In a number of vascular cryptogams a large, prominent **apical cell** may be present (Figs. 18-4, 20-4). Apical cells may be tetrahedral and pyramidal, giving rise to cells on three faces (Fig. 17-3A), or three-sided or lenticular, with two cutting faces (Fig. 17-3B). In many Anthophyta (flowering plants), the apex is differentiated into a superficial layer, the **tunica** (in which

FIG. 17-3. Two common types of apical cells or initials. A. Tetrahedral type from three faces of which derivative cells arise in stems (from all four sides in certain roots). B. Lenticular type from two faces of which derivatives are formed. (*Modified from Schüepp.*)

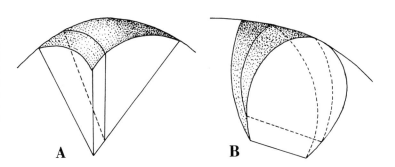

A   B

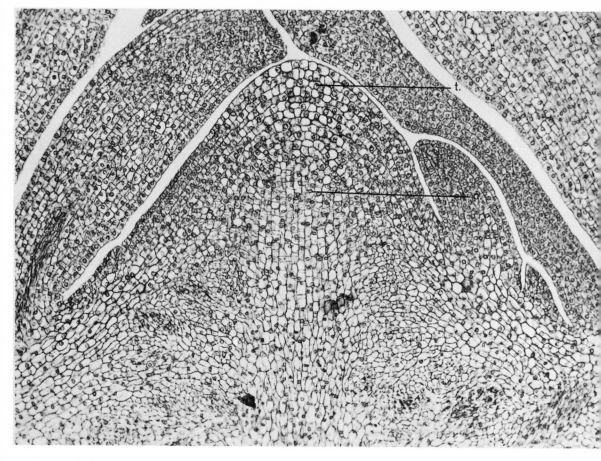

FIG. 17-4. *Yucca whipplei.* Median longisection stem apex; c., corpus; t., tunica. X 92.5.
(Courtesy of Dr. H. J. Arnott.)

most divisions are anticlinal), surrounding an internal **corpus;** the cell form and division patterns differ in these (Fig. 17-4).

At varying distances (in different species) from the apical meristem (Figs. 17-1, 17-2), the cells, although still meristematic, undergo divisions which result in their changing form. Thus, there are organized at a level below the apical meristem the three **primary meristems,** namely, the **protoderm, procambium** (sometimes called the provascular tissue), and the **ground meristem** (Figs. 17-1C, 17-2). The procambium, depending on the species, may have the form of a central strand, a ring of strands, or it may be a hollow cylinder. From these three regions, as cell division abates, there differentiate the **primary permanent tissues** of the stem.

The protoderm becomes differentiated into the **epidermis** (Fig. 17-1D). This may produce various types of appendages such as glandular and nonglandular hairs and scales. At maturity, the living epidermal cells have their walls impregnated with the fatty substance, cutin, and a common waxy layer, the **cuticle,** may cover the outer tangential epidermal walls. The epidermis is interrupted periodically by intercellular fissures surrounded by pairs of **guard cells** (Fig. 17-5). The opening and the guard cells together form the **stoma** (pl. stomata) (Gr. *stoma,* mouth).[7]

The ground meristem matures into the regions called the **cortex** and **pith.** The outermost cells of the cortex usually contain chloro-

[7] Sometimes the term stoma is used to refer only to the fissure itself.

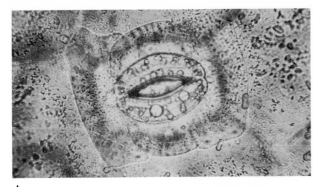

A

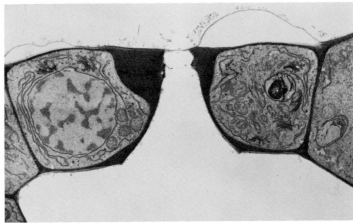

B

FIG. 17-5. Stomata. A. Surface view of stoma from stem epidermis of *Zebrina pendula*; note pore, guard cells, and accessory cells. X 250. B. Electron-micrograph of transection of stoma of *Lemna minor*. X 4500. (*Courtesy of Dr. H. J. Arnott.*)

plasts and, accordingly, are photosynthetic. The inner layers of the cortex often function in storage. The cortex is composed mostly of thin-walled living cells which together are called **parenchyma tissue.** Certain zones of the cortex may be composed of thick-walled cells which provide support and rigidity to the stem. The cell walls of the innermost layer of

the ground meristem in certain crytogams and in the rhizomes of other vascular plants may become specially thickened or otherwise modified to form an **endodermis** (Fig. 18-5B).

The **pith,** when present, occurs in the center of the stem. It is usually composed of relatively thin-walled parenchyma which functions in storage.

FIG. 17-6. *Zea mays;* corn. Transection of portion of phloem region of vascular bundle; c.c., companion cell; s.p., sieve plate; s.t., sieve tube; t., tracheid; v., vessel. X 300.

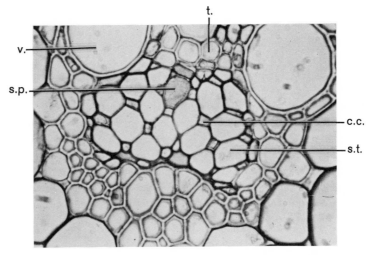

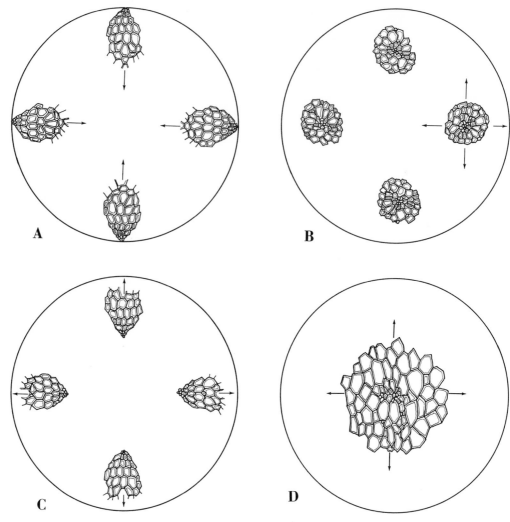

FIG. 17-7. Diagrammatic illustrations indicating (by arrows) the different directional patterns of primary xylem differentiation from procambium. A. Exarch. B. Mesarch. C. Endarch. D. Centrarch. Protoxylem cells small, metaxylem elements large, in each case. Synchronous type, consisting of metaxylem only, not illustrated.

The procambium or provascular tissue ultimately matures into vascular[8] tissue, the **primary xylem** and **phloem,** the former lignified and functioning in the conduction of water and (usually) inorganic salts and the latter cellulosic and functioning in the conduction of sugars and other complex compounds.

At any given level, the **primary phloem** usually differentiates from the procambium, on the outer tangential surface of the latter. The first phloem to mature, the **proto-**

---

[8] And other closely associated tissues such as the pith in certain roots.

phloem, does so before elongation of the stem has ceased. Thus, much of the protophloem may be crushed and obliterated. The **metaphloem** matures from procambium after elongation of the stem has stopped. The agent of conduction in the phloem is the **sieve element,** so called because of the presence of connecting strands which run from cell to cell in the sieve areas on either the terminal or lateral walls. Aggregates of sieve areas, which are particularly differentiated structurally from nonaggregated ones, are designated **sieve plates.** In angiosperms, the sieve cells are joined in series, with the transverse walls equipped with sieve plates, to form **sieve tubes** (Figs. 17-6, 17-8).

The sieve cells and sieve tube members, which are usually enucleate at maturity, are often flanked by smaller, nucleate **companion cells** (Figs. 17-6, 17-8). In addition, **parenchyma** cells (nonspecialized living cells which here function in storage) and lignified **fibers** (supporting cells) may be present in phloem.

With respect to the pattern or direction of differentiation of primary xylem from procambium, five relationships are known (Fig. 17-7). Their recognition depends on a distinction between two kinds of primary xylem, **protoxylem** and **metaxylem**. Protoxylem is the first-formed primary xylem, its elements usually smaller in diameter, differentiating before elongation of the organ has ceased, and lignified in annular or spiral fashion. In contrast, the metaxylem differentiates after the protoxylem, its elements are larger in diameter, they mature only after elongation of the organ has ceased, and their secondary wall

pattern is usually reticulate or pitted. However, there are transitions between protoxylem and metaxylem. The five patterns of primary xylem differentiation are **exarch,**[9] **mesarch, endarch, centrarch,** and **synchronous.** These are illustrated in Fig. 17-7 and explained in its legends.

The number of points at which protoxylem differentiates varies with the organ and the species. An axis with but one group of protoxylem is said to be **monarch;** those with two are **diarch,** with three, **triarch,** etc.

The primary xylem may contain the water-conducting elements, **tracheids** and/or **vessels** (Figs. 17-8, 17-11B), parenchyma cells, and fibers. One or another of these elements may be absent.

Tracheids are elongate, with tapering, interlocking end walls, nonliving at maturity, their secondary walls occurring in various patterns of cellulose and lignin deposition. These patterns of lignification, in order of increasing

---

[9] "Arch" here means first; hence, point of origin.

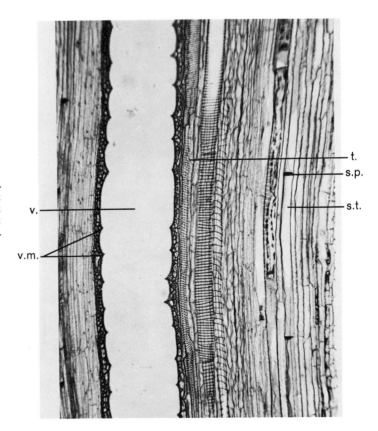

FIG. 17-8. *Cucurbita* (squash). Longisection of vascular tissue; s.p., sieve plate; s.t., sieve tube; t., tracheid; v., xylem vessel; v.m., limits of one vessel member. X 300.

amounts of lignin deposited, are annular, spiral (helical), reticulate, pitted (elongate to circular, often transitional) (Fig. 17-7). Intermediate patterns occur.

Vessels are composed of series of tracheid-like members, the **vessel members,** between the walls of which perforations occur (Fig. 17-8); these are thought to facilitate movement of liquids. Vessel members or elements differentiate from a series of procambium cells, while each tracheid arises from but a single one. There is strong evidence that vessels have arisen phylogenetically by actual dissolution of the closing membranes of pit pairs in the sloping, contiguous terminal walls of adjacent tracheids. Primitive vessels are composed of elongate tracheidlike segments, angular in transection, and are similar in pitting. The segments of the most specialized vessels are short, oval to circular in transection, have single large terminal perforations, and are quite unlike tracheids. Vessels have arisen both from tracheids with circular and from those with elongate pits, as well as from elements with secondary thickenings characteristic of protoxylem and early metaxylem.

The rigidity of the primary stem depends on the amount of xylem and the degree of its lignification as well as on the presence of supporting tissue within the vascular tissue or elsewhere. Fibers are elongate, heavily lignified cells, often with interlocking ends which strengthen stems. Fibers and other lignified cells in the cortex (collectively termed **sclerenchyma**) also may contribute to support of the primary stem.

(2) NODAL ANATOMY

The locus of leaf emergence on a stem is called the **node,** the portion of the stem which lacks leaves being the **internode.** In the preceding account of stem ontogeny, no consideration was given to the effect of the emergence of **leaf traces,** or vascular connections to the leaves, at or near the nodes, on the organization of the vascular tissue. In some plants, the traces are single and delicate, composed of but a few xylem and phloem cells, and their departure occasions little disturbance in the vascular tissue of the stem (Fig. 17-9A,C). This is true of the incipient or vestigial traces of Psilophyta (Chapter 18) and of the leaf traces of the Microphyllophyta (Chapter 19).

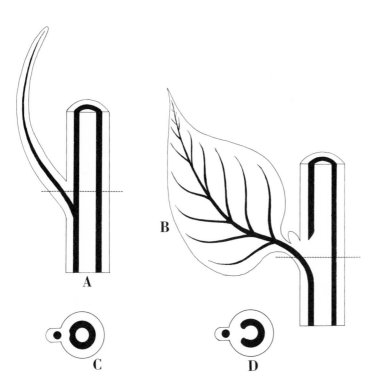

FIG. 17-9. A, B. Segments of longitudinal bisections of stems. A. Stem with microphyllous leaf. B. Stem with macrophyllous leaf. C, D. Transections at levels of A and B indicated by dotted lines. Steles, traces, and veins indicated in heavy black. Note leaf gaps in B and D and their absence in A and C.

In the remaining vascular plants, a significantly large branch or several branches of vascular tissue pass out[10] as leaf traces (Figs. 17-1, 17-9B,D). Parenchyma cells form a "**gap**"[11] at and above the point of departure of the trace from the stele.

(3) STELES

The xylem and phloem, the vascular tissue of the region of primary permanent tissues, together form the **stele** (L. *stela*, rod or column). Different arrangements of vascular tissue result in different stelar configurations among the vascular plants. These different types will be summarized at this point because they are often useful attributes in discussions of classification and relationship of vascular plants.

The following types of stele (Fig. 17-10) occur: (a) the protostele (including the haplostele, the actinostele, and plectostele); (b) the siphonostele (both amphiphloic and ectophloic); (c) the dictyostele; (d) the eustele, and (e) the atactostele.

---

[10] Although we speak of traces as "passing out," they, of course, do not move but differentiate in position from precursor strands of procambium.

[11] Literally, of course, not a gap.

(a) *Protosteles*

Protosteles are perhaps the simplest, and often considered to be the most primitive, type of stele. They are considered primitive because of their occurrence in certain Devonian fossils (in spite of the fact that siphonosteles, for example, occur in other Devonian plants) and because some see in them the counterpart of the anthocerotan columella (p. 217). A protostele is essentially a solid core of xylem surrounded by a cylinder of phloem (Fig. 17-10A); if this is circular in transection (Fig. 17-10A), it is called a **haplostele.** An **actinostele** (Fig. 17-10A') is simply protostele with radiating, coglike protuberances or ridges. A **plectostele** (Fig. 17-10A'') is a protostele in which phloem is interspersed in masses between the xylem. The xylem, although interrupted at a given level, forms a continuous system. Protosteles occur in the Psilophyta and Microphyllophyta and in the juvenile stems of other groups (and in many roots as well).

(b) *The Siphonostele*

In the siphonostele, the xylem and phloem form a cylinder around a central pith. The phloem may be both external and internal, as

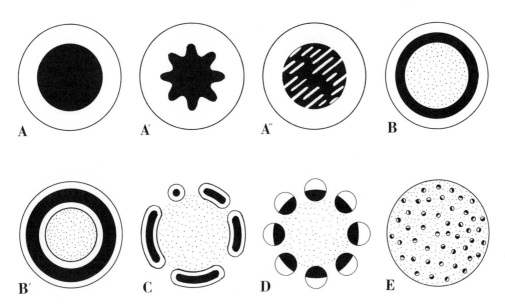

FIG. 17-10. Types of stele, diagrammatic transections. A–A''. Protosteles. A. Haplostele. A'. Actinostele. A''. Plectostele. B. Ectophloic siphonostele. B'. Amphiphloic siphonostele or solenostele. C. Dictyostele. D. Eustele. E. Atactostele. Xylem, black; phloem, white; pith, stippled.

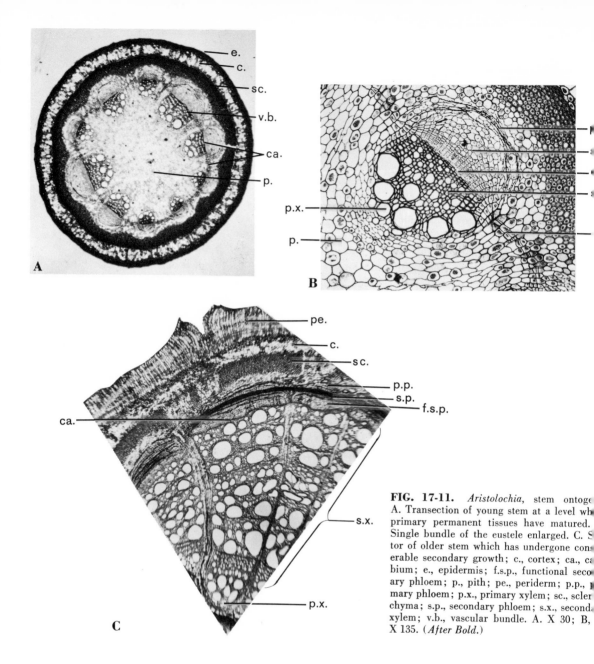

Labels in figure A: e., c., sc., v.b., ca., p., p.x., p.

Labels in figure C: pe., c., sc., p.p., s.p., f.s.p., ca., s.x., p.x.

FIG. 17-11. *Aristolochia*, stem ontoge[ny]. A. Transection of young stem at a level wh[ere] primary permanent tissues have matured. [B.] Single bundle of the eustele enlarged. C. S[ec]tor of older stem which has undergone cons[id]erable secondary growth; c., cortex; ca., ca[m]bium; e., epidermis; f.s.p., functional seco[nd]ary phloem; p., pith; pe., periderm; p.p., [pri]mary phloem; p.x., primary xylem; sc., scler[en]chyma; s.p., secondary phloem; s.x., second[ary] xylem; v.b., vascular bundle. A. X 30; B, [C.] X 135. (*After Bold.*)

it is in many ferns (Fig. 17-10B′) in which case the siphonostele is said to be **amphiphloic**. An amphiphloic siphonostele is sometimes called a **solenostele**. In **ectophloic siphonosteles** (Fig. 17-10B) the phloem is restricted to the outer surface of the xylem. The siphonostele is widely distributed, occurring in the ferns and in certain gymnosperms and flowering plants.

(c) The Dictyostele

In siphonostelic stems with short internodes, overlapping of the nodal leaf gaps results in dissection of the stele (Fig. 17-10C). As seen in transection, the stele appears as discrete strands or bundles. A siphonostele thus dissected is called a dictyostele.[12] This type of stele characterizes many ferns.

[12] The original definition of a dictyostele restricted the usage to netlike steles in which the separated strands of the dissected solenostele had, in transection, a concentric arrangement (phloem surrounding xylem) of vascular tissue resulting from the dissection of a solenostele. The term is sometimes used less restrictively to include also those gap-dissected siphonosteles with collateral xylem and phloem, derived presumably from ectophloic siphonosteles.

(d) The Eustele

Where the xylem and phloem occur in discrete collateral or bicollateral strands or bundles, the arrangement is called a eustele (Fig. 17-10D). The parenchyma between the bundles of a eustele may arise by overlapping of leaf gaps in an ectophloic siphonostele, independently of leaf gaps, or both types of parenchymatous gaps may be present. A eustele occurs in the internodes of *Equisetum* (Fig. 20-5) and in certain gymnosperms and flowering plants.

(e) The Atactostele

This arrangement of vascular tissues occurs in many monocotyledonous flowering plants. Here the discrete strands of xylem and phloem are scattered (Fig. 17-10E) through the stem.

The experimental investigations of Professor R. H. Wetmore and his associates on the causal relationship in the differentiation of vascular tissues have given us some insight into the factors involved. Using undifferentiated, parenchymatous **callus** in tissue culture, Wetmore and his associates have demonstrated that grafting (insertion) of buds of the same species will induce the differentiation of nodules of vascular tissue in the callus which would not otherwise develop. This indicates clearly that vascular differentiation is under chemical control. These investigators have shown further that localized application of auxin and sugar will result in localized induction of vascular tissues. The concentration of sugar (glucose or sucrose) appears to be critical. At 1.5–2% sucrose, xylem alone de-

velops. If the concentration be increased to 3–3.5%, the vascular nodules develop xylem toward the center of the callus and phloem toward the periphery, and a cambium may develop and join the ring of vascular nodules. Concentration of 4–4.5% sucrose stimulates production of a preponderance of phloem. Application to the callus of the auxin-sugar mixture through capillary pipettes resulted in the formation of a cylinder of xylem and phloem with cambium (see below) between; these simulated a siphonostele. These investigations are of significance in having demonstrated a causal role of a growth hormone (auxin) and sugars, the latter in varying concentrations, in the differentiation of vascular tissues.

(4) SECONDARY GROWTH

In most vascular cryptogams and in many flowering plants the axis is entirely primary in ontogeny, i.e., the component tissues differentiate entirely from the promeristem and primary meristems. In a few vascular cryptogams (e.g., *Isoetes*, p. 297, *Botrychium*, p. 327) and in many seed plants, however, the primary tissues (Fig. 17-11A, B) are augmented by the formation and differentiation of additional cells throughout the life of the individual. This is called **secondary growth** because the added cells are derived from the **cambium** and **cork cambium,** which are **secondary meristems.**

The cambium is a zone of meristematic cells between the primary xylem and phloem. At least that part of the cambium which lies be-

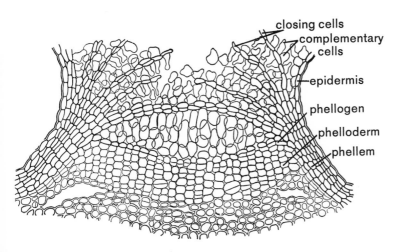

closing cells
complementary cells
epidermis
phellogen
phelloderm
phellem

FIG. 17-12. Transection of a lenticel of *Prunus avium* stem. (*After Devaux, from Eames and McDaniels.*)

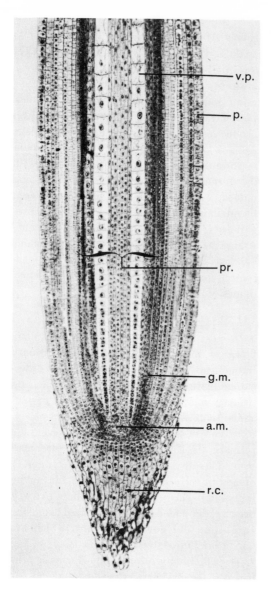

tiate into **secondary xylem** which lies between the cambium and the primary xylem (Fig. 17-11C). Fewer of the outer derivatives of the cambium differentiate into **secondary phloem**; this lies between the cambium and the primary phloem (Fig. 17-11C). Accordingly, the vascular tissues increase radially in thickness as long as secondary growth continues.

Where this is of long duration, stresses arise which rupture the epidermis and cortical tissue. This or other factors stimulate the organization of a peripheral zone of meristematic cells, the cork cambium or **phellogen**, either as a continuous cylinder or as localized strips. The outer derivatives of the phellogen are **cork cells** or **phellem**, the impervious walls of which are thickened with suberin. The internal derivatives are parenchyma cells which may augment the cortex of the stem. As the corky layers replace the epidermis, there are organized **lenticels** (Fig. 17-12) which apparently replace the stomata in function. Long-continued cambial activity results in extremely woody stems as in trees and shrubs, or, if the cambium adds more parenchyma than secondary xylem cells, the stem, although augmented in diameter, may become fleshy rather than woody.

B. The Root

The stems of all vascular plants except the Psilophyta (Chapter 18) and *Salvinia* (Chap-

FIG. 17-13. *Zea mays,* corn. Median longisection of root tip; a.m., apical meristem; g.m., ground meristem; p. protoderm; pr., procambium; v.p., xylem vessel precursors; r.c., root cap. X 40. (*Courtesy of Dr. W. G. Whaley.*)

tween the primary xylem and phloem originates from procambium. In axes with siphonosteles, the entire cambium would have such an origin. In eusteles and other dissected steles, the parenchyma cells between the vascular strands become meristematic at the inception of cambial activity within the strand so that a complete cylinder of cambium arises (Fig. 17-11). A preponderance of cells formed by tangential divisions of the cambium differen-

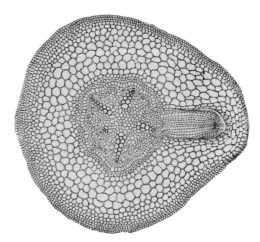

FIG. 17-14. *Phaseolus* sp., bean. Transection of root showing origin of branch roots. X 65. (*After Gibbs.*)

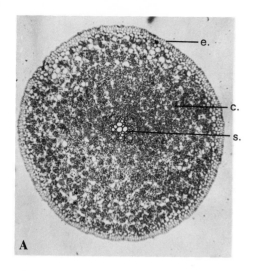
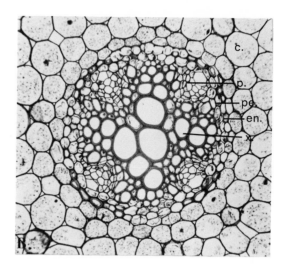

FIG. 17-15. *Ranunculus* sp. A. Transection of root. B. Stelar region of preceding; c., cortex; e., epidermis; en., endodermis; p., primary phloem; pe., pericycle; s., stele; x., primary xylem. A. X 25. B. X 200.

ter 23) bear roots. The latter differ externally from stems in not bearing leaves and in lacking nodes and internodes. Some of the epidermal cells of most roots, furthermore, produce absorptive protuberances called **root hairs.** The apical meristem of the root is covered by a mantle of cells, the **root cap** (Fig. 17-13).

Branch roots, in contrast to stem branches, originate endogenously from the **pericycle** (Fig. 17-14), a zone surrounding the vascular tissue of the stele and just within the endodermis; in some species they arise from the endodermis. They grow through the cortex and epidermis into the soil.

The procambium and primary vascular system in many roots is organized with a solid, central strand of xylem, which is exarch in ontogeny (Fig. 17-15). Roots may be monarch to polyarch. Between the protoxylem points in roots occur groups of primary phloem cells, so that primary xylem and phloem are radially alternate in roots (Fig. 17-15B) rather than collateral or bicollateral as they are in stems. The roots of some plants have a central pith.[13]

In all woody plants and in many herbaceous types, cambial activity in the root also results in secondary growth and increase in diameter and woodiness of that organ. Here the outer tissues (cortex and epidermis) may be sloughed off during secondary growth and replaced by corky layers which originate from a phellogen organized in the pericycle.

C. The Leaf

Leaves arise ontogenetically as meristematic emergences or **primordia** at the surface of young stems (Figs. 17-1, 17-2). Several layers near the stem surface may undergo active division to initiate the leaf. The primordium

---

[13] This is true of the roots of *Ophioglossum* (p. 326) and the Marattiales (p. 330) as well as of certain flowering plants. Monocotyledonous plants with pith-containing roots also have smaller roots which lack pith.

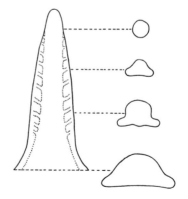

FIG. 17-16. Tobacco: leaf ontogeny. Diagrams of leaf primordium and transections at four levels from apex to base; note midrib and marginal meristem in three lower transections. (*After Avery.*)

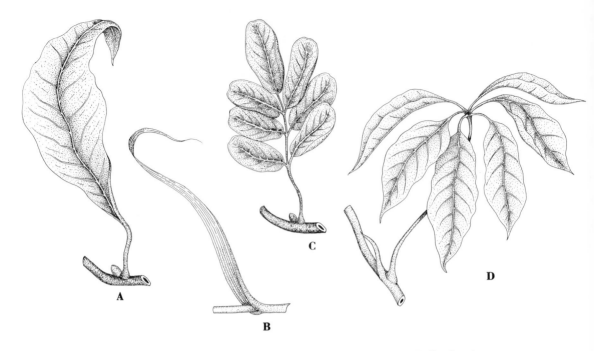

FIG. 17-17. Leaves; gross morphology. A. Simple petiolate leaf of croton. B. Sessile, simple leaf of a grass. C. Pinnately compound leaf of a legume, *Sophora*. D. Palmately compound leaf of *Scheffeleria* sp.

at first consists largely of axis but later there are organized on opposite sides of the latter **marginal meristems** from which the bulk of the leaf blade develops (Fig. 17-16). In some leaves, those of many ferns, for example, a prominent apical cell functions in leaf ontogeny.

At maturity, leaves vary widely in both external and internal organization (Fig. 17-17). They may be simple leaves, with undivided blades, or variously compound, with divided blades. They may be petiolate or sessile in their attachment to the axis.

The vascular tissue of the leaf, the **veins,** may be unbranched (Microphyllophyta, Arthrophyta) or variously branched. **Open dichotomous venation** (Fig. 17-18A) occurs in many ferns and *Ginkgo*. In many monocotyledonous flowering plants, the venation is **striate** (Fig. 17-18B), the main veins being elongate and connected at intervals by delicate, transverse, ladderlike veins. In certain ferns and in many dicotyledonous flowering plants, venation is **reticulate,** the veins being abundantly branched and anastomosing (Fig. 17-

18C). Intermediate types of venation also occur.

Histologically, most leaves are relatively simple, being covered by a more or less heavily cutinized epidermis (with stomata on the lower, upper, or on both epidermal layers); with veins and photosynthetic cells, the **mesophyll,** lie within. In some species the latter is differentiated into palisade and spongy zones (Fig. 17-19).

Comparative morphology distinguishes between two categories or leaves in vascular plants, **microphyllous** (in the Microphyllophyta and Arthrophyta[14]) and **macrophyllous** (megaphyllous) which occur in all other groups. Microphyllous leaves are usually of small size (although there are exceptions such as those of *Isoetes*, p. 297, and certain fossil Microphyllophyta, p. 308), and have single, unbranched veins, traces to which leave no gap in the stem stele (Fig. 17-9A,C). By contrast, macrophyllous leaves are usually large,

---

[14] Certain fossil Arthrophyta seem to have been macrophyllous.

have richly branching veins, and their leaf traces leave gaps (Fig. 17-9B,D) in the stem stele.[15]

Although ontogenetically similar, it has been suggested that microphyllous and macrophyllous leaves may be of quite different phylogenetic origin (see pp. 379–380).

The scalelike emergences on the stems of

certain Psilophyta (Figs. 18-1–18-3; 24-1), which lack veins, may well represent precursors of microphyllous leaves. In some species and for some of the scales, traces leave the stem stele but end in the cortex short of the leaf base. Microphyllous leaves differ from these only in that the trace continues into the leaf to form its single vein. Microphyllous leaves then, if this view is correct, would be simple enations or emergences from the stem surface which ultimately became vascularized.

Macrophyllous leaves, on the other hand,

---

[15] This last attribute is not always valid: leaf gaps are absent in macrophyllous plants with protosteles and polysteles, although grooves (corresponding to gaps) may be present in the steles or protosteles of macrophyllous plants.

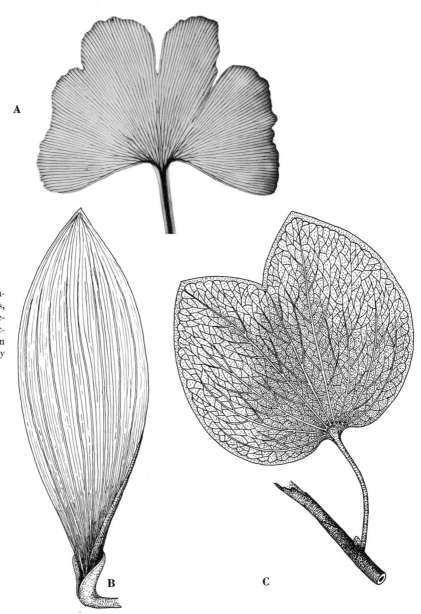

FIG. 17-18. Types of venation. A. Open-dichotomous, *Ginkgo biloba.* B. Striate venation in *Clintonia.* C. Reticulate or netted venation in *Bauhinia* leaf. (A. *Courtesy of Dr. H. J. Arnott.*)

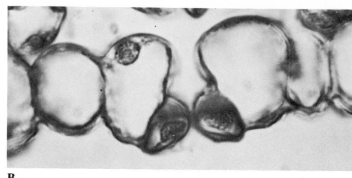

FIG. 17-19. *Ligustrum* sp. A. Transection of leaf blade. B. Enlarged view of stoma of same transection; l.e., lower epidermis; p., palisade mesophyll; s., stoma; sp., spongy mesophyll; u.e., upper epidermis; v., vein in transection. A. X 30. B. X 550. (*After Bold.*)

since the late nineteenth century, have usually been considered to represent modified stems which originated in evolution from the more distal branches of axes. In this development (Fig. 24-2), it has been suggested, the first step was a change from dichotomous to monopodial branching by dominance and **overtopping** of one dichotomy. The second modification was restriction of the remaining dichotomies to one plane, **planation.** Finally, there occurred lateral fusion and **"webbing"** to form the leaf blade. The presence of open dichotomous venation in the leaves of many ferns and the prolonged apical growth in development of fern leaves are cited as evidence for this interpretation. Although it was stated above that the phylogenetic origin of the microphyllous leaf was quite different from that

of the macrophyllous, there is an alternative interpretation, namely, their origin by reduction (Fig. 24-6). The phenomena of overtopping, planation, webbing, and reduction are important aspects of the **telome theory,** discussed in Chapter 24.

The preceding paragraphs have presented a brief summary of some fundamental concepts regarding the organization of the vegetative body of the vascular plants. More detailed discussion of the several topics briefly alluded to will be found in some of the reference texts on plant anatomy cited at the end of this chapter.

The organization and functioning of the reproductive structures of the vascular plants are discussed with the representative types where these are described in the remaining chapters of this text.

DISCUSSION QUESTIONS

1. Define vascular tissue and state the functions of its components.

2. What is usually meant by the term "land plants"? What divisions of the plant kingdom have terrestrial representatives?

3. What division of vascular plants had evolved by the Devonian?

4. What did Cryptogamia mean to Linnaeus?

5. What are cryptogams in current usage?

6. On what attributes is the division Tracheophyta based?

7. How may vascular plants originate in ontogeny?

8. Define or explain: rhizome, bud, axillary bud, leaf primordium, meristematic, promeristem, apical cell, primary meristems, tunica, corpus, protoderm, procambium, ground meristem, epidermis, cuticle.

9. Define or explain: primary xylem and phloem; secondary xylem and phloem; protophloem and metaphloem; protoxylem and metaxylem; sieve cell, sieve tube; companion cell, tracheid, vessel; exarch, endarch, and mesarch xylem development; monarch, diarch and triarch protosteles; node, internode, leaf trace, leaf gap.

10. Distinguish between microphyllous and macrophyllous leaves. What hypotheses are there in explanation of the origin of these leaf types?

11. What is the supposed phylogenetic relationship between tracheids and vessels?

12. Define and make three-dimensional diagrams of a protostele, haplostele, plectostele, actinostele, siphonostele, solenostele, dictyostele, eustele, and atactostele.

13. Define or explain: cambium, phellogen, cork cambium, collateral bundle, venation.

14. In what respects, internal and external, do roots and stems differ?

REFERENCE WORKS[16]

Andrews, H. N., Jr., *Studies in Paleobotany,* John Wiley and Sons, Inc., New York, 1961.

Arnold, C. A., *An Introduction to Paleobotany,* McGraw-Hill Book Co., Inc., New York, 1947.

Bower, F. O., *The Origin of a Land Flora,* Macmillan and Co., Ltd., London, 1908.

Bower, F. O., *Primitive Land Plants,* Macmillan and Co., Ltd., London, 1935.

Campbell, D. H., *The Structure and Development of Mosses and Ferns,* The Macmillan Company, New York, 1928.

Campbell, D. H., *The Evolution of the Land Plants (Embryophyta),* Stanford Univ. Press, Stanford, Calif., 1940.

Chamberlain, C. J., *Gymnosperms: Structure and Evolution,* Univ. of Chicago Press, 1935.

Darragh, W. C., *Principles of Paleobotany,* Chronica Botanica Co., Waltham, Mass., 1939.

Delevoryas, T., *Morphology and Evolution of Fossil Plants,* Holt, Rinehart and Winston, New York, 1962.

Eames, A. J., *Morphology of Vascular Plants,* McGraw-Hill Book Co., Inc., New York, 1936.

Eames, A. J., *Morphology of Angiosperms,* McGraw-Hill Book Co., Inc., New York, 1961.

Eames, A. J., and MacDaniels, L. H., *An Introduction to Plant Anatomy,* McGraw-Hill Book Co., Inc., New York, 1947.

Emberger, L., *Les Plantes Fossiles dans leves Rapports avec Les Vegetaux Vivants,* Masson et Cie, Paris, 1944.

Esau, K., *Plant Anatomy,* 2nd ed., John Wiley and Sons, Inc., New York, 1965.

Foster, A. S., and Gifford, E. M., *Comparative Morphology of Vascular Plants,* W. H. Freeman and Co., San Francisco, 1959.

Goebel, K., *Organography of Plants,* Part II, English ed. by I. B. Balfour, Oxford University Press, London, 1905.

Jeffrey, E. C., *The Anatomy of Woody Plants,* Univ. of Chicago Press, 1930.

Manton, I., *Problems of Cytology and Evolution in the Pteridophyta,* Cambridge Univ. Press, London, 1950.

Meeuse, A. D. J., *Fundamentals of Phytomorphology,* The Ronald Press Co., New York, 1966.

Scagel, R. F., *et al., An Evolutionary Survey of the Plant Kingdom,* Wadsworth Publishing Co., Inc., Belmont, Calif., 1965.

Schellbach, L., and Lacke, J., "Grand Canyon: Nature's Story of Creation," *National Geographic Magazine* 107:589–629, 1955.

Seward, A. C., *Plant Life Through the Ages,* Cambridge Univ. Press, London, 1933.

Smith, G. M., *Cryptogamic Botany,* Vol. II, *Bryophytes and Pteridophytes,* McGraw-Hill Book Co., Inc., New York, 1955.

Sporne, K. R. *The Morphology of Pteridophytes,* Hutchinson & Co., Ltd., London, 1962.

Verdoorn, F., *Manual of Pteridology,* Martinus Nijhoff, The Hague, The Netherlands, 1938.

Walton, J., *An Introduction to the Study of Fossil Plants,* A. & C. Black, Ltd., London, 1953.

Wardlaw, C. W., *Phylogeny and Morphogenesis,* The Macmillan Co., Ltd., London, 1952.

Wardlaw, C. W., *Embryogenesis in Plants,* John Wiley and Sons, Inc., New York, 1955.

Zimmerman, W., *Phylogenie der Pflanzen,* 2nd ed., Gustav Fischer, Verlagsbuchhandlung, Jena, Germany, 1959.

---

[16] For use with Chapters 17–32.

CHAPTER 18

Psilophyta

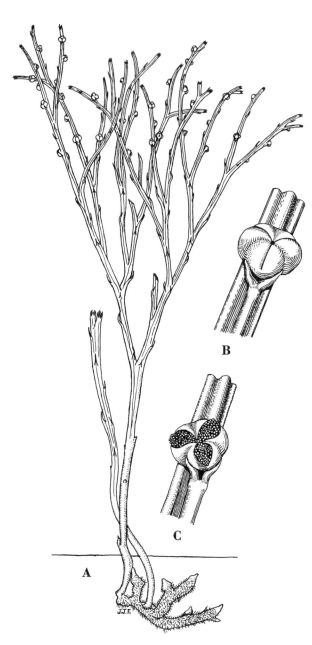

FIG. 18-1. *Psilotum nudum* (L.) Beauv. A. Rhizome and aerial branches of sporophyte. X 0.75. B, C. Details of sporangia and bracts; the sporangium in C, dehiscent. X 9.

Of the vascular plants, the members of the Psilophyta, both extant and extinct, have the least complex plant bodies.[1] Most of them are organized as dichotomously branching, leafless[2] axes which arise from subterranean rhizomes. Roots are absent. All share the common attribute of producing their sporangia terminally on branches of the axes; accordingly, their sporangia are said to be **cauline.** The gametophytes are subterranean, cylindrical, and nonphotosynthetic and the sperms multiflagellate.

Both extant and extinct members of the Psilophyta are usually included in the single class Psilopsida, the former in the order Psilotales and the latter in the order Psilophytales.

Order 1. Psilotales

FAMILY 1. PSILOTACEAE

Two genera, *Psilotum* and *Tmesipteris*, comprise the family Psilotaceae.

Psilotum

Psilotum (Gr. *psilos*, bare) (Figs. 18-1; 18-2) the **whisk fern,** occurs in Florida, Louisiana, and Texas, either epiphytically or in humus-rich soil. This is *P. nudum* (L.) Beauv. (Fig. 18-2A) which is widespread in tropical and subtropical regions. Another species, *P. complanatum* Sw. (Fig. 18-2B), occurs in Hawaii but is less abundantly and widely distributed. *Tmesipteris* (Gr. *tmesis*, act of cutting + Gr. *pteris*, fern) grows natively only in Australia, New Zealand, and on other southern Pacific islands. Because of its more ready availability and ease of culture in the green-

---

[1] Except for certain (presumably) secondarily reduced aquatics.

[2] *Tmesipteris*, perhaps, is an exception.

FIG. 18.2   A. *Psilotum nudum.* X 0.125. B. *Psilotum complanatum.* X 0.125.

house, *Psilotum* will be emphasized in the following account.

Vegetative morphology

The conspicuous plant body of *Psilotum*, which is the sporophyte, as is the case in all vascular plants, consists of dichotomously branched aerial axes a foot or more in height and of subterranean rhizomes which have epidermal cells bearing rhizoids (Figs. 18-1, 18-2); the latter may be one to three cells long. The aerial stems are ridged, often pentagonal in cross sections of the lower portions of the axis and triangular above. They bear small, scalelike appendages (Figs. 18-1, 18-3) which lack vascular tissue, although vascular

traces from the stele emerge toward the bases of some of the scale leaves in both species of *Psilotum*. Roots are absent.

Both rhizome and aerial branches develop by apical growth which may be traced to the activity of a single tetrahedral apical cell and its derivatives, all of which divide actively. A short distance posterior to the promeristem, differentiation becomes apparent (Fig. 18-4) in the meristematic tissues, in which three groups of cells are recognizable. The outermost single layer of cells are prismatic and radially elongate and comprise the protoderm. The central mass of elongate cells is the procambium; the cells between the procambium and protoderm are the ground meristem. In these three primary meristems (Fig. 18-4) the component cells continue to divide.

The organization of the aerial axis of *Psilotum* upon completion of differentiation is somewhat variable, according to the level between apex and base. The erect stems may be almost circular in transection as they emerge from the soil but toward the lowermost (first) dichotomy they are often pentagonal and between the more distal dichotomies, triangular.

The stele also changes at different levels and in different individuals. Thus, it may be triarch or tetrarch at soil level; of much greater diameter and pentarch to octarch approaching the first dichotomy; and tetrarch, triarch, or diarch in the most distal dichotomies (Fig. 18-5B). Furthermore, the stele is mesarch at

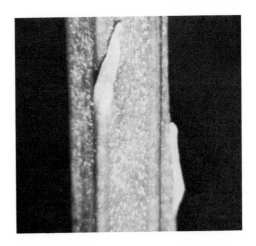

FIG. 18-3.   *Psilotum nudum.* Close-up of aerial axis showing ribs, stomata, and bracts. X 10.

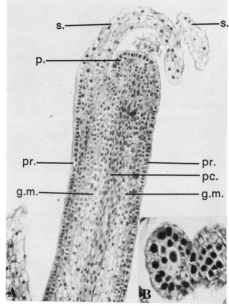

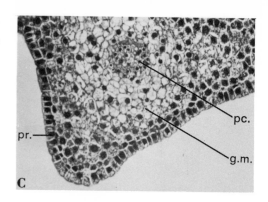

FIG. 18-4. *Psilotum nudum*. Ontogeny of the aerial axis. A. Median longisection of branch. X 60. B. Transection of promeristem; note apical cell. X 150. C. Portion of a transection at the level of the primary meristems. X 150; g.m., ground meristem; p., promeristem (note two apical cells which initiate dichotomy); pc., procambium; pr., protoderm; s., scale or bract.

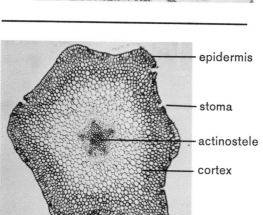

the base of the aerial shoot and this condition may extend beyond the first dichotomy. More distal portions of the axes are exarch.

The stele of *Psilotum* (Fig. 18-5A,B) has been interpreted as a protostele (actinostele) by some and as a siphonostele by others. This is because the stem center is composed of lignified, sclerenchymatous cells which may belong either to the xylem (protostele interpretation) or represent a sclerotic pith (siphonostele interpretation). It should be noted that the stele always develops from a solid core of procambium. The phloem of *Psilotum* has re-

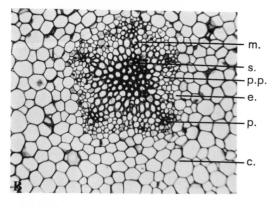

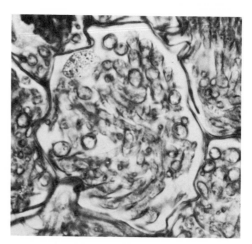

FIG. 18-5. *Psilotum nudum*. A. Transection of stem at the level of the primary permanent tissues. X 30. B. Stele of preceding, enlarged; c., cortex; e., endodermis; m., metaxylem; p., protoxylem; p.p., primary phloem; s., sclerenchyma. X 90.

FIG. 18-6. *Psilotum nudum*. Cell of cortex of rhizome filled with mycorrhizal fungus. X 770.

MORPHOLOGY OF PLANTS

cently been investigated. Sieve cells, with sieve areas in their oblique terminal walls, are present. Their nuclei disintegrate as the cells mature. A prominent endodermis surrounds the stele.

The cortex is massive as compared with the stele (Fig. 18-5A) and consists of a parenchymatous storage region adjacent to the endodermis. This is surrounded successively by a zone of sclerenchyma and by several layers of photosynthetic parenchyma cells. The latter represent the major photosynthetic region of the plant, and the increase of the internal surface of the cells by lobing suggests the chlorenchyma in the leaves of certain conifers. The cortical cells of rhizomes frequently contain fungi (Fig. 18-6), the role of which is not understood. The epidermis is heavily cutinized and interrupted here and there, between the ridges of the stem, by stomata and guard cells (Figs. 18-3, 18-5A, 18-7), the latter slightly sunken, as in many xerophytes. A small substomatal chamber is present beneath each stoma.

The scalelike appendages (Figs. 18-1, 18-3) of the stem lack vascular tissue and are made up entirely of photosynthetic tissues covered by an epidermis. As noted previously, traces may extend from the stem stele to the bases of some of the scales.

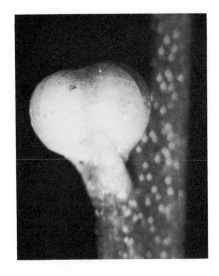

FIG. 18-7. *Psilotum nudum*. Mature and dehiscent sporangium; note abundant stomata on axis. X 15.

Reproduction: the sporophyte

Spores are produced in the globose, trilobed sporangia that are borne at the apices of short lateral branches (Figs. 18-1, 18-3, 18-7) and, therefore, are cauline. Two lateral emergences curve about the sporangium and its stalk. The latter is traversed centrally by a trace, which is connected with the stele of the main axis. The trace extends into the base of the sporangial partition and divides into three

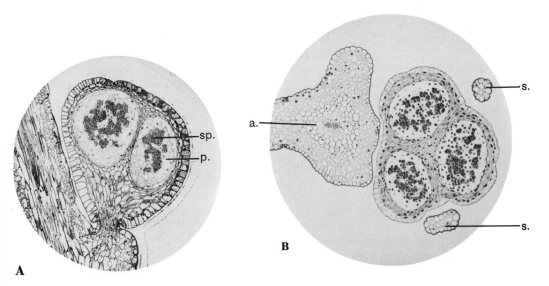

FIG. 18-8. *Psilotum nudum*. A. Longisection and B. Transection of sporangia containing sporocytes; a., axis; p., plasmodium; s., scale or bract; sp., sporogenous tissue. X 30.

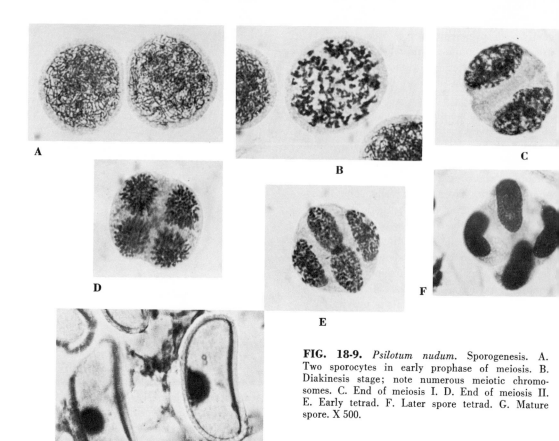

A

B

C

D

E

F

G

FIG. 18-9. *Psilotum nudum.* Sporogenesis. A. Two sporocytes in early prophase of meiosis. B. Diakinesis stage; note numerous meiotic chromosomes. C. End of meiosis I. D. End of meiosis II. E. Early tetrad. F. Later spore tetrad. G. Mature spore. X 500.

branches. The sporangium originates from superficial cells of the lateral branch and is **eusporangiate** in development. In this method of sporangium development (which is characteristic of all vascular plants except the leptosporangiate ferns, p. 341), a superficial cell or cells divide by periclinal division into an inner and outer cell layer. In subsequent development, the sporogenous tissue arises from the inner products of the initial periclinal divisions, and most of the sporangial wall arises from the outer. The wall of eusporangiate sporangia is always more than one layer of cells thick (Fig. 18-8B).

It is not entirely clear whether the three-lobed sporangium of *Psilotum* (Figs. 18-1, 18-7, 18-8) represents a single, partitioned sporangium or three single sporangia which have been united, and both interpretations have been suggested. In any case, as development proceeds, both the wall region and the sporogenous layers increase in thickness by

nuclear and cell division. Only a portion of the potentially sporogenous tissue functions as sporocytes. The remainder disintegrates (Fig. 18-8), forming a plasmodial mass at sporogenesis, during which the products of disintegration are absorbed by the sporocytes. The latter undergo the meiotic process (Fig. 18-9), forming tetrads of spores which ultimately separate. The mature spores (Fig. 18-9G) are colorless, kidney-shaped, and have transparent walls. During sporogenesis, the epidermal layer of the sporangium wall undergoes thickening by additional deposition of wall material. However, a single vertical layer remains thin-walled and, upon drying, serves as the site of dehiscence (Fig. 18-1C).

Reproduction: the gametophyte

The spores of *Psilotum* are slow to germinate; they have so far not been grown into mature gametophytes under laboratory conditions.[3] The gametophytes (Fig. 18-10) found in nature are cylindrical, rarely more than 2 mm. in diameter, are sometimes forked, and covered with numerous rhizoids. They lack chlorophyll and are saprophytic, possibly because of their association with an endophytic fungus (Fig. 18-10D). They have little internal differentiation. Their cylindrical form, dichotomous branching, and subterranean habitat render them difficult to distinguish from young rhizomes without microscopic examination. The occasional presence of typical xylem cells (tracheids) in the center of the gametophytes, along with their cylindrical form and rhizoids, has been interpreted as an

incipient or reduced stele and as support for the homologous theory of alternation of generations, according to which sporophytes and gametophytes are merely different manifestations of a single ancestral plant body. It should be noted that the gametophytes in which xylem tissue has been observed have been shown to be diploid; apparently most greenhouse specimens of *Psilotum* are tetraploid.

The sex organs develop from surface cells of the bisexual gametophytes (Fig. 18-10). The antheridia are hemispherical and slightly protuberant, the single layer of jacket cells enclosing a small number of coiled, multiflagellate sperms (Fig. 18-10C,D). The archegonia (Fig. 18-10B) are partially sunken

---

[3] Dr. D. W. Bierhorst has succeeded in growing gametophytes in the soil of potted greenhouse plants.

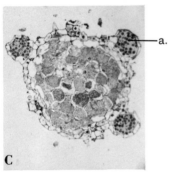

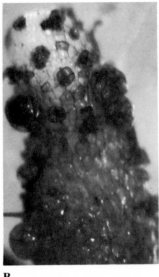

A

B

FIG. 18-10. *Psilotum nudum.* Gametophytes. A. Forked specimen with rhizoids and prominent antheridia. X 12. B. Apex of gametophyte with archegonia. X 42. C. Transection showing mycorrhizal fungi and antheridium (a.) X 110. D. Section of antheridium. X 450. (*Courtesy of Dr. D. W. Bierhorst.*)

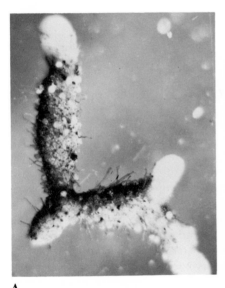

—a.

C

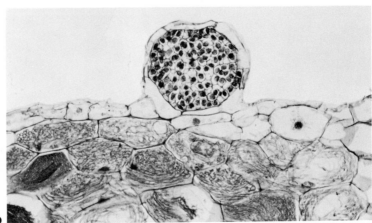

D

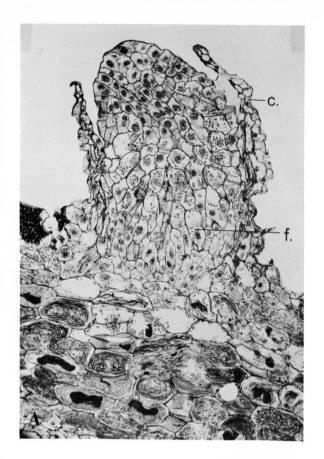

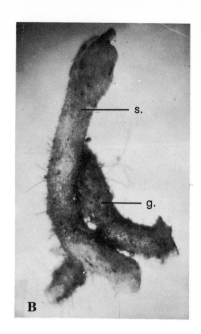

FIG. 18-11. *Psilotum nudum.* Development of the embryonic sporophyte. A. Longisection of barely emergent sporophyte. X 60. B. Gross appearance of young sporophyte (s.) attached to forked gametophyte (g.); c., calyptra; f., foot. X 12. (*Courtesy of Dr. D. W. Bierhorst.*)

within the gametophyte and have necks that are much shorter than those in the Hepatophyta and Bryophyta. The necks are composed of only four rows of neck cells.

Reproduction: embryogeny

Following fertilization, the zygote undergoes transverse division. The outer product of the division gives rise to the embryonic

stem; the derivatives of the inner one are organized as an enlarged foot. The primary stem is a branched rhizome which develops rhizoids and becomes infected with a fungus as it emerges from the gametophyte (Fig. 18-11). Some of the branch tips become negatively geotropic and produce aerial axes when they are exposed at the soil surface. By this time the embryonic stem usually has separated

FIG. 18-12. *Tmesipteris* sp. A. Living specimen from the Philippines. X 0.5. B. Enlarged view of bilobed sporangium and bract; note stomata. X 12. (*Courtesy of Mr. Donald Reynolds.*)

A   B

MORPHOLOGY OF PLANTS

from the foot, which remains within the gametophyte.

Tmesipteris

Tmesipteris (Fig. 18-12A) is an erect or pendulous epiphyte on the trunks of tropical tree ferns or it may be terrestrial and erect. The plant consists of branching, rhizoid-bearing rhizomes that anchor it and aerial branches which may be unbranched or undergo one or several dichotomies, depending on the species. From base to apex, the scalelike, nonvascular appendages are succeeded by small flattened leaves, each of which is traversed by a single, central unbranched vein connected to the stele by a trace. The fact that the stem apex itself is modified as a leaf has suggested that the "leaves" of *Tmesipteris* may represent flattened branchlets.

The sporangia of *Tmesipteris* also are subtended by a pair of bracts and are bilobed (Fig. 18-12B). The gametophytes are similar to those of *Psilotum*.

Summary

The more important features of *Psilotum* described above illustrate its anomalous position in comparison with other vascular cryptogams. In its lack of roots and vascularized leaves it is paralleled only by certain fossil genera such as *Rhynia* (see below). An additional characteristic it shares with them is the terminally cauline position of the sporangia. In this respect it and *Tmesipteris* are unlike other living vascular cryptogams, with the possible exception of *Equisetum*. The sporangium itself is primitive in lacking a tapetum, a special tissue for nutrition of the developing spores. The latter obtain metabolites through the disintegration of some of the sporogenous tissue prior to sporogenesis, as noted also in the liverwort, *Sphaerocarpos*. The branched cylindrical gametophytes, similar in some respects to the sporophyte, are almost unique in the plant kingdom.[4] It is possible that *Psilotum* represents a living remnant of members of the Devonian flora now extinct, and that it

---

[4] See, however, those of *Ophioglossum*, page 326, and those of certain species of *Schizaea*, page 353.

has survived to the present with few modifications from its progenitors. The fossil record sheds no light on this speculation.

Order 2. Psilophytales

The resistant nature of the xylem and other lignified and sclerotic tissues of vascular plants has resulted in their more abundant preservation in a form suitable for microscopic study. A relatively rich land flora of vascular plants has been described from early Devonian (Table 32-1) strata. Although there have been several reports of the occurrence of spores, pollen, and vascular tissues in the Cambrian, these require confirmation. Our knowledge of the Devonian flora is based largely on a remarkably well-preserved bog in the vicinity of Rhynie in Aberdeenshire, Scotland, the vegetation of which is sometimes called the Rhynie flora. These fossils were described by British paleobotanists about 60 years ago, and Devonian rocks in other parts of the world have yielded similar plants. It should be emphasized, however, that an earlier discovery of vascular plants in the Devonian was made by Dawson, who described the genus *Psilophyton* (Fig. 18-13) from eastern Canada in 1859.

Knowledge of the Devonian flora has profoundly influenced current ideas regarding the relationship of vascular plants, largely because these extinct plants furnish us with morphological features and potentialities which are developed more highly in extant genera.

The Psilophytales herein discussed belong to the families Psilophytaceae, Rhyniaceae, and Asteroxylaceae.

FAMILY 1. PSILOPHYTACEAE

Psilophyton

Although *Psilophyton* (Gr. *psilos*, naked + Gr. *phyton*, plant) (Fig. 18-13) had been described from Devonian strata in eastern Canada as early as 1859, its structure was so anomalous, as compared with other known vascular cryptogams, both extant and extinct, that it received little attention for more than

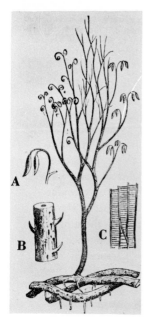

FIG. 18-13. *Psilophyton princeps* Dawson. Reconstruction based on fossil Devonian material. A. Details of pendulous sporangia. X 1. B. Detail of axis with spines. X 1. C. Tracheids from stele, much enlarged. Compare with Fig. 18-15 and comments in text. (*After Dawson.*)

leaves of *Psilotum*. The stem was protostelic with centrarch xylem.

The sporangium-bearing branches in the reconstruction probably belong to another plant, *Dawsonites arcuatus* Halle (Fig. 18-14). Recently, it has been shown that the sporangia of *Psilophyton* were lateral (Fig. 18-15), not terminal as in *Dawsonites* (Fig. 18-14) and *Rhynia* (Fig. 18-17), and hence more like those of *Psilotum*. Thus, there were apparently two series of Devonian psilophytes, one with terminal sporangia and one with lateral ones. The mesarch xylem and much-branched axes of *Dawsonites*, with their terminal sporangia, are not far removed from putative fern precursors (see Chapter 23).

FIG. 18-15. *Psilophyton princeps* Dawson. Reconstructed segment of a fertile axis showing globose and lateral sporangia. X 2.5. (*After Hueber.*)

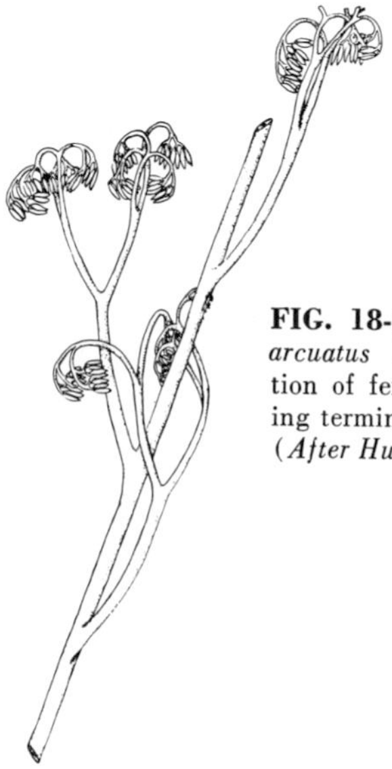

60 years until paleobotanists began to describe plant remains with somewhat similar attributes from the Devonian sandstones at Rhynie, Scotland.

Psilophyton, as now widely illustrated in reconstruction (Fig. 18-13), consisted of leafless horizontal rhizomes which bore erect, dichotomously branching, aerial branches with coiled or circinate developing apices. The aerial stems bore spiny scales or appendages which lacked vascular tissue as do the scale

FIG. 18-14. *Dawsonites arcuatus* Halle. Reconstruction of fertile branches bearing terminal sporangia. X 0.5. (*After Hueber.*)

FAMILY 2. ASTEROXYLACEAE

Asteroxylon

Asteroxylon, so named for the actinostele in its aerial branches (Fig. 18-16), was contemporaneous with *Rhynia* in the Devonian swamps of Rhynie. It, too, produced erect, branching aerial branches from smooth horizontal rhizomes. The former were densely clothed with small, *Lycopodium*-like leaves, which, however, lacked vascular tissue. The sporangia were probably borne on stalked lateral branches in the axils of the veinless leaves. One species of *Asteroxylon* attained a meter in height. It may be that further studies

276

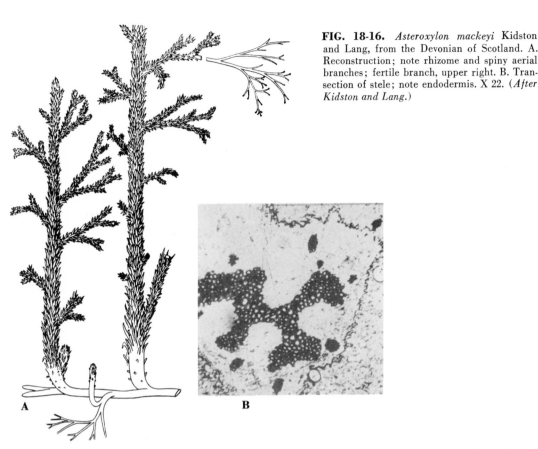

FIG. 18-16. *Asteroxylon mackeyi* Kidston and Lang, from the Devonian of Scotland. A. Reconstruction; note rhizome and spiny aerial branches; fertile branch, upper right. B. Transection of stele; note endodermis. X 22. (*After Kidston and Lang.*)

A   B

will confirm a suggestion that *Asteroxylon* has affinities with the Microphyllophyta (Chapter 19).

FAMILY 3. RHYNIACEAE

Rhynia

Although *Psilophyton* (Fig. 18-13) had been described as early as 1859, its structure was so anomalous, in comparison with that of other vascular cryptogams, that it received little attention until later, when paleobotanists began to describe genera with similar attributes from the Devonian rocks at Rhynie and elsewhere. The Carboniferous had long been known as the age of ferns; but the discovery that Devonian strata contain a rather diverse cryptogamic flora stimulated anew interest in the origin of vascular plants.

One of the best-known Devonian genera is *Rhynia* (after Rhynie). *Rhynia* (Fig. 18-17) probably was a marsh plant, perhaps not unlike our modern sedges or rushes in gross ap-

pearance and stature. Its most striking feature was its lack of leaves and roots, for the plant bodies consisted entirely of dichotomously branching aerial stems attached to rhizomes on which tufts of unicellular rhizoids served as organs of absorption. As in certain modern xerophytes, these plants had stems as the chief photosynthetic organs. Stomata in the epidermis of the aerial axes are well preserved in fossil specimens.

The Rhynie plants show internal structure particularly well (Fig. 18-18). The stem of species of *Rhynia* ranged from 2 to 5 mm. in diameter. Plant anatomists had postulated before the discovery of *Rhynia* that stems having a solid core of xylem surrounded by phloem (a protostele) represented the most primitive type of stele. The occurrence of such an anatomical pattern in the stems of many Devonian plants is striking confirmation of this theory. That these plants were sporophytes is evidenced by the abundant occurrence of spores in tetrads (Fig. 18-19) in association

FIG. 18-17. *Rhynia gwynne-vaughanii.* A. Reconstruction; note vegetative and fertile axes, the latter with terminal sporangia. B. Section of terminal sporangium filled with spores. (A. *Courtesy of the Chicago Natural History Museum.* B. *After Kidston and Lang.*)

A

B

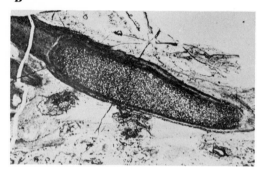

with the stems. The spores were produced in elongate sporangia (Fig. 18-17B) borne at the stem apices. The sporangia here are sporogenous stem apices. No special provision for sporangial dehiscence has been described,

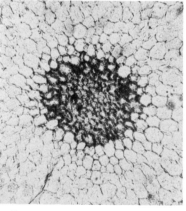

FIG. 18-19. *Rhynia* sp. Spore tetrads. X 250. (*Preparation by Dr. Richard Stearns.*)

and no germinating spores or mature gametophytes are known.

Summary

In summary, it may be stated that *Rhynia* and *Psilophyton* represent a type of Devonian cryptogam in which the sporophyte consisted exclusively of branched aerial and subterranean axes. Leaves and roots were absent. Furthermore, these primitive plants had protostelic organization and cauline sporangia borne at the branch tips.

When one reviews the living vascular cryptogams in search of genera with attributes similar to those of the Devonian genera just described, it becomes apparent that *Psilotum* especially, of the extant genera described in

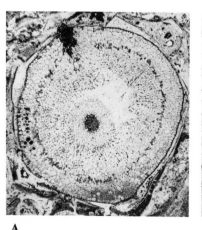

FIG. 18-18. *Rhynia* sp. A. Transection of axis; note central stele, three regions of cortex and epidermis. X 12.5. B. Stele enlarged; note centrarch xylem. X 150.

A

B

this text, seems to qualify. Here, too, one finds leaves and roots absent, as well as protostelic stems and terminal cauline sporangia. No fossil record of *Psilotum* has been discovered, however, so classification of that genus with *Rhynia* and *Psilophyton* in the same division, the Psilophyta, is based entirely on speculation. But it is quite apparent that *Psilotum* stands almost alone among other extant vascular cryptogams.

DISCUSSION QUESTIONS

1. Define eusporangiate sporangium development.

2. The gametophytes of *Psilotum* and *Tmesipteris* have never been grown to maturity, from spores, in laboratory culture. How would you attempt to accomplish this?

3. What significance has been attached to the occasional occurrence of tracheids in *Psilotum* gametophytes?

4. In what respects is *Psilotum* unusual among vascular plants?

5. Distinguish among rhizoids, rhizomes, and roots.

6. What structural adaptations related to photosynthesis occur in the stems of *Psilotum*?

7. What type of nutrition probably occurs in the *Psilotum* gametophyte? How could you prove it?

8. What does the fossil record indicate regarding the comparative age of algae and vascular plants?

9. What are the significant features of such Devonian fossils as *Psilophyton*, *Rhynia*, and *Asteroxylon*?

10. What evidence is there that *Rhynia* plants were sporophytes?

11. Does the fossil record shed any light regarding the precursors of the Devonian land plants?

CHAPTER 19

Division Microphyllophyta

Members of the division Microphyllophyta (Gr. *mikros*, small + Gr. *phyllon*, leaf + Gr. *phyton*, plant), a group accorded only subdivisional rank under the name Lycopsida in many schemes of classification (Table 32-2), are readily distinguishable from the Psilophyta by having vascularized leaves and roots and by the intimate association of their sporangia with fertile leaves known as **sporophylls** (Gr. *spora*, spore + Gr. *phyllon*, leaf). Some of these plants are commonly known as **club** and **spike mosses,**[1] because their small

[1] They were, in fact, classified with the mosses by Linnaeus.

size and their mosslike leaves, closely arranged on the stems, suggest mosses; furthermore, the aggregation of the sporophylls of certain species into terminal groups (Figs. 19-1, 19-2) has suggested the terms "club" or "spike."

Whether they are given class or divisional rank, two series are usually distinguished in the classification of these plants (Table 32-2). In one series, exemplified in this chapter by the extant *Selaginella* (Figs. 19-16, 19-17) and *Isoetes* (Fig. 19-34) and by the extinct *Selaginellites* and the Lepidodendrales, each leaf produces a small, basal protuberance, the **ligule** (L. *ligula*, little tongue) (Fig. 19-22B).

A B C

FIG. 19-1. A. *Lycopodium lucidulum*. Portion of plant; note aerial branches, rhizome, and roots. X 0.5. B. *Lycopodium complanatum*; note strobili on special branches. X 0.5. C. *Phylloglossum drummondii*. X 4. (C. *After Bower*.)

These genera are grouped in the class Glossopsida (Gr. *glossa*, tongue + Gr. *opsis*, appearance of), sometimes called the Ligulatae; in the other series, the Aglossopsida, the ligule is absent. The extant genera *Lycopodium* and *Phylloglossum* (Figs. 19-1, 19-2) and the extinct *Protolepidodendron* (Fig. 19-41) belong in the latter category.

Class 1. Aglossopsida

Order 1. Lycopodiales

FAMILY 1. LYCOPODIACEAE

Lycopodium

Introduction and vegetative morphology

Lycopodium (Figs. 19-1, 19-2) and *Phylloglossum* (Fig. 19-1C), the only living genera included in this class, comprise 180 species. *Phylloglossum*, of which but a single species is known, occurs only in Australasia. Species of *Lycopodium* are widely distributed and are familiarly known as ground pines, trailing evergreens, and club mosses. Most species are perennials, living upon the forest floor in temperate climates, but many tropical species are epiphytic. The plants are rather firm herbs with dichotomously or monopodially branched stems (Figs. 19-1, 19-2). In the latter case, the branch system consists of a main axis which supports minor branches.

The leaves are small (Figs. 19-1 to 19-3),

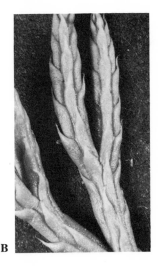

FIG. 19-2. A. *Lycopodium annotinum*; note terminal strobili. X 0.5. B. *L. obscurum*; note terminal strobili. X 0.5.

sessile, and spiral or whorled in arrangement. In *L. complanatum* L., the leaves are much reduced and almost scalelike (Fig. 19-3A). All species have branching rhizomes from which aerial branches develop. The roots are delicate and dichotomously branched, and are

FIG. 19-3. *Lycopodium*. Enlarged view of leafy axes. A. *L. obscurum*. B. *L. complanatum*. X 4.

scattered along the underground portions of the stem (Fig. 19-1A).

Development of both the stem and root of *Lycopodium* may be traced to an apical group of meristematic cells no one of which is specially differentiated. A central procambium strand develops some distance back from the promeristem in both stem and root and ultimately gives rise to an exarch[2] protostele in both (Fig. 19-4). The stem stele is bounded by several layers of pericycle cells and sharply delimited by a well-developed endodermis. The epidermis contains stomata and guard cells. The arrangement of xylem and phloem in the stem varies in different species, in accordance with the degree of ridging or dissection of the central xylem mass. It also varies within a species in accordance with stem diameter. In species in which the xylem seems to consist of discrete masses in transverse section (Fig. 19-4), serial transverse sections reveal that the *apparently* discrete units are lobes that join each other at different levels of the stem. In species with dissected xylem masses, phloem cells develop between them, forming a plectostele. In species with continuous xylem, the phloem is present external to the xylem. Functional phloem is, however, always

---

[2] Sometimes weakly mesarch.

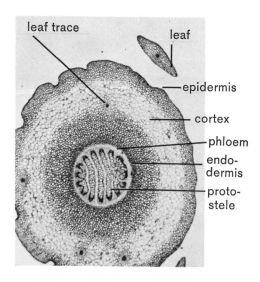

FIG. 19-4. *Lycopodium clavatum* L. Transection of stem; this type of protostele is a plectostele (see p. 259). X 25.

leaf trace
leaf
epidermis
cortex
phloem
endo-
dermis
proto-
stele

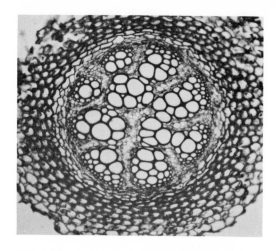

FIG. 19-5. *Lycopodium complanatum*. Transection of root. X 60. (*Courtesy of Mrs. Elizabeth Pixley.*)

separated from the xylem by a layer of parenchyma cells.

The roots of erect species of *Lycopodium* arise deep within the rhizomes from the surface of the stele. They grow through the cortex and emerge into the soil at points somewhat removed from the level of their origin. The root stele varies with the size of the root in a given species and also with the species. The exarch stele may be crescentic with phloem in the concavity of the xylem crescent as in *L. lucidulum* or a plectostele as in *L. complanatum* (Fig. 19-5); other configurations occur.

The tip of the root is covered by a root cap. The root hairs are anomalous in that they develop in pairs from the epidermal cells. Roots of *Lycopodium* usually branch dichotomously; the branches originate through the reorganization of the apical meristematic cells into two groups.

The leaves of *Lycopodium* arise by localized growth of groups of superficial cells near the stem apex. As they grow, each develops a central procambium strand which finally differentiates into a vascular strand of tracheids surrounded by scattered sieve elements and parenchyma. The chlorenchyma of the leaf is rather uniform in structure, small intercellular spaces being present. Depending on the species, the stomata occur either on the epidermis of both leaf surfaces or only on the lower epidermis. The vascular supply of the leaf is connected to the stem stele by a leaf trace (Fig.

19-4) which is connected with the protoxylem of the stem stele. Leaves with a single unbranched vein, the traces of which leave no parenchymatous gap in the stele above its point of departure, are said to be **microphyllous.** It should be emphasized at this point that small size is merely a secondary attribute of many microphyllous leaves; their possession of single, unbranched veins and the absence of leaf gaps near the point of departure of their traces are their distinguishing features.

Reproduction: the sporophyte

Species of *Lycopodium*, like *L. lucidulum* Michx. (Fig. 19-1A), in which the sporophylls are not localized in compact aggregations, in

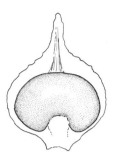

FIG. 19-7.   *Lycopodium complanatum.* Adaxial view of sporophyll. X 8.

axil of the leaf and stem (Fig. 19-6). In some species—*L. lucidulum*, for example, the fertile, sporangium-bearing leaves, the **sporophylls,** are entirely similar to sterile leaves and occur in zones among them (Fig. 19-6); such species are considered primitive. In species like *L. complanatum*, on the other hand, localization of the sporophylls into a terminal cone-like structure, the **strobilus** (Figs. 19-1B, 19-8), is accompanied by their modification into nonphotosynthetic, scalelike structures which are reduced in size (Fig. 19-7). This condition is interpreted as the most advanced in the genus. Some morphologists regard the *lucidulum* type as a strobilus comprising an entire plant. According to this view, the sterile

FIG. 19-6.   *Lycopodium lucidulum;* b., propagative gemma or bulbil; s., axillary sporangia (their sporophylls removed). X 4.

many instances produce special mechanisms for vegetative propagation, namely **gemmae** or **bulbils** (Fig. 19-6). These consist of a proximal, enlarged base and a distal, short axis with several pairs of leaves. The distal portion is abscised and may develop into a young sporophyte under favorable conditions.

The sporophyte of *Lycopodium* at maturity produces spores in rather massive, kidney-shaped sporangia which are often borne on short stalks either on the leaf base or in the

FIG. 19-8.   *Lycopodium.* Strobili of *L. annotinum,* left, and *L. complanatum,* right (enlarged). X 4.

leaves represent secondarily sterilized sporophylls.

It is clear that the compact type of strobilus is a stem with short internodes bearing sporophylls (Fig. 19-9). The strobilus develops from an apical meristem and its vascular structure is similar to that of the vegetative axis. Each sporophyll is supplied from the stele by a single trace, as are the vegetative leaves of the plant. The individual sporangium arises in eusporangiate fashion from a row of superficial cells on the adaxial surface of the leaf base or at the junction of the leaf and stem (Fig. 19-9). These cells usually undergo divisions parallel to the leaf surface; hence a single transverse row of cells, three cells deep, extends partially across the leaf base. The central row continues division and ultimately forms the sporogenous tissue (Fig. 19-10). The upper row also undergoes division and develops a three-layered sporangium wall. The innermost wall layer, next to the sporogenous tissue, functions as a nutritive layer, the **tapetum**. The lowermost of the original three cell layers contributes to the lower sporangial wall and stalk. As the sporangium develops, the sporogenous cells become isolated and spherical and ultimately produce a tetrad of spores each. These finally separate and secrete a wall with ornamenta-

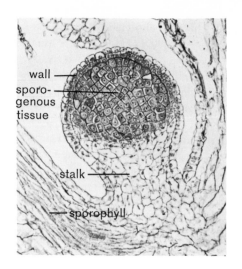

FIG. 19-10. *Lycopodium obscurum*. Longisection of immature sporangium. X 250.

tion which varies with the species. The spores are yellow at maturity. Dehiscence of the sporangium occurs along a line of cells running across the upper surface of the reniform sporangium. In species with compact strobili, this is preceded by slight elongation of the internodes and by drying and spreading of the sporophylls which are facilitated by the shrinkage of a cavity in the lower side of each sporophyll.

Reproduction: the gametophyte

The various species of *Lycopodium* vary in the speed with which their spores germinate and complete their development into mature gametophytes (Figs. 19-11, 19-15A,B). There is good evidence that speed of germination is correlated with thickness and/or permeability of the spore wall. Thus, the thin-walled spores of *L. cernuum* L. germinate soon after they have been planted.

Treatment of the spores of thick-walled species such as *L. complanatum, L. selago,* and *L. obscurum* with concentrated sulfuric acid, by scarification, and/or high temperatures have effected much more rapid germination in the laboratory than occurs in nature. Without treatment, the spores of some of these species may not germinate for from 5 to 7 years, during which they are washed down into the soil and buried by debris to depths of 10 or more centimeters. In nature,

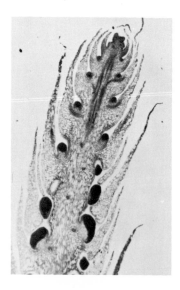

FIG. 19-9. *Lycopodium* sp. Median longisection of immature strobilus; note developing sporangia and sporophylls. X 30.

FIG. 19-11. Gametophytes of *Lycopodium. L. obscurum*, at the left; the others, *L. complanatum*; young sporophytes attached. X 0.5.

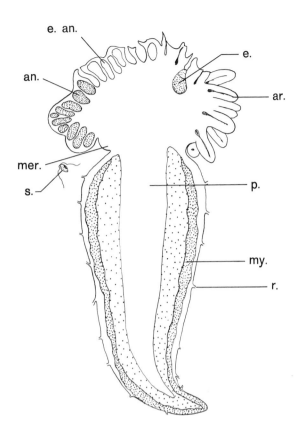

FIG. 19-12. *Lycopodium complanatum*. Median longitudinal section of gametophyte (diagrammatic). X 25; an., antheridium; ar., archegonium; e., embryo; e. an., empty antheridium; mer., meristematic collar; my., mycorrhizal zone; p., central pith-like region; r., rhizoid; s., sperm. (*After Bruchmann.*)

several types of gametophyte have been found: some are photosynthetic and at least in part epiterranean (*L. cernuum, L. innundatum*), while others are tuberous or branching cylinders, achlorophyllous and subterranean (*L. complanatum, L. obscurum*) (Fig. 19-11). Although the subterranean gametophytes in nature lack chlorophyll and are clearly heterotrophic, in laboratory cultures on the surface of agar their cells develop numerous chloroplasts. Furthermore, gametophytes grown in laboratory culture are much branched and differ markedly from the compact, fleshy forms of the same species found in nature. It has been demonstrated recently that if a fungus isolated from naturally occurring gametophytes is inoculated into axenic (pure) cultures of young gametophytes, the fungus will invade the lower (older) portions of the gametophytes. The morphology of the latter is then modified so that the gametophyte comes to consist of a dark-green fleshy base and a lighter green crown on which the sex organs are borne at maturity. The fungus has not been positively identified but is a member of the Phycomycota, possibly a species of *Pythium*. The form of the gametophytes of *Lycopodium*, accordingly, is readily affected by environmental stimuli.

Both antheridia and archegonia occur on the crowns of individual mature gametophytes (Fig. 19-12). The development of both antheridia and archegonia (Fig. 19-13) may be traced to single superficial cells. In each case, these undergo periclinal division; by further division, the inner of the two cells gives rise to the major portion of the antheridium and archegonium. The sex organs,

therefore, are partially embedded. The antheridia are massive and produce large numbers of biflagellate sperms which are liberated through the ruptured superficial wall

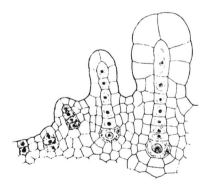

FIG. 19-13. *Lycopodium selago* L. Left to right: successively later stages in the development of archegonia. X 250. (*After Bruchmann.*)

cells. The archegonial necks vary among the several species in length and degree of emergence. The necks are composed of four or five rows of neck cells.

Reproduction: embryogeny

The occurrence of *Lycopodium* gametophytes, each with several attached sporophytes in various stages of development, indicates not only that the gametophytes are long-lived and active in the nutrition of the embryonic sporophyte, but also that the sex organs may function over long periods. The zygote divides by a transverse wall into an outer, **suspensor cell,** and an inner, **embryo-forming cell** (Fig. 19-14A). The latter develops the embryo itself; the former may divide once or twice. The embryo-forming cell gives rise to a massive foot, stem, and leaf (Fig. 19-14B,C). The first embryonic leaf may be called the **cotyledon.** The root develops adventitiously at the base of the cotyledon. The primary axis grows out of the gametophyte and up into the light. Axes and leaves of sporophytes borne on subterranean gametophytes remain colorless until they emerge above the substratum. The gametophyte may persist for a long time attached to the sporophyte (Figs. 19-11, 19-15B-D), but it ultimately disintegrates as the latter becomes established. The first leaves in some species differ from those on the mature plant in their scalelike habit as well as in the absence of vascular tissue and chlorophyll.

Recent studies indicate that sporophytes of *Lycopodium* may develop apogamously in laboratory cultures; whether or not this occurs also in nature has not been ascertained.

Summary

The axis of the sporophyte in many *Lycopodium* species, like that of *Psilotum*, is fundamentally protostelic. Its branching may be dichotomous or monopodial. Although the mature sporophyte has microphyllous leaves and roots, organs that are absent in *Psilotum*, there is evidence that these organs are secondary additions to the axis of *Lycopodium*. This is suggested by the absence of vascular tissue in the early leaves of the embryonic plant and the lack of a specially differentiated root-forming region in the embryo.

The several species show variation in the distribution of sporogenous tissue, apparently progressing from a scattered, zonate condition in *L. lucidulum* through stages in localization at the stem apex found in *L. innundatum* and *L. complanatum*. For the most part, the massive, short-stalked, reniform sporangia occur on the adaxial surface of the leaf base. Their development can be traced to a row of surface cells which divide periclinally to form a row of cells three tiers deep. The sporangial wall and the tapetum arise from the uppermost layer; the sporogenous tissue may be traced to the intermediate layer, a manifestation of the eusporangiate condition characteristic of a majority of vascular plants.

The spores of most species require long periods to develop mature gametophytes in nature. *Lycopodium cernuum, L. carolinianum,* and *L. innundatum* are exceptional in this respect. The gametophytes in nature are of several kinds, either photosynthetic and partially epiterranean (*L. cernuum*), or completely devoid of chlorophyll and subterranean (*L. complanatum* and *L. obscurum*). In the latter case, they may be either tuberous

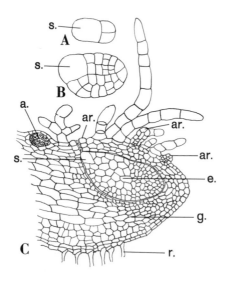

FIG. 19-14. *Lycopodium clavatum.* A–C. Successively older stages of embryogeny; a., antheridium; ar., archegonium; e., embryo; g., gametophyte; r., rhizoid; s., suspensor. A, B. X 120. C. X 60. (*After Bruchmann.*)

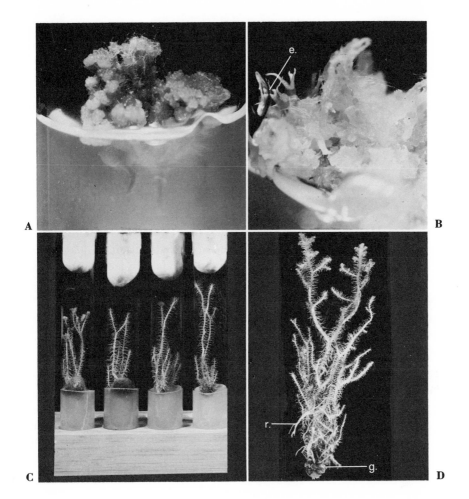

FIG. 19-15. *Lycopodium cernuum* L. Development of gametophytes and young sporophytes in culture. A. Gametophyte on agar; note club-shaped tips and rhizoids. X 2.3. B. Gametophyte with several embryos (e.) with first leaves or prophylls. X 4. C. Young sporophytes arising from gametophytes 2 months after spores were sown. D. Plants with immature strobili 28 months after spore germination; g., gametophyte; r., roots or rhizophore. (*Courtesy of Dr. Ralph H. Wetmore.*)

or branching cylindrical structures. Subterranean types are infected with a mycorrhizal fungus and are saprophytic.

In axenic laboratory cultures of these same species, however, the gametophytes are green. Invasion of young gametophytes by a phycomycetous fungus modifies the morphology of the gametophyte. The fungus is both inter- and intracellular. The sex organs are massive and partially embedded; the sperms are biflagellate. Each gametophyte may produce several sporophytes at intervals as long as a year apart. The gametophytes persist during the slow development of the embryonic sporophyte.

Class 2. Glossopsida

Order 1. *Selaginellales*

FAMILY 1. SELAGINELLACEAE

Selaginella

Introduction and vegetative morphology

Selaginella (Dim. of L. *selago*, name of plant resembling the savin, a juniper + L. *ella*, diminutive) (Figs. 19-16, 19-17) is one of three extant genera of the class Glossopsida, all the members of which have ligulate leaves (Fig. 19-22B,C). Although it

a single sporangium on the adaxial surface, *Selaginella* also has features which distinguish it from *Lycopodium*. The most significant of these is the production of two kinds of spores, a condition known as **heterospory,** which is associated with profound changes in the morphology and physiology of the gametophyte generation. Furthermore, both the vegetative leaves and the sporophylls of *Selaginella* have small, tonguelike **ligules** (Fig. 19-22B,C).

The genus *Selaginella*, sometimes called the **spike moss,** is a large one, including approximately 700 species which are developed most abundantly in tropical regions with heavy rainfall. In the United States, *S. apoda* (L.) Fern., an inhabitant of moist soils, is widely distributed, as is the xerophytic *S. rupestris* Spring, an inhabitant of exposed rocks. The so-called "resurrection plant" (Fig. 19-18), often sold as a novelty, is the xerophytic *S. lepidophylla* (Hook. and Grev.) Spring, which is native to the southwestern United States. A number of tropical species are cultivated in conservatories and in Wardian cases because of the beauty of their branches and foliage; *S. kraussiana* A. Br. and *S. uncinata* Spring are encountered frequently as a ground cover in greenhouses.[3]

FIG. 19-16. A. *Selaginella uncinata* Spring. B. *S. kraussiana* A. Br. X 0.66.

has such *Lycopodium*-like attributes as small microphyllous leaves, the herbaceous habit, and strobili composed of sporophylls bearing

---

[3] A magnificent collection of *Selaginella* (and ferns) is maintained in the conservatories at Garfield Park, Chicago, Ill.

FIG. 19-17. *Selaginella pallescens* Spring. A. Habit of growth. X 0.25. B. Single "frond" with strobili. X 0.33.

FIG. 19-18. *Selaginella lepidophylla* (Hook. and Grev.) Spring. The "resurrection plant." A. Moist. B. The same plant, air-dried. X 0.33.

A   B

Most species of *Selaginella* exhibit abundant branching, often in a single plane (Fig. 19-17A,B). The branches are arranged dichotomously or in monopodial or sympodial fashion, depending on the species. Branching and planation in some species result in the production of frondlike growths (Fig. 19-17) which may arise from a common center, simulating a fern. Other species are climbers, and still others are prostrate and creeping (Fig. 19-16).

Development of the stem may be traced either to a single apical cell and its derivatives or to a group of apical meristematic cells, depending on the species. In some species, the apical cell is later replaced by a group of meristematic initials. *Selaginella kraussiana* is typical of those with a single apical cell. Some distance back from the apical meristem, the central region of the stem differentiates as procambium from which the vascular tissues arise. In older regions of the axis (Fig. 19-19) in species like *S. caulescens* Spring, the central portion is separated from the cortex by a cylindrical cavity. The cortex and central tissues are connected by elongate endodermal cells which are called **trabeculae** (L. *trabecula*, little beam). Casparian thickenings are apparent on the walls of these cells.

The stele may be circular or ribbon-shaped in transection, depending on the species. The stele in *S. kraussiana* is a dual structure for part of the distance between successive branches. This duality results from a forking of the stele in precocious preparation of the trace to a more distal branch (Fig. 19-20). In other species there may be one or several steles, the **polystelic** condition. Each stele in *S. kraussiana* is surrounded by a single layer of pericycle cells, immediately within which the phloem is located. The central portion of each stele contains the xylem, which is exarch and monarch.[4] The cortex is composed of thin-walled, photosynthetic parenchyma cells, bounded externally by a cutinized epidermis with stomata. It should be noted that in some species of *Selaginella* (*S. rupestris* [L.] Spring, for example), series of procambium cells differentiate into vessels rather

---

[4] The xylem of the stem stele is mesarch in some species, among others, in *S. martensii*, *S. uncinata*, *S. emmeliana*, and *S. caulescens*.

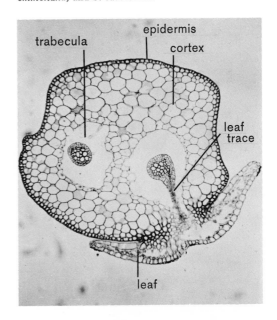

FIG. 19-19. *Selaginella caulescens.* Transection of a stem and leaf base. X 25.

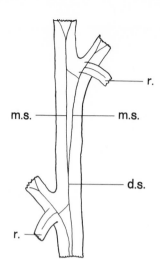

FIG. 19-20. *Selaginella kraussiana*. Diagrammatic segment of a main axis, its branches, and roots; note precocious forking of stele in anticipation of branching; d.s., single diarch stele; m.s., two monarch steles; r., root. (*Modified from Webster and Steeves.*)

than into tracheids. Vessels, it will be recalled, are composed of cell segments in which the common terminal walls have become perforate; they are multicellular in origin, and lacking in all but a few genera of vascular cryptogams.

In many species of *Selaginella*, prominent, leafless axes originate near the points of branch origin (Fig. 19-16A) and grow toward the substratum. Until recently, these were interpreted as specialized, root-bearing branches and termed **rhizophores.** A recent, intensive study of several species, including *S. kraussiana*, indicates that these are adventitious roots which fork repeatedly and dichotomously near their apices. Growth of both the main root and its smaller rootlets may be traced to a single, prominent apical cell. The root contains a protostele in which the central protoxylem is surrounded by metaxylem.

The ligulate leaves of *Selaginella* may be arranged either spirally, a primitive attribute, as in *S. rupestris*, or spirally and compressed in four rows, as in *S. kraussiana* (Fig. 19-21A). In the latter, the two dorsal rows of leaves are smaller than the two rows with ventral insertion. This condition is known as **anisophylly.** Others species of *Selaginella*, *S. rupestris*, for example, are **isophyllous** like *Lycopodium*. The leaves are sessile on the stem, alternately inserted, and each is traversed longitudinally by a single unbranched vein which is connected to the stele by a leaf trace (Fig. 19-19). The leaves, therefore, are microphyllous. Mention has already been made of the basal ligule on the adaxial surface of each leaf. Transverse sections of the leaf (Fig. 19-21B) reveal lower and upper epidermal cells containing chloroplasts, and between them the mesophyll composed of photosynthetic parenchyma cells with intercellular spaces. The mesophyll cells of differ-

FIG. 19-21. A. *Selaginella uncinata*. Leaf arrangement and dimorphism. X 6. B. *S. caulescens*. Transection of leaf. X 450.

A

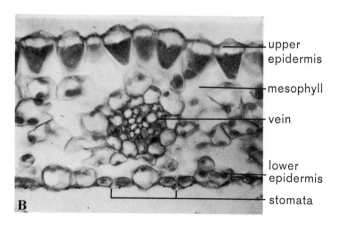

B

upper epidermis

mesophyll

vein

lower epidermis

stomata

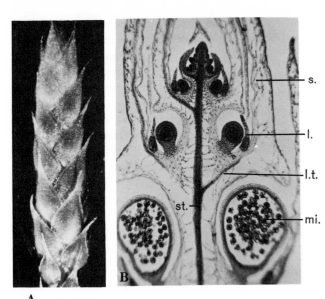

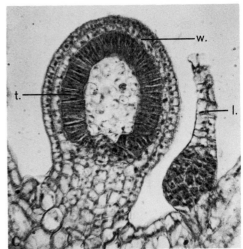

FIG. 19-22. *Selaginella pallescens.* A. Strobilus, enlarged. X 10. B. Median longisection of apex of immature strobilus. X 125. C. Median longisection of immature megasporangium and ligule. X 250; l., ligule; l.t., leaf trace; mi., microsporocytes; s., sporophyll; st., stele; t., tapetum; w., sporangial wall.

ent species vary in number of chloroplasts from one to several. The plastids are always rather massive, as compared with those of other vascular plants. Stomata are present on the abaxial surface of the leaf and are localized near the midrib (Fig. 19-21B).

Reproduction: the sporophyte

All species of *Selaginella* produce their sporangia in strobili (Figs. 19-17B, 19-22A). The sporophylls are scarcely different from vegetative leaves, and in some species they are arranged so loosely as to render the strobili inconspicuous. The sporophylls, like the vegetative leaves, are ligulate (Fig. 19-22B,C). Each bears a single sporangium near its adaxial base (Figs. 19-22B, 19-23, 19-25). Growth of the strobilus is apical (Fig. 19-22B); hence median sections of a young strobilus show various stages in the eusporangiate development of the sporangia. The sporangium wall is two-layered and separated from the sporogenous tissue by a tapetum (Fig. 19-22C).

The sporogenous tissue is segregated into individual cells which function as sporocytes as development proceeds. It subsequently becomes apparent that there are two types of

sporangia. In some, a small percentage of sporocytes may degenerate, the remainder undergoing meiosis and cytokinesis to produce many tetrads of spores (Figs. 19-22B, 19-23). In others (Figs. 19-23, 19-24), usually all except one of the sporocytes degenerate. The survivor undergoes meiosis and cytokinesis, producing a single spore tetrad the members of which gradually enlarge, ap-

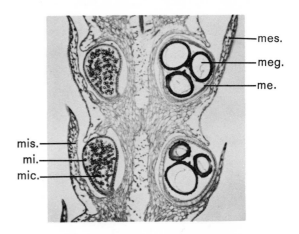

FIG. 19-23. *Selaginella* sp. Segment of a longisection of a strobilus; me., megasporangium; meg., megaspore; mes., megasporophyll; mi., microsporangium; mic., microspores; mis., microsporophyll. X 125.

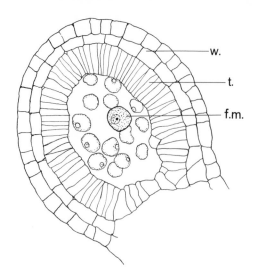

FIG. 19-24. *Selaginella* sp. Median longisection of young megasporangium; f.m., functional megasporocyte (the remainder, degenerating); t., tapetum; w., sporangial wall. X 400.

parently by appropriating the materials made available by the degeneration of the other sporocytes. Ultimately, the four spores in these sporangia grow large enough to cause bulging of the sporangial wall (Figs. 19-25B, 19-26). This account of the ontogeny of the two types of sporangia indicates that they are fundamentally similar through the sporocyte stage. The divergence in developement begins at that period. The greatly enlarged spores are called **megaspores** (sometimes, macrospores), and sporangia in which they develop and the sporophylls which subtend the spo-

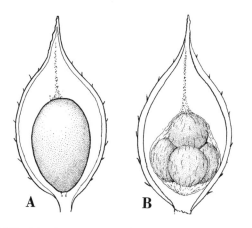

FIG. 19-25. *Selaginella pallescens.* A. Microsporophyll and microsporangium. B. Megasporophyll and megasporangium. Both in adaxial view. X 18.

rangia are known as **megasporangia** and **megasporophylls,** respectively. The smaller spores are called **microspores,** their sporangia are **microsporangia,** and their sporophylls are **microsporophylls.** The sporocytes that give rise to megaspores are called **megasporocytes;** those that form microspores are known as **microsporocytes.** This dimorphic condition of the spores is known as **heterospory** (Fig. 19-26).

The microsporangia may occur in the apical portion of the strobilus and the megasporangia below, or there may be two vertical rows of microsporophylls and two of megasporophylls; less regular arrangements may occur.

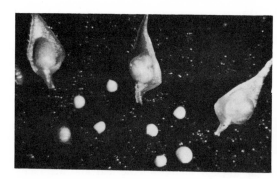

FIG. 19-26. *Selaginella pallescens.* Adaxial views of microsporophyll with microsporangium (left) and two megasporangia with megaspores (right); note eight megaspores (and their variant size) and the numerous microspores. X 8.

Of the living vascular plants so far discussed, *Selaginella* is the first to exhibit heterospory. While the ontogenetic cause of heterospory in *Selaginella* obviously is degeneration of a majority of sporocytes in certain sporangia and increase in size of the survivors, the factors which evoke this condition are obscure. That the number of degenerating megasporocytes is not absolutely fixed is indicated by the presence of as many as forty-two and as few as one megaspore in megasporangia of certain individuals.

As the microspores and megaspores mature, their walls thicken. Those of the microspores are red in certain species and those of the megaspores cream-colored. The tapetum of the megasporangium seems to play a role in the thickening of the megaspore walls. Both

FIG. 19-27. *Selaginella pallescens.* Development of microspore into ♂ gametophyte. A. Section of microspore; note small prothallial cell. B. Partially exposed ♂ gametophyte; note jacket cells and two antheridia. C. Microspore with mature ♂ gametophyte ready to liberate sperm. X 770.

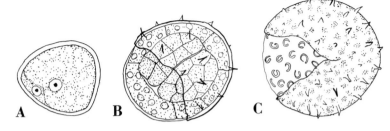

microspores and megaspores have prominent triradiate ridges which mark the lines of cytokinesis of the spores within the spore mother cell walls. Dehiscence of the sporangia is explosive; the spores are ejected through a vertical cleft in the sporangial wall.

Reproduction: the gametophytes

The development of unisexual gametophytes is an invariable result[5] of heterospory. Microspores develop into male gametophytes,

---

[5] Except in the fern *Platyzoma* (see p. 342).

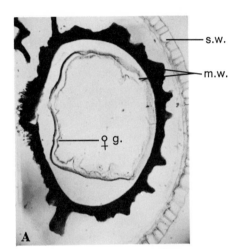

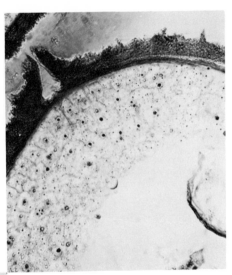

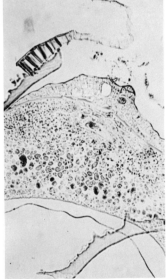

FIG. 19-28. *Selaginella* sp. A. Section of megaspore with free-nuclear female gametophyte. X 135. B. Section of megaspore at triradiate ridge; note partially cellular female gametophyte. X 250. C. Section of a megaspore with more mature female gametophyte; note two apical archegonia. X 200; ♀ g., female gametophyte; m.w., megaspore wall; s.w., sporangial wall. (C. *From a preparation by Dr. D. W. Bierhorst.*)

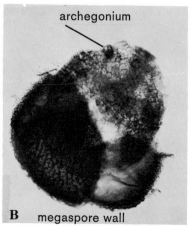

archegonium

megaspore wall

FIG. 19-29. *Selaginella pallescens.* Living megaspores with female gametophytes. A. ♀ gametophyte, immature; note rhizoids. X 35. B. ♀ gametophyte, mature. X 60.

A

B

and megaspores into female gametophytes. Unlike *Psilotum* and *Lycopodium*, spore germination in *Selaginella* frequently is precocious,[6] so that at the time of their ejection the spores are in various stages of gametophyte development. These intrasporangial stages are sometimes said to represent **primary germination.** Under certain condi-

tions, the gametophytes may reach maturity, as manifested by their production of sex organs, by the time of their dissemination from the sporangia. In two extreme instances, fertilization and embryo development have been reported to occur while the megaspores and their contained gametophytes were still within the opened walls of the megasporangium. Further comparative study of a number of species of *Selaginella* is desirable to establish the factors that effect the liberation

[6] The spores of *Pellia*, *Conocephalum*, and *Porella* among the Hepatopsida also exhibit a degree of precocity in their endogenous divisions (Chapter 15).

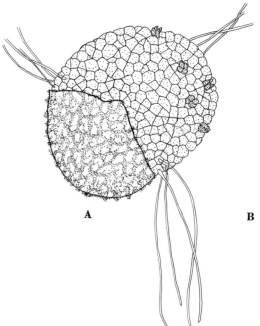

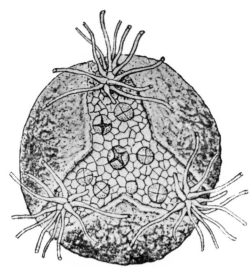

A

B

FIG. 19-30. *Selaginella pallescens.* A. Megaspore with mature ♀ gametophyte. X 35. B. The same stage in *S. martensii* Spring. X 175. (B. *After Bruchmann.*)

of the spores in relation to the degree of maturity of their enclosed gametophytes.

The mature microspore is uninucleate at first. Its development of the male gametophyte is initiated by an internal mitosis and cytokinesis that result in the formation of a small, peripheral **prothallial cell** and a large cell, the **antheridial cell** (Fig. 19-27A). The prothallial cell usually is interpreted as the sole remnant of the vegetative tissue of free-living gametophytes; it undergoes no further divisions. The antheridial cell, by anticlinal and periclinal divisions (Fig. 19-27B), forms a single-layered jacket enclosing 128 or 256 spermatogenous cells, each of which gives rise to a single biflagellate sperm. The microspore of *S. kraussiana* is shed from the microsporangium before the antheridium is fully formed. The latter matures in the microspores that fall into environments which favor further development. The prothallial cell and wall cells of the antheridium ultimately disintegrate; the sperms are liberated by rupture of the microspore wall (Fig. 19-27C).

The megaspores also begin their development into female gametophytes while still grouped together in the tetrad and before they have attained their maximum size. The young megaspore contains a large central vacuole surrounded by a thin peripheral layer of cytoplasm. The megaspore wall at maturity is composed of two layers, a thick, outer cream-colored exine and a more delicate inner layer, the intine.

The single nucleus undergoes mitosis which is not followed by cytokinesis. This process continues, and the cytoplasm, which gradually increases in amount, becomes multinucleate (Fig. 19-28). The occurrence of successive mitoses without ensuing cytokineses is known as **free-nuclear division.** With continued increase in number of nuclei and amount of cytoplasm, the nuclei lying in the portion of the megaspore near the triradiate ridge are gradually separated by cell walls (Fig. 19-28). This process continues until much of the megaspore lumen is filled with cellular tissue. This may not occur, however, until after fertilization.

The megaspore is finally ruptured in the region of the triradiate ridge by the protrusion of the developing female gametophyte (Figs. 19-28C, 19-29). It is in this region that the several archegonia develop. Gametophytes in megaspores that have been shed have been reported to develop chloroplasts and rhizoids if they come in contact with soil in the presence of light. Although rhizoids develop, the gametophytes are always achlorophyllous in the writer's experience. It is probable, moreover, that the gametophyte derives the bulk of its nutriment from the metabolites freed by degeneration of the supernumerary sporocytes, by the activity of the tapetum of the megasporangium, and from the food stored within the megaspores.

A number of superficial cells of the exposed portion of the female gametophyte develop into archegonia (Figs. 19-28C, 19-29, 19-30). These are largely embedded, except for their short necks which are two tiers high and composed of four rows of neck cells.

As noted previously, union of the sperm and egg may occur either after the mature gametophytes have been shed from the strobilus or, rarely, by sifting of the microspores containing male gametophytes into the open megasporangia. This transfer is in some respects suggestive of pollination in seed plants.

Reproduction: embryogeny

As in *Lycopodium*, the first division of the zygote in *Selaginella* gives rise to a suspensor initial near the neck of the archegonium; the lower cell and its derivatives form the embryo proper. In some species the suspensor remains relatively inactive as it does in *Lycopodium*, whereas in others it undergoes cell division with subsequent elongation, so that the developing embryos are thrust into the nutrient-filled vegetative tissue of the female gametophyte (Figs. 19-31, 19-32). The portion of the embryo opposite the suspensor becomes organized as a foot, and the remainder develops into an axis consisting largely of primary root (radicle) and stem bearing two cotyledons. As development continues, the

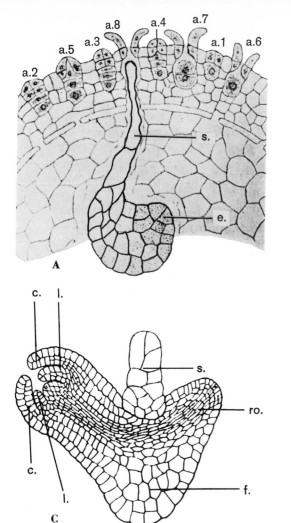

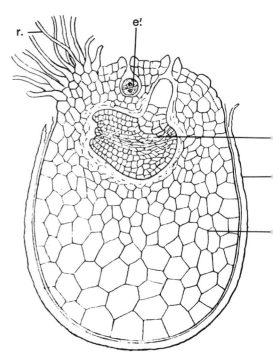

FIG. 19-31. *Selaginella.* Embryogeny. A. Early stages in *S. poulteri.* X. 225. B. *S. martensii.* Median section of megaspore and ♀ gametophyte with embryos. X 150. C. Median longisection of embryo of *S. martensii.* X 125; a.1–a.8, successively more mature archegonia; c., cotyledon or first embryonic leaf; e., successful embryo; e.', abortive embryo; f., foot; ♀ g., female gametophyte; l., ligule; m., megaspore wall; r., rhizoids; ro., primary root or radicle; s., suspensor. (*After Bruchmann.*)

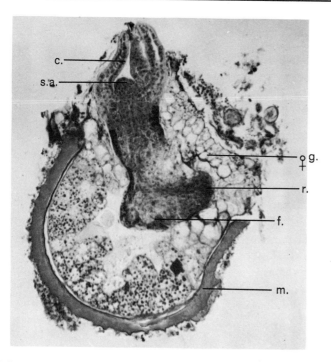

FIG. 19-32. *Selaginella* sp. Section of megaspore, ♀ gametophyte and embryo sporophyte; s.a., stem apex or promeristem; other labels same as in Fig. 19–31. (*After Steiner, Sussman, and Wagner.*)

FIG. 19-33. *Selaginella pallescens*. Germling sporophyte attached to ♀ gametophyte (within megaspore). X 5.

embryo, except for the foot, emerges from the female gametophyte and megaspore, and the young plant is soon established independently. This embryonic sporophyte, attached to the female gametophyte within the megaspore, looks strikingly like a minute seedling at this stage (Fig. 19-33).

Summary

Although *Selaginella* is similar to *Lycopodium* in a number of respects, it differs in the possession of ligulate leaves, frequently polystelic stems, vessels in its xylem, and especially in its heterospory. In accordance with the latter, the gametophytes are strictly unisexual. The ontogeny of the spores of *Selaginella* is instructive in providing a clue as to the possible origin of heterospory. In view of the similarity in development of both microsporangia and megasporangia through the sporocyte stage, along with the variation in megaspore number in certain individuals and species, it seems probable that heterospory here is occasioned by a difference in nutrition during sporogenesis. The ultimate causes of heterospory are not clear.

The precocious germination, and in rare instances maturation, of the spores into gametophytes before they are shed from the sporangia is a noteworthy departure from the reproductive cycle of *Lycopodium* and *Psilotum*. Spore dimorphism in *Selaginella* has resulted in gametophyte dimorphism. Both male and female gametophytes are much reduced in size, duration of existence, and complexity of structure as compared with free-living gametophytes, the male gametophyte especially so. It should be noted that single spores of homosporous plants (*Polytrichum, Sphaerocarpos,* and *Marchantia,* for example) may develop into unisexual gametophytes. In such homosporous plants, meiosis results in two members of every spore tetrad growing into male and the other two into female gametophytes. In *Selaginella* and other heterosporous plants, however, *all* the products of meiosis of a single sporocyte form *either* male or female gametophytes.

The major source of food for the female gametophyte, as well as for the developing embryo, is the material stored in the megaspore during its long period of enlargement. The food is sporophytic in origin. While the twice-reported transfer of microspores containing immature male gametophytes to the opened megasporangia, containing megaspores with female gametophytes, suggests pollination in the seed plants, as the occurrence of fertilization and embryo development within the megasporangium likewise do, there are significant differences.

Order 2. Isoetales

FAMILY 1. ISOETACEAE

Isoetes

Introduction and vegetative morphology

Although morphologists differ in their opinion regarding the relation of *Isoetes*[7] to other plants, there is considerable evidence that its affinities may be with the Microphyllophyta, in which division it is included in the present text. A related South American genus, *Stylites*, from a lake in the high Andes of Peru, was described in 1957.

---

[7] For a more detailed treatment of *Isoetes* see: Paolillo, D., *Developmental Anatomy of Isoetes*, Univ. of Illinois Press, Urbana, Ill., 1963.

A

B

FIG. 19-34. *Isoetes melanopoda.* A. In soil. X 0.25. B. Free of soil, showing "corm" and roots. X 0.5.

Isoetes is a genus containing 64 species familiarly known as **"quillworts"** because of their narrow, elongate leaves, the bases of which are rather spoonlike. Most species are either partially submerged aquatics (*I. engelmanni* A. Br.) or amphibious; a few, like *I. butleri* Engelm. are terrestrial. *Isoetes butleri* is perennial, but active growth occurs only during the early spring and late autumn rains. *Isoetes melanopoda* Gay and Durieu (Fig. 19-34) is an inhabitant of shallow granitic pools and is subject periodically to desiccation; *I. butleri* Engelm. occurs on moist soils.

The quill-like leaves are attached in spiral fashion to a subterranean cormlike structure (Fig. 19-34B). Their spiral arrangement is readily apparent in transverse sections through the overlapping leaf bases. Although the leaves in some species, as in *I. engelmanni,* attain a length as great as 2 feet, they are considered to be microphyllous, inasmuch as they have single, unbranched veins and the traces leave no gap in the vascular tissues of the stem. It is evident, in transverse section, that each leaf contains four longitudinally placed **lacunae** or air chambers; the vein is located in the solid tissue in the center of these. The tissue external to the air chambers is photosynthetic parenchyma. Leaves of terrestrial species have stomata in their epidermis.

The cormlike structure (Fig. 19-34B) on which the leaves are borne is difficult to in-

terpret morphologically. Its upper portion is considered to be a much shortened, fleshy, vertical stem with a broad and sunken apex. The nodes are so close together that the internodes are practically obliterated (Fig. 19-35A,B). Elongation of the upper portion of the axis is very slow, most of the derivatives of the apical meristem cells becoming involved in the formation of leaves and the portions of the stem immediately subtending the leaves. The vascular tissue is arranged as a central protostele (Fig. 19-35), the xylem of which consists of a large number of parenchyma cells and relatively few tracheids, a characteristic of aquatic plants in general. The xylem is surrounded by phloem. Outside the phloem there is a meristematic layer, the exact nature of which is somewhat in dispute. It functions as a **cambium** in that its divisions add to the tissues of the stem. Apparently the cambium derivatives develop as sieve elements, occasionally as tracheids, or as parenchyma cells adjacent to the phloem. Most of the cells produced by the cambium augment the cortex, the outer portion of which, with the older leaf bases, is sloughed off each growing season. No endodermis is present. The surface of the corm is covered by the remains of the leaves of previous seasons. The surface layers of the corm become suberized.

The lower portion of the corm is a bilobed or trilobed organ; its structure and homologies have received various interpretations. It often is referred to as the **rhizophore,** inasmuch as the delicate roots are borne in orderly series only on this region of the plant. The rhizophore end of the plant develops from its own meristem which is sunken in a groove (Fig. 19-35B). The youngest roots, therefore, occur near the deepest portion of the groove, and the older ones arise from the sides of the rhizophore lobes. The roots are endogenous in origin; each is connected to the central vascular tissue of the rhizophore by a trace (Fig. 19-35B).

The delicate roots are protected by root caps beneath which a group of apical cells is present; these add to both the root cap and the root itself. The roots branch dichotomously as a result of the organization of two groups of apical initials below the root cap. Mature

298

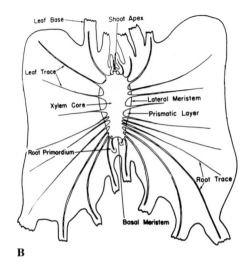

A   B

FIG. 19-35. *Isoetes butleri.* A. Almost median longisection of "corm." X 25. B. Diagrammatic median longisection; compare with section in A. C. Transection of a root; note large central lacuna and lateral stele. X 60. (B. *After Paolillo.*)

C

roots contain delicate protosteles which are excentric in position (Fig. 19-35C) because of the disintegration of the inner cortical cells on one side of the stele to form a lacuna. The stele is bounded by a well-differentiated endodermal layer. The cortex is surrounded by an epidermis. This unusual type of root, with its excentric stele and air chamber, is very similar in organization to the roots of fossil Lepidodendrales, also borne on rhizophores (Fig. 19-47B).

Reproduction: the sporophyte

Every leaf of *Isoetes* is potentially a sporophyll and the plants are heterosporous. The first-formed leaves of any season, the outermost, are frequently sterile, however. The next older leaves mature as megasporophylls (Fig. 19-36A) and are followed by microsporophylls (Fig. 19-36B) within. The last-formed leaves of the season frequently bear abortive sporangia. Microsporophylls and megasporophylls are indistinguishable at first. In each case, the single sporangium arises from superficial cells near the adaxial surface of the spoon-shaped leaf base; the cells undergo a

series of periclinal divisions. Development of the sporangium is eusporangiate. The sporangium is massive and larger than that in *Lycopodium* and *Selaginella*. It may attain a length of up to 7 mm. A small ligule arises just above the apex of the sporangium, and other superficial cells in that region grow down to form an indusiumlike covering, the **velum** (L. *velum*, veil) (Fig. 19-36). The sporangia are incompletely chambered by

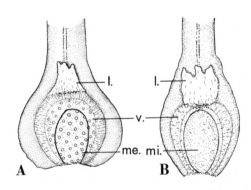

A   B

FIG. 19-36. *Isoetes* sp. Adaxial views of A. megasporophyll, and B. microsporophyll; l., ligule; me., megasporangium; mi., microsporangium; v., velum. X 3.

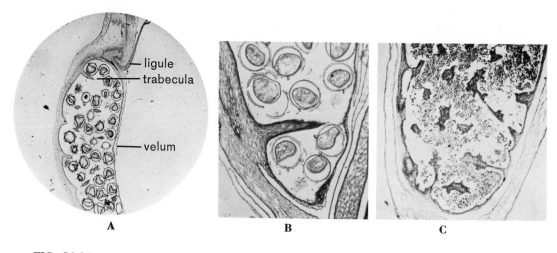

FIG. 19-37. *Isoetes* sp. A. Sagittal section of leaf base with megasporangium. X 12.5. B. Enlarged sectional view of megasporangium; note megaspores and trabecula. X 60. C. Segmented portion of microsporangium; note trabeculae and microspores. X 60.

strands of sterile tissue, the **trabeculae,** which extend from the walls partially across the sporangial lumen (Fig. 19-37); the sporangial walls and trabeculae are lined with a two-layered tapetum.

As in *Selaginella*, development of both microsporangia and megasporangia is similar through the sporocyte stage. Practically all of the microsporocytes undergo meiosis and form tetrads of microspores; hence tremendous numbers of spores, estimated to be between 150,000 and 1,000,000, develop in each microsporangium. Certain of the megasporocytes enlarge, but only a small number divide and form tetrads; the remainder disintegrate. Megasporangia of the several species produce between 50 and 300 megaspores. Both microspores and megaspores have walls with ornamentation that varies from species to species; the microspores are often covered with long spines, while the megaspores are ridged and grooved. There is no special mechanism of sporangial dehiscence, at least in aquatic species. The spores are liberated as the sporophylls and sporangial walls disintegrate at the end of the growing season. The spiny microspores are often found attached by their spines to the megaspores, an important adaptation in unisexual gametophytes.[8]

[8] Personal communication, Prof. David Bierhorst (November 17, 1964).

Reproduction: the gametophyte

Unlike *Selaginella*, the spores of *Isoetes* do not begin their development into gametophytes until they have been set free from their sporangia. The male gametophyte, as in *Selaginella*, is entirely enclosed within the microspore wall (Fig. 19-38A). It arises by internal divisions of the microspore protoplast to form a single prothallial cell and a single antheridial cell. The latter develops into an antheridium consisting of a single-layered wall enclosing four spermatogenous cells. Each of these gives rise to a single multiflagellate sperm at maturity.

Development of the female gametophyte of *Isoetes*, as of *Selaginella*, involves a series of free-nuclear divisions of the megaspore nucleus and its descendants. Cell wall formation occurs first in the region of the triradiate ridge and gradually extends through the remainder of the female gametophyte. It may still be incomplete in the basal portion of the gametophyte for some time after fertilization. The megaspore wall cracks open, exposing the cellular apex of the developing gametophyte which develops unicellular rhizoids. Certain superficial cells undergo division to form archegonia which are largely embedded (Fig. 19-38B,C). Their necks, composed of three or four tiers of four cells, are longer than those of *Selaginella*.

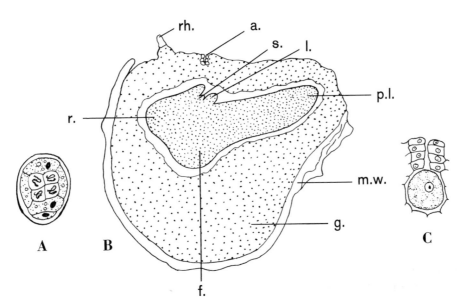

FIG. 19-38. A. *Isoetes lacustris* L. Section of microspore containing mature ♂ gametophyte; note prothallial cell, jacket cells, and four spermatogenous cells. B. *Isoetes lithophila* Pfeiffer. Sectional view of megaspore with mature ♀ gametophyte and young embryo; a., archegonial neck; f., foot; g., ♀ gameto- phyte; l., ligule; m.w., megaspore wall; p.l., pri- mary leaf or cotyledon; r., root; rh., rhizoid; s., stem apex. X 120. C. Single archegonium, median longi- tudinal section. X 300. (A. *After Liebig.* B, C, *After LaMotte.*)

Reproduction: embryogeny

Usually only one zygote in each female gametophyte develops into a sporophyte (Figs. 19-38B, 19-39). Nuclear and cell division by the zygote and its derivatives produce a spheri- cal mass of tissue which later differentiates into the embryonic regions of the sporophyte. These include a rather massive foot in contact with the starch-filled cells of the female ga- metophyte, an embryonic root, and a leaf or cotyledon. The stem develops secondarily in the region between the leaf and the root (Fig. 19-38B). Although the young sporophyte soon becomes established as an independent plant, it remains attached to the female gametophyte and megaspores for a considerable period (Fig. 19-38). It should be noted that no sus- pensor is present in the embryo of *Isoetes*.

FIG. 19-39. *Isoetes* sp. Young sporophyte attached to ♀ gametophyte within mega- spore; c., cotyledon; m., megaspore; r., root. X 5.

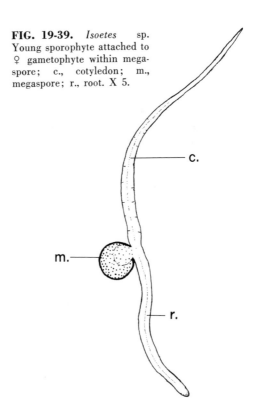

Summary

Although the leaves of *Isoetes* are markedly larger than those of *Selaginella* and *Lycopo-*

dium, they are microphyllous, as indicated by their single unbranched veins and the absence of gaps in the stele. All organs of the plant show evidences in their anatomical structure of adaptation to an aquatic habitat. Among these are air lacunae and the paucity of lignified xylem tissue. The leaves of *Isoetes* are ligulate and spirally inserted on a short, underground cormlike structure. Each leaf is potentially a sporophyll. Although growth in length of the corm is very limited, the presence of a cambiumlike layer contributes to its increase in girth. The cortex of the corm is composed of starch-filled cells, an indication that the perennial corm is primarily a storage organ. The stem is protostelic with few tracheids, most of the xylem cells maturing as parenchyma. The lower portion of the corm is called a rhizophore. This is a lobed structure on which the delicate roots are borne in orderly fashion. Both stem and root develop from a group of apical meristematic cells rather than one. Root branching is dichotomous. The roots are characterized by excentric steles and a central air chamber.

The sporangia are massive and heteromorphic. A variable number of megaspores matures in the megasporangium. The number is always larger than in *Selaginella*, and unlike the latter, the spores do not initiate development into gametophytes until they have been shed from their sporangia. Evidences of further reduction of the gametophytes, as compared with those of *Selaginella*, are present in *Isoetes*. Among these, the reduction of spermatogenous cells to four and the failure of the female gametophyte to project from the megaspore wall are noteworthy. Unlike both *Selaginella* and *Lycopodium*, the sperms of *Isoetes* are multiflagellate. The development of the embryo differs from these genera in the complete absence of a suspensor and in the long-delayed development of the stem. In spite of the differences just cited, there are many evidences of similarity in morphology between *Isoetes* and *Selaginella* and *Lycopodium*. The roots and rhizophore suggest the fossil Lepidodendrales. Some morphologists, however, on the basis of the multiflagellate sperms and anatomical considerations, are of the opinion that *Isoetes* is more closely related to certain ferns. This view seems to ignore such a fundamental attribute as the microphylly of *Isoetes* as contrasted with the macrophylly of ferns.

Fossil Microphyllophyta

Extinct representatives of the orders Lycopodiales, Selaginellales, and Isoetales have been preserved in the fossil record. In addition, members of three other microphyllophytan orders (of which no extant members have survived), the Protolepidodendrales, Lepidodendrales, and Pleuromeiales, have been preserved as fossils. The Microphyllophyta are known from Devonian strata and some, indeed, were contemporaneous with certain members of the Psilophyta.

The extinct Microphyllophyta will be briefly summarized in the remainder of this chapter.

Order 1. *Protolepidodendrales*

Members of this order occur in the earliest Devonian strata. They lacked ligules. *Baragwanathia*[9] (Fig. 19-40), described from Australia, is known from axes which bore spirally arranged, microphyllous leaves much like extant species of *Lycopodium* and of certain Selaginellas. The plant was herbaceous; seg-

---

[9] Originally described as from Silurian (Table 32-1); the strata are now considered to be Lower Devonian.

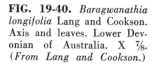

FIG. 19-40. *Baragwanathia longifolia* Lang and Cookson. Axis and leaves. Lower Devonian of Australia. X ⅞. (*From Lang and Cookson.*)

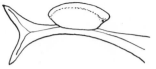

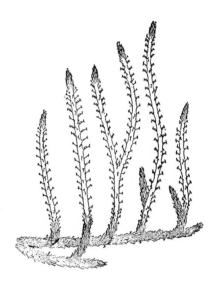

FIG. 19-41. *Protolepidodendron scharyanum* Krejci, Devonian. Rhizome and aerial branches (reconstruction). (*From Kräusel and Weyland.*)

ments of up to 28 cm. long have been found. Kidney-shaped sporangia were inserted in the axils of the leaves or on the bases of the leaf blades. The sporangia occurred in zones, as in *Lycopodium lucidulum. Baragwanathia* was probably homosporous.

Protolepidodendron (Fig. 19-41) specimens have been recovered from both Lower and Middle Devonian strata. The plant was herbaceous, from 20 to 30 cm. tall. The prostrate stems were densely clothed with spirally arranged leaves. The dichotomously branched erect axes, which contained protosteles, bore less densely arranged, forked microphyllous leaves. Some of these produced ovoid sporangia on the median adaxial surface (Fig. 19-42).

Order 2. *Lycopodiales*

Herbaceous, elongate plants, corresponding closely to the extant genus *Lycopodium*, have been described from upper Devonian rocks under the name of *Lycopodites* (Fig. 19-43).

Order 3. *Lepidodendrales*

The Lepidodendrales, all now extinct, were treelike Microphyllophyta which flourished in

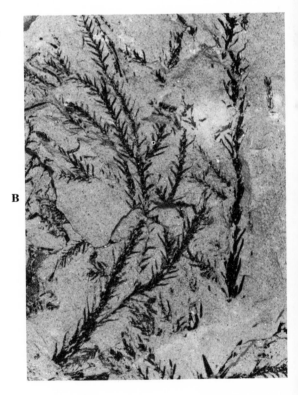

FIG. 19-43. A. *Lycopodites stackii* Kidston. X 0.5. B. *Lycopodites pendulus* Lesq. Upper Carboniferous, Yorkshire. X 2. (A. *After Bower.* B. *Courtesy of Dr. W. G. Chaloner.*)

A

B

FIG. 19-44. A. Carboniferous swamp forest as reconstructed at the Chicago Natural History Museum. B. Key to some of the organisms in A: 4, *Lepidodendron obovatum* Sternberg; 5, *Sigillaria rugosa* Brongniart; 6, *Sigillaria saulii* Brongniart; 8, *Sigillaria lacoei* Lesquereaux; 10, *Sigillaria* trunk; 12, *Lepidophloios laricinus* Sternberg; 13, *Selaginellites* sp. (4–13, lycopods); 14, *Neuropteris heterophylla* Brongniart; 15, *Neuropteris decipiens* Lesquereaux; 16, *Lyginopteris oldhamnia* Williamson (seed ferns); 17, *Caulopteris giffordii* Lesquereaux (fern); 20, *Sphenophyllum emarginatum* (Brongniart) Koenig; 21, *Calamites* sp. (20, 21, Arthrophyta); 22, *Cordaites borasifolium* (Sternberg) Unger (gymnosperm); 26, *Archeoblattina beecheri* Seelards, a roach. (Certain nonrelevant fossils not named here.) (*Courtesy of the Chicago Natural History Museum.*)

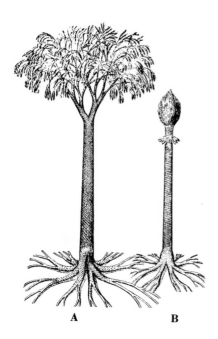

A   B

FIG. 19-45. A. *Lepidodendron obovatum* Sternb. B. *Sigillaria* sp. (*After Hirmer, from Smith.*)

many Carboniferous (Table 32-1) swamp forests (Fig. 19-44). The causes of their ultimately having become extinct are not clear.

Lepidodendron and Sigillaria

These are among the best known of the arborescent genera (Fig. 19-45). The tallest specimens probably approached 135 feet and the trunks, with a basal diameter of about 4–6 feet, were unbranched for a great distance from the base. At the apex repeated dichoto-

mies occurred; these bore leaves of varying size, ranging from a few millimeters to over a meter in length. The microphyllous leaves contained a single, unbranched vein, and arose from rhomboidal leaf bases which persisted, after the leaves were shed, in older regions of the stem (Fig. 19-46A). A trace scar occurs in each leaf scar.

From the base toward the top of the unbranched trunk the primary xylem and phloem varied in arrangement from that of an exarch protostele to a siphonostele (Fig. 19-46B) with an increasingly large pith. There was a large amount of secondary xylem at the base and progressively less toward the top of the trunk. In the branches, the siphonosteles became smaller in diameter, with less pith. Finally, in the ultimate dichotomies only primary growth in the form of protosteles is apparent. The broad, so-called cortex was composed of an extensive corky, periderm layer; the primary cortex was limited in extent.

The massive trunk rested on dichotomously branching bases (Fig. 19-47), formerly (before their relation to the erect system had been clarified) classified as the genus *Stigmaria*. These stigmarian bases are often considered to be rhizophores. They produced spirally arranged, rootlike appendages with internal organization quite similar to that of the roots of *Isoetes*.

The spores of *Lepidodendron* and other arborescent lycopods were formed in terminal strobili (Fig. 19-48) on the smaller branch-

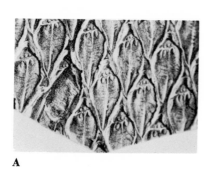

A

FIG. 19-46. A. Stem surface of *Lepidodendron* showing leaf scars. B. *Lepidodendron* sp. Transection of the stem; i.c., inner cortex; o.c., outer cortex; p., pith; p.x., primary xylem; s.x, secondary xylem. X 25.

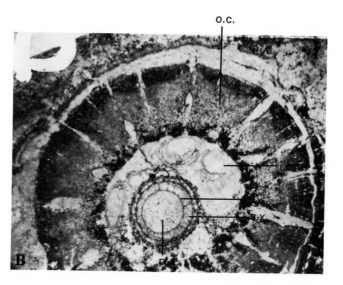

B

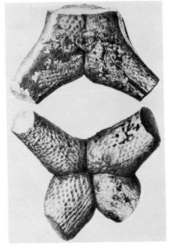

FIG. 19-47. A. Stumps of *Lepidodendron* trees resting on stigmarian bases; sandstone casts at Victoria Park, Glasgow, Scotland. B. *Stigmaria ficoides* Brong. bases; note root scars. (A. *Courtesy of Dr. H. N. Andrews, Jr.* B. *After Williamson, from Eames.*)

A

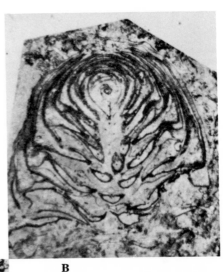

B

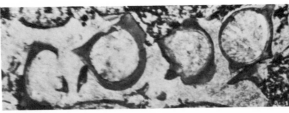

C

D

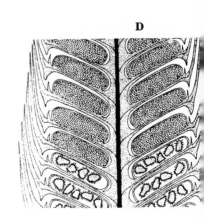

FIG. 19-48. A. *Lepidophloios.* Portion of branch system of arborescent lycopod; note cones on lateral branches at left. B. *Lepidostrobus.* Longisection of a fossil lycopod strobilus. X 8. C. *Sigillaria* sp. Megaspores. X 90. D. *Lepidostrobus.* Diagram of longisection of strobilus; note heterospory (A. *After Andrews.* D. *After Smith.*)

lets. Those of the related genus *Lepidophloios* are illustrated in Fig. 19-48B. These strobili were sometimes described under the generic name *Lepidostrobus* and were about 20 inches long. The sporophylls were ligulate and spirally arranged, and each bore adaxially a single sporangium. There is good evidence that *Lepidodendron* and related genera, *Sigillaria* (Fig. 19-48C), for example, were heterosporous.

A number of other arborescent Microphyllophyta were contemporaneous with *Lepidodendron*. *Sigillaria* differs in having vertically aligned series of leaf scars. *Bothrodendron* is of interest because four megaspores occurred in each megasporangium; megaspores of this plant with enclosed mature female gametophytes have been preserved as fossils.

Order 4. Selaginellales

A distinctly *Selaginella*-like plant has been described from the Carboniferous (Table 32-1) under the generic name *Selaginellites*. Specimens of *Selaginellites* (Fig. 19-49) are recognizable by their anisophyllous leaves which occur also in many (but not all) extant species of *Selaginella*. The cones of one species of *Selaginellites* (*S. crassicinctus* Hoskins and Abbott) bore megaspores near the base of the strobilus and microspores above (Fig. 19-49B. Four megaspores were present in each megasporangium. The megaspores were 800 μ in diameter and the microspores 80 μ.

A specimen described as *Selaginella amesiana* Darrah from Pennsylvanian (Table 32-1) rocks has well-preserved female gametophytes within the megaspores.

Order 5. Isoetales

Fossilized plant remains in Cretaceous (Table 32-1) deposits have been described either as *Isoetes* or *Isoetites*, an indication that the fossil plants were very similar to the extant genus.

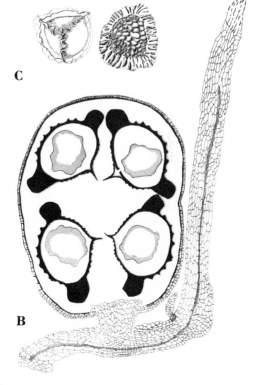

FIG. 19-49. A. *Selaginellites gutbieri* Göppert. Carboniferous. B, C. *S. crassicinctus.* Diagrammatic sagittal section of megasporangium; note mega-spores, megasporangium, and ligule; microspores above. (A. *From Geinitz.* B, C. *After Hoskins and Abbott.*)

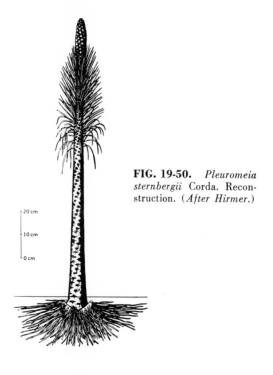

FIG. 19-50. *Pleuromeia sternbergii* Corda. Reconstruction. (*After Hirmer.*)

Order 6. Pleuromeiales

Pleuromeia, described from Triassic (Table 32-1) rocks (Fig. 19-50), was a plant a meter or more tall. The trunklike stem was unbranched and rested on four massive *Stigmaria*-like lobes. These bore numerous spirally arranged, delicate roots the internal structure of which was similar to those of *Isoetes* and *Lepidodendron*. Near the apex of the trunk were borne numerous slender, elongate leaves subtending a single terminal strobilus. *Pleuromeia* was heterosporous. The sporangia may have been abaxial on the sporophylls or deeply embedded on the adaxial surface. The highly compressed nature of the specimens is responsible for our lack of knowledge. *Pleuromeia* suggests an elongate *Isoetes*, or the latter is like a telescoped *Pleuromeia*.

Summary

The history of microphyllophytan plants extends from the Lower Devonian to the present, although a number of genera have become extinct and seemingly have been replaced by the extant genera *Lycopodium*, *Selaginella*, and *Isoetes*, the first two of these genera being very ancient, probably having persisted, with little modification, from the Carboniferous. Among the extinct genera, both ligulate and eligulate, homosporous and heterosporous, and herbaceous and arborescent types occurred. The last were striking plants, approaching 100 feet in height, and were abundant in Carboniferous forests. They rested on large, dichotomously branching systems known as stigmarian bases. Cambial activity was a noteworthy attribute of the treelike forms, but the bulk of the secondary tissues was periderm, not secondary xylem. All the fossil genera were clearly microphyllous, no leaf gaps occurring in the stem steles. The Microphyllophyta are an ancient group of plants, but in view of the few relicts which remain extant, they seem not to have been the progenitors of other vascular plants.

The genera of Microphyllophyta discussed in this chapter may be classified as follows:

Division Microphyllophyta
  Class 1. Aglossopsida
    Order 1. Protolepidodendrales
      Family 1. Protolepidodendraceae
        Genera: *Protolepidodendron*,
                Baragwanathia
    Order 2. Lycopodiales
      Family 1. Lycopodiaceae
        Genera: *Lycopodium, Lycopodites*
  Class 2. Glossopsida
    Order 1. Selaginellales
      Family 1. Selaginellaceae
        Genera: *Selaginella, Sellaginellites*
    Order 2. Isoetales
      Family 1. Isoetaceae
        Genera: *Isoetes, Stylites, Isoetites*
    Order 3. Lepidodendrales
      Family 1. Lepidodendraceae
        Genera: *Lepidodendron, Sigillaria,*
                Bothrodendron
    Order 4. Pleuromeiales
      Family 1. Pleuromeiaceae
        Genus: *Pleuromeia*

DISCUSSION QUESTIONS

1. What attributes distinguish the Microphyllophyta from the Psilophyta?

2. Compare *Psilotum* and *Lycopodium* with respect to vegetative structure and reproduction.

3. Define or explain strobilus, leaf trace, microphyllous leaf, suspensor, sporophyll.

4. What is meant by eusporangiate sporangium development?

5. Suggest the composition of a culture medium suitable for the cultivation of *Lycopodium* gametophytes.

6. What significance may be attached to the absence of vascular tissue from the first-formed leaves on the young sporophytes of *Lycopodium?*

7. On what basis is dichotomous branching considered to be a primitive attribute in vascular plants?

8. Can you suggest an adaptive advantage of the stroboloid arrangement of sporophylls in certain *Lycopodium* species as compared with the scattered, zonate arrangement?

9. Although the stems of *S. kraussiana* are distelic in the mature plants, the embryonic and juvenile stems are monostelic. Of what significance is this?

10. How does the xylem of *Selaginella* differ from that of *Psilotum* and *Lycopodium?*

11. What possible explanation is there for the fact that some *Lycopodium* gametophytes are chlorophyllous in laboratory culture but achlorophyllous in nature?

12. How do the leaves of *Selaginella* differ from those of *Lycopodium?*

13. What is the origin of the thick megaspore wall in *Selaginella?*

14. What light does ontogeny shed on the possible origin of heterospory? Explain.

15. Why are the gametophytes of *Selaginella* said to be "reduced"?

16. Distinguish between the terms primitive, advanced, specialized, generalized, simple, and reduced, as they are used in comparative morphology.

17. How do *Selaginella* megaspores with attached embryonic sporophytes differ from dicotyledonous seedlings?

18. Why are both *Selaginella* and *Lycopodium* considered to be microphyllous?

19. With the aid of labeled diagrams illustrate the reproductive cycle in *Selaginella.*

20. Define or explain heterospory, homospory, prothallial cell, free-nuclear division.

21. What attributes do *Selaginella* and *Lycopodium* have in common?

22. List the attributes shared by *Isoetes* and other Microphyllophyta.

23. What anatomical evidences of aquatic habitat are present in *Isoetes?*

24. In what respects does the development of the gametophytes in *Isoetes* differ from that in *Selaginella?*

25. On what basis are the leaves of *Isoetes* said to be microphyllous?

26. How do the sporangia of *Isoetes* differ from those of other Microphyllophyta?

27. Describe the structure of the corm of *Isoetes.*

28. What genera of extinct Microphyllophyta are known from the fossil record?

29. What significant attributes characterize them?

30. Why are the roots and rhizophore of *Isoetes* of interest in relation to the fossil record?

CHAPTER 20

Division Arthrophyta

The division Arthrophyta (Gr. *arthros,* jointed + Gr. *phyton,* plant) is the third group of vascular cryptogams known from Devonian (Table 32-1) strata. Arthrophytan plants were contemporaneous with the early Psilophyta and the Protolepidodendrales and Lepidodendrales of the Microphyllophyta. They became increasingly abundant and dominant during the Paleozoic (Table 32-1), but only a single genus, *Equisetum,* has survived in our present flora.

Order 1. Equisetales

FAMILY 1. EQUISETACEAE

Equisetum

Equisetum (L. *equus,* horse + L. *saeta,* bristle) (Figs. 20-1, 20-2) with 25 species, the only living member of the family Equisetaceae and order Equisetales, is widely distributed and the various species are familiarly known as **"horsetails"** (the branching species) and **"pipes"** and **"scouring rushes"** (the unbranched species). Some, like the common *E. arvense* L., grow both in moist and in somewhat xeric habitats, whereas others, like *E. sylvaticum* L., frequently flourish only in marshy situations. Temperate-zone species are relatively small in stature, rarely exceeding 4 feet in height. The tropical *E. giganteum* L. may exceed 5 meters in height and have stems up to 2.4 cm. in diameter.

The stem is the dominant organ of the plant body in the genus *Equisetum,* for the minute leaves, although photosynthetic for a short period after their formation, soon become dry and scalelike (Fig. 20-3). In *E. arvense* and other species, the plant consists of a subterranean, deep-growing rhizome and an erect aerial stem (Fig. 20-1A,B). Rhizome systems of *E. arvense* have been observed growing horizontally 6–7 feet below the surface of the soil and covering areas many hundreds of square feet in extent. The aerial stem may be richly branched, as in *E. arvense,* or branching may be rare, as in *E. hyemale* L. (Figs. 20-1C,D; 20-2B,C). The fact that unbranched species, under such stimulation as injury, develop branches at the nodes is often cited as evidence that branching is a primitive attribute in the genus, the branch primordia being present at the nodes.

Both the aerial stems and rhizomes have well-defined nodes and internodes (Figs. 20-1 to 20-3). The surface of the stem is ribbed or ridged, the ribs of successive internodes being arranged in alternate fashion. The bases of the leaves are fused and give the appearance of a scalloped collar. Both rhizomes and aerial stems bear the scalelike leaves. A few rudimentary stomata are present near the tips of the adaxial surface of the leaves of *E. arvense.* Stomata are present in two or three rows on both sides of the projecting midrib on the abaxial leaf surface. The central region of each leaf is photosynthetic when the leaves first appear.

The relation between the branches and leaves in *Equisetum* differs from that in all other vascular plants. In those of the latter which branch at the nodes, stem branches originate from the axils of the leaves, whereas in *Equisetum* they emerge from the region of the node between the leaves. As the branches elongate, they pierce the nodal leaf sheath.

Development of the stem originates in a single, pyramidal apical cell which divides regularly in three directions (Fig. 20-4). The derivatives of the apical cell divide in an anticlinal direction soon after they are delimited. One of the cells thus formed, in each case by further division, contributes to the internodal and the other to the nodal portion of the axis.

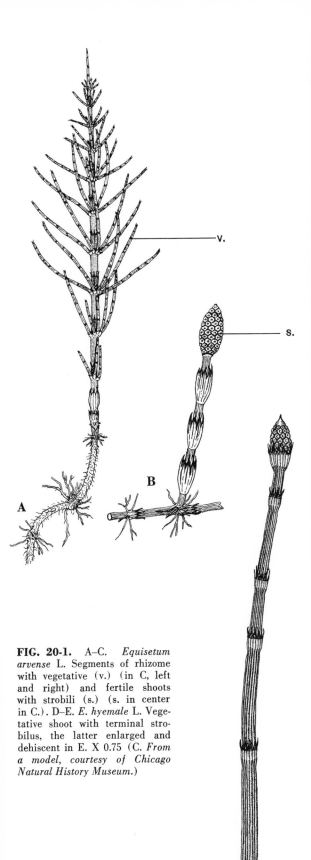

FIG. 20-1. A–C. *Equisetum arvense* L. Segments of rhizome with vegetative (v.) (in C, left and right) and fertile shoots with strobili (s.) (s. in center in C.). D–E. *E. hyemale* L. Vegetative shoot with terminal strobilus, the latter enlarged and dehiscent in E. X 0.75 (C. *From a model, courtesy of Chicago Natural History Museum.*)

v.

s.

A

B

C

D

E

A
B
C

FIG. 20-2. A. *Equisetum arvense.* Living vegetative shoots. X 0.33. B, C. Living stands of *E. hyemale;* plants in C with strobili. X 0.08.

The leaves originate as superficial, ringlike outgrowths of the nodal cells. A short distance back from the apical region, tissue differentiation is initiated in the axis. The surface cells form an epidermis with silicified cells. Certain of the epidermal cells undergo two successive divisions to form guard cells and their more superficial accessory cells. The latter are thickened with siliceous ribs. In *E. arvense* the

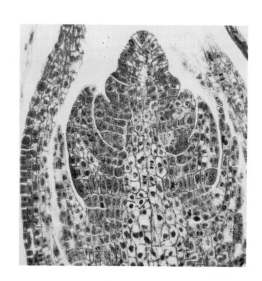

FIG. 20-4. *Equisetum hyemale.* Median longi-section of apex; note apical cell and origin of whorled laterals. X 125.

FIG. 20-3. *Equisetum hyemale.* Node and portions of adjacent internode, enlarged; note leaves, ridges, and stomata. X 3.

stomata are superficial but in *E. hyemale* they are sunken. Stomata are present most abundantly on the slopes of the ridges of the fluted stem surface (Fig. 20-3).

Figure 20-5A shows a transverse section of the vegetative stem of *E. arvense* taken from an internode where differentiation has been completed. The central region of the stem is

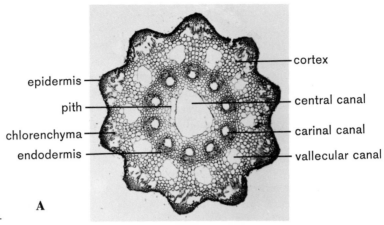

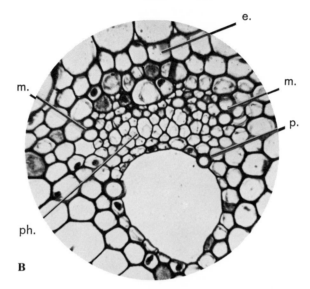

FIG. 20-5. *Equisetum arvense*. A. Transection of vegetative stem. X 30. B. Single vascular strand, enlarged. X 250; e., endodermis; m., metaxylem; p., protoxylem; ph., phloem.

hollow at maturity and is surrounded by the remains of the parenchymatous pith. This cavity is called the **central canal.** Outside the pith there is a ring of circular canals the position of which is directly internal to the surface ridges of the stem. These, therefore, are known as **carinal** (L. *carina,* keel) **canals,** and they mark the position of discrete strands of xylem and phloem. Experiments with dyes indicate that these canals have a role in conduction. Development of the xylem is endarch, for the first-formed annular and spiral protoxylem cells arise near the inner limit of each procambium strand (Fig. 20-5B). With the formation of the carinal canals, after differentiation of the protoxylem, the position of the protoxylem elements is disturbed. The phloem, which lies directly out-

side each carinal canal, is bordered laterally by two groups of metaxylem cells. Vessels, with not more than two component elements, occur in the nodal metaxylem; their perforations connect with the carinal canal. A second type of vessel occurs in the lateral xylem of the internodal vascular strands.

The pericycle is represented by a single layer of cells just within a rather prominent endodermis. In some species of *Equisetum* each vascular strand is completely surrounded by endodermis. In others, there are both outer and inner common, continuing endodermal layers and in still others, as in the aerial stems of *E. arvense,* only a continuous outer endodermal layer is present.

The cortex consists internally of parenchyma cells interrupted by large **vallecular**

canals which have a position corresponding with that of the depressions of the stem surface. Groups of outer cortical cells contain abundant chloroplasts. The walls of the cortical cells beneath the surface ridges are markedly thickened and contribute to the support and rigidity of the stem. The epidermal cells are heavily thickened with silicon dioxide and provided with stomata.

Although the xylem and phloem are present as discrete strands in the internodes of *Equisetum*, serial sections through the nodes reveal that they join there to form a short siphonostele. A diaphragm of tissue at the nodes interrupts the internodal canal. The vascular strands above and below the nodal region are joined to the siphonostele in alternate fashion. A ring of small protoxylem leaf traces leaves the stele at each node; branch traces originate between the leaf traces. The absence of leaf gaps indicates that the leaves are probably to be interpreted as microphyllous.[1] The internodal stele is known as a

eustele; here the parenchymatous gaps between the internodal bundles are neither leaf nor branch gaps. It is worthy of note that the internodes of the axis of the embryonic sporophyte at first contain a protostele; the eustele differentiates in later development.

Roots of mature plants are nodal, endogenous, and adventitious in origin and arise at the bases of lateral branches or their primordia. The root grows as a result of the activity of a single apical cell and its derivatives and is protostelic and exarch. Specially differentiated cubical cells of the root epidermis give rise to root hairs. The occasional branch roots develop endogenously from the pericycle.

Reproduction: the sporophyte

The sporogenous tissue in all species of *Equisetum* is localized in a strobilus, but the

---

[1] That the unbranched vein of *Equisetum* leaves may be reduced rather than primitive is suggested by

the presence of dichotomously branched veins in the leaves of the arthrophytan fossil *Sphenophyllum* (see p. 323). Furthermore, in the fossil arthrophyte *Hyeniopsis*, a well-developed branch may take the place of a leaf in the whorl.

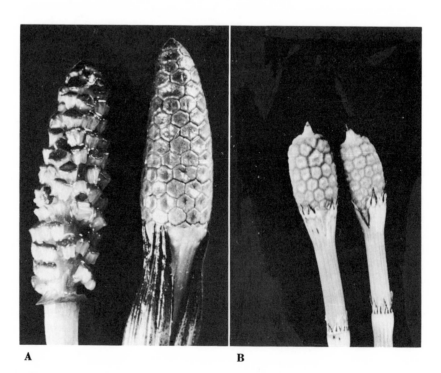

A **B**

FIG. 20-6. A. *Equisetum arvense*. Strobili, the one at the left about to shed spores. X 2. B. *E. hyemale*. Strobili. X 1.

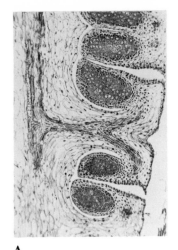 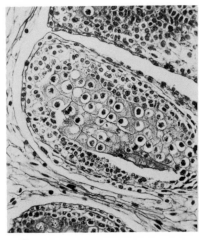

FIG. 20-7. A, B. *Equisetum hyemale*. Longisections of sporangiophores and immature sporangia; note traces to sporangia. A. X 60. B. X 125.

A   B

relation of the strobilus to the vegetative branches varies. In some species—*E. hyemale*, for example—the strobili develop at the tips of vegetative axes (Figs. 20-1C,D, 20-6A). In *E. arvense*, however, the strobilus is usually borne on a nonchlorophyllous fertile branch which develops from the rhizome as a unit (Fig. 20-1C). The latter later produces green vegetative branches after the strobilate branches have withered away. *Equisetum sylvaticum* is intermediate between these two extremes, in that the unbranched axis which bears the strobilus lacks chlorophyll at first. It becomes green and branched after the spores have been discharged.

In *E. arvense*, the strobilus-bearing branch is formed in the autumn preceding the spring in which it is to appear above the soil. As in the vegetative stem, growth of the strobilus is apical. In some species its axis continues to grow slightly beyond the apex of the strobilus. The axis of the strobilus produces a series of surface enlargements, each of which grows into a spore-producing appendage called a **sporangiophore**.[2] Mature spo-

rangiophores typically are hexagonal in surface view (Figs. 20-1; 20-6) because of mutual pressure. Between five and ten superficial and equidistant cells on the periphery of each sporangiophore function as sporangial initials; development of the sporangium is eusporangiate. Growth of the central portion of each sporangiophore is in a radial direction and inverts the young sporangia, so that their position at maturity is adaxial. Each sporangiophore is served by a trace which branches distally (Fig. 20-7A). The mature sporangia are elongate and fingerlike (Figs. 20-6A; 20-8).

The sporogenous tissue of the young sporangium (Fig. 20-8) is surrounded by a tapetum and a wall several cells in thickness. As development progresses, the cell walls of the tapetum disintegrate. There is thus formed a **tapetal plasmodium** which contributes to the nutrition of the sporogenous tissue and

---

[2] Professor R. L. Hauke, on the basis of unusual material of *E. littorale*, in which there were strobili with whorls of appendages transitional between leaf sheaths and typical sporangiophores, concluded that the appendages of the strobilus had dual potentialities. Accordingly, he considers the fertile appendages to be sporophylls. The term sporangiophore is used by those who are impressed with evidence from certain fossil Arthrophyta in which both branchlike sporangiophores and leaflike whorls occur in the strobilus.

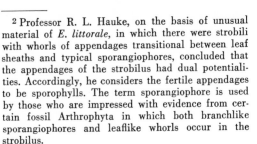 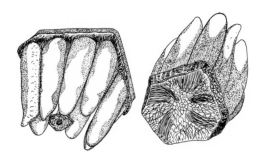

FIG. 20-8. *Equisetum arvense*. Enlarged views of sporangiophore and sporangia. X 10.

FIG. 20-9. *Equisetum arvense.* Spore and "elaters." X 420.

formation of the outermost layer of the spore wall. A number of the sporocytes abort, but those that remain undergo meiotic division, each producing a tetrad of spores. The haploid chromosome number is approximately $n = 108$ in *E. arvense* and *E. hyemale*.

The outermost layer of sporangial wall cells thickens spirally, and those beneath disintegrate. Dehiscence of the sporangium is longitudinal along a vertical line in that portion of the sporangial wall adjacent to the sporangiophore stalk. The wall structure of the mature spores is complex, the outermost wall layer consisting of four spirally arranged portions (Fig. 20-9). These separate at the time of sporangial dehiscence, so that each spore bears four somewhat spoonlike appendages sometimes called **"elaters."** The latter are hygroscopic and quickly affected by slight changes in humidity. When the spores are ready for dissemination, the internodes of the strobilus elongate slightly, thus separating the sporangiophores. The stalk of each now increases in length on its lower side, so that the apex of the sporangiophore is brought into

such a position that the sporangia are approximately perpendicular to the soil surface.

Reproduction: the gametophyte

The green spores of *Equisetum* germinate rapidly (Fig. 20-10) after their dissemination, provided that they are carried to suitable substrata. The spores are thin-walled and do not remain viable, without special treatment, for more than 15 days. In the case of *E. arvense,* which frequently is found in rather xeric situations, it is doubtful that any considerable number of spores produce mature gametophytes in such habitats. Vegetative multiplication by means of the rhizomes probably accounts for the formation of extensive colonies. Germinating spores and mature gametophytes of several species have been found on moist soil in nature. Naturally occurring gametophytes of *E. arvense* varied in size from that of a pinhead to 8 mm. in diameter. The spores of *E. arvense* and *E. hyemale,* among others, germinate rapidly in laboratory cultures on suitable media and on moist *Sphagnum* (Fig. 20-10). The developing gametophytes are extremely sensitive to such unfavorable environmental conditions as crowding, and their form is modified accordingly. However, well-isolated spores form rather disclike or cushionlike green gametophytes several millimeters in diameter (Figs. 20-11A,B, 20-15). They are anchored to the substratum by numerous unicellular rhizoids. The superficial cells of the gametophyte de-

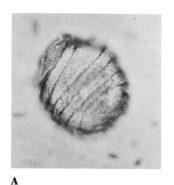

A

B

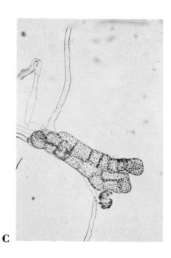

C

FIG. 20-10. *Equisetum hyemale.* A. Living spore with spiral "elaters." X 400. B. Spore germination. X 400. C. Young gametophyte. X 125.

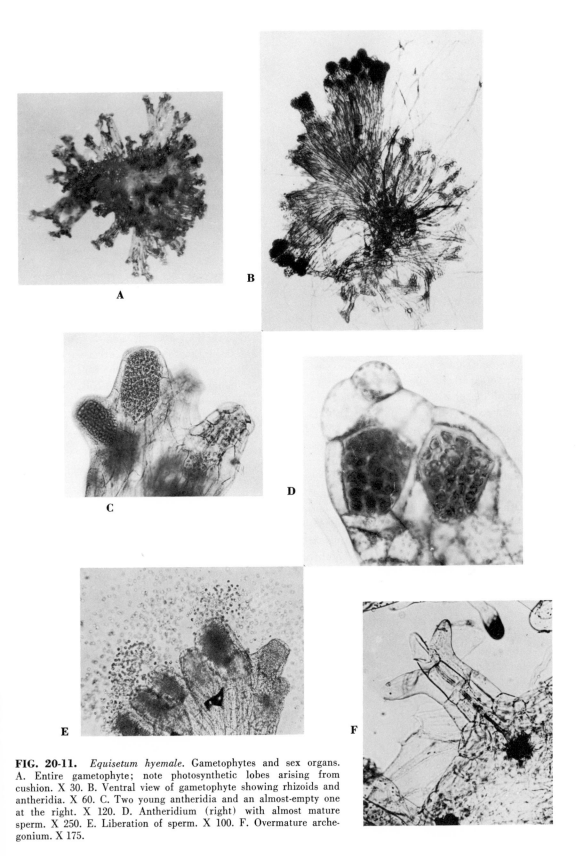

FIG. 20-11. *Equisetum hyemale.* Gametophytes and sex organs. A. Entire gametophyte; note photosynthetic lobes arising from cushion. X 30. B. Ventral view of gametophyte showing rhizoids and antheridia. X 60. C. Two young antheridia and an almost-empty one at the right. X 120. D. Antheridium (right) with almost mature sperm. X 250. E. Liberation of sperm. X 100. F. Overmature archegonium. X 175.

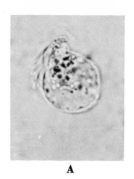

A   B

FIG. 20-12. *Equisetum arvense.* Sperm. A. Living. X 300. B. X 600.

velop lamellar lobes of photosynthetic cells which densely cover the moundlike basal portion which has a marginal meristem.

Under laboratory conditions, the antheridia may be produced on very young gametophytes. They always are borne at the apices of the erect surface lobes (Fig. 20-11C,D). The archegonia always occur near the bases of the photosynthetic lobes on the prostrate portion of the gametophyte where they may be recognized by their protuberant necks and widely flaring distal neck cells (Fig. 20-11F).

The gametophytes of *Equisetum* are usually reported to be bisexual but this requires careful further study. Crowding is said to evoke a preponderance of antheridial gametophytes. In the writer's experience, in many cultures of *E. arvense* and *E. hyemale,* in uncrowded cultures, some gametophytes bore only archegonia, some only antheridia, some both types of sex organs, and some were sterile.[3]

Each antheridium originates from a single superficial cell which undergoes division into an outer cell and an inner cell. The outer forms the wall of the upper portion of the antheridium; the inner, by successive divisions, forms the spermatogenous tissue (Fig. 20-11C-E). Each antheridium produces a large number of multiflagellate sperms which are liberated explosively when the mature antheridia are moistened (Fig. 20-11E). This is effected by absorption of water and increasing turgor of the cells of the antheridial jacket and by the inhibition of water and swelling of a hydrophilic substance surrounding the sperm cells. The sperms of *Equisetum*

[3] See p. 325, Addendum.

are relatively large (Fig. 20-12). When first liberated, they are surrounded by a spherical matrix (Fig. 20-12A) which swells and ultimately bursts, liberating the sperm protoplast, which becomes actively motile.

The archegonia (Figs. 20-11F, 20-13A) also arise from superficial cells. At maturity, their short necks, consisting of four vertical rows of neck cells, are protuberant; the venter is buried in the thallus. The eggs of several archegonia of a single gametophyte may be fertilized and may develop embryonic sporophytes (Figs. 20-13B; 20-14; 20-15).

Reproduction: embryogeny

Growth of the sporophyte is initiated by transverse division of the zygote, followed by divisions to form a quadrant. The two upper (outer) cells are often smaller than the two lower (inner) cells, and develop the first leaf sheath and stem in *E. arvense.* The lower cells develop the foot and the root, no suspensor being present (Figs. 20-13B, 20-14). In some species the primary axis ceases development after it has formed a limited number of nodes and internodes. In such forms, secondary axes are successively formed, one of which ultimately gives rise to the mature axis. The embryonic root grows through the gametophyte into the soil (Fig. 20-15A), thus establishing the independence of the young sporophyte. The gametophytes persist for some time in laboratory culture after sporophyte development has been initiated (Fig. 20-15B,C).

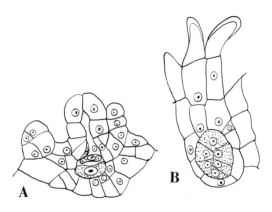

A   B

FIG. 20-13. A. *Equisetum arvense.* Immature archegonia. B. *E. hyemale.* Longitudinal section of archegonium with young sporophyte. (*From Jeffrey.*)

MORPHOLOGY OF PLANTS

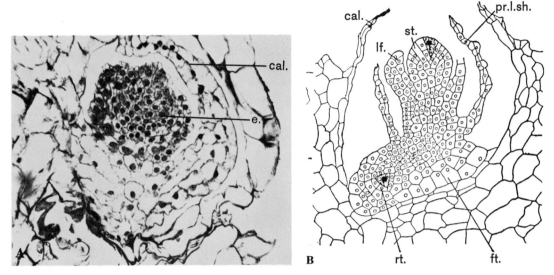

FIG. 20-14. *Equisetum arvense*. A. Almost-median section of embryonic sporophyte. B. Median section of older embryo. X 150; cal., calyptra; e., embryo; ft., foot; lf., leaf; pr. l. sh., primary leaf sheath; rt., root; st., stem. (B. *After Smith.*)

Summary

Equisetum, the only extant member of the Arthrophyta, differs from other seedless vascular plants, except certain *Lycopodium* species, in the whorled arrangement of its leaves and branches. Furthermore, its alternate arrangement of leaves and branches is anomalous among vascular plants. The leaves are reduced to scalelike appendages; each, however, receives a vascular trace and is provided with stomata. The burden of photosynthesis is borne by the axis. Except for the primary root, the roots are adventitious and arise at the bases of the lateral branches or their primordia. Both roots and stems develop as a result of the activity of apical cells and their derivatives. The root is protostelic, and the stem is eustelic at the internodes and siphonostelic at the nodes; the xylem is endarch in the stem. The parenchymatous gaps in the internodal steles are not related to either leaf or branch traces.

The sporogenous tissues of *Equisetum* always are localized in strobili; the relation of the latter to the vegetative branches is variable in the several species. The sporangium-bearing appendages are called sporangiophores; each has from five to ten sporangia. The sporangiophores differ from sporophylls, which are foliar, in being whorled branches of the strobilus axis. Sporangium development is

FIG. 20-15. A–C. *Equisetum hyemale*. Gametophytes with young sporophytes; note radicle in A. X 6.

eusporangiate and the spores are homosporous. The spores are anomalous in their possession of four hygroscopic appendages called "elaters."

The gametophytes of *Equisetum* are mound-like, chlorophyllous structures which have numerous erect, platelike lobes. The archegonia arise at the meristematic margin of the cushion between the bases of the lobes. The antheridia develop at the apices of the lobes. The sperms are multiflagellate. Suspensors are absent from the developing embryos, a number of which may be borne on a single gametophyte.

Fossil Arthrophyta

The fossil record includes specimens of Arthrophyta extending from the Lower Devonian through the end of the Paleozoic (Table 32-1, p. 512), although a few persisted into the early Triassic. Fossil Arthrophyta are usually readily recognized by their whorled branching, ribbed stems, and cauline sporangia. The Arthrophyta have been variously classified. In addition to the Equisetales, with both extinct and extant members, three orders known only through extinct genera will be described. These are the Hyeniales, Calamitales, and Sphenophyllales.

Order 1. Hyeniales

The stems of Hyeniales were jointed, but the dichotomously lobed or branching sterile

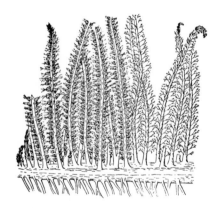

FIG. 20-16. *Hyenia elegans*. Portion of rhizome with aerial branches and roots. X 0.5. (*After Leclercq.*)

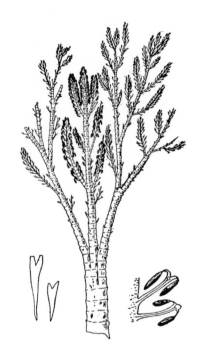

FIG. 20-17. *Calamophyton primaevum*. Kräusel and Weyland. Reconstruction. Vegetative leaves at left; sporangium-bearing appendages at the right. (*After Kräusel and Weyland, from Smith.*)

and fertile appendages were not always clearly whorled.

Protohyenia, the oldest known member of the order, has been described from the Lower Devonian. It was thus contemporaneous with Psilophyta and Microphyllophyta.

Hyenia (Fig. 20-16) is a Middle Devonian genus much like *Calamophyton*, from which it differs (as far as known) in its extended rhizome which bore many erect, unbranched shoots. From the rhizome arose numerous, dichotomously branching roots. The aerial branches of one species, *H. vogtii* Høeg, were branched and clothed with whorled, leaflike forked appendages. Some of the aerial branches produced whorled, dichotomously branching sporangiophores with inwardly directed sporangia.

Calamophyton (Fig. 20-17) is another well-known Middle Devonian arthrophyte. The stems of *Calamophyton bicephalum* Leclerq and Andrews were clearly jointed and the main axes at least 2 feet high. Whether or not they arose from a rhizome has not been ascertained. These axes were digitately, mono-

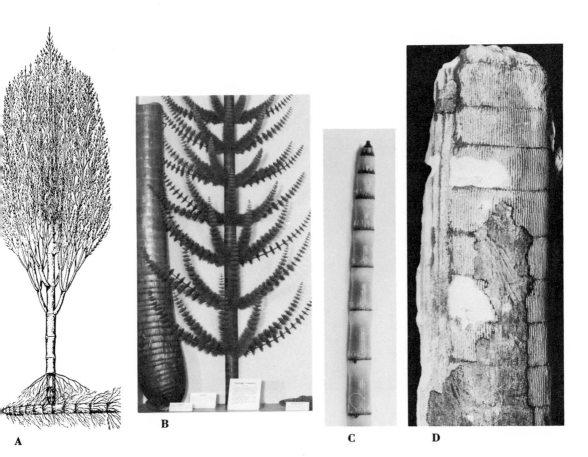

A

B

C   D

FIG. 20-18. *Calamites carinatus* Sternb. A. Reconstruction; note rhizome, roots, and whorled aerial branches. B. Model reconstruction: trunk at left, whorled branches (*Annularia*) at the right. C. *Equi-* *setum hyemale*, and D. Cast of *Calamites* stem for comparison. C. X 1. D. X 0.33. (A. *After Hirmer.* B. *Courtesy of the Chicago Natural History Museum.*)

podially, and dichotomously branched. The branchlets bore three-dimensionally branched, terete appendages, some of which recurved and terminated in sporangia. In *C. primaevum* Kräusel and Weyland, the ultimate branchlets gave rise to whorled, wedge-shaped leaves (Fig. 20-17). Whether *Calamophyton* was homosporous or heterosporous is not known.

Order 2. Calamitales

The giant, treelike Arthrophyta flourished from the Upper Devonian to the end of the Paleozoic (Table 32-1). *Calamites* (Fig 20-18), the giant horsetail, with a number of species, is abundant in both Mississippian and Pennsylvanian (Table 32-1) strata. *Calamites* (Gr. *kalamos*, reed) was treelike in habit, in some cases perhaps extending up

to 90 feet in height, with a trunk up to 1 foot in diameter. The aerial portion of the plant arose from a large underground rhizome as in *Equisetum*. The great diameter of the stems was the result of cambial activity which covered the primary, *Equisetum*-like stele with successive layers of secondary xylem (Fig. 20-19). The wood, however, gives no indication of annual zonation. As in *Equisetum*, the stem contained a large central canal and canals associated with the vascular tissues. Both rhizomes and aerial branches departed from the main axis in a series of whorls. The ultimate branches were clothed with circles of slender leaves with an internal structure which indicates that they were photosynthetic organs. The adventitious roots arose in whorls from the nodes of the rhizome.

The fertile appendages of *Calamites* were borne in compact strobili. These were com-

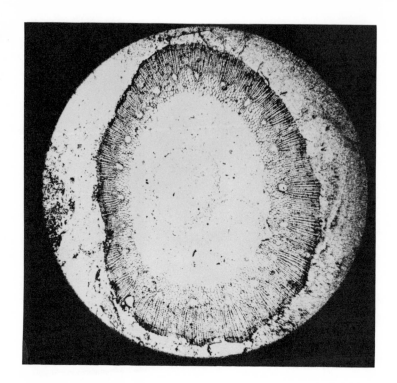

FIG. 20-19. *Calamites* sp. Transection of small stem; note canals associated with primary xylem. X 16.

posed of a central axis which had alternating cycles of bracts and sporangiophores (Fig. 20-20). The sporangiophores and bracts were supplied by separate traces from the stele. In some cases, the sporangiophores were peltate and had two sporangia on their adaxial surface. Sections of the sporangia indicate that they were much like those of *Equisetum* and that the sporangial wall was composed of a single layer of annularly thickened cells; at maturity some species of *Calamites* were heterosporous.

Order 3. Sphenophyllales

The members of the Sphenophyllales such as *Annularia* (Fig. 20-21) and *Sphenophyllum* (Fig. 20-22) were herbaceous, low-growing plants, probably not exceeding a meter in height, which occurred from Upper Devonian through early Triassic (Table 32-1). Some species of *Sphenophyllum* may have been climbers.

The axes were composed of clearly delimited nodes and ribbed internodes, the ribs, however, not alternating in successive internodes as they do in *Equisetum*. Each node bore a whorl of wedge-shaped leaves (Fig. 20-22B), which in some species were traversed by dichotomously branching veins in multiples of three. Successive whorls of leaves and the internodal ribs were not alternately

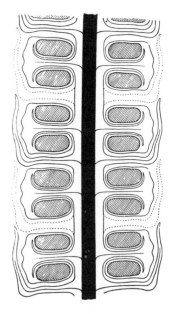

FIG. 20-20. *Calamostachys* sp. Median longitudinal portion of strobilus associated with *Calamites;* note bracts, sporangiophores, and sporangia. (*From Hirmer.*)

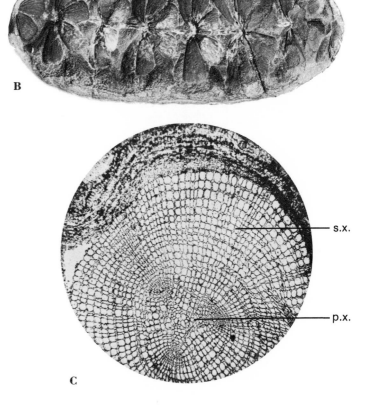

arranged. Internally, the slender stems contained an actinostele with exarch xylem. Older stems of certain species had considerable secondary xylem (Fig. 20-22C), a cambium, and secondary phloem. The roots also underwent some secondary growth.

The distal portions of certain branches of *Sphenophyllum* species were fertile; they were composed of an axis bearing whorled, leaflike bracts which subtended a whorl of sporangiophores (Fig. 20-23). The strobili are often assigned the name *Bowmanites*. In some species the sporangiophores arose from the adaxial face of the bracts. Each sporangiophore bore three sporangia in *S. dawsonii*

FIG. 20-21. A. *Annularia* sp. Foliage associated with *Calamites*. B. *Sphenophyllum*. X. 0.66.

s.x.

p.x.

FIG. 20-22. *Sphenophyllum* sp. A. Reconstruction; note stobilus. B. *S. emarginatum*. Portion of fossilized axis and leaves. X 1. C. Transection of stele; note triarch protostele surrounded by secondary xylem; p.x., primary xylem; s.x., secondary xylem. X 35. (A, B. *Courtesy of the Chicago Natural History Museum.*)

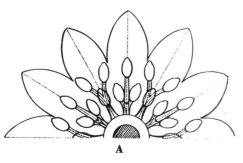

A

FIG. 20-23. A. *Spheno-phyllum* sp. Half of one whorl of bracts with sporangiophores. B. *Sphenophyl-lum* sp. Median longisection of portion of strobilus; note axis, bracts and sporangia. (A, B. *After Hirmer.*) C. *Sphenophyllum dawsonii.* Transection of strobilus. X 20.

C   **B**

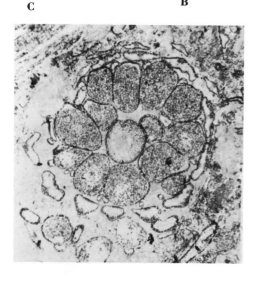

Williamson. The spores in some species were only slightly heterosporous; other species may have been homosporous.

Order 4. Equisetales

In addition to the extant *Equisetum*, a number of other members of this order survived beyond the Paleozoic. Among these may be cited *Equisetites* (Fig. 20-24), known from Mesozoic and Cenozoic strata, which like *Equisetum* was herbaceous. The leaves of *Equisetites* were insignificant and scalelike. Certain of the branches bore strobili. The

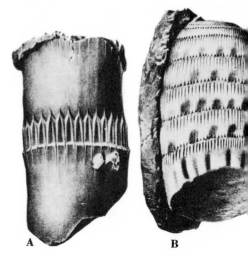

A   **B**

FIG. 20-24. *Equisetites.* A. *E. platyodon* Brong. B. *E. arenaceus* Jäger. (*After Hirmer.*)

Equisetales are thought by some to represent reduced forms of the more robust Calamitales.

Summary of Fossil Arthrophyta

The fossil record indicates that, although currently represented in our flora only by the small number of *Equisetum* species, the Arthrophyta were formerly an important assemblage. Arthrophytan forms are known from the Lower Devonian by their whorled appendages, and ribbed stems and were co-dominant with the Microphyllophyta and certain Pterophyta during the Carboniferous. Both woody (arborescent) and herbaceous and homosporous types have been described.

The members of the Arthrophyta treated in this chapter may be classified as follows:

Order 1. Hyeniales
    Family 1. Hyeniaceae
        Genera: *Protohyenia, Hyenia,*
            Calamophyton
Order 2. Calamitales
    Family 1. Calamitaceae
        Genus: *Calamites*
Order 3. Sphenophyllales
    Family 1. Sphenophyllaceae
        Genera: *Sphenophyllum, Annularia*
Order 4. Equisetales
    Family 1. Equisetaceae
        Genera: *Equisetites, Equisetum*

DISCUSSION QUESTIONS

1. What attributes distinguish *Equisetum* from other vascular cryptogams?

2. Why are the parenchymatous regions between the vascular bundles in *Equisetum* not considered to be leaf or branch gaps?

3. Define or explain carinal canal, vallecular canal, central canal.

4. What does the paucity of xylem in a stem, leaf, or root usually indicate?

5. How does the arrangement of branches with reference to the leaves mark *Equisetum* as unique?

6. Summarize the methods of nutrition of the gametophyte in *Lycopodium*, *Selaginella*, *Psilotum*, *Isoetes*, and *Equisetum*.

7. Describe the process of spore dissemination from the strobilus of *Equisetum*.

8. Can you give other examples, among the vascular plants, in which the stems are the chief photosynthetic organs?

9. What evidence can you cite to support the claim that the branched condition is primitive in *Equisetum?*

10. Describe the genera *Calamophyton*, *Sphenophyllum*, and *Calamites* with respect to vegetative structure and reproduction.

11. What attributes do these genera possess in common with *Equisetum?*

12. To what do you ascribe the absence of annual rings in the secondary xylem of *Calamites?*

13. Of what significance is the evidence that certain fossil Arthrophyta were slightly heterosporous?

14. Speculate regarding the nature of the gametophytes in fossil Arthrophyta.

Addendum:
This is substantiated by the current investigations of Duckett (personal communication) who has observed in 9 species in axenic culture gametophytes of 2 types, male or female. The male remain male, but the female gametophytes develop antheridia later (protogyny). This is similar to the fern, *Platyzoma* (p. 342).

CHAPTER 21

Division Pterophyta—I

Introduction

Because of their number and diversity, discussion of the final group of vascular cryptogams, the Pterophyta, will require this and the following two chapters. The Pterophyta, broadly speaking, the ferns, include approximately 10,000 species. Probable precursors of the Pterophyta flourished during the middle Devonian (Table 32-1). Consideration of these and of the remainder of the fossil record will be deferred to the end of Chapter 23 (p. 368).

Of the four divisions of vascular cryptogams, Psilophyta, Microphyllophyta, Arthrophyta, and Pterophyta, only the members of the last are macrophyllous (p. 264). The leaves in a number of genera are the largest and most complex in the plant kingdom. In many ferns, the leaves appear to be the dominant organs of the sporophyte, the stems being smaller and less prominent. All have branching veins and the traces of all mature fern leaves are associated with gaps in the stem steles.[1] They share the attribute of macrophylly with the phanerogams or seed plants. Those who classify all vascular plants in the single division Tracheophyta group ferns and seed plants together in the subdivision Pteropsida (Table 32-2).

Survey of the Pterophyta indicates that the group may be divided into two series on the basis of method of sporangium development. The first series, the class **Eusporangiopsida,** has a type of sporangium development essentially similar to that of the Psilophyta, Microphyllophyta, Arthrophyta, and seed plants. Furthermore, the sporangia are massive and entirely or partially embedded, and they contain an indefinitely large

number of spores surrounded by a several-layered sporangial wall, at least during early development. In the second series, the **Leptosporangiopsida** (Gr. *leptos*, fine or small), the sporangia develop from single cells which undergo periclinal divisions. Here the outer cell forms the major portion of the protuberant sporangium which is small in size, thin-walled (one-layered), and few-spored, the number usually definite and a multiple of two (frequently 32-64; or 512 as in *Osmunda,* p. 350). The vast majority of familiar cultivated and field ferns are members of the Leptosporangiopsida. The Eusporangiopsida will be discussed in this chapter and the Leptosporangiopsida in Chapters 22 and 23.

Class 1. Eusporangiopsida

The Eusporangiopsida include two orders with living plants, namely, the Ophioglossales and Marattiales. Each order is represented by two genera in the present text, namely, *Ophioglossum* and *Botrychium,* and *Marattia* and *Angiopteris,* respectively. The first two genera grow in the temperate zone, to the subarctic and the tropics; the last two are entirely tropical. A total of 10 genera and 280 species of ferns are included in the Eusporangiopsida, which, accordingly is a small group as compared with the Leptosporangiopsida.

Order 1. *Ophioglossales*

FAMILY 1. OPHIOGLOSSACEAE

Ophioglossum and *Botrychium*

Introduction and vegetative morphology

The genera *Ophioglossum* (Gr. *ophis,* serpent + Gr. *glossa,* tongue), the **adder's**

---

[1] Unless the stele be a protostele, in which case a groove is sometimes visible.

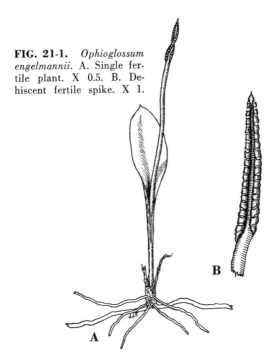

FIG. 21-1. *Ophioglossum engelmannii.* A. Single fertile plant. X 0.5. B. Dehiscent fertile spike. X 1.

FIG. 21-3. *Botrychium virginianum* (L.) Sw. Single plant with fertile spike. X 0.15. (*From a negative of Dr. C. J. Chamberlain, courtesy of Chicago Natural History Museum.*)

FIG. 21-2. *Ophioglossum engelmannii.* Living specimens. A. Fertile plant. X 0.5 B. Immature fertile spike. X 1.5.

tongue fern (Figs. 21-1, 21-2), and *Botrychium* (Gr. *botrychos*, grape), the **grape fern** (Fig. 21-3), are rather widely distributed in temperate North America. The former occurs in old fields and meadows, and the latter is frequently an inhabitant of the forest floor where it thrives in partial shade. *Ophioglossum engelmanni* Prantl is often quite abundant after spring and fall rains in partial shade, near and under cedar trees (*Juniperus*).

The leaves in both genera arise from a rather short, fleshy subterranean stem which bears fleshy, adventitious roots. The roots of some species of *Ophioglossum* produce adventitious buds that may develop new plantlets, a phenomenon which results in the formation of rather extensive colonies. Both *Botrychium* and *Ophioglossum* usually elevate only a single leaf from the perennial stems each growing season (Figs. 21-1 to 21-3). The leaves are annual in activity. Serial transverse sections of the axis of *O. engelmanni* reveal that the leaves arise in spiral order in five

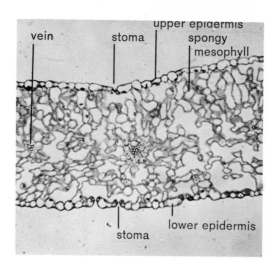

FIG. 21-4. *Ophioglossum engelmannii.* Transection of a leaf. X 65.

vertical rows, although usually only one leaf is present at a time. In *Botrychium virginianum* (L.) Sw. (Fig. 21-3), the leaf blade is large and dissected, but in other species of the genus the leaves are smaller and simpler. The leaf of *Ophioglossum engelmanni* is simple and entire. It has been suggested that simple leaves are reduced rather than primitive in these ferns.

Inasmuch as the leaf is the dominant and most conspicuous organ of these plants, its structure will be described first. The young leaves are rolled up and protected by the remains of the ensheathing stipular sheath of the preceding leaf as they emerge from the soil. The leaflets of *Botrychium* are characterized by open dichotomous venation; the leaf blade in *Ophioglossum* is traversed by a reticulate system of veins which are mostly united at the leaf margins. The leaves appear as primordia near the slow-growing stem tip several years before they are raised above the ground, and their development is extremely slow. The vascular tissue of the leaf is connected to that in the stem through the petiole. In *O. engelmannii,* the double leaf trace branches into four or more strands soon after it enters the petiole. The single trace in *Botrychium* divides into two as it enters the petiole. The leaf blade in *Ophioglossum* is covered by epidermal cells above and below (Fig. 21-4); the central portion is composed

of photosynthetic parenchyma cells which are not differentiated into palisade and spongy layers. Stomata occur abundantly on both surfaces of the leaf. The guard cells, alone among the epidermal cells, contain chloroplasts.

The underground stems of both *Ophioglossum* and *Botrychium* are erect, slow-growing, and fleshy. They are covered with the remains of previous seasons' leaves at their summits, and with rather closely arranged, fleshy roots below (Figs. 21-1, 21-2), one of the latter associated with each old leaf base. Development of the stem in both genera is localized in the division of single apical cells and their derivatives. These differentiate in older portions of the stem into stelar, cortical, and epidermal regions. The vascular tissue in the primary (embryonic) stems of some species is protostelic, but as the stem grows older, the vascular tissue formed later is arranged as a siphonostele. The siphonostele is much dissected (Fig. 21-5) into discrete strands in *Ophioglossum* because of the close proximity to each other of the roots, the nodes, and the points of departure of leaf traces, which in these macrophyllous plants, leave parenchymatous gaps in the stele above the point of their departure. The shortness of the internodes and the overlapping of leaf

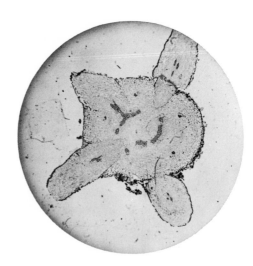

FIG. 21-5. *Ophioglossum engelmannii.* Transection of stem; note emergent roots and dissection of (ectophloic) siphonostele by gaps. X 12.5.

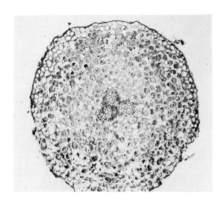

FIG. 21-6. *Ophioglossum engelmannii*. Transection of a root; note triarch stele and extensive cortex. X 30.

gaps result in the arrangement of vascular tissue as an eustele, with endarch maturation of the xylem. The phloem is external to the xylem. Endodermis and pericycle are absent in mature stems of *O. engelmanni*. In the stems of *Botrychium*, a cambium adds secondary vascular tissues to the primary ones. The cortex is parenchymatous and starch-filled. The stem surface is suberized in older portions by the formation of a periderm layer. *Botrychium* is the only extant fern genus with secondary vascular tissue and a periderm.

The roots in both genera also develop through the activity of single apical cells. They arise endogenously in the rhizome near the phloem in association with the leaves and below them. In *Ophioglossum*, the root (Fig. 21-6) may be monarch, diarch, or tetrarch; it is most often tetrarch in *Botrychium virginianum*. The phloem alternates with the xylem, and both are surrounded by one or more layers of pericycle cells. The stele is delimited from the cortex by a well-differentiated endodermis. The cortex is extensive and serves as a storage region. The epidermis is devoid of root hairs; in older regions of the root, the surface is suberized. Endophytic fungi usually are present in these genera.

Reproduction: the sporophyte

Both *Ophioglossum* and *Botrychium* are at once distinguishable from other Pterophyta by the arrangement of their sporogenous tissue, which is localized in a branched or

unbranched **fertile spike** (Figs. 21-1 to 21-3). The latter emerges at the junction of the leaf blade and petiole. Anatomical evidence has been interpreted as indicating that this structure represents a pair of fertile, lateral pinnae (leaflets). The fertile axis is unbranched in *O. engelmanni* (Figs. 21-1, 21-2) but compound in *B. virginianum* (Fig. 21-3). In the former, it has two longitudinal rows of deeply sunken sporangia (Fig. 21-2B) which arise in eusporangiate fashion. Their walls are composed of several layers of cells (Fig. 21-7). A branch of vascular tissue runs to the base of each sporangium. There is a one- or two-layered tapetumlike zone between the central sporogenous tissue and the wall. As the sporangium develops, the walls of the tapetal cells disintegrate and give rise to a tapetal plasmodium. A few of the sporogenous cells also disintegrate, but the remainder undergo meiosis and give rise to tetrads of spores. It has been reported recently that the haploid number of chromosomes in *O. vulgatum L.* is approximately 256. The cells of the sporophyte, therefore, contain more than 500 chromosomes; a tropical species, *O. petiolatum*, with over 1000 chromosomes, has the largest number yet observed in a naturally occurring vascular plant. The sporangia dehisce at maturity along a line perpendicular to the long axis of the fertile spike predetermined by the formation of several rows of thin-walled cells. Each sporangium may contain as many as 15,000 spores in some species.

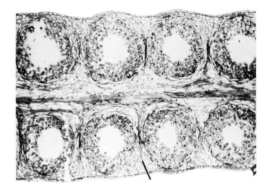

FIG. 21-7. *Ophioglossum* sp. Median longitudinal section of apex of fertile spike; note seriate eusporangiate sporangia and vascular traces. X 25.

Development of the gametophyte from the spores has never been followed completely in laboratory cultures; hence our knowledge of it is based largely on specimens collected in the field. In both *Ophioglossum* and *Botrychium*, the gametophyte is fleshy, subterranean, and nongreen and always is infected with the hyphae of an endophytic fungus. *Ophioglossum* gametophytes are cylindrical (Fig. 21-8), up to 2 inches in length, and branched in some individuals. The diameter of the largest is about one-quarter of an inch. The nutrition of the gametophyte here, as in *Psilotum* and some species of *Lycopodium*, apparently is saprophytic. However, small amounts of chlorophyll may develop in exposed portions of the gametophyte, the growth of which is apical.

Ophioglossum is bisexual, the antheridia and archegonia occurring together in various stages of development (Fig. 21-8). Both sex organs arise from cells on the surface of the gametophyte, but at maturity they are largely

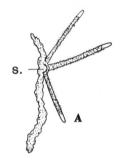
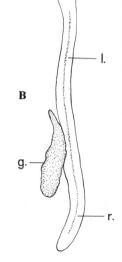

FIG. 21-9. A. *Ophioglossum vulgatum.* Gametophyte showing roots and minute stem (s.) of young sporophyte. X 2. B. *O. moluccanium* Schlecht. Embryonic sporophyte attached to gametophyte; g., gametophyte; l., primary leaf or cotyledon; r., primary root or radicle. (B. *Modified from Smith.*)

sunken within it, as in *Anthoceros.* The antheridia are massive and contain large numbers of multiflagellate sperms. Only the tips of the archegonial necks protrude above the gametophyte surface. There are four rows of neck cells. Fertilization has been observed to occur in the summer months in the northern hemisphere.

Reproduction: embryogeny

Development of the zygote into an embryonic sporophyte progresses slowly in various species of *Ophioglossum.* A small spherical mass of tissue is formed within the archegonial venter. This becomes differentiated into foot, root, and a leaf primordium. The apical initial of the stem appears later, and this perhaps foreshadows the inconspicuous state of that organ in the mature sporophyte (Fig. 21-9). Several years are required, in most species, for the production of a leaf with a fertile spike.

Order 2. Marattiales

FAMILY 1. MARATTIACEAE

Marattia and *Angiopteris*

Introduction and vegetative morphology

The members of the order Marattiales, family Marattiaceae, are more fernlike in habit than *Ophioglossum* especially because their

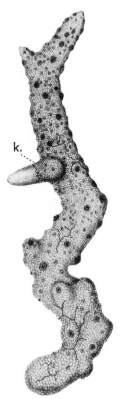

FIG. 21-8. *Ophioglossum vulgatum* L. Cylindrical gametophyte with antheridia (larger, darker) and archegonia; young embryo at k. X 20. (*After Bruchmann.*)

FIG. 21-10. A. *Marattia alata* Smith. X 0.2. B. *M. fraxinea.* Growing in Botanic Garden, Sydney, Australia (A. *After G. M. Smith*, B. *From a negative of Dr. C. J. Chamberlain, courtesy of the Chicago Natural History Museum.*)

sporangia are borne on the undersurface of the large fronds. The Marattiales are exclusively tropical in distribution. Two of the genera, *Marattia* (Fig. 21-10) and *Angiopteris* (Fig. 21-11), are sometimes available in university and other conservatories and as specimens in herbaria. *Angiopteris* grows natively in Hawaii, the Philippines, and other Pacific islands, while *Marattia* is more widely distributed in the tropics.

The stems are fleshy, tuberous, and erect or trunklike and covered by the persistent paired stipules at each leaf base from among which the fleshy roots emerge. The mature stems are dictyostelic, and the roots contain exarch actinosteles with as many as twelve protoxylem groups (*Marattia alata*), many more than occur in most ferns.

The large,[2] pinnately compound leaves, unlike those of the Ophioglossales, are curled or circinate in the bud, so that typical fernlike "fiddle heads" are produced. The venation is

___

[2] The fronds of a New Zealand species are 20–30 feet long and up to 15 feet in width.

FIG. 21-11. *Angiopteris evecta.* Growing in Missouri Botanic Garden. (*From a negative of Dr. C. J. Chamberlain, courtesy of the Chicago Natural History Museum.*)

dichotomous. Mucilage chambers occur throughout the rather fleshy plants.

Reproduction: the sporophyte

The eusporangiate sporangia are massive (Fig. 21-12) and closely appressed laterally. They are borne near the leaf margins along the veinlets. Approximately 512 sporocytes are differentiated within each sporangium. The latter is thick-walled and provided with a tapetum.

The sporangia of *Angiopteris*, although crowded together, retain their individuality and dehisce into two valves by vertical splitting (Fig. 21-12A,B). Those of *Marattia* are united into a compound unit called a **synangium** (Fig. 21-12C). The latter opens as a unit, exposing the vertically split, contiguous sporangia.

Reproduction: the gametophyte

The gametophytes are massive and liverwortlike (suggestive of *Pellia*), up to several centimeters long (Fig. 21-13). A fungus may be present within the gametophytic cells. The gametophytes are long-lived and many cells thick, except at the margins. Antheridia, which produce multiflagellate sperms, may develop on both surfaces of the protrandrous gametophytes; the archegonia occur only on the ventral surface. Both types of sex organs are immersed in the thallus as in the Ophioglossales and *Anthoceros*.

Reproduction: embryogeny

Usually only one zygote on each gametophyte develops into a juvenile sporophyte. The Marattiales differ in their embryogeny from

MORPHOLOGY OF PLANTS

C

FIG. 21-12. A, B. *Angiopteris* sp. Dehiscent sporangia. C. *Marattia* sp. Dehiscent synangium. A. X 5. B. X 25. C. X 5. (C. *After Bower.*)

A   **B**

the leptosporangiate ferns (p. 347) in that the primary leaf or cotyledon emerges from the dorsal surfaces of the gametophyte, rather than from the ventral.

Summary and Classification

The eusporangiate Pterophyta include two groups of living ferns exemplified in the preceding account by *Ophioglossum* and *Botrychium*, on the one hand, and by *Marattia* and *Angiopteris*, on the other. The first two genera bear their massive, eusporangiate sporangia on fertile spikes, whereas in the latter they occur separately, though contiguously, or in

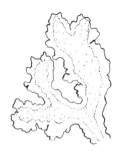

FIG. 21-13. *Marattia sambricina* Bl. Gametophyte 27 months after spore germination. X 4. (*After Stokey.*)

synangia on the lower surface near the margins of vegetative leaflets. In both cases, development and maturation of all the sporangia are synchronous, and each sporangium produces large numbers of spores.

The gametophytes of *Ophioglossum* and *Botrychium* are fleshy, subterranean, achlorophyllous, saprophytic structures. That of the former is cylindrical and radially organized, with sex organs well distributed over the surface. In *Botrychium virginianum*, the gametophyte has some degree of dorsiventrality, with the sex organs limited to the upper surface. The gametophytes of *Marattia* and *Angiopteris*, on the other hand, are epiterranean, chlorophyllous, and *Pellia*-like, although they also contain a mycorrhizal fungus. The archegonia are confined usually to the lower surface; the antheridia may occur on both surfaces.

These genera possess macrophyllous leaves which are the dominant organs of the sporophyte. This is attested by the profound disturbance of the stem stele by leaf gaps and the relatively slow development of the stem itself. The latter is especially apparent in the development of the embryonic sporophyte, in which leaf development far outstrips that of the stem. The first embryonic leaf emerges through the *dorsal* surface of the gametophyte in the Marattiales. Discussion of the fossil record of the eusporangiate ferns will be deferred to Chapter 23, page 368.

DISCUSSION QUESTIONS

1. Distinguish between macrophyllous and microphyllous leaves.

2. How does the venation of *Ophioglossum* differ from that of *Botrychium?* Which is considered to be more primitive, and on what basis?

3. Are microphyllous and macrophyllous leaves homologous in your opinion? Explain.

4. Can you suggest an explanation for the relatively small size of the stems in *Botrychium, Ophioglossum,* and the Marattiales?

5. Does the approximately simultaneous maturation of the spores in these genera occur in vascular plants previously studied? Can you suggest a biological disadvantage of this habit?

6. Can you suggest similarities between the gametophyte of *Ophioglossum* and that of other seedless vascular plants? Explain.

7. How does spore production in *Marattia* and *Angiopteris* differ from that in *Ophioglossum* and *Botrychium?*

8. In what respects are the gametophytes of these genera different?

9. Where would you search for *Botrychium* and *Ophioglossum* in nature?

CHAPTER 22

Division Pterophyta—II

Class 2. Leptosporangiopsida

As stated at the beginning of Chapter 21, the division Pterophyta may be subdivided into two classes, the Eusporangiopsida, described in the preceding chapter, and the Leptosporangiopsida, to be considered in the present and following chapter. The Leptosporangiopsida include all the ferns which have leptosporangiate sporangium development. In this type of sporangial ontogeny (Fig. 22-11), the sporangium arises from a single cell, derivatives of which protrude from the surface of the plant. An apical cell functions in sporangium development. Leptosporangiate sporangia are small, produce a definite number of spores (frequently 48 to 64), and have a wall one layer of cells in thickness. Other attributes, in addition to sporangial characters, serve to distinguish the Eusporangiopsida from the Leptosporangiopsida. These will be cited in the following account.

In number of genera, species, and individuals, the leptosporangiate ferns far outnumber the eusporangiate. Some 250 genera and 9000 species have been described. Leptosporangiopsida are most abundant in the tropics, but they are also well represented in the temperate zone. In habit, they vary from small, delicate, filmy plants to large tropical tree ferns with upright stems and enormous leaves; several are climbers. The Leptosporangiopsida include a number of families, of which many species are inhabitants of the tropics and, therefore, not readily available for study except in collections in herbaria and occasionally in conservatories. For this reason, the treatment of the group in this text will be restricted to a brief discussion of representatives that are readily available; specialized treatises listed on p. 267 give a more extensive treatment of the ferns.

In the present account, the class Leptosporangiopsida is considered to include three orders: (1) Filicales, (2) Marsileales, and (3) Salviniales. The Marsileales and Salviniales are discussed in Chapter 23.

Order 1. Filicales

With the exception of the five genera of "water ferns" classified in the Marsileales and Salviniales, the majority of leptosporangiate ferns are usually included in the very large order Filicales which contains many families and approximately 300 homosporous genera and one genus seemingly with incipient heterospory (p. 292). A number of these are known only through tropical representatives from remote places; material of these ferns is not readily available. The present discussion, accordingly, will emphasize certain widely distributed and generally available genera of the family Polypodiaceae and will be followed by briefer treatment of representatives of some of the other families.

FAMILY 1. POLYPODIACEAE

Introduction and vegetative morphology

A majority of the most familiar, naturally occurring, and widespread ferns of the temperate zone and tropics, as well as many cultivated varieties, are members of a vast assemblage of polypodiaceous ferns, so named from the genus *Polypodium* (Gr. *polys*, many + Gr. *pous*, foot). Among these are *Dryopteris* (Gr. *drys*, tree + Gr. *Pteris*, fern), *Adiantum* (Gr. *adiantos*, maidenhair), *Polystichum* (Gr. *polys*, many + Gr. *stichos*, row), *Woodsia* (after *Joseph Wood*, an English botanist), *Pteris* (Gr. *pteris*, fern), *Pteridium* (Gr. *pteris*), and *Nephrolepis* (Gr. *nephros*, kidney + Gr. *lepis*, scale). Most of these genera are plants of moist, mesic woodlands. *Adian-*

A

B

FIG. 22-1. A. *Adiantum capillus-veneris*. X 0.33.
B. *A. pedatum*. X 0.1.

tum capillus-veneris L. (Fig. 22-1A), the
Venus maidenhair, however, is an example
of a rather hydrophytic species and is widely
distributed on wet limestone cliffs; *A. pedatum*
(Fig. 22-1B) grows in moist, shady woods.
Pellaea atropurpurea (L.) Link., the **cliff
brake,** and *Polypodium polypodioides* (L.)
Watt., the **"resurrection fern,"** on the other

hand, are xerophytes. All temperate-zone
members of this alliance are perennial and a
few (*Polystichum, Cyrtomium*) are evergreen.
   Adiantum capillus-veneris (Fig. 22-1) and
Dryopteris dentata (Forsk.) C. Chr. (Fig.
22-2) will be emphasized as illustrative types
in the following account because they are
widespread and readily cultivated in green-

FIG. 22-2. *Dryopteris dentata,* a
species of shield fern. X 0.05.

houses. In both of them the stem is subterranean, although in the latter it may be exposed. The bases of the preceding seasons' leaves persist indefinitely and form a sort of jagged armor about the stems. The stem in *Dryopteris dentata* is ascending and relatively slow-growing, but in *Adiantum* it is a horizontal, rapidly elongating rhizome. Branching of the rhizome is abundant in *Adiantum* and results in colonization of the area around the original plant. The stems of both genera are clothed with a dense mass of adventitious roots which emerge from the stem between the leaf bases.

Growth of the stem in each case may be traced to the activity of single apical cells and their derivatives; these occur at the stem tip, often concealed by a dense growth of superficial multicellular scalelike organs known as **paleae.** The apical cell of leptosporangiate fern stems may be tetrahedral, and gives rise to three ranks of derivative cells, or it may cut off derivatives in only two planes as in the dorsiventral rhizome of *Pteridium*. Although the vascular tissues in the embryonic stems of all leptosporangiate ferns are reported to be protostelic, there is a gradual transition in older stems to a siphonostelic, solenostelic, or dictyostelic condition, depending on the species. In *Adiantum* (Fig. 22-3A), the vascular tissue is completely surrounded by a well-differentiated endodermis which separates it from the parenchymatous pith and cortex; in *Dryopteris*, the endodermis surrounds each

segment of the dictyostele (Fig. 22-3B). Portions of both of these may become sclerotic. *Adiantum* is solenostelic, while *Dryopteris* is dictyostelic. The xylem is mesarch in development and composed chiefly of large tracheids with abundant, transversely elongate bordered pits. In a few genera (*Pteridium*), the closing membranes of the pits of the sloping terminal tracheid walls are dissolved at maturity, resulting in direct continuity between adjoining elements. This condition results in the organization of primitive vessels, previously noted in *Selaginella* and *Equisetum* and characteristic of the xylem of many flowering plants. The sieve elements are elongate, lack companion cells, and have numerous sieve areas in their vertical walls.

All roots, with the exception of the embryonic radicle, are adventitious (Figs. 22-1, 22-2) and arise endogenously from the stem. They emerge between the leaf bases. Development of the root originates in a single apical cell; in this case, however, the latter cuts off derivatives in a direction perpendicular to the long axis of the root, thus adding cells to the root cap. The cells of the central procambium differentiate into an exarch protostele, the arrangement characteristic of the roots of most vascular plants. The roots of *Dryopteris dentata* are diarch. The stele is surrounded by a narrow pericycle, a prominent endodermis, cortex, and epidermis, the latter with root hairs. The inner portion of the cortex is often sclerotic. Branch roots originate from endo-

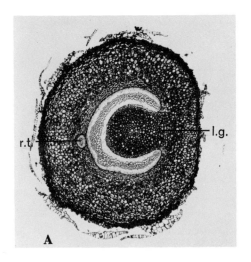

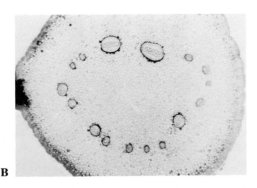

FIG. 22-3. A. *Adiantum* sp. Transection of rhizome; note amphiphloic siphonostele (solenostele). B. *Dryopteris* sp. Sector of transection of rhizome; note strands of dictyostele; l.g., leaf gap; r.t., root trace. X 20.

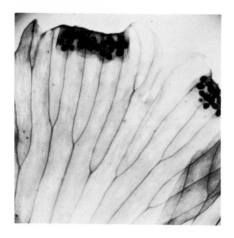

FIG. 22-4. *Adiantum capillus-veneris.* Cleared leaf segment (pinnule); note dichotomous venation and sori with false indusia. X 5.

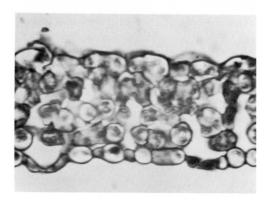

FIG. 22-5. *Dryopteris dentata.* Transection of leaf; note upper and lower epidermis, the latter with a stoma and mesophyll. X 400.

dermal cells opposite the protoxylem groups. Secondary growth is absent in both stems and roots of leptosporangiate ferns.

As in the eusporangiate ferns, the leaves of *Dryopteris* and *Adiantum* and other Leptosporangiopsida are the dominant organs of the sporophyte. The large compound leaves, circinately coiled in the bud (Figs. 22-2, 22-32), may be highly elaborate when mature. Complex, finely divided fern leaves are considered to represent the primitive condition. Simple leaves in ferns are probably reduced. The ultimate divisions of the compound leaves are called **pinnules.** The continuation of the petioles among the leaflets is the **rachis.** The fern leaf is often referred to as a **frond.**

FIG. 22-6. *Asplenium rhizophyllum.* The "walking fern"; note simple leaves developing new plantlets at their apices (arrows). X 0.25. (*Courtesy of Dr. Ilda McVeigh.*)

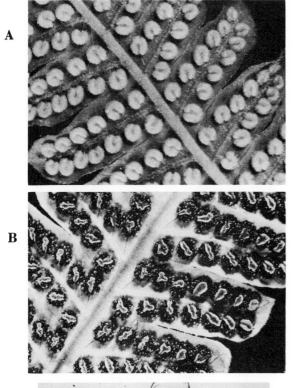

A

B

FIG. 22-7. *Dryopteris dentata.* A. Immature sori covered by indusia. X 5. B. Mature sori, indusia retracted. X 5. C. Transverse section of young leaf segment, receptacle, developing sporangia, and indusium. X 175.

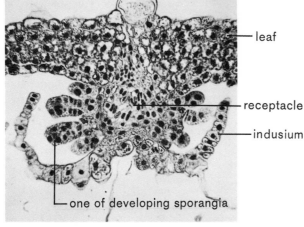

C

leaf

receptacle

indusium

one of developing sporangia

The petiole of each leaf is connected to the stem stele by one or more traces; these run throughout the rachis, giving rise to branches which traverse the pinnae and pinnules. In *Adiantum* the venation is dichotomous (Fig. 22-4A), while in *Dryopteris dentata* it is pinnate. Reticulate is thought to have been derived from dichotomous venation by development of branches between the dichotomies. Internally, the leaf blade consists of an upper and lower epidermis, the latter with abundant

stomata enclosing a relatively undifferentiated mesophyll (Fig. 22-5). The mesophyll of *Adiantum* is limited in extent; the abundant chloroplasts in the epidermal cells in this genus undoubtedly play a major role in photosynthesis. The veins are collateral in arrangement of xylem and phloem. The leaves arise close to the growing point of the stem and develop at first through the activity of a short-lived apical cell; a new group of leaves is produced each season. The simple leaves of the **walk-**

FIG. 22-8. *Polystichum acrostichoides* (Michx.) Schott. Portion of frond showing distal fertile pinnae. X ½.

ing fern, *Asplenium rhizophyllum* L., function in propagation (Fig. 22-6).

Reproduction: the sporophyte

After a series of entirely vegetative leaves has been produced from the stem of a young plant, all the leaves which develop subsequently in *Dryopteris, Adiantum,* and in most other genera, are usually both vegetative and fertile. In both genera, groups of sporangia known as **sori** (Gr. *soros,* heap) develop on the undersurface of ordinary leaves (Fig.

22-7). Some segregation of vegetative and reproductive functions is apparent in the distribution of sporogenous tissue in several other genera of polypodiaceous ferns. In the **Christmas fern,** *Polystichum acrostichoides* (Michx.) Schott (Fig. 22-8), for example, only the distal pinnae of each frond are fertile. *Onoclea sensibilis* L., the **sensitive fern,** and *Pteretis pensylvanicum* (Willd.) Fern., the **ostrich fern,** superficially suggest *Osmunda cinnamonea* L., the **cinnamon fern** (p. 347), in that they produce sporangia on markedly modified fronds, the remaining leaves being purely vegetative.

In *Adiantum* (Fig. 22-9) and *Pteris* (Fig. 22-10), the sori are almost marginal and are covered during development by a revolute leaf margin known as a **false indusium.** The sporangia are actually borne on this false indusium in *Adiantum.* In *Dryopteris dentata* (Fig. 22-7), the sori lie over the veins of the pinnules, and each is covered by a shieldlike flap of tissue, the **true indusium** (L. *indusium,* tunic), a single layer of cells in thickness, and of epidermal origin. The sporangia in both genera arise from the lower leaf surface (Fig. 22-7C) and the region of their origin is known as the **receptacle.** The order of development in both cases is said to be **mixed,** inasmuch as sporangial development follows no definite order with relation to the receptacle, both immature and mature sporangia being present in contrast to the

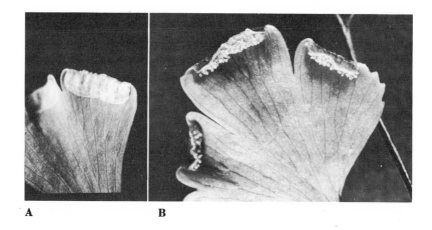

A   B

FIG. 22-9. *Adiantum capillus-veneris.* Fertile leaf segments. A. Sorus covered by false indusium. B. Mature sori. X 6.

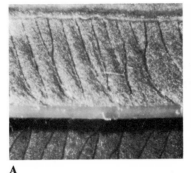 

FIG. 22-10. *Pteris vittata.* A. Margin of pinna with false indusium covering immature sporangia. B. Margin of pinna with indusium rolled back revealing sporangia. X 4.

A   B

simultaneous maturation of the sporangia in the Eusporangiopsida and *Osmunda* which is called **simple.**

The details of development of the leptosporangiate sporangium are illustrated in Fig. 22-11. Each sporangium arises from a superficial cell of the receptacle which projects above the surface and undergoes periclinal division. The entire sporangium usually develops from the outer product of this division. This cell becomes divided by three somewhat anticlinal walls that cut out a central apical cell (Fig. 22-11C). The apical cell undergoes division in three directions,

forming a stalk. The apical cell now divides in a direction perpendicular to the stalk to form an apical wall initial, beneath which lies the **primary archesporial cell** (Fig. 22-11E). The latter gives rise, by periclinal divisions, to the four **primary tapetal cells** (Fig. 22-11F) which subsequently undergo division, forming a two-layered **tapetum** (Fig. 22-11F). The central sporogenous cell now divides repeatedly and forms the sporocytes, which vary in number from 12 to 16. Each of these separates, undergoes meiosis, forming a tetrad of spores which ultimately separate and thicken their walls (Fig. 22-12).

FIG. 22-11. *Dryopteris dentata.* A–G. Successive stages in leptosporangiate sporangium development. A–E. X 770. F. X 410. G. X 190.

A   B   C   D

primary
archesporial cell

wall cell
(annulus)

tapetum

sporocyte

stalk

E   F   G

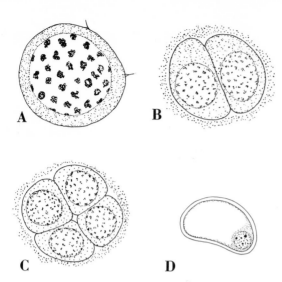

FIG. 22-12. *Dryopteris dentata.* Sporogenesis. A. Sporocyte in prophase of meiosis. B. End of meiosis I. C. Spore tetrad. D. Immature spore. X 1500.

The chromosome number of the Venus maidenhair, *A. capillus-veneris*, has been determined to be $n = 30$, a rather low number among the Leptosporangiopsida. The tapetal cells elongate radially during sporogenesis and finally become disorganized, presumably functioning in the nutrition of the developing spores.

During sporogenesis, the cells of the sporangial jacket divide by anticlinal division and the products increase in size, as do the cells of the stalk. At maturity the sporangium is a slightly flattened spheroid or ellipsoid (Fig. 22-13A). The wall cells on the flattened faces are large and have undulate walls. A vertical row of specially differentiated cells, the **annulus,** forms an incomplete ring about the sporangium (Fig. 22-11G; 22-13A). The radial and inner tangential walls of these cells are markedly thickened. Between the last cell of the annulus and the base of the stalk there are a number (often four) of thin-walled cells, the **lip cells** or **stomium** (Fig. 22-13A).

As the spores mature, they become invested with a dark, brown-black wall, and color of the entire sorus changes from a delicate whitish-green to dark brown. When the spores on a majority of the sporangia are mature, the indusium in *Dryopteris* contracts (Fig. 22-7B), exposing them to the air. In *Adiantum*

(Fig. 22-9) and *Pteris* (Fig. 22-10), the revolute leaf edge unfolds slightly when the spores are mature.

Spore dissemination in both genera is accomplished by dehiscence of the sporangia which depends on loss of water. The annulus and lip cells are directly concerned in the process. The loss of water through the thin outer tangential walls of the cells of the annulus shortens its length so that the sporangial wall is ruptured transversely in the region of the lip cells (Fig. 22-13B); the outer wall cells of the sporangium are also ruptured. As the annulus continues to shorten (Fig. 22-13C), its outer tangential cell walls become increasingly concave because they are adherent to the water within the annulus cells, the amount of which is lessening through evaporation. Ultimately a point is reached at which the tensile resistance of the water within the annulus cells is no longer sufficient to prevent the separation of the outer tangential walls from its surface; at this point the water vaporizes, reducing the tension on the outer tangential cell walls of the annulus which snaps back or catapults to its original position (Fig. 22-13D), thus ejecting the spores.

Although the number of spores produced by a single sporangium in most leptosporangiate ferns is small, frequently 48 to 64, as compared with those of eusporangiate genera (1500 to 2000 in *Botrychium*, for example), the large number of sporangia in a sorus, along with the enormous number of sori on the pinnules of a single mature plant, results in the production of a surprisingly large number of spores by a single individual. It has been estimated that one mature plant of *Dryopteris* produces 50,000,000 spores each season.

An Australian fern, *Platyzoma microphyllum* R. Br., produces spores of two size classes with a volume ratio of 1 : 7.5. These spores grow into unisexual gametophytes, the smaller into filamentous male gametophytes lacking rhizoids and the larger into spatulate ones bearing archegonia and later, antheridia.

Reproduction: the gametophyte

In spite of this enormous number of spores, relatively few complete their development

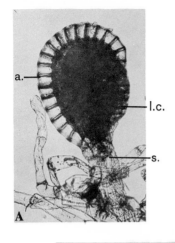

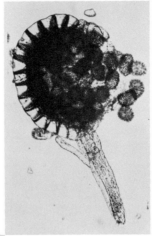

B

C

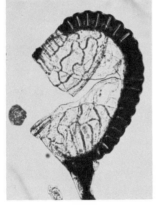

D

FIG. 22-13. *Dryopteris dentata*. Sporangial structure and dehiscence. A. Mature sporangium. B. Contraction of annulus and rupture of lip cells. C. Further contraction of annulus and opening of sporangium. D. Re-elongation of annulus; sporangium empty; a., annulus; l.c., lip cell; s., stalk. X 135.

into mature gametophytes because so many are borne by air currents to places unfavorable for germination. Gametophytes are sometimes present on moist soil or in rock crevices in the vicinity of fern colonies growing in nature. As a matter of fact, fern gametophytes seem not to be abundant or conspicuous in the wild, at least in the temperate zone.

The processes of spore germination and gametophyte development may be followed readily in laboratory cultures of spores of *Dryopteris, Adiantum,* and other leptosporangiate ferns planted on agar or moist soil, or on the surface of moist flower pots or other crockery. Some stages in their development are illustrated in Fig. 22-14. In crowded cultures, the developing gametophytes may remain irregularly filamentous, but when they are well spaced they typically become cordate.

Spore germination frequently results in the formation of a small, protonemalike chain of bulbous cells rich in chloroplasts (Fig. 22-

14A). A rhizoid usually develops early from the basal cell, and more rhizoids develop later from the ventral cells of the gametophyte. The form of the gametophyte and abundance of rhizoids are affected by quality and intensity of light. The spores will not germinate in darkness. Higher intensities of white and blue light evoke the development of the flat, thallose form. They also increase the number of rhizoids. In low light intensities, especially of red light, the gametophyte remains filamentous and few rhizoids form.

Under favorable conditions, oblique divisions in the terminal cell of the young filamentous gametophyte result in the production of an apical cell which cuts off segments in two directions. The derivatives continue to divide, forming a spatulate plant body (Fig. 22-14B,C) one layer of cells in thickness except in the central region near the apical notch.

The **prothallia,** or prothalli, as the ga-

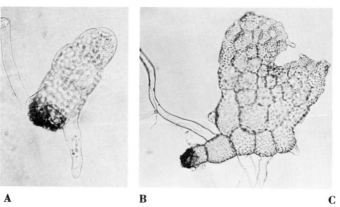
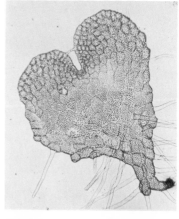

A   B   C

FIG. 22-14. *Dryopteris dentata.* Spore germination and gametophyte development. A. Early germination; note chlorophyllous branch and rhizoids. X 325. B. Early gametophyte, 25 days after spores were planted. X 250. C. Almost-mature gametophyte (45 days). X 45. D. Mature gametophytes on the surface of an agar culture. X 3.5.

D

metophytes are often called, are usually bisexual but usually somewhat protandrous. This is especially noticeable in crowded cultures in which minute filamentous gametophytes tend to develop antheridia precociously. In uncrowded cultures, the sex organs appear in laboratory cultures on agar in about 45 days. Both types are normally borne on the ventral surface, although deviations may appear in the moist atmosphere of Petri-dish cultures.

In general, the antheridia (Fig. 22-15) are

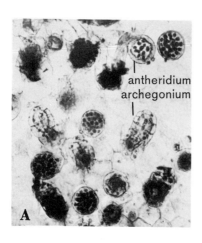
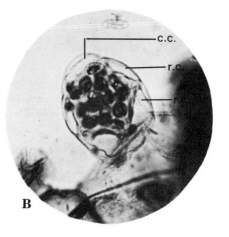

antheridium
archegonium

c.c.

r.c.

r.c.

A   B

FIG. 22-15. *Dryopteris dentata.* A. Ventral view of gametophyte near apical notch, showing sex organs. X 135. B. Antheridium enlarged. X 500; c.c., cover cell; r.c., ring cells.

produced nearer the posterior portion of the gametophyte than the archegonia, which develop on the thickened, central cushion nearer the apex. Like the sporangia, the antheridia are protuberant, whereas only the necks of the archegonia project from the thallus surface (Figs. 22-15; 22-16A). Both antheridia and archegonia originate from single superficial cells of the gametophyte. The antheridial initial protrudes to form a hemispherical cell which undergoes transverse division. The outer product of division develops into the antheridium, as shown in Fig. 22-15B. The antheridial wall is composed of three cells, two of them ringlike and the uppermost a cover or lid cell. Liquid water is necessary for antheridial dehiscence, which is effected by the swelling of the component cells (both wall and sperm) and rupture of the cap cell. The extruded multiflagellate sperms (Fig. 22-16B,C) rapidly become motile and subsequently slough off their spheres of attached cytoplasm.

An antheridium-inducing factor has been isolated from the gametophytes of the bracken fern, *Pteridium aquilinum* (L.) Kuhn, and from the culture medium in which the gametophytes were grown. This substance stimu-lates the precocious formation of antheridia on gametophytes only 10–14 days old. Normally, antheridia do not appear until at least 6 weeks after the spores germinate. The antheridium-evoking substance from *Pteridium* was also efficacious when applied to certain species of other genera (including *Dryopteris*) but had no effect on the gametophytes of certain other fern families (Osmundaceae, Schizaeaceae, and Cyatheaceae). Two genera of one of these families have been shown to produce antheridium-inducing substances which differ from that of *Pteridium*.

It has recently been reported that seven types of gibberellins evoked antheridium formation in gametophytes of the fern *Anemia*, while controls grown without the gibberellins were sterile. Gibberellins had the same effect on species of two other genera of the same family to which *Anemia* belongs[1] but no stimulatory effect on antheridium production in 40 species from seven other fern families.

The archegonia arise from surface cells close to the growing point of the prothallium (Fig. 22-15A). Each initial undergoes periclinal division into a superficial and a hypog-

---

[1] Schizaeaceae, page 353.

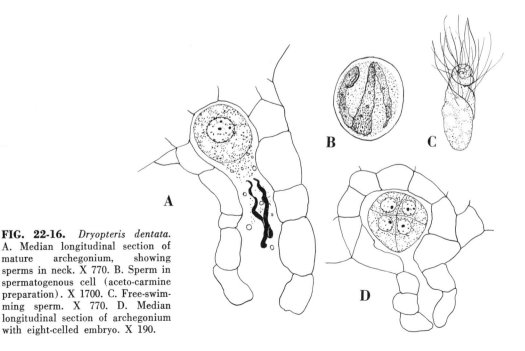

FIG. 22-16. *Dryopteris dentata.* A. Median longitudinal section of mature archegonium, showing sperms in neck. X 770. B. Sperm in spermatogenous cell (aceto-carmine preparation). X 1700. C. Free-swimming sperm. X 770. D. Median longitudinal section of archegonium with eight-celled embryo. X 190.

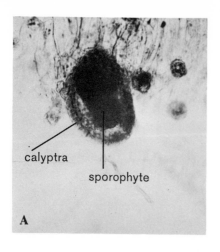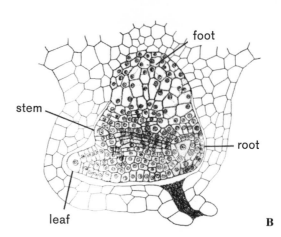

A

calyptra

sporophyte

stem

leaf

foot

root

B

FIG. 22-17. A. *Dryopteris* sp. Ventral view of gametophyte, showing young sporophyte within calyptra. X 25. B. Median longisection of embryonic sporophyte of a fern (from a sagittal section of a gametophyte) ; stage similar to that in A. X 160. (B. *After Haupt.*)

enous cell, the latter dividing only once. The outermost cell undergoes two successive perpendicular anticlinal divisions, forming initials of the four rows of neck cells which arise by division of these initials. The hypogenous cell divides periclinally to form the neck canal initial and the central cell. The neck canal initial undergoes nuclear division to form two neck canal nuclei, but cytokinesis is often suppressed. The central cell divides, forming the egg and ventral canal cells. On immersion in water, the distal tiers of neck

cells are ruptured, apparently by the swelling of the disintegrated neck and ventral canal cells which are extruded and leave a canallike passageway to the egg (Fig. 22-16A).

It was demonstrated long ago that the movement of sperms toward archegonia is not fortuitious but the result of a chemotactic response. The chemical stimulant secreted from the archegonium can be replaced by malic acid in laboratory experiments.

The moist habitat of the gametophytes, along with the ventral position of the sex organs, enhances the opportunities for fertilization (Fig. 22-16A). Further growth of the gametophyte ceases after its archegonia have been fertilized.

Reproduction: embryogeny

Although it seems probable that more than one egg on each gametophyte is fertilized, only one zygote normally completes its development into an embryonic sporophyte.

The zygote secretes a cell membrane soon after fertilization and after an interval undergoes mitosis and cytokinesis in a direction parallel to the neck of the archegonium. Cell divisions at right angles to the original direction of division and to each other result in the formation of a quadrant (Fig. 22-16D). Subsequent development of the cells of this quadrant indicates that already at this stage

FIG. 22-18. *Dryopteris dentata.* Ventral view of gametophyte with attached juvenile sporophyte; note cotyledon (primary leaf), radicle, and region of the foot. X 10.

differentiation has occurred in preparation for the development of the organs of the older embryo.[2] The origin and development of these organs are depicted in Fig. 22-17 and explained in its labeling.

The archegonial venter and sterile gametophytic tissue keep pace for a short time with the developing embryo (Fig. 22-17), but soon the radicle and cotyledon burst forth, the former penetrating the substratum and the latter emerging usually through the apical notch (Fig. 22-18). The gametophyte persists in some cases until several leaves have been formed, but it ultimately turns brown and the embryonic sporophyte initiates an independent existence.

The early embryonic leaves are simpler in form than the mature leaves of the parent species, but gradually leaves are produced which are characteristic of the mature plant. Other than the primary root, fern roots are adventitious. Once established, the young sporophyte embarks on a perennial existence in most leptosporangiate ferns.

The genera *Dryopteris* and *Adiantum*, just described, have been chosen to serve as representatives of the more advanced leptosporangiate ferns, the Polypodiaceae. Their distinctive characters are their method of sporangium development from a single cell; the mixed sori, the size, annulus position, and transverse dehiscence of the sporangium; and the small number of spores produced in each. The gametophytes of these genera, as compared with the photosynthetic gametophytes of the eusporangiate Marattiales, differ in their more delicate structure, less massive form, absence of a midrib, and in their protuberant and smaller antheridia. Furthermore, they are more rapid in their development and more ephemeral in their existence. Their dorsiventrality is marked. The precocity with which the organs of the embryo are organized in the early divisions of the zygote is also unlike the embryogeny of the eusporangiate ferns and *Osmunda*, in which differentiation appears later.

---

[2] In some species there is doubt that the organs of the juvenile sporophyte are blocked out as early as the quadrant stage.

Other Filicales

The family Polypodiaceae, as represented by *Adiantum* and *Dryopteris*, described above, is the largest family of the Filicales in number of genera and species. Most of the attributes described for *Adiantum* and *Dryopteris* are in marked contrast to those of the eusporangiate ferns. Some of the other families of Filicales to be described briefly below are in some respects intermediate in several of their attributes between the Eusporangiopsida and Leptosporangiopsida.

FAMILY 2. OSMUNDACEAE

Osmunda

Vegetative morphology

In most classifications of the Filicales, the Osmundaceae with *Osmunda* (*Osmunder*, Saxon equivalent to the god Thor) and *Todea* (after Henry Tode, German botanist) are placed at the beginning of the series in recognition of certain attributes which are interpreted as intermediate between the eusporangiate and leptosporangiate Pterophyta.

The genus *Osmunda* is cosmopolitan. Three species are distributed widely in the United States, namely, *O. regalis* L., the **royal** or **flowering fern**; *O. cinnamomea* L., the **cinnamon fern**; and *O. claytoniana* L., the **interrupted fern** (Fig. 22-19).

These perennial ferns are found usually in rather hydric habitats in which the magnificent ascending fronds attain a large size, often reaching 6 feet in length. In the northeastern United States, the several species of *Osmunda* are planted as ornamentals in semishaded locations. The striking leaves of *Osmunda* are either once or twice pinnately compound, depending on the species. Each growing season, the underground stem produces a group of circinately coiled fronds which unfold, photosynthesize, and produce spores. The leaves are annual and die at the end of the season; but the long-persistent leaf bases surround the stem and, together with the wiry roots, form prominent mounds. Mature pinnae are rather leathery in texture. Their venation is open-dichotomous, as in *Botrychium*.

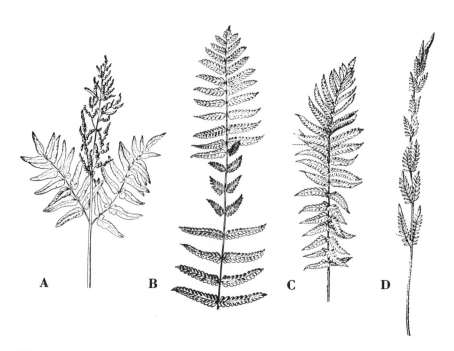

FIG. 22-19. A. *Osmunda regalis* L. The royal or flowering fern. B. *O. claytoniana* L. The interrupted fern. C, D. *O. cinnamomea* L. The cinnamon fern; sterile frond at C; fertile frond at D. A. X 0.3. B–D. X 0.12. (*After Gleason.*)

The dense covering of the wiry roots and persistent leaf bases, noted above, effectively protects the vertical underground stem of *Osmunda*. The roots, leaf bases, and stem are so intimately associated that sections of all are usually available for study in a single preparation (Fig. 22-20). The vascular tissue of the mature *Osmunda* stem, as viewed in transverse section, is composed of a circle of strands separated by narrow parenchymatous leaf gaps. Leaf traces which have occasioned the gaps may be observed in section at various points in the cortex, through which they pass into the leaf bases. Three-dimensional and longitudinal views of the stele indicate that it is a siphonostele dissected by leaf gaps, as in *Ophioglossum*. The xylem strands are mesarch (Fig. 22-20B), with the protoxylem surrounded by metaxylem, the latter composed largely of scalariform-pitted tracheids. A prominent endodermis delimits the stele from the cortical region of the stem. Within it there are several layers of parenchyma cells, the pericycle, the phloem cells, and the mesarch xylem. The inner cortex is composed of parenchyma and darkly stained sclerenchyma tissue. The spirally arranged leaves are connected to

the stele by C-shaped traces. Near each leaf base, two roots, with their vascular supply derived from the leaf trace, originate endogenously and grow between the leaf bases into the soil.

The roots contain exarch protosteles which are diarch or triarch. The development of both root and stem is localized in single apical cells. In certain individual roots, however, as many as four apical cells may be present, an attribute suggestive of ferns of the *Marattia* group.

Reproduction: the sporophyte

Further striking modifications of leaf structure are associated with sporangium production in *Osmunda*. The location of the sporangia varies in the several species. In all cases the sporangia do not occur in sori but are in marginal zones without indusia. In *O. regalis*, only the most distal pinnae and pinnules are fertile (Figs. 22-19A; 22-21A). In *O. claytoniana* (Fig. 22-19B), on the other hand, certain intermediate pairs or pinnae bear sporangia, whereas the proximal and distal ones are sterile. Finally, in *O. cinnamomea*

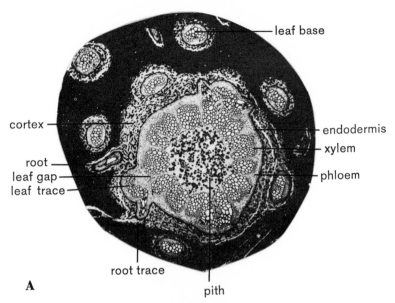

leaf base

cortex —

root —
leaf gap —
leaf trace —

root trace

pith

endodermis

xylem

phloem

FIG. 22-20. *Osmunda* sp. A.
Transection of rhizome; note associated roots and leaf bases. X 18. B.
Portion of stele enlarged; note
mesarch xylem and stages in departure of leaf and root traces. X
40.

A

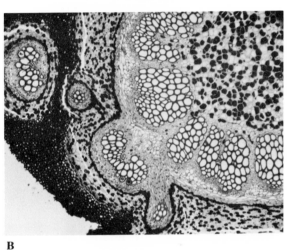

B

FIG. 22-21. *Osmunda
regalis.* A. Tip of fertile
frond; note transition between vegetative and spo-
rangium-bearing pinnules.
X 1. B. Dehiscent spo-
rangia, living. X 10.

A

B

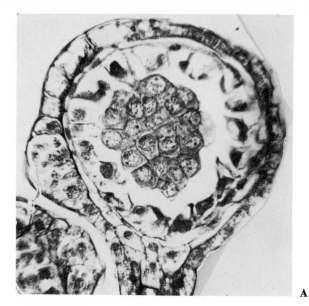

B

FIG. 22-22. *Osmunda regalis.* A. Section of sporangium at sporocyte stage; note two-layered wall; bulging, unilateral annulus (left); tapetum; sporocytes; and sporangial stalk. X 135. B. Wall of mature sporangium showing unilateral annulus. X 60. (B. *After Andrews.*)

A

(Fig. 22-19C), the sporangia are borne only upon special fertile spore-bearing leaves, the vegetative tissues and functions of which are greatly restricted. Intermediate stages in these dimorphic phenomena are readily observable on examination of several individuals (Fig. 22-21B).

The sporangia themselves originate superficially on the pinna surface. Although prominent single initial cells may be present in each sporangial precursor, adjacent cells also contribute to the formation of the sporangium, which becomes protuberant and rather massive, in comparison with that in other leptosporangiate ferns. Furthermore, the sporangial stalk is also thicker (Fig. 22-22A) than in other leptosporangiate ferns, and the wall is two-layered. A central sporogenous cell in each sporangium undergoes repeated divisions until approximately 128 sporogenous cells are produced. The outermost layer of these functions somewhat as a tapetal plasmodium during sporogenesis, and, in addition, a true tapetum is present. The large and prominent chromosomes are relatively few in number ($n = 22$). Each sporangium produces between 256 and 512 spores. These are green at maturity and are shed by dehiscence of the sporangium along a vertical line running between a unilateral group of thick-walled annulus cells and the stalk of the sporangium (Fig. 22-22B).

Reproduction: the gametophyte

As is the case with the chlorophyllous spores of *Equisetum*, those of *Osmunda* do not remain viable very long if stored. They germinate very readily, however, if transferred to agar, soil, or other environments with adequate moisture (Fig. 22-23).

The young gametophyte at first consists of a short chain of cells with a basal rhizoid, but an apical cell is organized soon by successive oblique divisions of the terminal cell. This gives rise to a spatulate gametophyte at the tip of which several apical cells may function. Their derivatives build up a relatively massive green gametophyte, suggestive of *Marattia* and *Angiopteris* (Figs. 22-24). Prominent, ventrally projecting midribs are present in the gametophytes of *Osmunda*, which are liverwortlike and long-lived and may be perennial. Vegetative propagation of the gametophytes by separation of marginal lobes has been observed.

There is some evidence that the gametophytes are protandrous; well-separated individuals are always bisexual. The antheridia

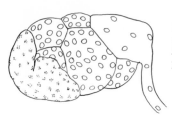

FIG. 22-23. *Osmunda regalis.* Spore germination, 2 weeks after spores were planted on agar. X 315.

FIG. 22-24. *Osmunda regalis* L. Mature gametophyte growing on agar. X 2.

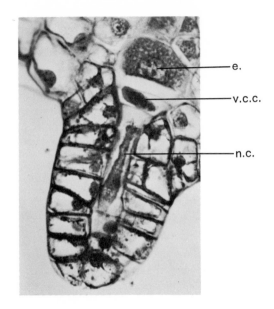

FIG. 22-26. *Osmunda* sp. Median longisection of an archegonium; e., egg; n.c., neck canal cell; v.c.c., ventral canal cell. X 500.

(Fig. 22-25A, 22-27A) are borne on the underside of the gametophyte near the margins, and the archegonia (Fig. 22-25B) are on or near the midrib. The protuberant antheridia have a single layer of jacket cells, one of which, near the apex, is thrown off as the antheridium dehisces. Approximately 100 spermatogenous cells fill the antheridium; each gives rise to a single, coiled, multiflagellate sperm. The archegonial venters are sunken in the superficial tissue on the ventral surface of the gametophytes. The single binucleate neck canal cell is surrounded by four rows of neck cells about six to eight tiers high (Fig. 22-26).

Reproduction: embryogeny

The zygote undergoes two successive vertical divisions parallel in direction to the axis of the archegonium but perpendicular to each other. The next divisions are transverse, so that an octant stage develops (Fig. 22-27B). The outermost four cells (nearest the neck) gradually develop the stem, leaf, and primary root of the embryo, and the four basal cells form a foot. Growth of the embryo is relatively slow in *Osmunda* as compared with

other leptosporangiate ferns. The archegonium functions as a calyptra during early embryogeny, but it is ultimately ruptured by the developing embryo which protrudes from the gametophyte and becomes established as an independent plant (Fig. 22-27C).

The primary embryonic leaf and those which follow it during the juvenile phases of development are much simpler than those of the adult plant (Fig. 22-27C). The stem of the young sporophyte is protostelic at first, and the dissected siphonostelic condition does not arise until considerable development has occurred.

FIG. 22-25. *Osmunda regalis*. A. Ventral view of portion of a gametophyte; note antheridia at margins and archegonia (enlarged in B) along midrib. A. X 45. B. X 120.

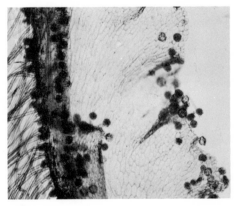

A

B

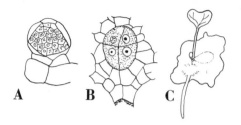

FIG. 22-27. A. *Osmunda cinnamomea.* Mature antheridium. X 215. B. *O. claytoniana* L. Section of eight-celled embryo in archegonium. C. *O. claytoniana.* Gametophyte with young sporophyte emerging. X 4. (*From Campbell.*)

SUMMARY

Osmunda and the Osmundaceae differ from polypodiaceous ferns like *Adiantum* and *Dryopteris* in a number of respects. The sporangia are not in sori and all mature their spores simultaneously as in eusporangiate ferns. Furthermore, the sporangia, which have two wall layers, are not typically leptosporangiate in development because several cells, in addition to an apical cell, function in its development. In addition, as many as 512 spores may mature in each sporangium. The spores are thin-walled and green like those of *Equisetum.* The sporangium opens by a vertical cleft and the annulus consists of a lateral group of thick-walled cells.

The gametophytes are longer-lived and more massive than those of leptosporangiate ferns. The antheridia produce more sperms and the rhizoids contain chloroplasts. The archegonial necks are straight instead of curved as in the Polypodiaceae.

The embryo of *Osmunda* differentiates later

FIG. 22-28. A. *Anemia mexicana* Klotzsch. X 0.16. B, C. *Lygodium japonicum* (Thunb.) SW. climbing fern. B. Habit of growth. X 0.03. C. Detail of sterile (below) and fertile (above) leaflets. X 0.5. (A. *After Correll.* C. *Courtesy of Dr. C. A. Brown, after Brown and Correll.*)

in development than the quadrant or octant stage. Finally, the primary leaf or cotyledon does not grow up through the apical notch as in the Polypodiaceae, but laterally around the margin of the gametophyte.

FAMILY 3. SCHIZAEACEAE

Of the genera of this family, *Lygodium* (Gr. *lygodes*, like a willow) and *Anemia* (Gr. *aneimon*, unclad, referring to the naked sporangia) (Fig. 22-28) are perhaps the best-known and most readily available for study. One species of *Schizaea* (Gr. *schizein*, to split) (Fig. 22-29) is native to the United States, occurring in the pine barrens of New Jersey. Although a single species of *Lygodium*, the climbing fern, *L. palmatum* (Bernh.) SW., is native to the United States, *L. japonicum* (Thunb.) SW. (Fig. 22-28B,C) is widely cultivated in conservatories and in many gardens in the southern United States and in some places[3] has escaped from cultivation, as a wild form. *Anemia mexicana* is native to the extreme southern United States in Florida and Texas; its sporangia occur on much-reduced leaf segments (Fig. 22-28C).

In these ferns, the sporangia are borne on the leaf margins and either lack an indusium or have a false one. The sporangia produce up to 216 spores; an apical group of thick-walled cells (Fig. 22-30) serves as an annulus. Sporangial dehiscence is vertical. All the sporangia mature simultaneously (simple type) as in the Eusporangiopsida and Osmundaceae.

---

[3] Georgia and Texas, among others.

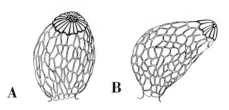

FIG. 22-30. A. *Anemia mexicana*, sporangium. B. *Lygodium palmatum*, sporangium. (*After Andrews.*)

The gametophytes of the genus *Schizaea* are of great interest and of two types. Some like those of *S. pusilla* Pursh are chlorophyllous and filamentous, much like moss protonemata. In *S. melanesica* Selling, in contrast, the gametophytes are upright, subterranean, and fleshy, cylindrical structures much like those of *Psilotum*.[4] Furthermore, the subterranean gametophytes of *S. pusilla* contain endophytic fungi. The occurrence of such radially symmetrical gametophytes in the Pterophyta is interpreted as a primitive attribute which may indicate common ancestry with other vascular cryptogams with similar gametophytes.

FAMILY 4. HYMENOPHYLLACEAE

The Hymenophyllaceae, the filmy ferns, are largely tropical and include (among others) two genera of delicate-leaved ferns, *Hymenophyllum* (Gr. *hymen*, membrane + Gr. *phyllon*, leaf) (Fig. 22-31A) and *Trichomanes* (Gr. for waterwort) (Fig. 22-31B), both of which are represented in the flora of the United States. *Trichomanes* occurs in extremely moist habitats such as on rocks bathed in spray from waterfalls. As the familial name implies, the leaves are delicate, often but a single layer of cells thick except at the midveins. The sporangia are borne at the margin of the leaves on elongate receptacles covered during development by cuplike or two-lipped indusia. Development of the sporangia on the receptacle is orderly, the oldest being at the apex and the younger sporangia arising on the flanks of the receptacle, with the youngest at the base. This represents **gradate** organization of the sorus, in contrast to the simple sori of the Eusporangiopsida. Up to 512 spores may be produced

---

[4] Bierhorst, D. W., "The Fleshy, Cylindrical, Subterranean Gametophyte of *Schizaea melanesica*," *Amer. J. Bot.*, 53: 123–133, 1966.

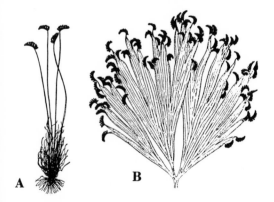

FIG. 22-29. *Schizaea*. A. *S. pusilla* Pursh. B. Leaf of *S. elegans* (Vahl.) SW. X 0.3. (*After Smith.*)

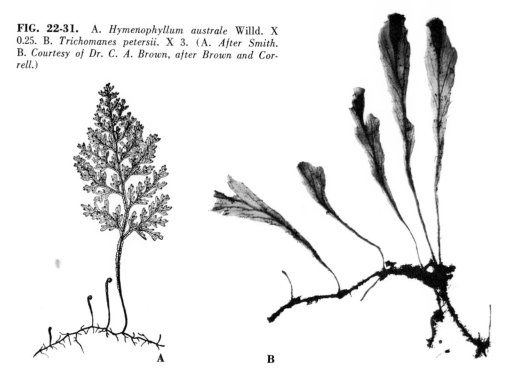

FIG. 22-31. A. *Hymenophyllum australe* Willd. X 0.25. B. *Trichomanes petersii.* X 3. (A. *After Smith.* B. *Courtesy of Dr. C. A. Brown, after Brown and Correll.*)

A   B

in each sporangium. The annulus is obliquely vertical and the sporangium opens transversely. The spores may undergo the early stages of germination before they are shed from the sporangia.

The green gametophytes are branching and straplike (*Hymenophyllum*) or branching filaments (*Trichomanes*).

FAMILIES 5 AND 6. CYATHEACEAE AND DICKSONIACEAE

The Dicksoniaceae are included in the Cyatheaceae in some systems of classification. To these families belong the tree ferns (as well as some species with massive prostrate stems). Tree ferns (Fig. 22-32) grow natively in tropical rain forests where large specimens may exceed 60 feet in height. They are widely cultivated in conservatories and out-of-doors in mild, moist climates like those of the Pacific coast.[5] *Cyathea* (Gr. *kyathos,* cup), *Alsophila* (Gr. *alsos,* grove + Gr. *philein,* to love), and *Cibotium* (Gr. *kibotion,* little box) are often present in conservatory collections. The trunks (stems) are rarely branched and

[5] A group of tree ferns has been planted in San Francisco's Golden Gate Park.

are covered by a dense mat of adventitious roots which arise in association with the leaf bases. Roots at the distal portion of the trunk never reach the soil. Creeping stems arise on the trunks some distance above the soil, run downward, then outward and initiate new erect stems. The lower portion of the stem, which is smaller in diameter than the upper, is supported by a dense, buttresslike covering of persistent roots. In spite of their massive size, tree ferns lack a cambium and secondary growth. Anatomically, the young stems are simple and protostelic, but as the stem continues to grow, the stele increases in diameter, becoming dictyostelic and, finally, polycyclic and quite complex.

The apex of the trunk supports a crown of leaves which are circinately vernate when young. The leaves may approach 15 feet in length and are pinnately compound.

The sporangia are borne in gradate sori. In the Dicksoniaceae these are marginal and subtended by cuplike indusia, while the Cyatheaceae they are abaxial and may or may not have indusia. The annulus is obliquely vertical and the transverse sporangial dehiscense is initiated in the region of special thin-walled lip cells or stomium, as in the Polypodiaceae.

The gametophytes are heart-shaped and organized much like those of the Polypodiaceae. The archegonia have long, scarcely curved necks like those of *Osmunda.*

Summary of Filicales

The Filicales include all the homosporous leptosporangiate ferns. These are widely distributed in both the tropics and temperate zones and are almost exclusively perennial plants. In colder climates, with few exceptions (*Cyrtomium, Polystichum,* for example), the leaves die at the end of the growing season, and are replaced by a new set of leaves the following spring.

The stems of Filicales may be prominent and trunklike (Cyatheaceae and Dicksoniaceae) or rhizomes, or underground, vertical stems. Their ontogeny may be traced in every case to an apical cell. The stele in juvenile sporophytes is usually a protostele. As the stem increases in size, a siphonostele, dictyostele, or complex polystele may develop. Secondary growth is absent.

The roots of Filicales are adventitious. All develop from the activity of prominent apical cells and have exarch protosteles.

Filicalean leaves are formed early in ontogeny at the stem apex and have circinate vernation. Compound leaves are considered to be more primitive than simple leaves which are interpreted as reductions. Similarly, open-dichotomous, as opposed to reticulate, vena-

FIG. 22-32. *Cyathea* sp. Tree ferns. Insert, an enlarged view of tree fern bud or fiddle head. (*From a negative of Dr. C. J. Chamberlain, courtesy of the Chicago Natural History Museum.*)

tion is considered to represent the primitive condition.

The sporangia occur on the margins or abaxial surfaces of ordinary vegetative leaves or somewhat modified leaves or segments thereof. Marginal sori are considered more primitive than superficial ones because they correspond in position, in macrophyllous leaves, to the terminal sporangia of branches (see p. 386). They arise from receptacles in discrete groups or sori or may be in continuous zones or rows. They may or may not be covered during development by indusia. The sporangia in certain families (Osmundaceae, Schizaeaceae, for example) are in some aspects suggestive of eusporangiate sporangia. The sori may be simple, gradate, or mixed in order of development. Dehiscence is either vertical or transverse.

The gametophytes of Filicales show considerable range of organization. There are differences in spore germination and early development (bipolar, tripolar, and unipolar germination; time of initiation of spatulate stage). The gametophytes may be filamentous (*Schizaea*), ribbonlike (*Hymenophyllum*), or cordate, the latter with entire or incised margins and they may bear unicellular and/or multicellular branched or unbranched hairs. The gametophytes may be massive and long-lived (Osmundaceae) or rather delicate and ephemeral (Schizaeaceae, Hymenophyllaceae, and Polypodiaceae). The rhizoids may be brown-walled or colorless. The gametophytes of almost all Filicales are bisexual.[6] The antheridia may have many wall cells (Osmundaceae) or only three (Polypodiaceae) or four. The archegonia may have long, straight necks (Osmundaceae) or shorter, curved ones (Polypodiaceae). The taxonomy of Filicales is based largely on sporophytic attributes, but gametophytic characteristics are being increasingly studied.

Finally, in embryogeny of the Filicales, differentiation into the organs of the young sporophyte may occur as early as the quadrant or octant stage, or it may be delayed.

---

[6] The gametophytes of the Australian *Platyzoma microphyllum* have recently been described as dimorphic with individuals unisexual, the male gametophytes being smaller than the female (p. 342).

The Fern Life Cycle

The life cycle of *Adiantum* and *Dryopteris* and of most other Filicales is fundamentally similar to that of other vascular cryptogams in that it involves a regular alternation of a diploid, spore-producing generation and a haploid, gamete-producing one. This type of life cycle has been so greatly emphasized in biological teaching that we often gain the impression that it is obligate and inexorable. Furthermore, we are so prone to contrast the two alternants in the life cycle that they sometimes seem like different organisms rather than merely successive morphological expressions of the same one. This tendency to contrast has, of course, been enhanced by the antithetic theory of alternation of generations discussed at two previous points in this text (p. 223 and p. 247).

The purpose of the following paragraphs is to present a somewhat different interpretation of life cycle phenomena, with the ferns as a point of departure.

Deviations from the life cycle described for *Adiantum* and *Dryopteris* occur in nature or they may be induced. These deviations have been grouped together under the phenomena **apogamy** and **apospory,** alluded to earlier (p. 248). Apogamy denotes a deviation from the life cycle in which the transition from the gametophytic phase to the sporophyte is accomplished without sexual union of gametes and their nuclei. By apospory, on the other hand, is meant the transition from sporophyte to gametophyte in a manner other than through the medium of spores.

Apospory is known to occur among both Hepatophyta and Bryophyta, as well as in the vascular cryptogams and seed plants. Injured sporophytes of *Anthoceros* develop gametophytic thalli, and injured moss setae and capsules may develop protonemata. In certain fern varieties, prothallia may develop at the leaf margins or from transformed sporangia. Examples of apogamy are best known from certain varieties of ferns. In most of these, the gametophytes do not produce archegonia, although antheridia may be developed abundantly. The thickened central region of the gametophyte develops directly into a sporophyte without the occurrence of sexual union.

The phenomena of apogamy and apospory have an important bearing on such fundamental questions as the nature and relation of the alternating generations and the chromosome cycle. Are apogamously produced sporophytes haploid or diploid? If the former is the case, what is the nature of chromosome behavior during sporogenesis? In the latter case, are the prothallia diploid or haploid, and if diploid, what is the origin of the diploid condition? In spite of the investigations of numerous cytologists, the chromosome cycle in apogamous and aposporous ferns has not been clarified until recently. It has been shown for the **holly fern,** *Cyrtomium falcatum* Presl. (Fig. 22-33), for example, that the chromosome number of both sporophytes and gametophytes is the same, both being diploid. The gametophytes give rise to sporophytes apogamously. However, only the spores from certain types of sporangia in a sorus develop into gametophytes. Spores from other types of sporangia usually abort. In the sporangia that produce fertile spores, the first three divisions of the primary archesporial cell are normal; hence eight cells are produced. When these undergo nuclear division in preparation for the formation of sixteen spore mother cells, nuclear division is arrested at prophase or metaphase, with the result that in all eight sporogenous cells the nuclei are precociously reorganized. These contain double the chromosome complement of the original cells. These eight cells (second eight-celled stage) now function directly as sporocytes, undergoing meiosis with regular chromosome pairing and production of thirty-two spores, each of which, however, contains a nucleus with the chromosome number characteristic of the sporophyte. This temporary doubling, in the abortive fourth nuclear division, makes normal meiosis possible and also explains the similarity of chromosome number in gametophyte and sporophyte. A number of other ferns have been shown to have a similar chromosome cycle.[7]

FIG. 22-33. *Cyrtomium falcatum* Presl., the holly fern, an apogamous species. X 0.1.

In *Polypodium dispersum* Evans, in contrast to *Cyrtomium falcatum*, both sporophyte and gametophyte are haploid, the sporophytes arising from gametophytes lacking sex organs. No change of chromosomes occurs at spore production or at the time the sporophyte is initiated by the gametophyte.

Thus, at least three types of life cycle occur among leptosporangiate ferns: (1) The widespread cycle which involves regular alternation of diploid sporophytes and haploid gametophytes, as in *Dryopteris* and *Adiantum* (pp. 340–347); (2) the *Cyrtomium falcatum* type in which both sporophyte and gametophyte are diploid; and (3) the *Polypodium dispersum* type in which both sporophyte and gametophyte are haploid. The last two life cycles involve obligate apogamy.

Apogamy may be induced at will in other, normally sexual species. This has been accomplished by withholding water from the surface of gametophyte cultures, thus preventing swimming and functioning of the sperms. It has been demonstrated recently that when gametophytes of ten species of ferns (including *Pteridium aquilinum, Osmunda cinnamomea, Dryopteris marginalis,* and *Adiantum pedatum*) are grown in an inorganic medium supplemented with about 2.5% sugar (glucose, fructose, sucrose, or maltose) they produce sporophytes apogamously. The role of the sugar is not one of effecting a change in osmotic pressure but probably acting as a respiratory substrate. Control cultures grown in

---

[7] Another type of apogamous fern life cycle has recently been described in which the basic (presumably haploid) chromosome number is preserved by mitosis throughout both generations; meiosis is absent.

inorganic medium without sugar did not show apogamy.

A further factor effecting apogamy has been shown to be high light intensity. It has been suggested that this operates by increasing the rate of photosynthesis. Adding sugars to an inorganic medium may thus replace the factor of intense illumination.

Apospory, which occurs less frequently in nature than apogamy, also may be induced in many ferns. This is most readily accomplished by removing the leaves from young sporophytes and placing them on agar media. After an interval, leaf cells in contact with the agar give rise to filaments which ultimately grow into typical, cordate gametophytes.

The apogamous production of sporophytes and the aposporous development of gametophytes, such that gametophytes and sporophytes have the same chromosomal constitution, are strong evidence in support of the homologous theory of alternation of generations. The facts that sporophytes can directly transform some of their tissue into gametophytes (apospory), that gametophytes can directly transform their tissues into sporophytes (apogamy), and that the same chromosome complement may be present in both phases without modifying their fundamental morphology, all seem to indicate that the two alternating generations are fundamentally similar.

These phenomena then serve to focus our attention once again on the nature of alternation of generations and the causal relationships involved. It was suggested early in this century, on the basis of the isomorphic alternation known for certain algae, that the explanation for the profound morphological differences between the sporophyte and gametophyte in land plants was environmental. In the algae, it was argued, both generations develop as free-living plants from reproductive cells set free in the same environment; thus, the morphology of these algal sporophytes and gametophytes was similar. (Heteromorphic alternation in algae like the kelps, certain red algae, and some species of *Bryopsis* was unknown at the time.) In contrast, it was suggested that while the spore of land plants germinated freely into the gametophyte

in nature, the zygote always underwent the early phases of its development into a sporophyte within the confines of a pressure-exerting archegonium or calyptra. This difference of environment during development of sporophyte and gametophyte of land plants was suggested as the cause of their divergence in morphology.

In efforts to test this hypothesis, spores have been injected into the thickened midregion of fern gametophytes; although gametophytes ultimately arose from the injection site, it has not been possible to trace their origin with certainty. On the other hand, surgical removal of the archegonial neck, resulting in less pressure and constraint on the zygote, resulted in the latter's producing a mass of tissue in which differentiation into organs of the sporophyte was somewhat delayed, but finally did occur. However, zygotes removed completely from archegonia developed into prothalloid masses which did not become organized as sporophytes. There is evidence then, that the retention of the zygote within the calyptra and gametophyte has an important morphogenetic role.

It was long ago suggested that the chromosomal differences which normally obtain (the gametophyte being haploid and the sporophyte diploid) determine the difference in morphological expression, and this often is strongly emphasized. Several lines of evidence are available, however, in opposition to this suggestion. The occurrence in nature of gametophytes and sporophytes with the same chromosome complement, as in the case of *Cyrtomium* already discussed, is one negating factor. A second is the induction in apospory of regeneration of diploid fern leaves into diploid gametophytes. Finally, a polyploid series of haploid, diploid, and tetraploid gametophytes and diploid, tetraploid, and octoploid sporophytes of the same species has been obtained by experimental induction of apospory (followed by fertilizations) in the laboratory. In these investigations, gametophytes were still gametophytes whether haploid, diploid, or tetraploid, and diploid, tetraploid, and octoploid sporophytes themselves were little modified in morphology. These last results suggest that chromosomal or differences in *quantity* of DNA *of themselves* do not explain the differences between sporophyte and gametophyte.

It has recently been suggested that the cytoplasm of the egg cell itself may be the site of morphogenetic determination, but this would not explain the apogamous development of sporophytes from the vegetative tissues of fern gametophytes. The most significant causal agent so far discovered seems to be the enclosure of the zygote and young embryo by the archegonial jacket or calyptra. A similar force seems to be involved in the regeneration of juvenile plants from undifferentiated callus of angiosperms (p. 251).

Finally, in addition to the evidences of similarity of the alternants provided by apogamy and apospory, one additional point is relevant. It has been demonstrated that fern gametophytes may be stimulated to form vascular tissue (tracheids) by treatments with sucrose and an auxin (naphthalene acetic acid). Furthermore, by planting them in an erect position in inorganic agar medium with a 1.0% supplement of sucrose, the gametophytes become cylindrical and develop tracheids within. They thus approach in organization the axes of sporophytes and, at the same time, suggest the cylindrical organization of the gametophytes of *Psilotum* and *Ophioglossum*.

Accordingly, although the phenomenon of alternation of generations has been described and investigated for more than a century, we still lack precise data regarding the causal factors involved. It seems increasingly clear, however, on the basis of the evidence at hand, that sporophytes and gametophytes in a given life cycle are not so fundamentally different from each other as sometimes has been suggested or implied.

DISCUSSION QUESTIONS

1. How do eusporangiate and leptosporangiate sporangium development and sporangia differ? Are the differences always absolute?

2. Define or explain sorus, receptacle, indusium, false indusium, annulus, lip cells, circinate vernation.

3. Define apogamy and apospory. What is the phylogenetic significance of these phenomena?

4. How would you go about inducing apogamy in *Adiantum* and *Dryopteris*?

5. Define and give an example of simple and gradate sori.

6. Why are the sori of *Dryopteris* and *Adiantum* said to be "mixed"?

7. How do the gametophytes of *Dryopteris* and *Adiantum* differ from those of *Ophioglossum* and *Botrychium*? From those of *Osmunda*? From those of *Angiopteris* and *Marattia*? From those of *Schizaea*?

8. Why is the fern gametophyte called a "prothallus" or "prothallium"?

9. Where would you look for fern gametophytes in nature?

10. How would you go about propagating ferns from spores?

11. What genera of ferns grow in the vicinity of your home or campus?

12. What is meant by the "octant" stage in the embryogeny of leptosporangiate ferns?

13. To what group of nonvascular cryptogams does the fern gametophyte show some similarity? How does it differ?

14. Comment on the significance of the location of sporangia in various species of *Osmunda*.

15. What features of *Osmunda* suggest eusporangiate ferns?

16. How do the gametophytes of *Osmunda* differ from those of *Dryopteris* and *Adiantum*?

17. Could the trunks of tree ferns be used as lumber? Explain.

18. What attributes are considered primitive in fern sporophytes?

19. What variations occur in the gametophyte generations of ferns?

20. What significance do you attribute to the occurrence of tracheids in fern gametophytes? Under what conditions do tracheids develop? Cite the gametophyte of another vascular cryptogam which may contain xylem.

21. How would you induce apospory in a fern?

22. Comment regarding the causal factors involved in the dimorphism of the alternating generations in ferns.

CHAPTER 23

Division Pterophyta—III

It should be reiterated at this point that the division Pterophyta contains two classes, the Eusporangiopsida (discussed in Chapter 21) and the Leptosporangiopsida. The homosporous Leptosporangiopsida (the order Filicales) were treated in the preceding chapter. The present one includes a discussion of the heterosporous orders, Marsileales and Salviniales, sometimes called the waterferns, and concludes with a consideration of the fossil record of Pterophyta.

Order 2. Marsileales[1]

FAMILY 1. MARSILEACEAE

Introduction and vegetative morphology

The genera *Marsilea* (after Count *F. L. Marsigli*, an Italian naturalist), *Regnellidium* (after *A. F. Regnell*), and *Pilularia* (L. *pilula*, little ball[2]) comprise the single family, Mar-

sileaceae. All are amphibious, growing in shallow ponds and ditches, and are also able to survive when the water level falls, as long as the soil is moist; one species of *Marsilea*, however, is xerophytic. *Marsilea*[3] (Fig. 23-1), widely distributed throughout the world, occurs in the southern and Pacific regions of the United States; *Regnellidium* (Figs. 23-2, 23-3A) is native to the Amazon region of Brazil; *Pilularia* (Fig. 23-3B), the pillwort, occurs in Europe, Africa, and Australia; in the United States it grows natively in Texas, Oregon, California, Kansas, Arkansas, and Georgia.

Marsilea at first glance is decidedly unfern-like in appearance (Fig. 23-1); its compound leaves frequently suggest four-leaved clovers to the uninitiated. It grows readily under greenhouse conditions and is fairly hardy in colder climates, where it perennates by means

---

[1] The Filicales (Chapter 22) are the first order of Leptosporangiopsida.
[2] In reference to the sporocarp.

[3] For a recent summary on *Marsilea* see: Gupta, K. M., *Marsilea*, Bot. Monograph No. 2. Council of Scientific and Industrial Res., New Delhi. 1962.

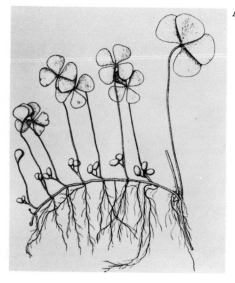

A

FIG. 23-1. A. *Marsilea quadrifolia*, X ⅔. B. *Marsilea vestita* Hook. and Grev. Habit of fertile branch with vegetative leaves and sporocarps. X ⅐. (A. *After Eames.*)

sporocarp

B

FIG. 23-2. *Regnellidium diphyllum.* Living plants. X 0.33.

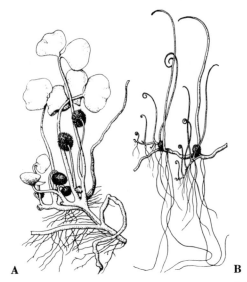

A   B

FIG. 23-3. A. *Regnellidium diphyllum.* B. *Pilularia* sp. Both with sporocarps. X 0.5 (*After Eames.*)

of its stems which are embedded in soil or mud.

The plant body consists of an elongate, branching, stolonlike stem (Fig. 23-1B) which grows either on the surface of the mud or slightly below it. The leaves are in two rows, alternately inserted on opposite sides of the stem, from which they arise in circinate fashion. The internodes are frequently very long. In mature plants, three kinds of leaves may develop: (1) floating leaves; (2) submerged leaves; and (3) aerial leaves. The first two, of course, occur in aquatic habitats and the last when the plant is terrestrial.

In submerged plants, the petioles are relatively flaccid, have air chambers, and the leaflets float on the surface of the water; stomata are restricted to the upper surface. The petioles of aerial leaves, however, lack air chambers and are sufficiently rigid to support the leaflets in an erect position; here

sunken stomata occur on both the dorsal and ventral leaf surfaces. The four leaflets of each leaf do not actually arise at one locus from the petiole; two are slightly higher than the others and are inserted in alternate fashion, the leaflet veins are dichotomously branched but laterally and marginally united to some extent to form a loose reticulum. A transection of the leaf (Fig. 23-4) reveals the presence of an upper and lower epidermis, both with slightly sunken stomata. The mesophyll is differentiated into palisade and spongy areas. Each petiole is traversed by a V-shaped vascular trace which leaves a gap above the place of its departure from the stem stele. The submerged leaves have smaller blades than either of the other two types.

Growth of leaves, stem, and root originates in apical cells and their derivatives. The vas-

FIG. 23-4. *Marsilea* sp. Transection of leaf; l.e., lower epidermis; p.m., palisade mesophyll; s., stoma; s.m., spongy mesophyll; u.e., upper epidermis; v., vein. X 90.

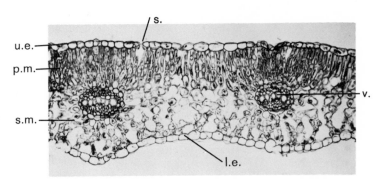

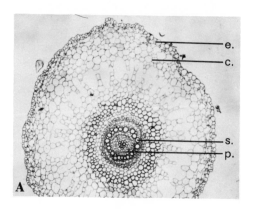

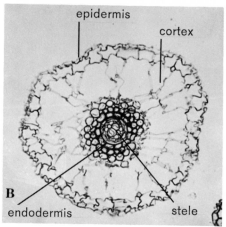

epidermis

cortex

e.

c.

s.

p.

A

B

endodermis

stele

FIG. 23-5. *Marsilea* sp. A. Transection of stem. X 60. B. Transection of root. X 125; c., cortex with air chambers; e., epidermis; p., pith; s., stele.

cular tissue of the mature stem (Fig. 23-5A) is arranged in the form of an amphiphloic siphonostele. Both inner and outer phloem are covered by a single layer of pericycle cells, which, in turn, are covered by a single endodermal layer. In some species the xylem is exarch. The pith may be parenchymatous or sclerotic, usually the latter, in stems growing in nonsubmerged soil. The continuity of the cortex is interrupted by large air chambers, and it is outwardly bounded by an epidermis. Stem branches always arise at the bases of leaves.

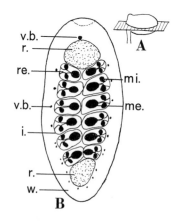

v.b.

r.

re.

v.b.

i.

r.

w.

A

mi.

me.

B

FIG. 23-6. *Marsilea* sp. A. Diagram indicating sectional plane. B. Section of sporocarp; i., indusium; me., megasporangium; mi., microsporangium; r., gelatinous ring; re., receptacle; v.b., vascular bundle; w., wall of sporocarp. (*Adapted from Eames.*)

The adventitious roots emerge at the nodes and are monarch or diarch protosteles with exarch arrangement (Fig. 23-5B). Vessels have recently been reported to be present in the roots of *Marsilea*. Here, too, the stele is surrounded by a single layer of pericycle and an endodermis. The inner cortex is sclerotic; the outer contains air chambers.

Reproduction: the sporophyte

The sporangia of *Marsilea* are borne in specialized structures known as **sporocarps,** which occur on short lateral branches of the petioles (Fig. 23-1). They appear after a long period of vegetative development, usually on terrestrial individuals. The sporocarps at first are relatively soft and green, but they become hard, brown, and nutlike at maturity. They may be borne singly or in clusters, depending on the species. Anatomical and ontogenetic evidence indicates that the sporocarp probably represents a fertile pinna which has become folded with the margins united, thus enclosing the fertile (abaxial) surface of the leaflet. Each lateral half of the sporocarp bears a row of elongate sori (Fig. 23-6) with ridgelike receptacles. The sori of one half alternate with those of the other, but all are close together and there is overlapping. Each sorus is covered with a delicate indusium; the indusia of adjacent sori are partially fused together, so that each receptacle and its sporangia lie in a cavity (Fig. 23-6).

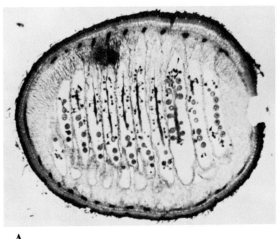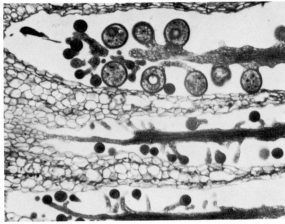

A   B

FIG. 23-7. *Marsilea* sp. A. Sagittal section of developing sporocarp; note receptacles, bearing megasporangia and smaller microsporangia, enclosed by indusia. X 8. B. Portions of three receptacles, enlarged. X 30.

Sporangial initials develop first at the apex of each ridgelike receptacle; subsequently, additional initials on the flanks initiate sporangium development in gradate order (Fig. 23-7).

The sporangia develop according to the leptosporangiate method, and all produce between 32 and 64 spores. In the sporangia at the apex of the receptacle, however, all the spores except one degenerate, their contents mingling with those of the tapetal cells which have formed a plasmodium late in sporogenesis. The surviving spore, probably as a result of absorbing large quantities of nutriment, increases to many times its original size, becoming somewhat ellipsoidal. A single megaspore, therefore, matures in each of the sporangia at the apex of the linear receptacle (Figs. 23-6, 23-7). The mature megaspore has a rounded protuberance at one end on which the triradiate ridges remain visible. The wall in this region is delicate, but over the remainder of the spore protoplast it is extremely thick. The megaspores are sufficiently large to be readily visible to the unaided eye. The single nucleus of the megaspore lies in dense cytoplasm and in the region of the protuberance. The bulk of the spore cavity is filled with starch grains; only a small amount of cytoplasm is present.

All the spores in the sporangia on the flanks of the receptacle mature; and they are many times smaller than the megaspores. Each of these microspores has a single central nucleus and rather dense cytoplasm containing starch grains. Hence *Marsilea* is heterosporous, as are *Selaginella* and *Isoetes* among extant microphyllous plants.

As the spores mature, changes occur in the sterile tissues of the sporocarp. The outer layers become stony, and their cell walls thicken markedly. The other tissues, except for the sori and indusia, disintegrate and gelatinize. Both microsporangia and megasporangia lack a highly differentiated annulus, an indication of the fact that the spores are not discharged vigorously and explosively from the sporangia.

In nature, the sporocarps persist in the water and soil after the vegetative portions of the plants which produced them have disappeared. It is probable that bacterial action plays a role in rotting the sporocarp wall and in thus effecting spore dissemination. This process may be hastened in the laboratory by cutting away a small portion of the stony wall and immersing the sporocarps in water. After such treatment, water is imbibed by the hydrophilic colloids in the sporocarp. Within a short time, the attendant swelling forces the two halves of the sporocarp apart and a gelatinous ring (which soon breaks) emerges,

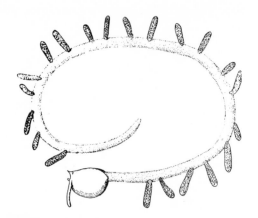

bearing the sori (Fig. 23-8). Several hours after their emergence, the sporangial walls become gelatinous, with the result that large numbers of free microspores and megaspores

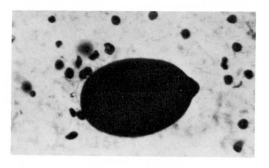

FIG. 23-9. *Marsilea* sp. Megaspore and microspores. X 50.

are shed into the common soral cavity still enclosed by the indusium. The latter disintegrates ultimately, and the microspores and

megaspores are liberated into the water (Fig. 23-9).

Reproduction: the gametophytes

Unlike those of *Selaginella*, but like those of *Isoetes*, the spores of *Marsilea* do not germinate until they have been shed from the sporocarp. Development into gametophytes is then very rapid. Formation of the male gametophyte by the microspore is initiated by a nuclear and cell division to form unequal cells within the microspore wall; the smaller cell is the prothallial cell. As in *Isoetes* and *Selaginella*, this cell fails to divide again and is interpreted as the sole remnant of vegetative tissue in the male gametophyte. The larger cell divides in two, and each of the resulting cells by further division (Fig. 23-10A, B) forms an antheridium which is covered with jacket cells that surround the sixteen spermatogenous cells. The microspore wall now ruptures and the mature antheridia protrude (Figs. 23-10B, 23-11A). The prothallial cells and jacket cells now disintegrate and the large sperms, which have previously developed singly in each spermatogenous cell, become actively motile and swim away (Figs. 23-10C, 23-11B). The sperms are tightly coiled and have a number of flagella on the apical nuclear portion (Figs. 23-10C, 23-12E). The development of the male gametophyte and liberation of the sperms may take place in as short a time as 12 hours.

In the development of the female gametophyte by the megaspore, a limited number of nuclear and cell divisions occur within the hemispherical protuberance, resulting in the formation of a small amount of vegetative

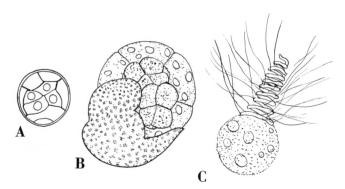

FIG. 23-10. *Marsilea vestita.* Development of the ♂ gametophyte. A. Section of the microspore with male gametophyte; note prothallial cell and two rudimentary antheridia. X 260. B. Microspore with emergent ♂ gametophyte. X 430. C. Living sperm. X 2266. (A. *Adapted from Sharp.*)

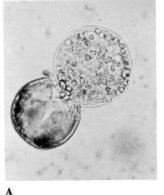

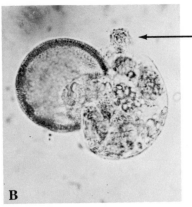

FIG. 23-11. A, B. *Marsilea* sp. Microspores with maturing male gametophytes, the one at B, liberating a sperm (arrow). X 175.

tissue bearing a single apical archegonium (Fig. 23-12A, B). Enlargement of these cells ruptures the megaspore wall, which is delicate in the region of the protuberance. The megaspore that bears the mature female gametophyte becomes surrounded by a gelatinous matrix which is usually thickest in the region of the female gametophyte (Fig. 23-12C). A more watery, central region of the matrix lies directly above the archegonium. The liberated sperms (Fig. 23-12D), apparently attracted chemotactically, swarm into the matrix

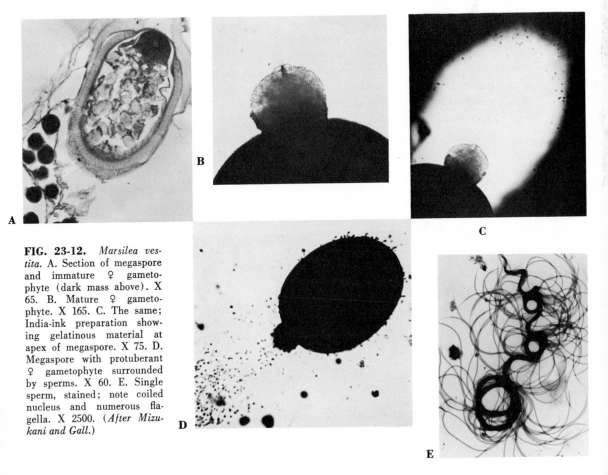

FIG. 23-12. *Marsilea vestita.* A. Section of megaspore and immature ♀ gametophyte (dark mass above). X 65. B. Mature ♀ gametophyte. X 165. C. The same; India-ink preparation showing gelatinous material at apex of megaspore. X 75. D. Megaspore with protuberant ♀ gametophyte surrounded by sperms. X 60. E. Single sperm, stained; note coiled nucleus and numerous flagella. X 2500. (*After Mizukani and Gall.*)

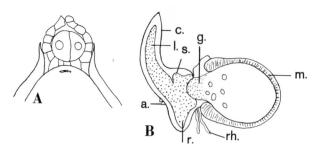

FIG. 23-13. A. *Marsilea vestita.* Median longitudinal section of ♀ gametophyte; archegonium with early embryo. X 280. B. *Marsilea* sp. Median longitudinal section of megaspore, ♀ gametophyte, and embryo; a., archegonium; c., calyptra-like sheath; g., ♀ gametophyte; l., primary leaf or cotyledon; m., megaspore wall; r., root; rh., rhizoid; s., stem. (A. *From Campbell.* B. *From Sachs.*)

in the vicinity of the archegonium. One of them makes its way to the egg cell and fertilization occurs.

Reproduction: embryogeny

Development of the embryo is initiated several hours after fertilization by nuclear and cell division of the zygote (Fig. 23-13A). Cytokinesis is usually in a direction parallel to the long axis of the archegonium and megaspore, which are typically horizontal. A second division, also parallel to the archegonial axis but in a plane perpendicular to that of the first division, results in the formation of four cells. These by further division develop the foot, leaf (cotyledon), stem, and root of the embryonic sporophyte, as indicated in Fig. 23-13B. The vegetative cells of the gametophyte are stimulated to divide as the embryonic sporophyte develops, and they form a sheathing calyptra (Fig. 23-13B)

around the latter. The surface cells of this gametophytic tissue develop rhizoids (Figs. 23-13B, 23-14); both rhizoids and other gametophytic cells develop chloroplasts. The calyptra is relatively persistent but disappears about the same time that the embryonic root penetrates the substratum. Growth of the embryonic sporophyte is rapid (Fig. 23-14A–B). One series of germling sporophytes of *M. vestita* planted in April produced mature plants bearing sporocarps by the following October.

Regnellidium and Pilularia

The genera of Marsileales form an interesting evolutionary series with respect to their leaves. *Marsilea* usually has two pairs of pinnae on its compound leaves but occasionally may have three pairs. In *Regnellidium* (Fig. 23-2), a deeply bilobed leaf occurs. Finally, in *Pilularia* (Fig. 23-3), no leaf blade develops, and the petiole and rachis are the photosynthetic organs. The organization of the sporocarp, maturation of the gametophytes, and the embryogeny of *Regnellidium* and *Pilularia*, in general, resemble corresponding phases in *Marsilea.*

Summary of Marsileales

Although decidedly not fernlike in appearance, the vegetative structure and sporangial development of *Marsilea* are very similar to those of other leptosporangiate ferns. The cloverlike leaves represent sterile pinnae with a dichotomous venation that is closed at the margins and to some extent laterally. Vernation of the leaves is circinate. The stems are amphiphloic siphonosteles, inter-

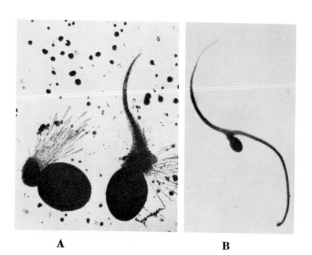

A	B

FIG. 23-14. *Marsilea vestita.* A, B. Megaspores with ♀ gametophytes after fertilization; the one to the right in A has an advanced embryo, cotyledon, and root, which are visible. X 30.

rupted by leaf gaps which usually do not overlap because of the great length of the internodes. The leaves arise alternately in two rows from the stolonlike stems. Both roots and stems afford anatomical evidence of aquatic habitat in the form of air chambers; the vascular tissue, however, is unusually abundant for a hydrophytic plant. The roots contain vessels. *Marsilea* is representative of the leptosporangiate ferns in which heterospory has been developed. The sporangia are borne in sclerotic, modified fused pinnae which comprise the sporocarp. With it have appeared such concomitant attributes as unisexual gametophytes, reduction in vegetative functions, tissue, and duration of the gametophytes. Gametogenesis and embrvogeny are extremely rapid in *Marsilea*.

Order 3. Salviniales

The order Salviniales contains two genera, *Salvinia* (after *Antonio M. Salvini*) and *Azolla* (Gr. *azo*, parched, killed by drought) both small, floating aquatics. Most species of *Salvinia* are native to Africa, but one species occurs in the United States. *Salvinia* is widely distributed in greenhouses and aquaria. Two species of *Azolla* occur in the United States, *A. caroliniana* Willd. in the eastern states and *A. filiculoides* Lam. in the western. Ponds and swamps are often colored red by "blooms" of *Azolla* in intense light.

Salvinia (Fig. 23-15) is rootless, the *apparent* roots being morphologically filiform leaf segments. The leaves are in whorls of three, two of which are floating and the third submerged. It is the latter which is divided into rootlike lobes. The floating leaves are concave and covered with hairs and waxy papillae (Fig. 23-15B).

Azolla (Fig. 23-16) consists of branching stems densely clothed with alternate bilobed leaves which suggest those of certain Jungermanniaceae (p. 207). Each leaf is composed of a chlorophyllous dorsal lobe and a submerged achlorophyllous ventral lobe. The dorsal lobes contain cavities in which occur filaments of the blue-green alga *Anabaena;* their role has not been determined with certainty, but it has been suggested that they fix gaseous nitrogen.

True roots, which arise endogenously at intervals along the stem, occur in *Azolla*. The roots bear root hairs as long as they exist. Both stem and root have exarch protosteles.

Salvinia and *Azolla* produce their sporangia in sporocarps, but these differ from those of *Marsilea* in that the sporocarp wall of the Salviniales is a modified indusium. Both genera are heterosporous, and at maturity the sporocarps bear only megaspores or microspores. Sporangium development, of course, is leptosporangiate. The individual gametophytes are unisexual and much reduced like those of the Marsileales. The account of reproduction of *Azolla* and *Salvinia* is terminated at this point because material with reproductive stages is rarely available for laboratory study. There seems to be no reason why cultivation of these plants in the laboratory, with variation of nitrogen level of the culture medium, temperature, and photo-

FIG. 23-15. *Salvinia natans.* A. X 1. B. X 3.

A   B

FIG. 23-16.
Azolla caroliniana.
A. X 0.8. B. X 3.

A   B

period, should not provide a readily available supply of plants in reproductive stages.

Fossil Pterophyta[4]

The Carboniferous (Table 32-1) has often been spoken of as "The Age of Ferns" because of the abundant and striking remains of fernlike foliage encountered in strata of that age. However, the discovery that some Carboniferous plants (the pteridosperms or seed ferns) with fernlike leaves bore seeds and that others had gymnospermlike xylem[5] has made this appellation suspect.

The Pterophyta (ferns, *sensu lato*), it will be recalled, are the only macrophyllous vascular cryptogams. The macrophyllous leaf, it was suggested late in the nineteenth century, is a modified branch system (p. 380). Accordingly, one would hope that the fossil record of ferns would provide some evidence for the method of origin of their complex leaves, and this, indeed, seems to be the case.

As noted in Chapter 17, when land plants

became prominent in the Devonian (Table 32-1), in addition to the Psilophyta, Microphyllophyta, and Arthrophyta, certain fernlike plants were contemporaneous. Examples of these and of fernlike plants of later strata will be briefly discussed in the following paragraphs.

A great many of the fernlike fossils are **form genera,** so called because they are known only as stem, petiole, rachis, or leaf fragments; accordingly, there are disagreements regarding the growth habit of the plants in their entirety and with respect to their classification. The following categorization should, therefore, be regarded as extremely tentative. The orders Protopteridiales,[6] Cladoxylales, and Coenopteridales, have no living members.

These early fern precursors had lateral branch systems which were either three-dimensional or flattened in one plane; the branchlets were at first stemlike rather than bladelike. The xylem was characteristically mesarch and prominently lobed and dissected in some forms. The sporangia were large and terminal. Representatives of these will be described first in the following account, which will conclude with consideration

---

[4] For an informative discussion see *Origin and Evolution of Ferns.* Memoirs of the Torrey Botanical Club 21, No. 5, 1964.

[5] *Archaeopteris* (see p. 445).

[6] Sometimes spelled Protopteridales.

of several fossil ferns from orders with extant members.

Order 1. Protopteridiales

To the Protopteridiales have been assigned several Middle- and Upper-Devonian (Table 32-1) genera with a growth habit suggestive of the Psilophyta. These genera include *Protopteridium* (Gr. *protos*, before + NL. *Pteridium*), *Eospermatopteris* (Gr. *eo*, dawn + Gr. *sperma*, seed Gr. *pteris*, fern), and *Aneurophyton* (Gr. *a*, lacking + Gr. *neuron*, nerve + Gr. *phyton*, plant), the last two perhaps identical.

The main axes of *Protopteridium* were dichotomously or monopodially branched (Fig. 23-17). The ultimate divisions of the axis were pinnately branched, circinately vernate, and with bladelike segments. The sporangia were elongate and pedicellate on certain of the branchlets (Fig. 23-17). These attributes suggest *Dawsonites* (p. 276).

Eospermatopteris (Fig. 23-18) was a treelike plant estimated to be between 20 and 40 feet tall. The trunks bore a terminal crown of frondlike branches, 6–9 feet long with

FIG. 23-18. *Eospermatopteris* sp. Reconstruction. (*After Goldring, from Andrews.*)

circinate vernation. These were decidedly fernlike in gross appearance. However, the ultimate divisions of the fronds lacked blades and were dichotomously branched. Certain of them terminated in large, ovoid sporangia up to 6 mm. long and 3 mm. in diameter.

The branching axes of the Protopteridiales, then, appoached the organization of modern ferns but lacked the laminate leaves of the latter.

Order 2. Cladoxylales

Representatives of the Cladoxylales are found from Middle- and Upper-Devonian through the Mississippian (Table 32-1). *Cladoxylon*[7] *scoparium* Kräusel and Weyland (Fig. 23-19A) is one of the most completely known species. The axes were dichotomously branched, had secondary thickening, and

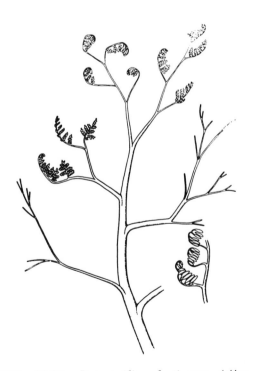

FIG. 23-17. *Protopteridium hostimense.* (*After Kräusel and Weyland, from Delevoryas.*)

---

[7] *Cladoxylon* (Gr. *klad*, sprout or branch + Gr. *xylon*, post).

bore dichotomously lobed leaves. Certain of these were fertile and fanlike (Fig. 23-14B), ovoid sporangia being borne at the tips of the dichotomies. *Cladoxylon* not only gives evidence of planation and webbing of axes, but is of interest because of its terminal, cauline sporangia.

The genus *Pseudosporochnus* (Gr. *pseudes*, false + *Sporochnus*, a genus of *Phaeophyta*), from the Middle Devonian (Table 32-1), was until recently assigned to the Psilophyta. Discovery of abundant material of a new species, *P. nodosus* Leclercq and Banks (in Belgium) and intensive study of it have led to the conclusion that *Pseudosporochnus* is a member of the Pterophyta, order Cladoxylales, rather than of the Psilophyta. This conclusion is based on the complex morphology of the frond and on anatomical evidence including the nature of the stele and leaf trace, the latter like that of the zygopterids, to be described below (p. 371).

Pseudosporochnus nodosus (Fig. 23-30) was a large plant, but the over-all height is not known. At the base of the trunklike stem there was a mass of thick, dichotomously branching roots. The main stem was unbranched but bore at its apex a crown of three-dimensional branches of three orders, diminishing in diameter of their axes (Fig. 23-20). The ultimate segments were dichotomizing sterile, vegetative, bladelike segments (called fronds). Other ultimate branchlets were fertile, terminating in eight pedicellate, ovoidal sporangia (Fig. 23-20). Some fronds were mixed sterile and fertile. The fronds were supplied with leaf traces, the latter, of course, lacking in the Psilophyta. The xylem of the axes is arranged in a series of radially arranged plates which is typical of *Cladoxylon*. The planate fronds also are pterophytan, rather than psilophytan. *Pseudosporochnus* is more primitive than *Cladoxylon* in its nonbladelike fertile branchlets.

FIG. 23-20. *Pseudosporochnus nodosus* Leclercq and Banks. Restoration. (*After Leclercq and Banks.*)

Order 3. Coenopteridales

Members of this order occur in strata from the Devonian through the Permian (Table 32-1) but are predominantly Carboniferous. The fossils included in the Coenopteridales are known, especially anatomically, from petrifactions of their stems, petioles, and rachides. The vascular pattern in the latter was complex, bilaterally symmetrical in either one or two planes (Fig. 23-21). The stems usually seem to have contained protosteles. The fronds were not organized in one plane in all the genera and the sporangia were borne terminally on small branchlets. The genera of Coenopteridales are segregated largely on the vascular pattern (stele) of their rachides which in transection ranged from simple-elliptical (Fig. 23-21A) to star- (Fig. 23-21B) and "H"-shaped.

Of the many genera of Coenopteridales, *Zygopteris* is one of the best known. *Zygopteris* (Gr. *zygon*, yoke + Gr. *pteris*, *fern*), from the Carboniferous and Permian, was originally described from a petiole fragment with an H-shaped vascular pattern in transection. *Zygopteris* included species which were arborescent and which had circinate leaves. The trunks were densely covered with leaf bases and adventitious roots. The stem contained a protostele and the primary xylem may have been covered by secondary xylem in some species, an unusual phenomenon for Pterophyta. The fronds of *Zygopteris* were called *Etapteris* (Gr. *eta*, H + Gr. *pteris*, fern) before their organic connection to *Zygopteris* had been established. Some *Etapteris* fronds were composed of several-times pinnate segments, the members of the several orders of pinnation lying in different planes

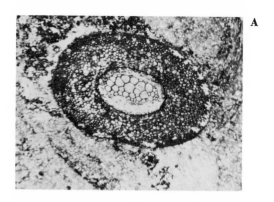

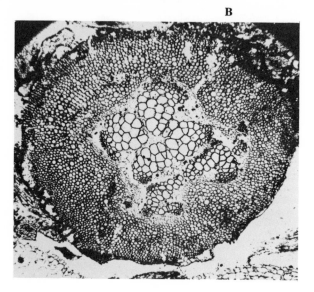

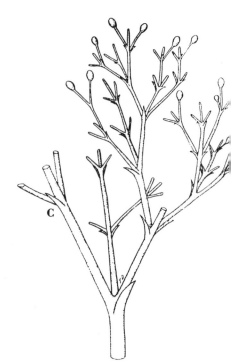

FIG. 23-21. A. *Botryopteris ramosa.* Section of rachis. X 45. B. *Stauropteris* sp. Section of rachis. X 60. C. *Stauropteris oldhamnia.* Reconstruction. (*After Zimmerman, from Delevoryas.*)

from each other and that of the rachis so that the leaves were three-dimensional (Fig. 23-22). Because of this they are sometimes called **phyllophores** rather than leaves. As far as known, these ferns were homosporous (Fig. 23-22B).

The genera of fossil ferns described above belong to orders which contain no living members. There are known, in addition, a number of extinct ferns belonging to orders with living members.

Order 4. Marattiales

Psaronius (NL., a precious stone[8]) (Fig. 23-23) was an arborescent genus of Marattiales; trunks of *Psaronius* 2 feet in diameter

are well preserved in Carboniferous and Permian strata. The general growth habit was apparently much like that of extant tree ferns (members of the Filicales). The stems were exceedingly complex anatomically, containing a series of roughly concentric solenosteles in the distal portion. These were dissected by gaps to form dictyosteles. The large fronds were several times pinnately compound with bladelike pinnules. Synangia occurred on the abaxial surface of some of these pinnules.

A *Marattia*-like genus, *Marattiopsis*, occurred in the Mesozoic along with several other extinct Marattiales.

Orders 5, 6. Filicales and Salviniales

A number of representatives of filicalean families occur in fossiliferous strata. Several

---

[8] From the speckled appearance of petrified specimens when polished.

MORPHOLOGY OF PLANTS

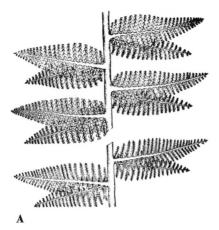

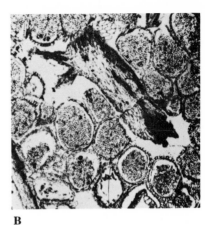

FIG. 23-22. A. *Etapteris lacattei* Renault. Portion of axis. B. *Botryopteris* sp., sporangia. X 60. (A. *After Hirmer, from Wettstein.*)

A   B

schizaeacean genera have been described from the Carboniferous, Triassic, Jurassic, and Cretaceous (Table 32-1). *Anemia*, a living genus, has, for example, the fossil species, *A. fremonti* in Cretaceous strata.

Several Osmundaceae are known, beginning with Permian representatives like *Thamnopteris* (Gr. *thamnos*, frequent + Gr. *pteris*, fern) (Fig. 23-24). *Osmundites* (*Osmunda* + Gr. *ites*, fossil) with the relationship of roots and stem very much like that in the extant *Osmunda* occurs in Jurassic to Tertiary (Table 32-1) strata. Comparative studies of the steles in fossil Osmundaceae indicate that the pith has arisen within the stele by replacement of tracheids by parenchyma cells.

Polypodiaceous ferns are known from the Jurassic, but really abundant and diversified remains do not occur earlier than the Cenozoic (Table 32-1). For this reason, the Polypodiaceae are often called "the modern ferns."

Finally, although the fossil record of the Marsileales seems to be unknown, both *Salvinia* and *Azolla* have been found in Tertiary strata.

FIG. 23-23. *Psaronius* sp. Reconstruction. (*After Morgan, from Andrews.*)

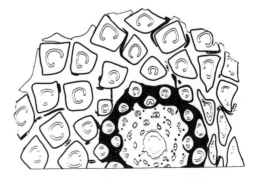

FIG. 23-24. *Thamnopteris schlechtendalii.* Transection of stem and leaf bases of a Permian osmundaceous fern. (*After Delevoryas.*)

Classification and Summary of Pterophyta

The extant ferns discussed in this and Chapters 21 and 22 may be classified as follows:

Division Pterophyta
    Class 1. Eusporangiopsida
        Order 1. Ophioglossales
            Family 1. Ophioglossaceae
                Genera: *Ophioglossum, Botrychium*
        Order 2. Marattiales
            Family 1. Marattiaceae
                Genera: *Marattia, Angiopteris*
    Class 2. Leptosporangiopsida
        Order 1. Filicales
            Family 1. Osmundaceae
                Genera: *Osmunda, Todea*
            Family 2. Polypodiaceae
                Genera: *Polypodium, Dryopteris, Adiantum, Onoclea, Pteretis, Pellaea, Polystichum, Pteris, Pteridium, Woodsia, Nephrolepis,* etc.
            Family 3. Schizaeaceae
                Genera: *Schizaea, Lygodium*
            Family 4. Hymenophyllaceae
                Genera: *Hymenophyllum, Trichomanes*
            Family 5. Cyatheaceae
                Genus: *Cyathea*
            Family 6. Dicksoniaceae
                Genus: *Dicksonia*
        Order 2. Marsileales
            Family 1. Marsileaceae
                Genera: *Marsilea, Regnellidium, Pilularia*
        Order 3. Salviniales
            Family 1. Salviniaceae
                Genera: *Salvinia, Azolla*

The division Pterophyta is here conceived to include all macrophyllous vascular cryptogams. This definition of the scope of the group is at variance with that of other botanists who, in a broader definition of its limits, classify all macrophyllous plants, both spore-bearing and seed-bearing, together in a single taxon. Discussion of the reasons for excluding the seed plants from the same divi-sion as the spore-bearing plants cannot be summarized profitably until one has become familiar with the seed plants, and accordingly it is deferred to a later chapter.

A comparative and orderly review of the Pterophyta may be instructive at this point, not only as a recapitulation but also as a prelude to the discussion of the entire group of vascular cryptogams and their phylogeny which follows in the next chapter. The comparison is based on discussion of the following topics: the sporophyte and its vegetative and reproductive features; the gametophyte; and embryogeny.

The vegetative sporophyte

The plant bodies of the Pterophyta exhibit a remarkable range in habit and complexity. At one extreme, perhaps, are the minute sporophytes of the hydrophytic genera *Salvinia* and *Azolla*, which are dwarfed by such plant bodies as those of *Dicksonia* and *Cyathea*, the tree ferns. The remaining genera, for the most part, are intermediate between these extremes and rarely exceed 6–8 feet in height, with the exception of tropical species of *Lygodium*, a climber, the leaves of which may attain a length of 100 feet! It is of interest to note that in spite of the great size of certain of these genera, secondary growth by cambial activity is absent from members of the division, except for the relatively abortive fashion in which it occurs in *Botrychium*, and, perhaps, in the extinct *Zygopteris*. With rare exceptions, the ferns are perennial and long-lived.

The dominant organ of the sporophyte is the macrophyllous leaf. In no group of vascular plants other than the Pterophyta has the leaf attained such predominance and elaborate form. In many cases, the leaves rival the stems of other plants in duration of development and regular ontogeny from apical initials. In almost all the genera except *Ophioglossum*, vernation is typically circinate. The dominant role of the leaf is reflected further in the large trace or traces which pass into the petioles and the profound disturbances (gaps) they occasion in the stelar tissues of the stem. Leaf form varies from such simple types as those of some species of *Ophioglos-*

sum and certain species of *Polypodium*, through pinnately once-divided leaves like those of *Polystichum acrostichoides,* to such extreme division of the blades as is evident in *Lygodium, Trichomanes,* and *Hymenophyllum.* There is evidence that in some forms (*Ophioglossum*) the leaves have become secondarily simplified, although the juvenile, embryonic leaves of most genera are also simple. Both open-dichotomous (*Angiopteris, Osmunda, Adiantum*) and closed-reticulate venation (*Ophioglossum, Dryopteris*) are present in the leaves of Pterophyta.

The form of the stem varies from the minute, poorly developed type observable in *Ophioglossum, Lygodium,* and *Ceratopteris* through the rather massive erect or ascending types in *Osmunda,* the horizontal rhizomes and rootstocks of such genera as *Adiantum* and *Dryopteris,* to the erect trunks of tree ferns. The range of stelar structure in fern stems is extensive. Most genera have protostelic stems in the juvenile stages, evidence that the protostele is truly primitive. The protostelic condition persists in the adult in such genera as *Lygodium,* but in a great majority of ferns the stems contain siphonosteles (*Adiantum*) which may be dissected into dictyosteles (*Dryopteris*), depending on the proximity of the nodes to each other. In a number of genera there has taken place a proliferation of the vascular tissues to form a complex system, polystelic in arrangement (*Pteridium*). Ontogeny of the stem, with few exceptions, originates in a single prominent apical cell. In *Pteridium,* and in the roots of *Marsilea,* as in *Selaginella* and *Equisetum,* perforation of the terminal walls of tracheids has resulted in the development of a primitive type of vessel, a xylem element otherwise absent in the vascular cryptogams. The dominance of the leaves, the relatively great size of the vascular traces passing into their petioles, and the resulting dissection of the cauline steles have impelled some morphologists to suggest that the stem in such genera as *Ophioglossum* is composed largely of overlapping leaf bases.

Except for the primary root (radicle) of the embryonic sporophyte, the root system of ferns is entirely adventitious. The thin, often blackish or brownish, wiry roots arise at and between the leaf bases, usually endogenously. The roots, and for that matter, the plant bodies of the Ophioglossales differ in their fleshiness from those of most other Pterophyta. Ontogeny of the root is initiated by a single apical cell or several such cells (*Osmunda*) and results in the development of an exarch protostele. The root, therefore, is thought to be a conservative organ. The roots (and stems) of a number of ferns (*Ophioglossum* and *Botrychium*) become infected with a fungus which invades the cortical cells and functions in mycorrhizal fashion. *Salvinia,* at maturity, is one of the few rootless genera, although it has an embryonic root.

Reproduction: the sporophyte

The sporogenous tissue of the fern sporophyte varies in its distribution. *Ophioglossum* and *Botrychium,* of the genera discussed in this text, are unique in the localization of their sporogenous tissues on an organ known as the fertile spike. A physiologically similar, but morphologically dissimilar, dimorphism occurs, however, in varying degrees in several species of *Osmunda, Onoclea,* and *Pteretis.* In genera with sporangia distributed abaxially on the foliage leaves, the sporangia may be uniformly arranged (*Dryopteris*) or restricted to the apical pinnae (*Polystichum acrostichoides*). The receptacular regions which give rise to the sporangia may be marginal or amarginal, and the sori bear varying relationships to the leaf veins.

Two series on the basis of sporangium development, the class Eusporangiopsida and the class Leptosporangiopsida, are apparent among the Pterophyta. The development of the sporangium of *Osmunda* suggests an intermediate condition. It is noteworthy that leptosporangiate sporangium development is restricted to the pterophytan series, a point of great importance in discussions of the phylogeny of seed plants, in which it is frequently disregarded. Leptosporangiate and eusporangiate sporangia differ in respects other than origin in ontogeny. These include size, wall thickness, and spore number. Among the Pterophyta, the sporangia may develop simultaneously, the simple type (*Ophioglos-*

sum); in basipetal succession, the gradate type (*Marsilea*); or in no special order, the mixed type (most Polypodiaceae).

Heterospory is present in the Leptosporangiopsida only in the filicalean genus *Platyzoma* (p. 292), *Marsilea* (and its related genera), *Salvinia*, and *Azolla*. In all of these genera, the early stages in ontogeny of the megasporangia and microsporangia are similar. However, following meiosis, only one spore survives, enlarges, and functions in the megasporangium. Spore germination in all these genera occurs only after the spores have been shed, as in the microphyllous genus *Isoetes*.

Reproduction: the gametophyte

Review of the genera of Pterophyta which have been described reveals a great range in the organization and physiological attributes of the gametophyte generation. The gametophytes of most species of *Ophioglossum* and *Botrychium* are long-lived, slow-growing, subterranean, and, with few exceptions, entirely lacking in photosynthetic tissues. Their saprophytic nutrition is probably connected with the presence of an endophytic fungus in the gametophyte tissues. The gametophytes of the heterosporous genera also are saprophytic, but in this case, the ultimate source of the nutriment is the parent sporophyte which has stored it in the microspores and megaspores. It is true, however, that photosynthetic tissue appears late in the development of the female gametophyte of *Marsilea* and also in that of *Salvinia*. The gametophytes of *Marattia* and *Angiopteris* and those of the homosporous leptosporangiate ferns are photoautotrophic. Those of *Marattia* and *Osmunda* are relatively massive, long-lived, and hepatopsidan as compared with the delicate, rather ephemeral, cordate gametophytes of *Adiantum* and *Dryopteris*. The antheridia of the eusporangiate genera are partially embedded, massive and contain large numbers of sperms. The antheridia of most homosporous leptosporangiate forms are smaller, protuberant, and they contain fewer sperms. *Osmunda*, again, is intermediate in these respects.

Reproduction: the embryo

The development of the embryonic sporophyte varies in the several groups of Pterophyta. Embryo development in *Ophioglossum* and *Botrychium* is of relatively long duration as compared with that in the polypodiaceous series. Furthermore, the first division of the zygote is transverse with reference to the long axis of the archegonium in *Ophioglossum* and *Botrychium*, and a suspensor functions in some species of *Botrychium*. Finally, the primary organs of the sporophyte cannot be traced back as clearly to early derivatives of the zygote in eusporangiate ferns as they can regularly be in the development of the embryo of many Leptosporangiopsida. The embryogeny of *Marattia* and *Angiopteris* is similar in many respects to that of *Ophioglossum* and *Botrychium*, but the embryos of the former lack a foot. *Osmunda*, again, is intermediate between the eusporangiate and leptosporangiate ferns with respect to its embryogeny. Although quadrant and octant stages of equal-sized cells are formed, the primary organs of the sporophyte cannot be referred back to one of these with certainty. Emergence of the primary leaf is slow, as compared with that in other Leptosporangiopsida, and the leaf grows laterally around the gametophyte in *Osmunda* rather than anteriorly upward through the apical notch, as in Polypodiaceae. In the Marattiales, the cotyledon emerges from the dorsal surface of the gametophyte. In conclusion, it should be noted that detailed knowledge of the morphology of a more extensive series of genera than has been described in this and the preceding two chapters is a necessary precursor to a more complete discussion of the variation and phylogeny of the Pterophyta.

DISCUSSION QUESTIONS

1. How does venation in *Marsilea* differ from that in *Adiantum?* Which do you consider more primitive and for what reason?

2. Describe the structure of the sporocarp of *Marsilea.*

3. What evidence indicates that the sporocarp of *Marsilea* is a folded pinna?

4. What is meant by the terms simple, gradate, and mixed as applied to sporangium development? Illustrate with examples from the genera described above.

5. How does the ontogeny of the functional megaspores differ in *Selaginella* and *Marsilea?*

6. A student argues that inasmuch as heterospory is obviously an advanced condition derived from homospory, *Selaginella, Isoetes,* and *Marsilea* should be classified together, as distinct from other extant vascular cryptogams. Give reasons against supporting such a classification.

7. Would you consider the male gametophyte of

Selaginella or that of *Marsilea* to be more primitive? Give the reasons for your answer.

8. Sporocarps of *Marsilea,* stored in alcohol for 20 years, have germinated when placed in water. How do you explain this?

9. A layman, observing the sporocarps of *Marsilea* for the first time, referred to them as "seeds." How do they differ from seeds?

10. How do the sporangia of *Lygodium* differ from those of *Dryopteris* and *Adiantum?*

11. In what conservatories and cities of the United States are there living specimens of tree ferns?

12. Cite examples of hydrophytic, mesophytic, and xerophytic Pterophyta.

13. What does the fossil record reveal regarding the nature and time of appearance of Pterophyta?

14. What is their possible origin?

15. Was the Carboniferous the "Age of Ferns" without qualification? Explain.

CHAPTER 24

The Vascular Cryptogams: Recapitulation

Chapters 18 through 23 have presented a discussion of the structure and reproduction of representatives, both extinct and extant, of the divisions Psilophyta, Microphyllophyta, Arthrophyta, and Pterophyta. The present chapter presents a brief comparative summary of the more important features of these organisms, the vascular cryptogams, and discusses their phylogenetic implications.

The Life Cycle

In some schemes of classification (other than the one used in this book), Table 32-2, p. 516, the seedless vascular plants are grouped together in a single division, Pteridophyta. Although the plants so classified have been regrouped as four separate phyletic lines (divisions) in the present volume, it should be emphasized that they do have in common the same balance between the alternating generations in their life cycles. In all vascular cryptogams, the sporophyte is the dominant phase in the life cycle; the gametophyte is clearly simpler and more ephemeral. In all cases, however, the latter is separated ultimately from the parent sporophyte, unlike the female gametophyte in the seed plants, in which it is permanently retained. In the Hepatophyta and the Bryophyta, on the other hand, the gametophyte is dominant. That the life cycle is not entirely inflexible and obligate is evidenced by numerous examples of apogamy and some of apospory. **Apogamy,** the development of a sporophyte from a gametophyte in which no fertilization took place, occurs regularly in certain species of polypodiaceous ferns, and there is evidence of its presence in species of *Marsilea* and *Selaginella*

as well. Furthermore, apogamy has been induced in normally sexual genera. **Apospory,** the development of a gametophyte directly from sporophytic tissue and not from a spore, is less widespread. It, too, occurs in nature and may be induced. These phenomena have focused attention on the question of the origin and relation of the two alternating phases and have resulted in speculations regarding the type of life cycle in the first land plants or their immediate ancestors.

There seems to be rather general agreement that primitive plants were at least potentially sexual and gametophytic and haploid. The initiation of the sexual process would obviously result in the existence of a diploid cell, the zygote. In organisms with zygotic meiosis, the diploid zygote is but a transitory phase which is obliterated in the meiotic process. It seems clear that the inception of sexuality and the first occurrence of meiosis must have been closely related in time, if not simultaneous, in view of their complementary functions and invariable coexistence.[1] An extensive diploid sporophyte generation appears to have been a secondary adjunct to the life cycle with sexuality. Its origin is postulated to have been occasioned by a delay in meiosis in the zygote and the interpolation of a more or less extensive series of mitoses and cytokineses between fertilization and meiosis, with the result that diploid cells other than the zygote arose for the first time. Meiosis then occurred in all these diploid cells, however numerous. This, of course, represents the type of life cycle

---

[1] See, however: Wagner, W. H., Jr., and A. J. Sharp, "A Remarkably Reduced Vascular Plant in the United States," *Science*, 142:1483–1484, 1963; this is the gametophyte of a fern, *Vittaria lineata* (L.) J. E. Smith.

present in all organisms with sporic meiosis. Finally, gradual extension of the duration and importance of the diploid sporophytic phase, concomitant with the suppression of the haploid phase, is thought to have resulted in the type of life cycle in which gametic meiosis occurs. It should be emphasized that the preceding statements are mere conjectures, none of which is verifiable experimentally. The credence with which they frequently are received and repeated might well be tempered by this consideration and others, among them the following: The great majority of animals are diploid organisms with gametic meiosis. It is scarcely conceivable that their present life cycles have evolved from genera with zygotic and sporic meiosis, especially in the absence of any examples of the latter among living animals. Furthermore, that diploidy of zygotes, resulting from failure of meiosis, might of itself have been insufficient to explain the origin of a sporophyte, especially of the type in heteromorphic alternation, is suggested by polyploidy and the phenomena of apogamy and apospory noted above.

In addition to these speculations concerning the *origin* of the alternate phases, there have been many conjectures regarding the fundamental *relationship* between them. Speculations about the relation of the sporophyte and gametophyte to each other often are summarized as two theories, namely, the antithetic and homologous theories, referred to briefly in Chapters 8 and 16. According to the **antithetic theory,** the gametophyte and sporophyte are essentially different manifestations of a single organism. The sporophyte is looked upon not as a modified or changed gametophyte but rather as a phase *sui generis*, which has been interpolated between successive gametophytic phases through delay in meiosis, as suggested above. Furthermore, by some proponents of this theory, the sporophyte is thought to have been entirely a reproductive phase originally, in which asexual spores in large numbers were produced as a result of delayed meiosis. Assumption by sporophytes of such vegetative functions as photosynthesis and translocation, among others, is viewed as secondary. These are interpreted as acquired functions taken up by primarily sporogenous

tissues. It should be emphasized that this view of the sporophyte was originally proposed by a student of the land plants long before the complexity of algal life cycles was appreciated fully. The antithetic theory of the nature of alternation of generations, perhaps in somewhat modified form, is much in evidence at present in many morphological discussions. It is sometimes called the **interpolation theory.**

In opposition to the views summarized above, it has been emphasized by some morphologists that alternating gametophytes and sporophytes are fundamentally similar. The sporophyte is looked upon as a somewhat modified or transformed gametophyte, modified in accordance with its function of spore production. According to the **homologous theory** of the nature of alternation of generations, vegetative and reproductive functions coexist in primitive sporophytes, although the balance between them may be variable. Certainly algal sporophytes are photosynthetic. Conceding that the alternants among the land plants are, indeed, heteromorphic, possibly because of the stimulus of a terrestrial environment, proponents of this theory also point to the algae, in which numerous cases of both isomorphic and heteromorphic alternation of generations in a uniform aquatic habitat are known. It has been suggested that one important factor effecting heteromorphism is the permanent retention of the sporophyte within or upon the gametophyte, as in the diploid carposporophyte of the Rhodophycophyta and the sporophytes of Hepatophyta and Bryophyta, and its retention during embryogeny in the vascular cryptogams and seed plants. However, marked heteromorphism is present in the kelps (*Laminaria*) in which the two generations are entirely independent of each other. This discussion of alternation of generations is presented not with the purpose of settling the problem but rather to indicate the complexity of the considerations involved. The apparent independence of alternation of generations from chromosome number has already been emphasized (p. 358). It seems quite possible that different life-cycle patterns may have arisen as a result of different circumstances and different stimuli in different organisms, and that a comprehensive explanation may be unattainable.

The Sporophyte

VEGETATIVE ORGANS

Comparison of the several divisions in which the vascular cryptogams have been classified indicates that the stem is certainly the dominant organ of the sporophyte, except in the Pterophyta in which it may be equaled or surpassed in stature and anatomical complexity by the macrophyllous leaves.[2] In the living Psilophyta, Microphyllophyta, and Arthrophyta, examples of erect and ascending, vinelike, rhizomatous, and stolonlike stems occur. With the exception of the tree ferns, the stems of the Pterophyta are mostly subterranean, vertical, or horizontal, or at the surface of the ground. Dichotomous branching of the stems, by the equal division of single apical cells or groups of meristematic cells, is considered primitive as compared with monopodial and sympodial types. *Equisetum*, with its whorls of branches and leaves, the latter alternating in origin with the former, is unique among vascular plants.

A considerable range in disposition of the vascular tissues is apparent in the members of the several divisions. The most primitive genera and the juvenile stages of most others usually have stems that contain protosteles. Examples of increasingly complex types of steles—namely, siphonosteles, both amphiphloic and ectophloic, dictyosteles, eusteles, polysteles, and atactosteles—have been described. Branch gaps occur in all the groups, but foliar gaps are present only in the Pterophyta. Thickening of the stem by addition of secondary tissues through the activity of a cambium is rare among living vascular cryptogams, and where it occurs (*Isoetes, Botrychium*) it does not result in any considerable increase in girth. The unicellular tracheid is the conducting element of the xylem of all these forms. In *Selaginella, Equisetum,* and *Pteridium* and the roots of *Marsilea,* however,

---

[2] Inasmuch as these are probably planate axes, the stem may be considered to be universally dominant.

perforation of walls of tracheids has resulted in the formation of vessels.

It is clear that the structures designated by the term "leaf" are not necessarily morphologically equivalent in the vascular plants. It will be recalled that in contrast with the microphyllous leaves of such plants as *Lycopodium* and *Selaginella,* which are relatively small, determinate in growth, and traversed by unbranched veins that leave no leaf gaps in the stem steles (Fig. 17-9A,C), macrophyllous leaves are typically larger, their development is more extended, if not indeterminate (*Lygodium*), their vascular system is richly branched, and their traces profoundly modify the stem stele from which they depart, leaving parenchymatous gaps (Fig. 17-9B,D). Because both these structures are called "leaves," are we, therefore, to consider them homologous? Morphologists have given different answers to this question. It is agreed by some of them that microphyllous leaves are to be interpreted as localized, superficial enations of stems which ultimately became vascularized (Fig. 24-1), and that macrophyllous leaves are to be interpreted as branches of stems which have undergone flattening by limitation of branching to one plane and webbing by extension of parenchymatous tissues between the branching steles (Fig. 24-2). The evidence for this interpretation of the macrophyllous leaf is based on its extensive, much-branched vascular supply, on the fact that its trace, like the branch trace of microphyllous plants, ef-

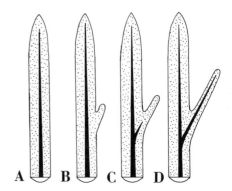

FIG. 24-1. A–D. Evolutionary origin of a microphyllous leaf, according to the enation theory; the emergence at C corresponds to that occurring sometimes in *Psilotum;* that at D corresponds to leaves of *Lycopodium* and *Selaginella.* (*After Stewart.*)

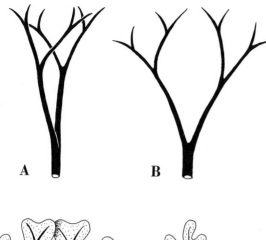

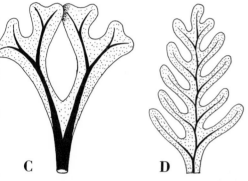

FIG. 24-2. A–D. Evolutionary origin of a macrophyllous leaf by flattening (planation) and parenchymatous webbing of a dichotomously branched axis. (*After Stewart.*)

fects a break in the stele where it originates,[3] and, finally, on its relatively large size and indeterminate development, all supported by the study of the fossil record. According to this view, at least the main branching veins even of an undivided fern leaf represent the direction of the branching of a primitive axis which has become webbed between the vein branches. These views regarding leaves are in accord with the **telome theory** which emphasizes the shoot or axis as the fundamental unit in the organization of plants. This will be considered in more detail further on in the discussion (p. 383).

Roots are present in all the divisions of vascular cryptogams save the Psilophyta,[4] in which the underground rhizomes, provided with rhizoidal appendages, carry on the func-

[3] Macrophyllous leaves do not leave gaps in protosteles, although grooves may be present.

[4] And in mature plants of *Salvinia*.

tion of absorption with sufficient efficiency to support the aerial portions of the plant. That the root is probably an organ of the vascular cryptogams which developed later than leaves and stems is suggested by the minor and relatively transitory role of the primary root or radicle in many genera; furthermore, the root sometimes arises in embryogeny later than the stem, never vice versa. The root system of the vascular cryptogams is almost exclusively adventitious in origin. Internally, the roots are exarch and protostelic without exception, and they develop entirely from primary meristems. It has been suggested that the root arose as a modified rhizome branch which became covered with a root cap.

SPOROGENOUS TISSUE

Review of Chapters 18 through 23 reveals considerable variation in the location and nature of the sporogenous tissues in the extant vascular cryptogams. Examples of little or no segregation of vegetative and sporogenous tissues are available in such instances as *Lycopodium lucidulum* and many polypodiaceous and marattiaceous ferns. Even in the primitive *Psilotum* and *Tmesipteris*, however, the sporogenous tissue is restricted to special, determinate lateral branches. The dimorphism observable in such plants as *Lycopodium complanatum*, species of *Osmunda*, the fertile spike of the *Ophioglossum-Botrychium* type, and the strobili of the Microphyllophyta and *Equisetum* is a manifestation of segregation of vegetative and reproductive functions at the organ level. Furthermore, examples of both cauline (*Psilotum*) and foliar (Microphyllophyta, polypodiaceous ferns) sporangia are present.

With reference to method of sporangial ontogeny, all the vascular cryptogams (and seed plants) are eusporangiate, with the exception of the Leptosporangiopsida among the Pterophyta. There is good evidence that heterospory developed independently in the Microphyllophyta, the Arthrophyta (fossil forms), and the Pterophyta. Spore ontogeny in the heterosporous genera indicates that the *immediate* cause of heterospory lies in differences in spore number and nutrition and that these are expressed ultimately by spore size.

The Gametophyte

Considerable morphological and physiological variation is apparent among the gametophytes of the vascular cryptogams. Cylindrical form, radial symmetry, and saprophytism characterize the gametophytes of *Psilotum*, of certain species of *Lycopodium*,[5] *Ophioglossum*, and *Schizaea*. Dorsiventral and photosynthetic gametophytes are present in *Equisetum* and in marattiaceous and homosporous leptosporangiate ferns. The presence of heterospory is associated with marked reduction in the morphological complexity and duration of the gametophyte, as is evident in *Selaginella*, *Isoetes*, and *Marsilea*. Furthermore, unisexual gametophytes inevitably accompany heterospory. The nutrition in these gametophytes is based largely on metabolites stored by the

[5] In nature.

parent sporophyte in the spores. Although the gametophytes of *Psilotum* and species of *Lycopodium*, *Ophioglossum* and *Botrychium* are relatively long-lived, as compared with those of other genera, the gametophyte generation in general is of lesser duration and complexity than are the persistent perennial sporophytes of the vascular cryptogams.

The archegonia of the female gametophytes produced in heterosporous ferns are in general smaller and less complex than those in homosporous types. Both biflagellate (*Lycopodium*, *Selaginella*) and multiflagellate sperms (*Isoetes*, *Equisetum*, Pterophyta) occur among vascular cryptogams.

The Embryo

The embryogeny of the vascular cryptogams exemplifies both slow (*Lycopodium*, *Psilotum*, *Ophioglossum*) and relatively

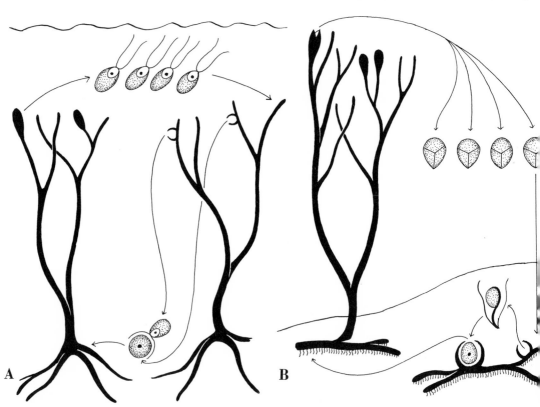

FIG. 24-3. A. Hypothetical *aquatic* algal ancestor of the vascular plants. The two alternants are isomorphic; the one at the left is the zoospore-producing sporophyte, while the one at the right is the gametophyte, in this case oogamous. B. Primitive vascular plant derived from A. The sporophyte now has aerial branches and is producing air-borne spores (instead of zoospores); these develop into minute, *aquatic*, oogamous gametophytes; alternation here is heteromorphic. w.s., surface of the water. (*After Stewart, from Zimmerman.*)

rapidly growing (*Selaginella, Equisetum,* polypodiaceous ferns) types. Nutrition of the embryo in heterosporous forms is based on metabolites of the parent sporophyte.

Phylogenetic Considerations

The preceding paragraphs and Chapters 17–23 have reviewed the ontogeny of the vegetative organs of the vascular plant—its stem, root, and leaf, and the reproductive features of representatives of the several groups of vascular cryptogams. At this point, it is appropriate to turn to a consideration of the phylogenetic origin of vascular plants and that of their component organs.

The fossil record indicates clearly that life was aquatic in origin, and that it was largely restricted to an aquatic habitat for more than 2.5 billion years. At the end of this period, colonization of the land began. The emigrants were with great probability algae or modified algal descendants. There have been many suggestions regarding the course of evolution of the land flora from its algal progenitors. These have largely been incorporated into a synthesis known as the **telome theory** or concept by the eminent morphologist, Dr. Walter Zimmerman. The telome theory attempts to interpret extant plants in terms of their origin from extinct precursors. The major components of this concept will now be summarized.

According to the telome concept, the vascular plants evolved from algal precursors (Fig. 24-3). The ultimate branchlets of the dichotomies are called **telomes** and the connecting axes between dichotomies are called **mesomes** (Fig. 24-4). Telomes may be sterile or fertile.

The Psilophyta (Chapter 18) are, perhaps, closest to the hypothetical ancestor but differ in having developed heteromorphic alternation with a dominant sporophyte and a small gametophyte.[6] In these plants, as exemplified

---

[6] According to the telome concept, the Hepatophyta and Bryophyta also evolved from algal precursors with isomorphic alternation, but in this case the gametophyte remained dominant and the sporophyte became reduced to a single epiphytic, or partially parasitic, telome.

by *Psilotum* (Figs. 18-1, 18-2) and *Rhynia* (Fig. 18-18), there is no distinction between root and leaf, the plant body consisting of a three-dimensional system of mesomes and telomes. The vascular tissue is in the form of a simple protostele. With the land habit, there developed cuticle and stomata on the aerial mesomes and telomes and rhizoids in the subterranean ones. The gametophyte of primitive land plants has not been preserved in the fossil record, perhaps because of its delicate nature, as in its algal precursor.

Evolution of the primitive psilophytan sporophyte of the type just described into the microphyllophytan, arthrophytan, and pteridophytan types of plant body[7] is postulated by the telome concept to have involved a number of fundamental processes, among them the following: (1) **overtopping** (Fig. 24-5A–C); (2) **planation** (Fig. 24-5D, E); (3) **webbing** (Figs. 24-2C, D; 24-10); and (4) **reduction** (Fig. 24-6). These processes have occurred independently and in differing order and number in the evolution of vascular plants.

---

[7] Also the plant bodies of gymnosperms and angiosperms.

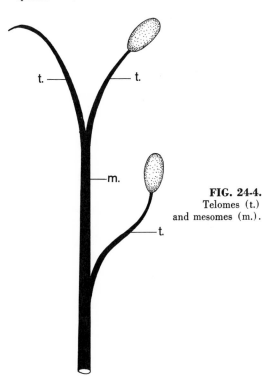

FIG. 24-4.
Telomes (t.)
and mesomes (m.).

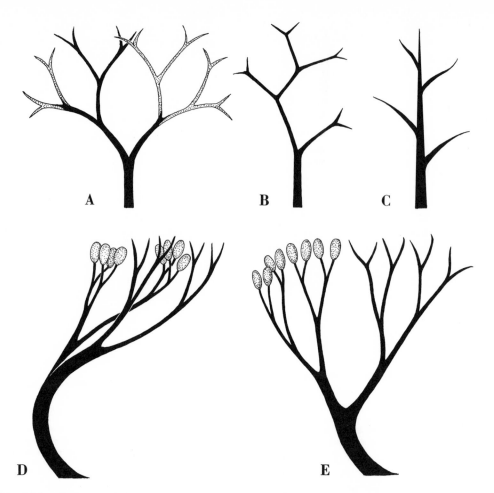

FIG. 24-5. Basic morphological modification of axes, according to the telome theory. A–C. Overtopping. A. Uniform dichotomous branching. B, C. Dominance of one arm of successive dichotomies leading to sympodial (B) and, ultimately, to monopodial branching. D, E. Planation. Note fertile and sterile telomes. (*After Stewart, from Zimmerman.*)

Thus, in the evolution of macrophyllous leaves from three-dimensional branches,[8] overtopping and planation have probably occurred (Fig. 24-2), and in that order. On the other hand, reduction may well account for the origin of microphyllous leaves (Fig. 24-6).

Some of these same processes have operated in the evolution of the reproductive organs of vascular plants according to the telome concept. The cauline sporangium of the Psilophyta and the axillary sporangium of the Microphyllophyta, according to this concept, arose as a result of reduction (Figs. 24-7, 24-8). The arthrophytan sporangiophore, it is proposed, also arose through these modifying forces (Fig. 24-9). In the Pterophyta, planation and webbing may well have de-

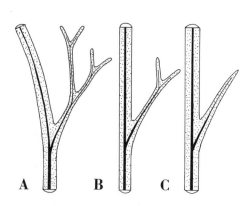

FIG. 24-6. A–C. Hypothetical origin of a microphyllous leaf by reduction; compare with Fig. 24-1. (*After Stewart, from Bower and Zimmerman.*)

[8] A combination of two or more branches is called a telome truss.

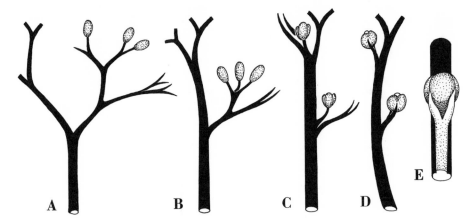

FIG. 24-7. A–E. Proposed evolutionary steps leading to the development of the *Psilotum* type of sporangium. (*After Stewart, modified from Emberger.*)

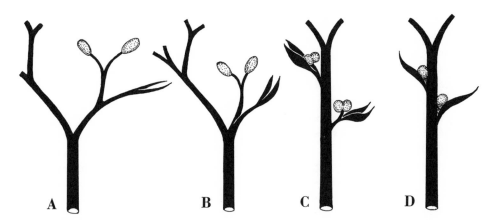

FIG. 24-8. A–D. Proposed evolutionary steps in modification of a primitive axis (composed of fertile and sterile telomes) into the *Tmesipteris* (C) and *Lycopodium* (D) type of sporangial position. (*After Stewart, from Zimmerman.*)

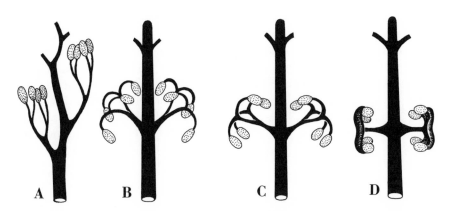

FIG. 24-9. A–D. Proposed evolutionary steps in development of a primitive axis (A), composed of fertile and sterile telomes, into several types of arthrophytan sporangiophores. (*After Stewart, from Zimmerman.*)

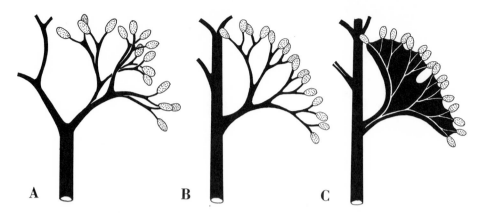

FIG. 24-10. A–C. Proposed course of evolutionary development of a pterophytan pinnule with marginal sporangia from a primitive axis composed of fertile and sterile telomes. (*After Stewart, from Zimmerman.*)

veloped the type of sporangial arrangement (Fig. 24-10) seen in *Cladoxylon scoparium* (Fig. 23-19B).

Zimmerman has also interpreted the vascular system in light of the telome theory.[9] For example, he looks upon polystelic stems as having resulted from syngenesis or fusions of haplosteles. However, his conclusions with respect to the origin of stelar types have not been received with enthusiasm.

The telome concept is a unifying synthesis which seeks to interpret the diversities of organization of extant plants as modifications from a primitive stock of Psilophytalike plants, probably precursors of known Psilophyta. With respect to its postulates regarding the origin of microphyllous leaves, it is in marked contradiction to the enation theory (p. 265) and the evidence on which the latter is based.

It has recently been suggested that if microphyllous and macrophyllous leaves are fundamentally similar in organization, differing only in number of component telomes,

then we ought not to contrast them as strongly as we currently do. The same argument has been applied to sporangial position which, in the last analysis, is really always at the tip of a telome. Similarly, the telome theory disagrees with the interpretation of the evolution of stelar types accepted by most morphologists. In spite of these difficulties, the telome concept certainly is and has been a stimulating and thought-provoking synthesis which has played and continues to play an important role in morphology.

In concluding this brief summary of the vascular cryptogams, it seems clear that comparison of representatives of the divisions Psilophyta, Microphyllophyta, Arthrophyta, and Pterophyta offers little evidence for close relationship of these plants. The fossil record indicates that these four phyletic series had been established by the Devonian (Table 32-1). Psilophytalike organisms may well have been the precursors from which these four lines developed. Their diversities seem clearly to overshadow in significance the combination of attributes they share, namely: vascular tissue, lack of seeds, and similarity in balance of the alternating generations.

---

[9] For an excellent and lucid presentation of the telome theory see Stewart, W. N., 1964, cited completely at the end of this chapter.

DISCUSSION QUESTIONS

1. a. What is meant by the term cryptogam, in current usage?

b. What did it mean originally?

c. What is meant by the term vascular cryptogam?

d. What are nonvascular cryptogams?

e. How is the term used currently?

2. Define or explain the terms apogamy and apospory. Where do these phenomena occur in the plant kingdom?

3. Briefly summarize and distinguish between the antithetic and homologous theories regarding the nature and origin of alternating generations.

4. Explain the following statement: "It seems clear that the initiation of sexuality and meiosis must have been closely related if not simultaneous, in view of their complementary functions."

5. In what way are the phenomena of apogamy and apospory interpreted as evidence in support of the homologous theory of alternation?

6. What bearing does the observed presence of chlorophyll and starch in liverwort sporophytes have on the question of the relation between the alternating generations and their origin?

7. Why is the stem often said to be the dominant organ of the sporophyte in Psilophyta, Microphyl-lophyta, and Arthrophyta? Why not in the Pterophyta?

8. Distinguish between protosteles, siphonosteles, dictyosteles, eusteles, and polysteles. Give examples of each from among the vascular cryptogams.

9. On what evidence are macrophyllous leaves considered to be homologous with branch systems?

10. Speculate regarding the possible origin of the root as an organ of the sporophyte.

11. Discuss the distribution of sporogenous tissue in the vascular cryptogams, citing illustrative examples.

12. Distinguish between cauline and foliar sporangia, giving examples. How do you interpret those of *Equisetum?* What bearing does the telome concept have on these considerations?

13. What evidence can you cite as to the origin of heterospory? Is the ontogeny of heterospory always the same? Explain.

14. Compare the gametophytes of vascular cryptogams as to habitat, form, and nutrition, giving examples.

15. State the major propositions of the telome concept.

16. Compare the origin of microphyllous leaves according to the enation and telome theories.

REFERENCE WORKS

Fritsch, F. E., "Studies in the Comparative Morphology of the Algae. IV. Algae and Archegoniate Plants," *Annals of Botany, N. S.* 9:1–29, 1945.

Stewart, W. M., "An Upward Outlook in Plant Morphology," *Phytomorphology* 14:120–134, 1964.

Wardlaw, C. W., *Phylogeny and Morphogenesis,* Macmillan and Co. Ltd., London, 1952.

Wilson, C. L., "The Telome Theory," *Botanical Review* 19:417–437, 1953.

Zimmerman, W., "The Main Results of The 'Telome Theory,'" *The Palaeobotanist* 1:456–470, 1952.

Zimmerman, W., *Die Phylogenie der Pflanzen,* Gustav Fischer Verlagsbuchhandlung, Jena, Germany, 1959.

CHAPTER 25

Introduction to Seed Plants; Division Cycadophyta

Introduction to Seed Plants

The members of the plant kingdom discussed as representative morphological types in Chapters 2–24 all are seedless plants, the *apparently* obscure (in the eighteenth century!) reproductive organs and life cycle of which suggested to Linnaeus the name **Cryptogamia** (Gr. *kryptos*, hidden + Gr. *gamos*, marriage). The seed plants were later called **Phanerogamae** (Gr. *phaneros*, visible + Gr. *gamos*), an allusion to the prominence of their supposed sexual organs, which in fact are sporebearing organs.

The seed plants are vascular plants usually containing abundant xylem and phloem, except in secondarily reduced aquatics. This attribute they share with the vascular cryptogams with which they sometimes are grouped in a single division, Tracheophyta (Table 32-2). This category has not been adopted in the present text, because in the author's opinion, such a grouping places too much weight on one attribute. The habit of producing seeds formerly was considered to be such an important indication of relationship that all seed-bearing plants were once classified in a single division, Spermatophyta (Table 32-2). However, this division has been replaced in many modern classifications by a still more inclusive taxon, the Pteropsida, under the division Tracheophyta. In spite of its lower rank, the Pteropsida includes a wider assemblage of plants, namely, the macrophyllous ferns as well as the seed plants. This arrangement reflects the views of those who see in the extinct seed ferns (p. 404) a possible bridge between the ferns and the living seed plants. In most systems of classification, the seed plants in which the seeds are not enclosed in a sporophyll are usually grouped in a taxon, Gymnospermae (Table 32-2). This is not done in this text because it is considered that this practice also places too much emphasis on a single attribute.

The formal taxonomic designation "Gymnospermae" (Gr. *gymnos*, naked + Gr. *sperma*, seed) and the informal term "gymnosperm" refer to the lack of enclosure of the seeds of certain plants (Fig. 25-22). By contrast, the terms "Angiospermae" (Gr. *angeion*, a vessel + Gr. *sperma*) and "angiosperm" signify that in other seed plants the seeds are enclosed in a structure variously known as the carpel or carpels, or pistil (Fig. 30-2). Angiosperms, the division Anthophyta, comprise the "flowering plants" to be discussed in Chapters 30 and 31.

Such topics as the origin and evolution of the seed and the origin and relationships of the seed plants are deferred to Chapter 31, a point by which, it is hoped, the reader will have assimilated adequate basic information to profit from such a discussion.

The classification of the seed plants used in the present text recognizes the important diversities apparent among the plants formerly included under the taxon Gymnospermae. The production of seeds is considered to occur in plants of several *divisions*, namely: The Cycadophyta, Ginkgophyta, Coniferophyta, and Gnetophyta (all four gymnospermous) and the Anthophyta (angiospermous).

The Cycadophyta, perhaps an unnatural group, include both extinct and extant gymnospermous seed plants with complex, fernlike foliage. Three classes, the Pteridospermopsida (seed ferns), Cycadeoidopsida (cycadeoids), and Cycadeopsida (cycads) comprise the division. The first and second classes are known only from fossils; the third, in addition to fossil members, includes a single order (Cycadales) with living genera. Because of their familiarity and availability, the living Cycadales will be discussed first in introducing the seed plants. Treatment of the remaining Cycadophyta will conclude the present chapter.

Class 1. Cycadopsida

Order 1. *Cycadales*

FAMILY 1. CYCADACEAE

The Cycadales, commonly called the **cycads,** include a small group of nine or ten[1] genera and 100 species of tropical plants which superficially suggest both ferns and palms insofar as the general form of the plant body is concerned (Figs. 25-1, 25-2). They are sometimes regarded as "living fossils," and it has been predicted that they will be extinct in the future. There is good evidence, indeed, that one of the genera, *Microcycas*, endemic to Cuba, is rapidly approaching extinction at present. Once widely distributed and important components of the earth's vegetation, they now are reduced in number of genera, species, and individuals. Only one genus, *Zamia* (L. *zamiae*, erroneous reading in Pliny for *azaniae*, pine nuts), is

represented in the flora of the United States (in Florida), although the other genera are cultivated in conservatories and tropical gardens.[2]

In addition to *Zamia*, other cycads of Mexico and the West Indies are the genera *Dioon* (Gr. *dis*, two + Gr. *ōion*, egg) (Fig. 25-2A, C), *Ceratozamia* (Gr. *keras*, horn + *Zamia*) (Fig. 25-2B), and *Microcycas* (Gr. *mikros*, small + *Cycas*). In the southern hemisphere, cycads occur especially in Australia and Africa. *Stangeria* (after Dr. Stanger[3]) (originally described as and considered to be a fern until it produced strobili!) and *Encephalartos* (Gr. *encephalos*, brain + Gr. *artos*, bread) are native to South Africa. *Bowenia* (after G. T. Bowen[4]), *Macrozamia* (Gr. *makros*, long + *Zamia*), and *Cycas* occur in Australia. *Cycas* (Gr. *kykos*, a palm) extends northward to Southern Japan; one species grows natively in Madagascar.

The genus *Cycas* (Fig. 25-3) is widely planted as an ornamental in warmer portions of the United States. *Zamia* has been selected as representative of the cycads in this book because it usually is to be found in university greenhouses or may be obtained readily.

---

[1] A tenth genus, *Lepidozamia*, is sometimes recognized.

[2] Such as the Fairchild Tropical Gardens, Coral Gables, Florida (which has all ten genera in cultivation); Biscayne Park, Miami, Florida; and the Huntington Botanical Gardens, San Marino, California.

[3] Surveyor General of Natal who sent the plant to England in 1851.

[4] First governor of Queensland.

A   B

FIG. 25-1. *Zamia floridana* A. DC. A. Plant with microstrobili. B. Plant with megastrobilus. X 0.1.

A

B

C

FIG. 25-2. A. *Dioon edule* Lindbl. X 0.015. B. *Ceratozamia mexicana.* X 0.015. C. *Dioon edule* with maturing microstrobilus. X ¹⁄₁₂. (C. Courtesy of Chicago Natural History Museum.)

FIG. 25-3. *Cycas revoluta* Th. A. Plant with crown of new leaves. X 0.015. B. Detail of circinately vernate pinnae. X 2. (A. *Courtesy of Dr. Elsie Quarterman. B. Courtesy of Dr. Edgar E. Webber.*)

A   B

Furthermore, the small stature of the plants makes it feasible to maintain a supply of fruiting specimens in limited space.

Two or more species of *Zamia* occur in Florida. Of these, *Z. floridana* A. DC. and *Z. umbrosa* Small have been studied with respect to reproduction. *Zamia* is widely distributed in the West Indies, Mexico, and northern South America to Chile.

Vegetative morphology

The plant body of *Zamia* (Fig. 25-1) consists of a relatively short, vertical, approximately conical stem which tapers toward the base; the latter bears a number of fleshy roots. Remains of leaves of former seasons are visible on the upper portions of the tuberous stem, and the apex supports a crown of spirally arranged, leathery, dark-green leaves. The latter are pinnately compound and decidedly fernlike in appearance. The leaves of *Cycas* (Fig. 25-3B) are even more fernlike because of the circinate vernation of the young pinnae.

As in the Pterophyta, the leaves of a majority of cycads are the most striking and dominant organs of the plant. They are arranged spirally on the axis, and under usual greenhouse conditions both *Zamia* and

Cycas produce a new crown of leaves annually. Leaf crowns of preceding seasons may persist but they finally become reflexed and abscised. The veins run in a direction parallel to the long axes of the pinnae; they arise from basal dichotomies. The leaflets of *Zamia* display histological features usually associated with xerophytism (Fig. 25-4). The epidermis of both surfaces is thickened heavily on the outer walls. Stomata are present only on the lower surface of the pinnae and are sunken. A thick-walled **hypodermis,** an additional protective layer, lies beneath the upper epidermis. The

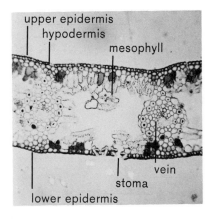

FIG. 25-4. *Zamia* sp. Transection of a pinna. X 60.

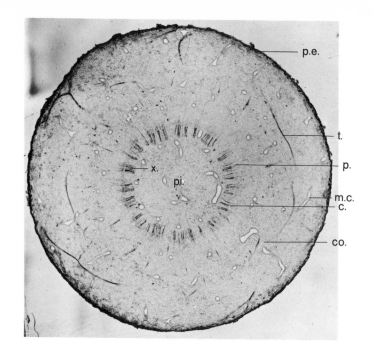

FIG. 25.5 *Zamia* sp. Transection of a stem; c., cambium; co., cortex; m.c., mucilage canal; p., phloem; pe., periderm; pi., pith; t., leaf trace; x., xylem. X 0.75 (*From a preparation and negative of Dr. C. J. Chamberlain, courtesy of the Chicago Natural History Museum.*)

mesophyll is differentiated into palisade and spongy zones.

The apex of the cycad stem is occupied by a dome of meristematic cells rather than by the single apical initial that is characteristic of so many vascular cryptogams. The meristematic zone differentiates into permanent tissues during the formation of strobili, and new apical meristems arise successively from subapical meristematic cells lateral to the original meristem. A transverse section of the mature stem of *Zamia* (Fig. 25-5) reveals a surprising paucity of xylem. The latter is composed largely of scalariform-pitted tracheids. A large part of the stem is occupied by the central pith and the extensive cortex, the cells of which are full of stored metabolites. The stem surface is protected by an impermeable periderm layer. Mucilage canals are abundant in the cortex and pith. The cortex is traversed by leaf traces which have an unusual path. Each leaf of *Zamia* receives from seven to nine traces which depart from different points in the stele and girdle it, rising slightly as they approach the leaf base, which may be 180° from the point of origin of some of the traces.

The vascular cylinder of the stem is interrupted by numerous leaf gaps formed in association with the traces. Although a cambium is present between the xylem and phloem, it is relatively inactive, so that the amount of vascular tissue remains small, and clearly defined growth rings are absent from the xylem of *Zamia*. The center of the stem is a parenchymatous pith.

The roots of cycads are fleshy, although considerable secondary xylem is produced. In some genera, *Cycas*, for example, certain root branches are **apogeotropic,** growing upon and above the soil. Such roots develop tubercular nodules which contain bacteria at first and later filaments of the blue-green alga, *Anabaena*. The relationships of the bacteria and *Anabaena* with the host have not been ascertained, but the alga fixes gaseous nitrogen.

Reproduction: the sporophyte

In *Zamia* and other cycads, and in all seed plants, two kinds of spores, with respect to function, are produced: one type is genetically conditioned to produce male gametophytes and the other female gametophytes. This obligate unisexuality differs from that present in *Marchantia* (p. 192) and *Polytrichum* (p. 233), however, in that *all four* spores arising from one sporocyte in the seed plants grow into either male or female gametophytes. Accordingly, segregation of sex does not occur at the time of meiosis in seed plants as it does in *Marchantia* and *Polytrichum*. Furthermore, in seed plants, the spores which produce male gametophytes arise in sporangia different from those in which female gametophyte-producing spores develop.

It will be recalled that in the vascular cryptogams *Selaginella, Isoetes, Marsilea, Azolla,* and *Salvinia,*[5] a similar dichotomy of spore function prevails, but in those genera it is associated with a dimorphism in the spores themselves, a phenomenon known as heterospory. Now careful measurements of the two kinds of spores in seed plants reveals little significant size difference between the male- and female-gametophyte-producing spores. Accordingly, it has been suggested that seed plants are homosporous. It is clear, however, that their so-called homospory differs profoundly from that of other homosporous plants, as noted above. In current usage, as in this text, the two kinds of spores of seed plants are considered to be *functionally* heterosporous, in spite of the absence of marked differences in their size. It has been suggested that the permanent retention of the female gametophyte-producing spore within its sporangium in seed plants accounts for diminution of its size. As a matter of fact, this spore in seed plants *ultimately* (during gametogenesis) achieves much greater size than the microspore. The *time* of its increase in size is later than in heterosporous cryptogams (see p. 292).

Those who are unwilling to accept this broader usage of heterospory have suggested the terms "androspores" and "gynospores" for the spores of seed plants. The assignment to spores of prefixes denoting sex cannot be supported, in the writer's opinion.

After due consideration of these points, the spores which develop into male gametophytes are called **microspores** and those which develop into female gametophytes are designated **megaspores** in the present volume, on the basis of their homology with those of vascular cryptogams and in light of the *ultimate* increase in size of the megaspore.

The microsporangia and megasporangia of *Zamia* are segregated in different strobili which are produced by different individuals (Fig. 25-1). This segregation is known as **dioecism** (Gr. *dis*, two + Gr. *oikos*, house). The microstrobili (Fig. 25-1A, 25-6A) are borne among the leaves at the stem apex in *Zamia*. They appear in summer (July) at first as small, conical emergences and gradually enlarge, finally becoming as long as 10 cm. They are brown, rather fleshy throughout development, and are composed of a central axis to which the spirally arranged microsporophylls are attached (Fig. 25-8A). Each microsporophyll has two groups of microsporangia on its abaxial surface (Fig. 25-6B), a total of between 28 and 50. Each microsporangium is supported by a short thick stalk and its development is eusporangiate. The number of spores is large and the sporangial wall is composed of several layers. A tapetum functions in nutrition during microsporogenesis, the cells disintegrating to form a tapetal plasmodium. The microsporocytes undergo meiosis, each giving rise to a tetrad of

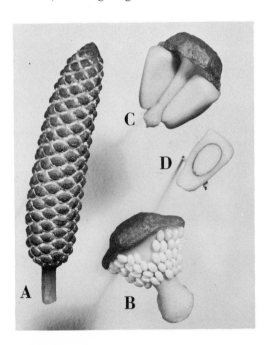

FIG. 25-6. *Zamia floridana.* A. Microstrobilus at pollen-shedding stage. X 0.5. B. Adaxial view of microsporophyll with microsporangia. X 2. C. Megasporophyll and ovules before fertilization. X 2. D. Section of an ovule. X 0.75. (*Courtesy of the Chicago Natural History Museum.*)

---

[5] And in a number of extinct plants.

FIG. 25-7. *Zamia floridana*. Portion of plant showing stem, leaf bases, and megastrobilus (at the time of fertilization). X 0.25 (*Courtesy of the Chicago Natural History Museum.*)

microspores which finally separate from each other. The walls of mature microspores are composed of several layers.

The megastrobili, which appear among the leaves of plants other than those that bear the microstrobili, are massive in construction

(Figs. 25-1B, 25-7, 25-9A). The megasporophylls are dark-brown, peltate structures attached to the axis of the strobilus by stipes (Fig. 25-8). Each megasporophyll bears two white ovoidal bodies, the **ovules** (Figs. 25-6C, 25-9), which are attached to the adaxial surface of the megasporophyll by extremely short stalks. A median longitudinal section of a young ovule shortly after the appearance of the megastrobilus is shown in Fig. 25-10A. The central cells of the young ovule contain dense protoplasmic contents. These cells comprise the young megasporangium in which the megasporocyte has not yet differentiated. The megasporangium tissue is surrounded by a multicellular covering, the **integument,** which is incompletely closed, leaving a minute passageway, the micropyle. This is at the pole opposite the point of attachment of the ovule. The ovule of *Zamia* and of other seed plants is a megasporangium surrounded by an integumentary layer or layers. In the cycads, six to nine vascular bundles arranged in a circle run vertically through the integument. This may indicate a phylogenetic union of previously distinct entities (see p. 404). The ovule of *Zamia* is about 1 cm. long at the time of pollination. Ovules occur only in seed plants. Their possible origin is discussed on page 404.

Somewhat later in its development, one of

FIG. 25-8. *Zamia* sp. A. Transection of young microstrobilus. B. Transection of young megastrobilus. X 3.

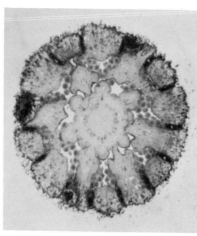

A

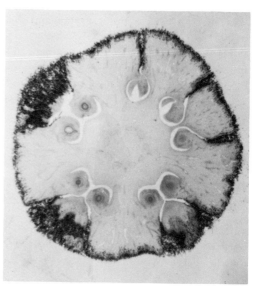

B

A   B

Soon after the formation of the linear tetrad, three of the four megaspores degenerate. The survivor, usually the one farthest from the micropyle, appears to appropriate the products of the degeneration of the nonfunctional megaspores and it increases in size as a result. This increase in size also depends on the transfer of nutriment from the fleshy megasporangial tissues to the megaspore. The latter never contains large amounts of stored metabolites, as is the case ·in megaspores of the heterosporous cryptogams. This surviving megaspore, which gives rise to the female gametophyte, is known as the **functional megaspore.**

FIG. 25-9. *Zamia* sp. A. Megastrobilus just before pollination. X 1. B. Two megasporophylls and ovules of same. X 3.

the deeper cells of the megasporangium enlarges, functions as a megasporocyte, and undergoes two successive nuclear and cell divisions during which meiosis takes place. The products of these divisions are arranged in linear fashion (Fig. 25-10B). They are interpreted usually as four megaspores arranged as a **linear tetrad.** The cell which gives rise to the linear tetrad is known as the **megasporocyte.** As noted above, the name megaspore has been assigned to the cells of the linear tetrad on the basis of comparison with the heterosporous cryptogams in which the megaspores are markedly larger than the microspores.

Reproduction: the gametophyte

As in *Selaginella,* the microspores begin their development into male gametophytes, and the megaspores theirs into female gametophytes, while still enclosed by their respective sporangia. The early stages of the male gametophytes are intrasporal, and those of the female are permanently so in seed plants. As the microspore (Fig. 25-11A) separates from the tetrad, it is uninucleate. A single nuclear division and cytokinesis then take place within the microspore (Fig. 25-11B). This results in the formation of a small **prothallial cell** and a larger cell. The male gametophyte is considered to consist of a single vegetative cell, the prothallial cell, and an antheridial remnant. A second nuclear and cell division in the large cell forms a small **generative cell** and a large **tube cell** (Figs. 25-11C, 25-12). When the male gametophytes have attained this stage of development, the microsporophylls separate slightly, apparently by elongation of the internodes of the strobilus axis, thus exposing the microsporangia to the air. During microsporogenesis and subsequently, the surface cells of the microsporangium thicken, except for a vertical belt over the summit. When the microsporangia are exposed, drying effects their bi-valvelike rupture along a vertical line of dehiscence. The microspore walls containing the immature male gametophyte thus are shed from the microsporangium in the three-celled stage. They are known as **pollen grains** at the time of shedding. In the vicinity of Miami,

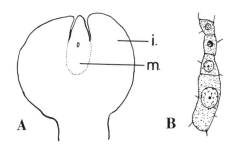

FIG. 25-10. *Zamia floridana.* A. Diagrammatic, median longitudinal section of ovule showing integument (i.) and megasporangium (m.), with single megaspore mother cell. B. Linear tetrad of megaspores; the lowermost, the functional megaspore. X 620. (*After F. Grace Smith.*)

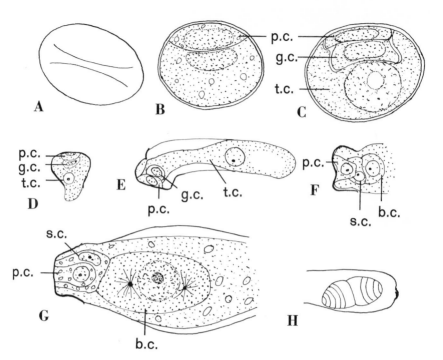

FIG. 25-11. *Zamia* sp. Development of ♂ gametophyte. A. Surface view of microspore. B. Sectional view of microspore showing prothallial cell. C. Sectional view of microspore (pollen grain) at shedding stage; note immature ♂ gametophyte, consisting of prothallial cell, generative cell, and tube cell. D, E. Germination of pollen grain with development of the tube-like haustorial protuberance; note migration of tube nucleus. F. Pollen-grain end of ♂ gametophyte some time after pollination; note prothallial cell, stalk cell, and body cell. G. Pollengrain end of ♂ gametophyte; note prothallial cell, stalk cell, and body-cell nucleus in prophase. H. Two sperm cells in pollen tube; b.c., body cell; g.c., generative cell; p.c., prothallial cell; s.c., stalk cell; t.c., tube cell. A–C. X 1030. D–H. X 400. (*After Webber.*)

Florida, this occurs between December and February each year. A pollen grain is a microspore wall containing an immature male gametophyte. The wall of the pollen grain consists of several layers.

During pollination, changes take place in the megastrobili and the ovules within them. A slight elongation of the internodes, beginning at the base of the megastrobilus and extending gradually to the higher nodes, separates the hitherto contiguous sporophylls by ¼- to ⅛-inch crevices (Fig. 25-13). It is

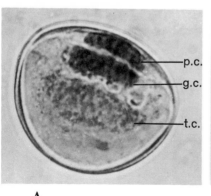

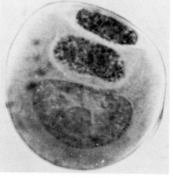

FIG. 25-12. A. *Zamia* sp. Pollen grain at shedding stage. B. *Ceratozamia mexicana.* Pollen grain at shedding stage. X 1400; g.c., generative cell; p.c., prothallial cell; t.c., tube cell.

FIG. 25-13. *Zamia floridana*. Megastrobili at pollination (January); note fissures between megasporophylls. X 0.75.

through the latter that the windborne pollen grains sift into the megastrobilus. During this period, the cells at the apex of the megasporangium (sometimes called the nucellus) disintegrate, and a droplet of colloidal material known as the **pollination droplet** is secreted. The breakdown of these cells results in the formation of a small depression, the **pollen chamber,** at the apex of the megasporangium. A number of pollen grains come to rest in the pollination droplet when it protrudes through the micropyle, the latter a tubular passageway through the integument. As the pollination drop dries, it contracts, carrying the pollen grains into the pollen chamber. The actual transfer of the pollen grains from the microsporangia to the micropyle of the ovule is known as **pollination.**

When the pollen grains have come to rest on the walls and base of the pollen chambers, their protoplasts protrude from the pointed pole through the portion of the wall lacking an outer layer to form tubelike haustoria into which the tube nuclei migrate in each case (Fig. 25-11D). These **pollen tubes** digest their way through the sterile tissue of the megasporangium, at first in a radial direction, but then curving toward the base of the ovule (Fig. 25-15). That they accumulate

some of the substance digested from the megasporangium tissue is indicated by the appearance of starch grains in the elongating pollen tubes. The tubes are unbranched or sparingly branched. As many as fourteen pollen tubes may be present within the apical tissues of a single ovule. The tubes may attain a length of 2–4 mm. Shortly after the pollen tube has been initiated, about a week after pollination, the generative cell divides to form a **stalk-** and **body cell** (Figs. 25-11E, F, 25-17A); the former name is based on the supposed homology with an antheridial stalk, while the latter refers to the antheridium itself. It has recently been suggested that the stalk cell is a sterile spermatogenous cell, while the body cell, of course, is a fertile one. Hence, the stalk cell is sometimes referred to as the **sterile cell** and the body cell as the **spermatogenous cell.** The body cell enlarges gradually as the pollen tube lengthens. The prothallial, stalk, and body cells all remain at the pollen grain region of the elongating pollen tube (Fig. 25-11F, G).

Meanwhile, the thin-walled functional megaspore within the megasporangium has begun to enlarge. The tissue immediately surrounding it becomes vacuolated, forming a so-called **spongy layer.** The latter seems to function like a tapetum, its protoplasmic contents contributing to the enlargement and subsequent development of the functional megaspore. The nucleus of the megaspore now begins a period of repeated free-nuclear divisions. This results, at first, in the formation of a number of nuclei which lie in a peripheral layer of cytoplasm just within the cell wall of the original megaspore; the center of the latter is occupied by a large vacuole. As free-nuclear divisions continue, however, additional cytoplasm is synthesized, so that the vacuole is obliterated gradually, and the megaspore lumen, which has been increasing constantly by absorption of the surrounding megasporangial tissues, is ultimately filled with large numbers of nuclei and watery cytoplasm (Fig. 25-14).

The wall of the enlarging megaspore gradually thickens until, as the female gametophyte matures, it may be more than 4.5 microns thick and composed of two layers. Inasmuch as the megaspore is never discharged from the

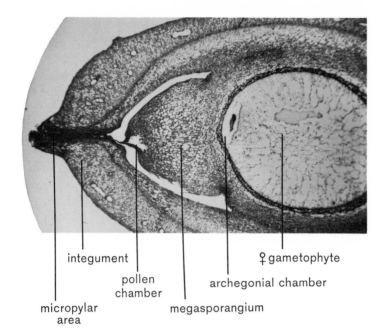

FIG. 25-14. *Zamia* sp. Longisection of ovule, made just as ♀ gametophyte became cellular. X 60.

integument

pollen chamber

♀ gametophyte

archegonial chamber

micropylar area

megasporangium

megasporangium, the thickening of the megaspore wall is considered to be a vestigial attribute persisting from free-spored precursors.

Cell wall formation is then initiated in the free-nuclear female gametophyte, at first between the peripheral nuclei, and it continues in a centripetal direction until the female gametophyte is entirely cellular (Figs. 25-14, 25-15). Four (sometimes fewer) cells at the micropylar pole of the female gametophyte now function as archegonial initials. Each of them, by cell and nuclear division, forms an extremely large archegonium (Figs. 25-15, 25-16A) consisting of two **neck cells** and a large **central cell.** Just before maturation, the nucleus of each central cell undergoes mitosis, forming the egg and ventral canal nuclei which usually are not separated by cytokinesis.

The vegetative cells of the female gametophyte which surround each archegonium form a **jacket layer,** the cells of which presumably function in the transfer of nutriments to the developing egg and proembryo. The egg cytoplasm projects into these cells through small pitlike apertures. The egg cell may attain dimensions of 3.0 by 1.5 mm. and is readily visible to the naked eye. The egg nucleus may attain a diameter of 550 microns.

Megasporogenesis and the maturation of the female gametophyte occupy about 5 months in *Zamia floridana*. During this period, all the component tissues of the ovule increase greatly by cell division, as do the megasporophylls and the strobilus axis. It has been demonstrated that the epidermis of the integument of the ovule has stomata and that

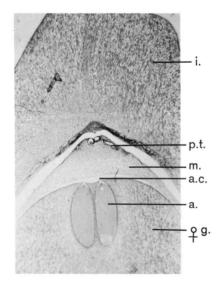

FIG. 25-15. *Zamia* sp. Longisection of ovule apex containing mature ♀ gametophyte; a., archegonium; a.c., archegonial chamber; ♀ g., female gametophyte; i., integument; m., megasporangium; p.t., pollen tube. X 120.

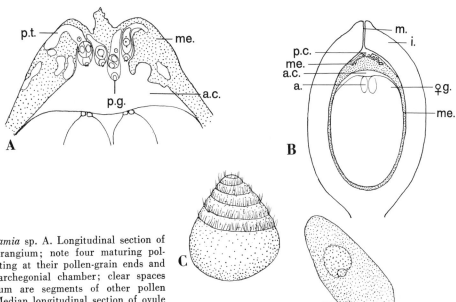

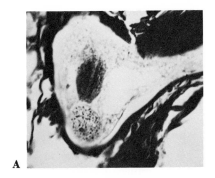

FIG. 25-16. *Zamia* sp. A. Longitudinal section of apex of megasporangium; note four maturing pollen tubes, elongating at their pollen-grain ends and protruding into archegonial chamber; clear spaces in megasporangium are segments of other pollen tubes. X 10. B. Median longitudinal section of ovule before fertilization. X 2. C. Single sperm cell. X 250. D. Egg cell at karyogamy; remains flagellar band near apex. X 18; a., archegonium; a.c., archegonial chamber; ♀ g., female gametophyte; i., integument; m., micropyle; me., megasporangium; p.c., pollen chamber; p.g., pollen-grain end; p.t., pollen tube. (*Modified from Webber.*)

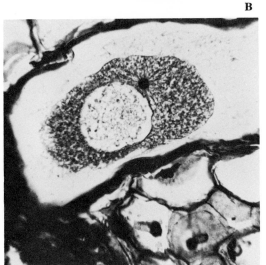

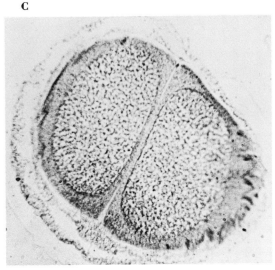

FIG. 25-17. *Zamia* sp. A. Germinating pollen grain in megasporangium; stalk cell, below; partial section of body cell, above. X 250. B. Body cell within pollen tube; its nucleus in early prophase; note centriole and asters. X 250. C. Transection of pollen tube and body cell with two sperm cells enclosed; note transections of flagella-bearing band in one sperm. X 250.

stomata also may be present on the surface of the megasporangium. Median sections of ovules containing mature female gametophytes are shown in Figs. 25-15 and 25-16A.

During the development of the female gametophyte, the haustorial pollen tubes progressively digest the tissues of the megasporangium. As the archegonia mature, the cells of the apex of the female gametophyte increase slightly in size and number so that the group of archegonia comes to lie in a slight depression, the **archegonial chamber** (Figs. 25-15, 25-16B), which is about 2 mm. in diameter and 1 mm. deep. Soon after this, the pollen tubes complete digestion of the megasporangium and the pollen and archegonial chambers (Fig. 25-16B) then become continuous.

Just prior to this, usually late in May, the body cell divides to form two **sperm cells** (Figs. 25-11G, H, 25-17A, B, C). These contain very large nuclei invested with a delicate layer of cytoplasm. During the enlargement of the body cell and its nuclear division, two centrosomelike bodies with astral radiations appear in the body cell and one becomes associated with each sperm. After the division, each of these bodies disintegrates into a mass of granules which become arranged in spiral fashion to form a flagella-bearing organelle about part of the sperm nucleus. Each of these spirals ultimately generates a great many short flagella (cilia) (Fig. 25-16C).

The mature sperms now are liberated from the body cell, become motile, and swim actively within the pollen tube. The sperms may attain a diameter of 300 microns, the largest known in the plant kingdom. The pollen tubes are extremely turgid, probably because of the high osmotic value of the substances which have been digested and absorbed. This is evidenced by the fact that the sperms continue their motility in a 10 percent solution of cane sugar. The pollen tubes finally burst and discharge the sperm.

Plants with pollen tubes are said to be **siphonogamous;** this means that the male gametes are conveyed by a tube to the egg cells. Strictly speaking, this does not occur in the cycads or *Ginkgo* (p. 419) but it does in *Pinus* (p. 435), *Ephedra* (p. 457), and in the Anthophyta (p. 485).

There is no liquid water in the archegonial chamber at fertilization. Observations of living material indicate that the sperms swim actively in the pollen tubes before the latter burst and discharge them with some liquid into the archegonial chamber, that the neck cells shrink, and that a portion of the egg cytoplasm protrudes into the archegonial chamber, drawing the sperm or sperms into the egg cytoplasm. This process is of sufficient violence to sever the flagellar band from the surface of the sperm in some cases (Fig. 25-16D). A sperm nucleus migrates to the vicinity of the egg nucleus, now of tremendous size, and nuclear union occurs (Fig. 25-16D). It should be emphasized at this point that pollination (the transfer of the immature male gametophyte to the micropyle of the ovule) and fertilization (nuclear union and the culmination of sexuality) are very different processes. In *Zamia*, they are separated by an interval of 5 months. Figures 25-15 and 25-16B show median longitudinal sections of an ovule at about the time of fertilization. The archegonia are readily visible to the unaided eye at this stage.

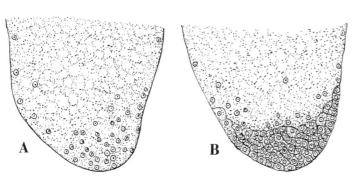

A   **B**

FIG. 25-18. *Zamia umbrosa* Small. Early embryogeny. A. Base of archegonium with free nuclei of proembryo. X 50. B. Cellular proembryo. X 46. (*After Bryan.*)

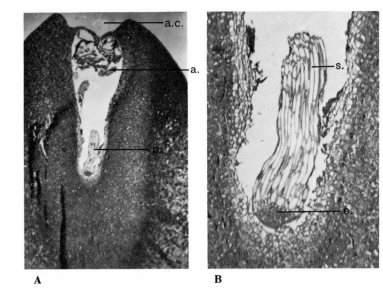

FIG. 25-19. *Zamia* sp. A. Longisection of apex of ♀ gametophyte after fertilization. X 40. B. Enlarged view of embryo in A. X 160; a., region of archegonia (now disorganized); a.c., archegonial chamber; e., embryoforming cells; p., proembryo; s., suspensor.

A   B

Reproduction: embryogeny and seed development

In the development of the zygote into the embryo in *Zamia* and other cycads, the zygote nucleus enters a period of free-nuclear mitoses which is variable in extent. In *Zamia*, approximately 256 nuclei are formed in the egg cell (Fig. 25-18A). Development of the embryonic sporophyte has recently been studied in *Zamia umbrosa*. Wall formation here is initiated among the free nuclei near the base of each archegonium and extends gradually toward the neck end. Some free nuclei may remain unenclosed by walls (Fig. 25-18B). The lowermost cells of this intra-archegonial proembryo function as a meristematic zone which is covered by a caplike layer. An intermediate layer of meristematic cells toward the neck region of the archegonium ceases to divide; its component cells increase in length and force the basal meristematic cells and their cap out through the base of the egg cell into the vegetative tissues of the female gametophyte (Fig. 25-19). This elongating zone of the proembryo, the **suspensor,** is augmented from the meristematic zone below.

Although the zygotes of all the archegonia of one female gametophyte may initiate embryo formation, only one embryo normally is present in the maturing seed (Fig. 25-20), the

others having aborted. The embryo grows at the expense of the female gametophyte tissues which are gradually digested. The uppermost cells (those nearest the archegonial neck) of the proembryo function as a sort of buffer zone which resists the pressure of the elongating suspensor sufficiently to cause it to become coiled.

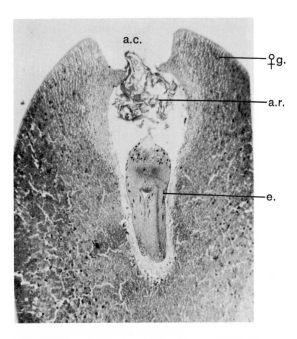

FIG. 25-20. *Zamia* sp. Longisection of upper half of female gametophyte with differentiating embryo. X 80; a.c., archegonial chamber; a.r., archegonial remnants; e., embryo; ♀ g., female gametophyte.

The terminal, embryo-forming cells of the proembryo organize two **cotyledons** between which is a minute terminal bud, the **plumule** (Figs. 25-20, 25-21). The axis of the embryo consists of a **hypocotyl** which extends from the cotyledonary node to the **radicle,** the embryonic root. The latter is covered with a special sheath, the **coleorhiza.** During the development of the embryo within it, the entire ovule increases in size, and changes occur in the massive integument in which three layers are more clearly differentiated (Fig. 25-21). The outermost of these becomes fleshy and bright yellow-orange in color. The middle layer is hard and stony, and the innermost remains soft. A median longitudinal section of the mature ovule or seed (Fig. 25-21) reveals that it contains an embryonic sporophyte embedded in vegetative tissue of the female gametophyte, the latter surrounded by the remains of the megasporangium and an integument. This statement regarding the seed of *Zamia* will serve to define seed structure in all gymnosperms.

As the seeds ripen (Fig. 25-22), the megasporophylls separate and the seeds are abscised. Germination follows immediately, and no fixed dormant period occurs, except as it may be evoked by the environment. The first manifestation of it is the protrusion of the

coleorhiza and enclosed root through the micropyle. The coleorhiza soon grows downward and is penetrated by the enclosed primary root. The tips of the cotyledons remain embedded within the seed, where they function in absorbing food stored in the female gametophyte cells. After some weeks the proximal portions of the cotyledons emerge and ultimately the first foliage leaf appears. Further growth and development of other foliage leaves are very slow in *Zamia*. A number of years are required for the young sporophyte to develop strobili.

Although *Zamia* has been chosen as representative of the cycads, several other genera may be available for observation in tropical regions or in conservatory collections. *Cycas* is of phylogenetic interest because its megasporophylls (Fig. 25-23) are woolly, modified, pinnately compound structures, loosely aggregated at the crown of the plant, and not

A

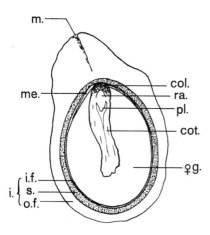

FIG. 25-21. *Zamia* sp. Median longitudinal section of recently shed seed; col., coleorhiza; cot., cotyledons; ♀ g., female gametophyte; i., integument; i.f., inner fleshy layer; m., micropyle; me., megasporangium remains; o.f., outer fleshy layer; pl., plumule; ra., radicle or embryonic root; s., stony layer. X $\frac{5}{12}$.

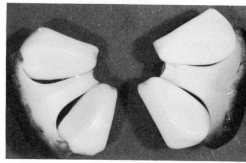

B

FIG. 25-22. *Zamia* sp. A. Transection of megastrobilus with maturing seeds. X 1. B. Two megasporophylls with mature seed. X 1.

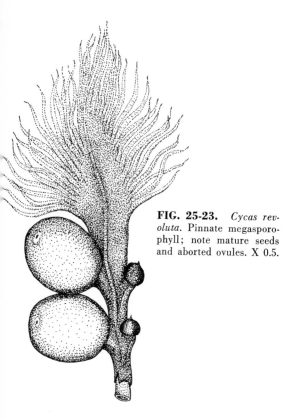

FIG. 25-23. *Cycas revoluta.* Pinnate megasporophyll; note mature seeds and aborted ovules. X 0.5.

Summary of Extant Cycadopsida

In general appearance, *Zamia, Cycas, Dioon,* and other cycads are suggestive of *Marattia*-like ferns. The tuberous, armored, sparingly branched stems, the pinnately compound leaves and circinate young pinnae contribute to this similarity. The stems are characterized by relative paucity of vascular tissue, in spite of the presence of a cambium, and by their girdling leaf traces. The primary stele is an endarch siphonostele interrupted by large and persistent leaf gaps.

All cycads are dioecious, microsporangia and megasporangia being produced on separate strobili (loosely grouped megasporophylls in *Cycas*) which occur on separate individuals. Sporangial development is of the eusporangiate type. The megasporangia are covered by a massive protective layer, the integument, which surrounds them completely except for a minute passageway, the micropyle. Such covered megasporangia are known as ovules. The megasporangium wall is not specially differentiated. The megasporocyte gives rise to a linear tetrad of megaspores, only one of which is functional. The megaspore does not contain large amounts of stored metabolites, is not markedly larger than the microspore, is relatively thin-walled, and permanently retained within the megasporangium, in contrast to the megaspores of nonseed plants. As a result, the female gametophyte also develops to maturity within the megasporangium, and fertilization and development of the embryonic sporophyte also take place within the megasporangium and its integument. The thickening of the megaspore wall as the female gametophyte matures is interpreted as a vestige from free-spored precursors. The permanent retention of these structures within the megasporangium has resulted in the seed habit. It will be recalled that a tendency toward such retention was noted in *Selaginella*; partial retention occurred in certain extinct Microphyllophyta. That the seed habit probably arose independently in more than one group of plants is suggested by the study of paleobotany.

The male gametophyte of *Zamia* and other

borne in strobili. The microsporophylls of *Cycas* and both types of sporophylls in the remaining genera of cycads are localized in strobili.

Variations of number of ovules and mature seeds in the megasporophylls of the several species of *Cycas* have been interpreted as evidence as to how the markedly nonfoliar megasporophylls of other genera may have evolved (Fig. 25-24). This evidence has, however, been challenged.

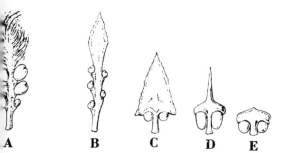

A   B   C   D   E

FIG. 25-24. Scheme deriving *Zamia* type (E) of megasporophyll from that of *Cycas.* A. *Cycas revoluta.* B. *C. media.* C. *Dioon.* D. *Macrozamia.* (*After Meeuse.*)

cycads also reveals innovations not present among the vascular cryptogams. Foremost among these is the development of a pollen tube; its primary function seems to be nutritive, inasmuch as it serves as a haustorial organ which digests the tissues of the megasporangium. Its elongation at the pollen grain end just prior to fertilization brings the male gametes into close proximity to the archegonia. The sperms of *Zamia* are multiciliate and actively motile, although their movement is confined to the pollen tubes. The number of sperms produced by each male gametophyte of *Zamia* is reduced, as compared with the vascular cryptogams, two being produced in all the cycads except the genus *Microcycas*, which is said to produce 16 to 22 sperms. In this respect, the male gametophyte of *Microcycas* would be the most primitive among the seed plants.

In addition to the permanent retention of the female gametophyte within the megasporangium, there are two other adaptive modifications, the pollen chamber and the archegonial chamber. Another departure in *Zamia* is the free-nuclear phase in embryogeny, an attribute of gymnosperms not paralleled in the vascular cryptogams. Finally, the abscission of the ovule containing the embryonic sporophyte within the female gametophyte and remains of the megasporangium, all covered by the integument, produces the characteristic structures known as seeds.

Some Primitive Fossil Seed Plants

The Cycadophyta includes three classes, the Pteridospermopsida, Cycadeoidopsida, and the Cycadopsida. Of these, only the order Cycadales of the Cycadopsida contains living representatives. These have been discussed in earlier pages of the present chapter. The extinct Cycadophyta will now be briefly summarized.

Class 1. Pteridospermopsida

The **Pteridosperms** or **seed ferns,** sometimes called the Cycadofilicales, were plants with fernlike foliage which bore seeds. Before

FIG. 25-25. *Emplectopteris triangularis* Halle. Fernlike leaf with seeds. (*After Andrews.*)

their existence was proven, early in the twentieth century, by the discovery of seeds attached to fernlike fronds (Fig. 25-25), the abundance of the latter in the Carboniferous (Table 32-1) earlier suggested the designation "Age of Ferns" for strata of that period. After the discovery of the seed ferns, it became uncertain whether sterile fernlike foliage might be pterophytan or pteridospermopsidan.

The existence of seeds and seed ferns in the Carboniferous raises the question of the origin of the seed habit. The ontogenetic precursor of the seed is the ovule which we have defined as a megasporangium covered with one or more integuments. The megasporangium is naked in cryptogams and provided with a covering in phanerogams (cf. Figs. 19-25B, and 25-10, 25-16B). The origin of the integument remains obscure. It has been suggested that in groups of megasporangia the peripheral ones became sterile and surrounded a central one as an incipient integument. This integument at first was not fused with the megasporangium except at the base; fusion of the two was a later development. The Lower Carboniferous seed, *Genomosperma* (Gr. *genos*, kind + Gr. *sperma*) (Fig. 25-26) may be cited in possible illustration of this hypothesis. Here the megasporangium is surrounded by eight sterile structures. In addition to the integument, the presence at the apex of the megasporangium of a special

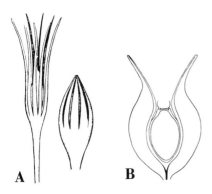

FIG. 25-26. A. *Genomosperma kidstonii* (Calder) Long (seed about 15 mm. long) and *G. latens* Long. B. *Lyrasperma scotica* Long. Diagrammatic longisection of seed. (A. *After Andrews.* B. *After Long, from Delevoryas.*)

receptive chamber for pollen distinguishes ovules from megasporangia. In *Genomosperma* there was such a chamber. Another Lower Carboniferous seed, *Lyrasperma* (Fig. 25-26B), is significant in these connections. Here the integument is more completely united with the megasporangium and a pollen chamber also is present.

Of the class Pteridospermopsida, the seed-fern *Lyginopteris* (Gr. *lygginos*, twisted or winding + Gr. *pteris*), among other genera, is one of the most completely known. *Lygin-*

opteris (Fig. 25-27), as reconstructed from fragments of leaves, stems, and roots as well as of reproductive structures, was somewhat like a modern tree fern in possessing an aerial stem. The latter, however, was more slender than those of tree ferns and probably was supported by other vegetation. The stems contained mesarch siphonosteles (Fig. 25-28) which were augmented by limited secondary growth. The leaves were large, with a dichotomously divided rachis, each branch being pinnately subdivided. Their blades were differentiated internally into palisade and spongy layers. The roots were adventitious, some of them arising from the stems above the soil and in association with leaf bases. Secondary growth occurred also in the root.

The reproductive structures of *Lyginopteris* are represented by fossil branches bearing microsporangia and by seeds. The small (5.5 mm. long) seeds (form genus *Lagenostoma*) were borne in a group of cupulelike bracts (Fig. 25-29A,B), a characteristic of many seed ferns. The integument was fused to the megasporangium except at the tip. Here the latter was prolonged as a central column within the pollen chamber. Pollen grains have been observed within the latter. The occurrence of characteristic glands (Fig. 25-29A) on the

A

B

FIG. 25-27. *Lyginopteris oldhamnia,* a seed fern. A. Habit of growth. B. Details of fronds and sporophylls; at the left, note frond of the seed fern *Neuropteris heterophylla.* (*Courtesy of the Chicago Natural History Museum.*)

FIG. 25-28. *Lyginopteris old-hamnia.* Transection of small stem; i.c., inner cortex; o.c., outer cortex; p., pith; s.x., secondary xylem.

cupule and on leaf fragments and stems helped prove the co-identity of *Lyginopteris* and *Lagenostoma.* The microsporangiate phase of *Lyginopteris* is not known with certainty; the form genus *Telangium* has been suggested as a possibility. This consists of six to twenty-five erect, fusiform sporangia borne on a disc at the tip of an ultimate division of a frond. *Telangium,* up to the present, however, has not been found in organic connection with *Lyginopteris.*

Approximately eight to ten genera of seed ferns have been found with seeds attached to their fernlike foliage. The seeds may be termi-nal on bladeless branches of the frond, as in *Lyginopteris,* or they may replace the terminal leaflet on a pinnate branch of the frond, as in *Neuropteris* (Figs. 25-27, 25-30B).

The Carboniferous genus *Medullosa* (Fig. 25-31) differs from *Lyginopteris* anatomically, its stem being polystelic instead of monostelic. The seeds were larger than those of *Lyginopteris;* some immature ovules have been found which contained female gametophytes and archegonia. Some species of the form genus *Neuropteris* probably represent fronds which grew on medullosan stems.

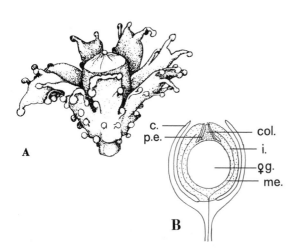

FIG. 25-29. A. *Lyginopteris oldhamnia.* Seed and surrounding structure. B. *L. lomaxii.* Diagrammatic, median longitudinal section of cupule and seed; c., cupule; col., central column of pollen chamber; ♀ g., female gametophyte with embryo; i., integument; me., megasporangium; p.c., pollen chamber. (A. *After Oliver and Scott, from Andrews.* B. *After Oliver, from Arnold.*)

FIG. 25-30. *Neuropteris* sp. A. Portion of fossilized leaf. B. Tip of pinna with terminal seed. (A. *Courtesy of the Chicago Natural History Museum.* B. *After Delevoryas.*)

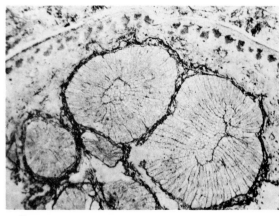

B

FIG. 25-31. *Medullosa noei*. A. Habit of growth, reconstruction. B. *Medullosa* sp. Transection of portion of polystelic axis. (A. *After Stewart and Delevoryas*.)

A

The seed ferns continued into the Mesozoic (Table 32-1). One of the most spectacular of these is the genus *Caytonia* (Fig. 25-32) from the Middle Jurassic, first described in 1925 from the Yorkshire coast of England. The leaves of *Caytonia* were palmately compound. The microsporangia were borne in groups of four (Fig. 25-32A) on branching axes. The ovule-bearing axes (Fig. 25-32A) consisted of two rows of saclike structures within each of which ovules were attached. These sacs surrounding the ovules at first suggested angio-

spermy. However, in pollination, pollen was transferred directly to the ovules within the sacs.[6] The latter are now considered homologous with the cupules of *Lyginopteris* and earlier seed ferns. It is of interest, in this connection, that intracarpellary pollen grains have been reported in several angiosperms, so that *Caytonia* and its relatives are significant in discussions of the origin of angiospermy.

As a group, the seed ferns are distinguish-

[6] In contrast to pollination in angiosperms (Fig. 25-2, and p. 483).

FIG. 25-32. A. *Caytonia nathorstii* Thomas. Axis with "fruits." X ⅔. B. *C. nathorstii*. Young "fruit." X 5. C. *Caytonia sewardii* Thomas. Section of "fruit" with orthotropous ovules; note opening in "fruit" for pollination. X 4. D. *Caytonanthus kochii* Harris. Portion of microsporangiate axis. (A–C. *After Thomas*. D. *After Harris*.)

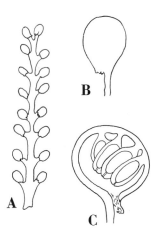

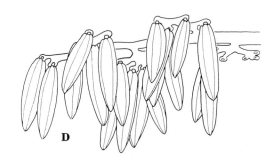

A

B

C

D

able from other gymnospermous plants by their fernlike foliage which bore seeds directly among the bladelike branches or on modified branches of the leaves. Neither the microspores nor ovules were associated in strobili as they are in Cycadales and Cycadeoidales. Fertilization may well háve occurred after the ovules had been abscised. The pteridosperms reached a degree of prominence in the Carboniferous and then declined, only a few persisting into the Mesozoic (Table 32-1).

Inasmuch as pteridosperms were contemporaneous with many ferns, it is doubtful that the latter could have been their progenitors. It is more probable that the Pteridospermophyta and Pterophyta developed from common Devonian precursors.

Class 2. Cycadeoidopsida

The Cycadeoidopsida include the single order Cycadeoidales.

The Cycadeoidales, in some texts called the Bennettitales, were prominent during the Mesozoic (Table 32-1) which, plantwise, is sometimes called the "Age of Cycads."

These cycadeoids were cycadlike in a number of respects but differed from living cycads in others. Like the ferns, pteridosperms, and cycads, the cycadeoids had fernlike compound leaves that arose from short, rarely branched columnar trunks which were covered with the tough bases of leaves of earlier seasons (Fig. 25-33). In several genera, the trunks were more slender and were sparingly branched (Fig. 25-35). As in modern cycads, the trunks contained a massive central pith surrounded by groups of primary xylem which were buried by secondary growth. Extensions of the pith interrupted the woody cylinders. Unlike modern cycads, which have slowly ascending, girdling leaf traces, those of the cycadeoids passed directly into the leaf bases. The pinnately compound leaves were of firm texture and probably reached a length of 10 feet in some individuals. The stomata of Cycadeoidales, unlike those of Cycadales, were complex with the guard cells heavily cutinized.

Some cycadeoids were monoecious, unlike modern cycads, while others were dioecious.

FIG. 25-33. *Cycadeoidea marylandica* Fontaine. The earliest described American fossil cycad, collected between Baltimore and Washington, D.C. (*From Wieland.*)

The microsporangia and ovules were associated on compound lateral branches that arose among the leaf bases (Fig. 25-34). The central portion of the reproductive axis was occupied by a conical receptacle in which the ovules were borne among sterile appendages, the latter sometimes interpreted as sterile ovules (Fig. 25-34B). A rather long, micropylelike tube projected outward between the interovular appendages. Surrounding the ovule-bearing axis was an enclosing fleshy structure which bore the microsporangia (Fig. 25-34A). It has been suggested that this was abscised before pollination, thus exposing the ovule to pollen from other plants. The microsporangial structure and ovules were both enclosed in a common whorl of hairy, bractlike appendages. Seeds of certain cycadeoids contained dicotyledonous embryos. The three best-known genera are *Cycadeoidea* (*Bennettites* of some authors) (Figs. 25-33, 25-34), the cycadlike stems of which were robust and rarely branched; *Wielandiella,* in which the stem was slender, elongate, and branched; and *Williamsonia* (Fig. 25-35) in which the stems were columnar as

FIG. 25-34. *Cycadeoidea* sp. A. Diagram of median longisection of a cone; ovules surrounded by microsporangiate complex. B. Longisection of ovulate complex; some ovules with embryos. Microsporangiate covering probably abscised; o., ovule. (*After Delevoryas.*)

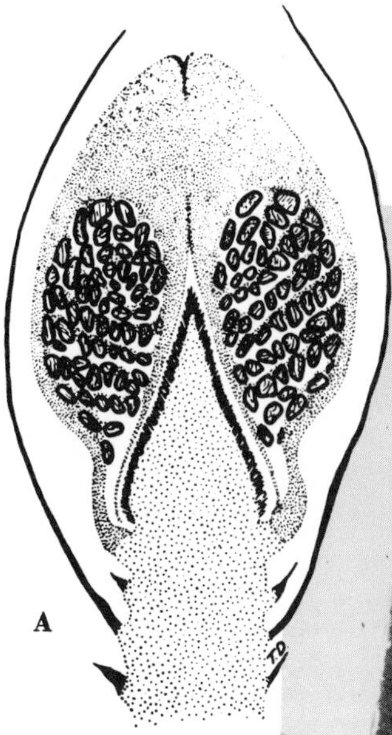

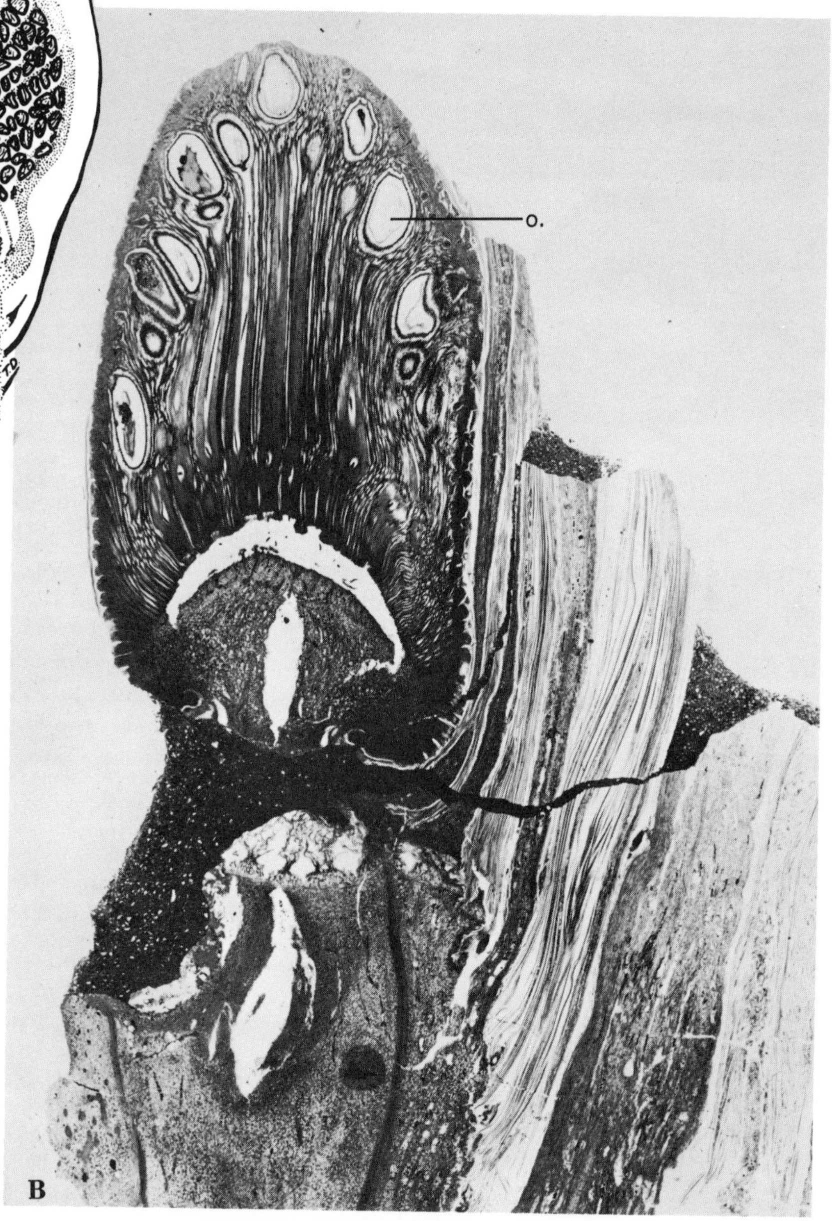

in *Dioon*. Both monoecious and dioecious species are known. The cycadeoids probably arose late in the Paleozoic but did not attain prominence until the Triassic (Table 32-1). They were also dominant in the Jurassic and persisted through Cretaceous times.

Class 3. Cycadopsida

Fossilized material of true cycads, order Cycadales (as distinct from cycadeoids), occurs prominently in the early Mesozoic (Triassic).

FIG. 25-35. *William-sonia* sp. Reconstruction of a portion of branching axes with leaves and strobili. (*Courtesy of the Chicago Natural History Museum.*)

It has been suggested that cycads arose from the pteridosperm complex and that the strobili of cycads with their reduced peltate sporophylls represent a reduction from the frondlike ovulate structures of pteridosperms (Figs. 25-25, 25-27B). Evidence of reduction of megasporophylls is available even among living cycads in such a series as that illustrated in Fig. 25-24, but, as noted earlier (p. 403), this has been challenged.

Bjuvia simplex Florin (Fig. 25-36) is an example of a fossil cycad; a reconstruction of this plant suggests the extant *Cycas*. The columnar, armored trunk bore a crown of pinnately compound leaves. The megasporophylls, each with two pairs of ovules, were in a terminal cluster. Fossil cycads, like the extant relatives, had simple stomata. In this and in their fruiting structures they differed markedly from the cycadeoids, fossil cycadlike plants, discussed above (p. 408).

Classification

The classification of members of the Cycadophyta discussed in this chapter is as follows:

Division Cycadophyta
    Class 1. Pteridospermopsida
        Order 1. Pteridospermales
            Family 1. Pteridospermaceae
                Genera: *Lyginopteris, Medullosa, Neuropteris, Caytonia*
    Class 2. Cycadeoidopsida
        Order 1. Cycadeoidales
            Family 1. Cycadeoidaceae
                Genera: *Cycadeoidea, Williamsonia, Wielandiella*
    Class 2. Cycadeoidopsida
        Order 1. Cycadales
            Family 1. Cycadaceae
                Genera: *Cycas, Dioon, Microcycas, Zamia, Macrozamia, Ceratozamia, Encephalartos, Bowenia, Stangeria,* and *Bjuvia*

FIG. 25-36. *Bjuvea simplex* Florin. Reconstruction. (*After Florin.*)

DISCUSSION QUESTIONS

1. What vegetative attributes of cycads suggest *Marattia*-like ferns?

2. In what respect are the leaf traces of *Zamia* anomalous?

3. How do the stem and root apex of *Zamia* differ from those of many vascular cryptogams?

4. What evidence can you cite to indicate that cycad leaves are macrophyllous?

5. Define or explain the terms endarch siphonostele, periderm, dioecism, ovule, seed, micropyle, pollen grain, free-nuclear embryogeny, pollination, linear tetrad.

6. What conditions must prevail for seed formation to occur?

7. A possible approach to the seed habit is cited in certain Microphyllophyta which are heterosporous. Would you search for the origin of the seed plants in that group? Explain.

8. Compare the female gametophyte of *Zamia* with the gametophytes of *Dryopteris*, *Selaginella*, and *Isoetes* with reference to both vegetative and reproductive aspects.

9. Compare the male gametophyte of *Zamia* with that of heterosporous cryptogams.

10. What adaptive advantages accrue to the plant which produces seeds?

11. Where would one find cycads in nature?

12. Distinguish between the pollen and archegonial chambers. Cite as many differences in these structures as you can.

13. In what respects do the Cycadopsida, Pteridospermopsida, and Cycadeoidopsida differ from each other?

14. What is the evolutionary significance of the Pteridospermopsida?

REFERENCE WORKS ON SEED PLANTS[7]

Arnold, C. A., "Origin and Relationship of the Cycads," *Phytomorphology* 3:51–65, 1953.

Benson, L., *"Plant Classification,"* D. C. Heath and Company, 1957.

Campbell, D. H., *The Evolution of the Land Plants (Embryophyta)*, Stanford Univ. Press, Stanford, Calif., 1940.

Chamberlain, C. J., *The Living Cycads*, Univ. of Chicago Press, 1919.

Chamberlain, C. J., *Gymnosperms: Structure and Evolution*, Univ. of Chicago Press, 1935.

Coulter, J. M., and Chamberlain, C. J., *Morphology of Gymnosperms*, Univ. of Chicago Press, 1917.

Davis, P. H., and V. H. Heywood, *Principles of Angiosperm Taxonomy*, D. Van Nostrand, Inc., Princeton, N.J., 1963.

Eames, A. J., *Morphology of the Angiosperms*, McGraw-Hill Book Co., Inc., New York, 1961.

Eames, A. J., and MacDaniels, L. H., *An Introduction to Plant Anatomy*, McGraw-Hill Book Co., Inc., New York, 1947.

Esau, K., *Plant Anatomy*, 2nd ed., John Wiley and Sons, Inc., New York, 1965.

Foster, A. S., and Gifford, E. M., Jr., *Comparative Morphology of Vascular Plants*, W. H. Freeman and Co., New York, 1959.

Haupt, A. W., *Plant Morphology*, McGraw-Hill Book Co., Inc., New York, 1953.

Jeffrey, E. C., *The Anatomy of Woody Plants*, Univ. of Chicago Press, 1930.

Johansen, D. A., *Plant Embryology*, Chronica Botanica Co., Waltham, Mass., 1950.

Lawrence, G. H. M., *Taxonomy of Vascular Plants*, Macmillan Company, New York, 1951.

[7] These references may be consulted as supplementary to Chapters 25–31.

Maheshwari, P., *An Introduction to the Embryology of Angiosperms*, McGraw-Hill Book Co., Inc., New York, 1950.

Meeuse, A. D. J., *Fundamentals of Phytomorphology*, The Ronald Press Co., New York, 1966.

Scagel, R. F. *et al.*, *An Evolutionary Survey of the Plant Kingdom*, Wadsworth Publishing Co., Inc., Belmont, Calif., 1965.

Seward, A. C., "The Story of the Maidenhair Tree," *Smithsonian Report*, Washington, D.C., pp. 441–460, 1938.

Wardlaw, C. W., *Embryogenesis in Plants*, John Wiley and Sons, Inc., New York, 1955.

Zimmerman, W., *Phylogenie der Pflanzen*, 2nd ed., Gustav Fischer Verlagsbuchhandlung, Jena, Germany, 1959.

CHAPTER 26

Division Ginkgophyta

Class 1. Ginkgopsida

Whereas the Cycadophyta, discussed in the preceding chapter, had comparatively small, sparsely branched stems and large, pinnately compound leaves, *Ginkgo* (Chinese, *yin*, silver + *hing*, apricot), the sole extant genus of the Ginkgophyta, is characterized by large, richly branched stems and smaller simple leaves, attributes which suggest the Coniferophyta with which *Ginkgo* is sometimes classified. Furthermore, the extensive pith, scanty xylem, and large cortex of cycadean stems are in marked contrast to the small pith, abundant xylem, and narrow cortex in stems of *Ginkgo*.

Ginkgo is the only member of the single order Ginkgoales, family Ginkgoaceae. *Ginkgo biloba* L., the **maidenhair tree** (Fig. 26-1), has often been called a living fossil. There has been considerable doubt that it still occurs in habitats where it has not been cultivated, although there are reports of specimens in the wild in Eastern China, near the borders of the Anhwei, Kiangsu, and Chekiang provinces south of the Yangtze River.[1] The fossil record indicates that *Ginkgo* and related genera were

---

[1] For an informative account of the history of *Ginkgo*, see: Li, Hui-Lin, "A Horticultural and Botanical History of *Ginkgo*," *Bulletin of the Morris Arboretum*, 7:3–12, 1956.

FIG. 26-1. *Ginkgo biloba* L. Large trees photographed in China by the botanical explorer, Meyer. (*Courtesy of the Chicago Natural History Museum.*)

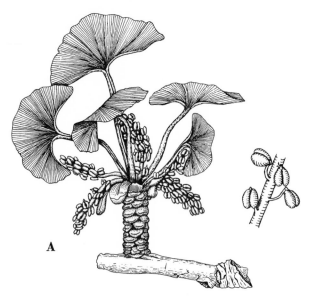

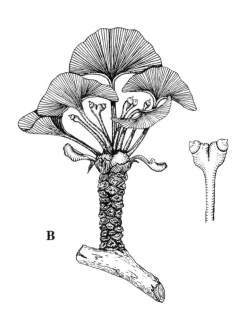

FIG. 26-2. *Ginkgo biloba* L. A. Portion of long shoot and spur shoot in spring, showing numerous terminal bud-scale scars, bud scales, emerging leaves, and microstrobili; detail of axis and four microsporophylls at the right. B. Similar portion of ovulate plant, showing paired pedunculate ovules; detail of latter at the right. X 1.

distributed widely, especially in the northern hemisphere, in earlier geological periods, some records extending back to the Permian (Table 32-1).

The name "maidenhair tree" is an allusion to the similarity in appearance between certain

leaves of *Ginkgo* trees and the leaflets of the maidenhair fern, *Adiantum*. The tree is widely cultivated in the United States and readily grown from seed. In Washington, D.C., and in New York City, a large number of trees have been planted along some of the streets. The leaves are a beautiful yellow-golden color in the autumn. Many oriental peoples have cultivated *Ginkgo* in their temple grounds. The Japanese once believed that *Ginkgo* exuded water during a fire, probably because these trees are more resistant than others to the disastrous effects of fire.

Vegetative morphology

Mature specimens of *Ginkgo* (Fig. 26-1) in cultivation may attain a height of more than a hundred feet. The form of young trees is narrowly conical, with the branches ascending; but in older specimens, especially ovule-bearing trees, the form is rounded, with the branches somewhat spreading and drooping.

Growth and development of the aerial portions of *Ginkgo*, as in all woody plants of the temperate zone, are marked by seasonal periodicity. *Ginkgo* trees are deciduous, producing entirely new leaves each year; these persist for only one growing season. During the fall and winter, the delicate growing tips of the stems are enclosed by leaf primorida which will emerge the following spring, and these in turn are covered by the resistant **bud scales** characteristic of woody plants. With the removal of growth each spring, the bud scales are shed, and the embryonic stem tips undergo rapid cell division and enlargement, thus exposing the rudimentary leaves.

Examination of branches in the leafy condition reveals that there is a dimorphism of branching (Fig. 26-2). The elongate main axes are known as **long shoots.** These produce a series of spirally arranged leaves on widely separated nodes during their first year of growth. Older portions of the long shoots bear a large number of short lateral branches, the **spur shoots.**[2] These develop from the lateral buds of long shoots after the first sea-

[2] See Gunckel, J. E., and K. V. Thimann, "Studies of Development in Long Shoots and Short Shoots of *Ginkgo biloba* L. III. Auxin Production in Shoot Growth," *Am. J. Bot.*, 36:145–151, 1949.

son. Each spur shoot produces a terminal cluster of as many as sixteen leaves every season. Growth in length of the spur shoots is extremely slow. However, on proper stimulation, such as injury to the terminal bud of a long shoot, spur shoots may metamorphose into long shoots.

Development of both spur shoots and long shoots may be traced to the activity of a group of meristematic cells and their derivatives, the apical meristem. The young leaves are initiated very close to the stem apex in *Ginkgo*. The vascular system is arranged in the form of a dissected siphonostele in primary growth. The primary xylem is endarch, and the stele is interrupted by the departure of traces, two to each leaf.

As in stem development in all woody perennial plants, the completion of primary differentiation is followed early by the initiation of activity by the **cambium**; in fact, these two processes overlap, in part. The latter is a zone of meristematic cells of the procambium, between the primary xylem and phloem, which has remained undifferentiated. Frequently, if not always, cambial activity, with resulting differentiation of secondary xylem and phloem, commences before primary differentiation has been completed. The **secondary tissues** (Fig. 26-3) which have developed from cambium derivatives are external to the earlier produced primary xylem. Cambial activity is seasonal; hence in older stems the annual zones of secondary xylem are readily distinguishable. Comparison of transverse sections of spur and long shoots of the same age indicates that considerably more secondary xylem (wood) is produced by the cambium of the long shoots. The pith and cortex of the spur shoots are persistent and more extensive than those of the long shoots. With the addition of secondary vascular tissues and expansion of the inner portion of the stem, the outermost cells of the cortex become organized into the **phellogen** or **cork cambium.** This is a meristematic cylinder, derivatives of which augment the cortex and replace the epidermis of the primary stem with phellem or cork cells. Abundant **lenticels,** which facilitate gaseous interchange, develop in the stems after the phellogen becomes active.

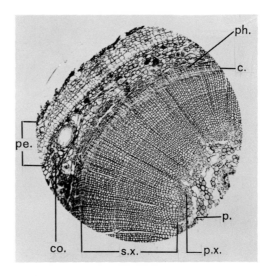

FIG. 26-3. *Ginkgo biloba.* Transection of a long shoot early in its second year; c., cambium; co., cortex; p., pith., pe., periderm; ph. secondary phloem; p.x., primary xylem; s.x., secondary xylem. X 30.

A number of meristematic cells also comprise the apical meristem of the root, which is covered by a protective cap. Each root contains an exarch protostele which is diarch in arrangement of the protoxylem. The primary tissues of the root also are supplemented by secondary tissues developed by cambial activity.

The leaves of *Ginkgo* are perhaps its most distinctive attribute that is readily observable. Leaves of seedlings and those of long shoots are deeply bilobed. Those of spur shoots are entire or obscurely lobed (Figs. 26-2, 25-5). The two vascular traces of the petiole fork as they enter the blade, where they undergo repeated dichotomies (Fig. 17-18A). There are occasional connections between the dichoto-

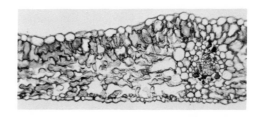

FIG. 26-4. *Ginkgo biloba.* Transection of a leaf; note upper and lower epidermis, the latter with stomata; palisade and spongy mesophyll; and transection of vein. X 65.

A

B   C

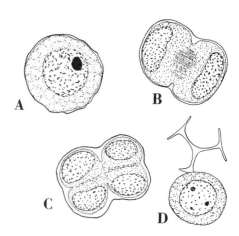

FIG. 26-5. *Ginkgo biloba.* A. Spur shoot with microstrobili. B. Spur shoot with ovules. A., B., X 0.5. C. Close-up of ovules. X 3.

mies. The mesophyll cells are differentiated internally (Fig. 26-4) into palisade and spongy layers in the leaves of long shoots but are less differentiated in leaves of the spur shoots. Stomata occur almost exclusively on the abaxial surfaces of the leaves. All the organs of *Ginkgo* are traversed by a series of mucilage canals in which a sticky substance is secreted.

Reproduction: the sporophyte

Like the cycads, which are dioecious, the microsporangia and ovules of *Ginkgo* are borne on separate individuals (Fig. 26-5). Structural differences have been reported in the chromosomal complements of the microsporangiate and ovulate trees. The latter are said to have four satellited chromosomes and the microsporangiate trees only three.

The microsporangia develop in lax strobili (Figs. 26-2A, 26-5A); the ovules occur in pendulous pairs at the tips of short, petiolelike stalks. Both arise among the vegetative leaves of spur shoots and emerge with the latter in the spring. The microstrobili of a given season develop during the summer preceding their emergence from the meristem of the spur shoot and attain considerable size by late autumn. They pass the winter in the microsporocyte stage, meiosis and microsporogenesis (Fig.

26-6) occurring the following spring. Each microstrobilus is composed of an axis which bears spirally arranged microsporophylls, the latter stalked and humped (Fig. 26-2A). Each microsporophyll bears two elongate microsporangia. The development of the latter is eusporangiate. The wall of the microsporangium is composed of five or six layers of cells within which there is a tapetum. Dehiscence

A   B

C   D

FIG. 26-6. *Ginkgo biloba.* Microsporogenesis (aceto-carmine preparations). A. Microsporocyte. B. End of meiosis I. C. Formation of tetrad of microspores. D. Single microspore and remains of common tetrad walls. X 1030.

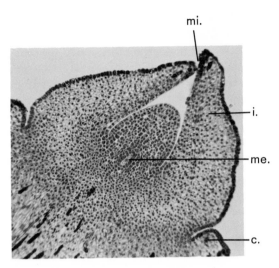

mi.

i.

me.

c.

FIG. 26-7. *Ginkgo biloba.* Median longisection of young ovule; c., collar; i., integument; me., megasporocyte; mi., micropyle. X 125.

of the microsporangia is by a vertical fissure.

The ovules are not borne in strobili but occur in pairs, terminally, at the tips of stalks or peduncles which emerge among the leaf bases of the spur shoots in early spring (Figs. 26-2B, 26-5B). Two vascular bundles traverse both the stalk of the microsporophyll and the peduncle which bears the ovules. The vascular bundles terminate at the base of the megasporangia. An enlarged, collarlike rim is present at the base of each ovule (Figs. 26-2B, 26-7). In certain abnormal individuals the collar may be expanded and bladelike. This suggests that the collar may represent the remnant of an expanded sporophyll. The ovule itself consists of a massive integument which rather loosely surrounds the elongate megasporangium except at its tip, where it leaves a micropyle (Fig. 26-7). As in all seed plants, a single megasporocyte is differentiated, here deep within the megasporangium. The sterile cells of the megasporangium which surround the megasporocyte form a spongy tissue. Soon after the ovules emerge from the buds of the spur shoots, certain of the apical cells of the megasporangia degenerate into mucilaginous masses, forming a deep pollen chamber in each ovule (Fig. 26-9A). Meiosis and megasporogenesis, in which a linear tetrad of megaspores is formed, occur at the time of pollination or soon after.

Reproduction: the gametophytes

Development of the uninucleate microspores (Fig. 26-8A) into male gametophytes is initiated, as in *Zamia*, soon after the completion of microsporogenesis and before the microspores are shed. The mature microspores are slightly protuberant at one pole, which is covered only by a single delicate layer, the **intine** (Fig. 26-8A). The outer layer, the **exine,** is absent from this portion of the microspore surface. Development of the male gametophyte begins with an intrasporal nuclear and cell division which delimits a small prothallial cell from a larger cell. The latter undergoes a second nuclear and cell division to form a second prothallial cell and an antheridial initial (Fig. 26-8B). The first prothallial cell sometimes degenerates promptly, but the second is more persistent. The antheridial cell now divides again, forming a small generative cell adjacent to the second prothallial cell, and a tube cell (Fig. 26-8C). The immature male gametophyte in the microspore wall, now called the pollen grain, is shed in this four-celled condition.

The pollen, which is light and wind-borne, is produced in large amounts by the microsporangiate trees. In the vicinity of Nashville, Tennessee, pollination takes place about April 15 each year, although there is variation in accordance with the temperature. Some of the

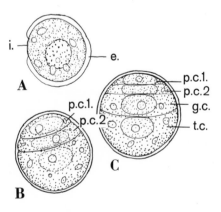

i.

e.

A

p.c.1

p.c.1.

p.c.2

p.c.2

B

C

p.c.1.
p.c.2
g.c.
t.c.

FIG. 26-8. *Ginkgo biloba.* Intrasporangial stages of ♂ gametophyte development (I_2–KI preparations). A. Microspore. B, C. Later stages. C. At shedding stage; e., exine; g.c., generative cells; i., intine; p.c.1, p.c.2, first and second prothallial cells; t.c., tube cell. X 1033.

pollen grains reach the apex of each megasporangium and become lodged in the mucilaginous material at the apex of the pollen chamber. It has been reported that as this material dries, it contracts and draws the pollen grains into the pollen chamber in contact with the megasporangial cells. A pollen tube, formed in the region of the pollen grain covered only by the intine, digests its way into the tissues of the megasporangium, much as in *Zamia*, apparently in *Ginkgo* also serving in an haustorial capacity. Maturation of the male gametophyte is completed as the pollen tube grows through the tissues of the megasporangium.

It will be recalled that each ovule contains either a megasporocyte (Fig. 26-7) or a linear tetrad at the time of pollination. As in *Zamia*, usually only one of the megaspores functions in developing a female gametophyte. It also

will be recalled that the interval between pollination and fertilization in *Zamia* is about 5 months, and that during this period the functional megaspore develops into the female gametophyte. Similarly, in *Ginkgo*, it takes from early April until August (in the southeastern United States[3]) for the megaspore to produce a mature female gametophyte.

Development of the female gametophyte involves an extended period of free-nuclear division (Fig. 26-9) during the early stages of which the nuclei are arranged around the periphery of the enlarging megaspore. The latter increases in size at the expense of the surrounding megasporangial tissue, the portion immediately surrounding the megaspore being called the spongy tissue. The period of free-

---

[3] Nashville, Tennessee; correspondingly later, northward.

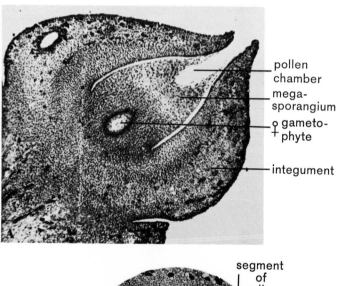

pollen chamber

mega-sporangium

♀ gameto-phyte

integument

FIG. 26-9. *Ginkgo biloba.* A. Median longisection of ovule with initiation of free-nuclear ♀ gametophyte. X 125. B. The same, slightly later. X 60.

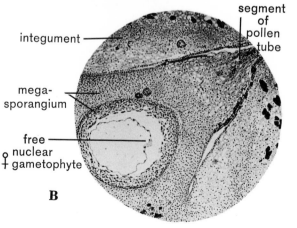

segment of pollen tube

integument

mega-sporangium

free ♀ nuclear gametophyte

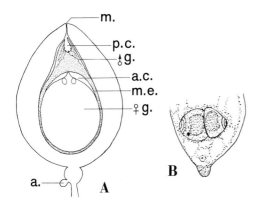

FIG. 26-10. *Ginkgo biloba.* A. Diagrammatic median longitudinal section of entire ovule before fertilization; a., aborted ovule; a.c., archegonial chamber; m., micropyle; me., megasporangium; ♂ g., male gametophyte in megasporangium; ♀ g., female gametophyte in archegonium; p.c., pollen chamber. B. Pollen-grain end of mature ♂ gametophyte; note prothallial-cell nucleus (second) and two sperm cells. X 300. (B. *After Hirase.*)

nuclear division is of about 2 months' duration, during which all the tissues of the ovule enlarge; approximately 8000 free nuclei are formed. Cell wall formation begins at the periphery of the female gametophyte near the megaspore wall. The latter may thicken up to 7 microns by the time of fertilization and consists of two distinct layers. The formation of cells in the female gametophyte gradually extends centripetally. Inasmuch as the innermost nuclei near the center of the gametophyte are finally surrounded by complete individual cell walls, the mature cellular gametophyte (Fig. 26-10) may be split readily into two portions. Nuclear and cell division continue, especially in the micropylar end of the female gametophyte. Although surrounded by the remains of the megasporangium as well as by the massive integument, the vegetative cells of the female gametophyte are green. Extraction of the pigment and study of its absorption spectra indicate that chlorophylls *a* and *b* are present.[4] Whether or not extensive photosynthesis occurs has not been ascertained. It is probable that nutrition of the female gametophyte of *Ginkgo*, as in *Zamia* and other seed plants, is based largely on material derived from the parent sporophyte.

4 Unpublished data of Dr. John Ridgway.

Two archegonia develop at the micropylar pole of each female gametophyte, but occasionally there are three or four (Figs. 26-11, 26-12). The archegonia are large but not as large as those of *Zamia*. Each has four neck cells and a jacket layer. However, in *Ginkgo*, the division of the central cell nucleus into egg and ventral canal nuclei generally is followed by cytokinesis, so that a ventral canal cell is formed. The latter disintegrates before fertilization. At that time, the archegonia lie in a somewhat circular groove, the archegonial chamber (Figs. 26-10A, 26-12). The vegetative tissue between the archegonia elongates, forming a short **column**[5] the apex of which extends to the megasporangial tissues (Figs. 26-10A, 26-12), and ultimately into the pollen chamber.

During the development of the female gametophyte, the male gametophyte has been digesting its way through the apical portion of the enlarging megasporangium. Early in this process, the generative cell divides into two cells, the stalk- and body cells, as in *Zamia*. Division of the body cell into two sperms does not occur until shortly before fertilization. After the nuclear division that forms the sperms, large granules, which appear prior to the division of the body cell, move to the sur-

5 Sometimes called a "tent pole."

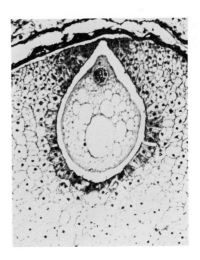

FIG. 26-11. *Ginkgo biloba.* Apex of nearly mature ♀ gametophyte; central-cell nucleus in prophase of division forming egg and ventral-canal nuclei. X 80.

face of the sperm cells where they form elongate, spirally coiled bands of cilia over a small portion of the sperm surface (Fig. 26-10B). All the nuclei of the male gametophyte, excepting sometimes the tube nucleus, remain at the pollen-grain end of the tube until just before fertilization. The function of the pollen tube, therefore, is primarily haustorial.

It has been reported that the archegonial chamber may be filled with fluid at fertilization. Just prior to this, the egg cytoplasm protrudes as a beak-shaped mass, forcing apart the four neck cells which have previously enlarged to form a hemispherical projection. The egg nucleus may extend into the protuberant cytoplasm. When a sperm has been engulfed by the latter, the egg cytoplasm and nucleus withdraw into the egg cell; the nuclear portion of the sperm is included and unites with the egg nucleus.

The time and place of fertilization in *Ginkgo* are of interest. Fertilization may occur in one and the same tree at various times between August and October (in different seasons), and while the ovules are still attached to the tree or after they have been abscised and have fallen to the ground. In the latter case, they are not unlike the vascular cryptogams. The variation in timing of fertilization and embryogeny in *Ginkgo* is probably correlated with variation in the time of pollination.

Reproduction: embryogeny

Soon after nuclear union, the zygote nucleus enters upon a period of free-nuclear division, the division products being uniformly distributed throughout the cytoplasm of the egg. Eight successive nuclear divisions occur, so that approximately 256 proembryonic nuclei are formed. Cell walls then segregate the nuclei, and the entire embryo becomes cellular (Fig. 26-12). The cells of the embryo in the region of the base of the archegonium divide rapidly; those in the neck region elongate slightly but do not divide. The cells in the intermediate zone then enlarge somewhat, but a highly organized suspensor, such as is found in *Zamia*, does not occur in *Ginkgo*. The actively dividing basal portion of the embryo grows through the base of the archegonium, digesting the vegetative tissues of the female gametophyte (Fig. 26-12) as it develops. The zygotes of both archegonia may initiate embryos, but usually only one is present in the mature seeds. Relatively early in development, the surviving embryo is differentiated into a root, a short hypocotyl, two cotyledons, and a short epicotyl terminated by the primordia of approximately the first five foliage leaves (Figs. 26-13, 26-14).

During the development of the embryo, the integument increases greatly and its three component layers are clearly differentiated. The

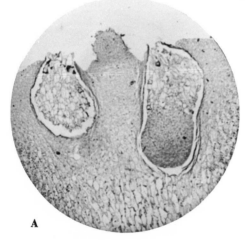
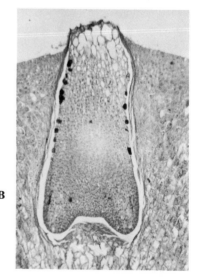

A   **B**

FIG. 26-12. *Ginkgo biloba.* A. Apex of ♀ gametophyte; note "tent pole"-like protuberance and two archegonia, the one at the left, abortive, the one at the right, with a cellular proembryo. X 125. B. More advanced embryo than in A; cotyledons and hypocotyl developed. X 160.

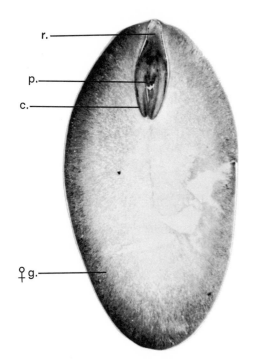

FIG. 26-13. *Ginkgo biloba.* Longisection of ♀ gametophyte and embryo of seed, some weeks after shedding; c., cotyledons; ♀ g., female gametophyte; p., plumule; r., radicle. X 4.

outermost and most extensive becomes fleshy and a mottled green-purple. The innermost layer is rather dry and papery, and the middle layer is stony, as in the cycads. The mature seeds have the appearance of small plums (Figs. 26-14, 26-15). A median section of a seed is shown in Fig. 26-14. The fleshy layer

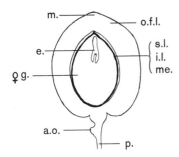

FIG. 26-14. *Ginkgo biloba.* Diagram of a median longitudinal section of mature seed. a.o., aborted ovule; e., embryo; ♀ g., female gametophyte; i.l., inner layer; m., micropyle; me., megasporangium remains; o.f.l., outer fleshy layer; s.l., stony layer of integument; p., peduncle.

FIG. 26-15. *Ginkgo biloba.* Branch with mature seeds. X 0.33. (*Courtesy of the Chicago Natural History Museum.*)

has a foul odor and may cause nausea and skin eruptions in certain individuals. The embryo and female gametophyte, however, are edible.

As in the cycads, there apparently is no genetically determined period of dormancy in the embryos of *Ginkgo*, although the environment may impose dormancy secondarily. Embryogeny is continuous, therefore, merging with germination, the latter in this case not a "renewal of growth" but merely the emergence of the growing embryo from the seed.

In seed germination, *Ginkgo* is **hypogean,** the cotyledons remaining within the seed except for the proximal portions; from it they digest and absorb the remains of the female gametophyte, translocating it in soluble form to other parts of the developing seedling. The

FIG. 26-16. *Baiera gracilis.* Ginkgophyta. Fossilized leaf. X 0.66. (*After Seward.*)

primary root emerges early and functions as a tap root. The seedling leaves are deeply bilobed like those at the tips of the long shoots in the mature trees.

Fossil Precursors of Ginkgo

Although the extant *Ginkgo* is restricted (except in cultivation) to a localized area of

A

B

FIG. 26-17. *Ginkgoites digitata.* A, B. Fossilized leaves. X 0.66. (*After Seward.*)

eastern China, the fossil record indicates it was much more widely distributed earlier in geologic time. The leaves of living *Ginkgo* vary in extent of lobing. A number of *Ginkgo*-like leaves found in the Mesozoic and Tertiary (Table 32-1) seem closely related to the extant genus. Many of these fossil leaves occur in the western United States, in Japan, and in eastern Greenland. Study of these indicates that dissection and lobing of the leaf blades are primitive attributes. The extinct genus *Baiera* (Fig. 26-16), a ginkgophyte, had wedge-shaped leaves which lacked petioles. Approximately nineteen extinct genera of Ginkgophytan plants including *Ginkgoites* (Fig. 26-17) have been described. Unfortunately, we lack adequate data regarding their reproductive structures.

Summary and Classification

Although the reproductive processes in *Ginkgo* are similar in many respects to those in *Zamia* and other cycads, its vegetative structure is in marked contrast. *Ginkgo* plants are large, richly branched trees, with an active vascular cambium that functions in stems and roots throughout the life of the plant in adding secondary xylem and phloem. The leaves are either almost entire or bilobed, never compound as in the cycads. The spur shoots superficially resemble the cycad stems in their armored surfaces and leaf crowns as well as in their extensive pith and cortex and the paucity of xylem.

Next to those of the cycads, the sperms of *Ginkgo* are the largest in the plant kingdom, and, with those of the cycads, the only ciliate sperms among the living seed plants. The male gametophyte of *Ginkgo,* with its two prothallial cells, is considered to be more primitive than those of cycads which have one. The occurrence of cytokinesis to form a ventral canal *cell* in the archegonium of *Ginkgo* is also a feature more primitive than that seen in other gymnospermous seed plants. An actively functioning suspensor is absent in the developing embryo of *Ginkgo*. The latter also differs from the Cycadophyta and vascular cryptogams in its extremely woody and deciduous habit, in which attributes it resembles the Coniferophyta (Chapter 27).

The fossil history of *Ginkgo*-like plants has been traced back to Permian times.

Ginkgo may be classified as follows:

Division Ginkgophyta
  Class 1. Ginkgopsida
    Order 1. Ginkgoales
      Family 1. Ginkgoaceae
        Genera: *Ginkgo, Baiera, Ginkgoites*

DISCUSSION QUESTIONS

1. Why is *Ginkgo* sometimes called a "living fossil"?

2. What is the origin of the common name for *Ginkgo?*

3. Where does *Ginkgo* grow natively? Where is the tree nearest to your campus?

4. Of what possible significance are the collars at the bases of the ovules?

5. What structures are visible in a median longitudinal section of the ovule made at pollination?

6. Describe the development of the male and female gametophytes and fertilization in *Ginkgo*. Make labeled drawings to illustrate these phenomena.

7. Compare the embryogeny of *Ginkgo* with that of *Zamia.*

8. In what respects are the gametophytes of *Ginkgo* more primitive than those of *Zamia?* On what assumptions do you base your answer?

9. Why is it so easy to split the mature female gametophyte of *Ginkgo* into two portions?

10. What significance do you attach to the chlorophyll of the female gametophyte of *Ginkgo?* Describe procedures to demonstrate the nature of the pigment.

11. Draw and label a mature seed of *Ginkgo* as it would appear in a median longitudinal section.

12. Devise a definition of a seed as you have observed its structure.

13. Define the terms epigean, hypogean, epicotyl, hypocotyl, radicle, cotyledons, coleorhiza.

14. How do the archegonial chambers of *Zamia* and *Ginkgo* differ?

15. Is dormancy a necessary attribute of seeds? In what plants are the seeds not characterized by dormancy?

CHAPTER 27

Division Coniferophyta

The Coniferophyta may in the future be proven to be more ancient than the Cycadophyta; they differ from the latter in a number of attributes. These may be summarized comparatively as follows:

Cycadophyta	Coniferophyta
1. Leaves, large, complex fern-frondlike, compound.	1. Leaves simple, often scale- or needlelike.
2. Xylem loosely arranged with abundant parenchyma; with broad parenchymatous rays.	2. Xylem compact, composed mostly of tracheids; rays narrow.
3. Pith and cortex extensive, as compared with xylem and phloem.	3. Pith and cortex restricted, xylem composing bulk of stem.
4. Leaf bases persistent, forming an "armor" on the stem.	4. Leaf bases not persistent.
5. Stem not differentiated into long and spur shoots.	5. Stem often differentiated into long and spur shoots.
6. Leaf traces numerous and complex.	6. ·Leaf traces few, simple.
7. Ovules borne singly on leaves, in *simple* strobili, or on a conical axis.	7. Ovules often borne in *compound* strobili or ovules borne singly.

As treated in this text, the division Coniferophyta includes three classes, namely, the Cordaitopsida, Coniferopsida, and Taxopsida. The first of these contains no extant members and will be discussed at the end of this chapter.

Class 1. Coniferopsida

Whereas the cycads are represented by only nine or ten living genera with 100 species and *Ginkgo* by a single living species, some 50 genera and 550 species of the class Coniferopsida have been described. Among these are such familiar trees as *Tsuga* (hemlock), *Abies* (fir), *Picea* (spruce), *Juniperus* (juniper, red cedar), *Sequoiadendron* (redwood, big tree), and other widely cultivated forms. Although the genera just listed are evergreen in habit, others, like *Larix* (larch, tamarack) and *Taxodium* (cypress) are deciduous. Certain Coniferophyta from the southern hemisphere— among them *Araucaria* and *Podocarpus*—are

often cultivated in warm climates and in conservatories and botanical gardens. Members of the Coniferopsida form extensive forests in western North America and in parts of Europe and Asia. Many are large trees, but a few— some of the junipers (*Juniperus*), for example —are shrublike. In the southern hemisphere, conifers are abundant in temperate South America, New Zealand, and Australia.

Pinus and its relatives may be the dominant type in many forested regions. The great value of these trees as lumber, in the manufacture of paper, and for naval stores and other commercial enterprises has markedly reduced the extent of naturally occurring stands in areas readily accessible to transportation. *Pinus* has been chosen as the representative genus of Coniferophyta because of the great detail in which its structure and reproduction are known and because of its widespread distribution in the northern hemisphere. Representatives of other families are treated after the discussion of *Pinus*.

Order 1. Coniferales

FAMILY 1. ABIETACEAE

Pinus

A relatively large number of species of *Pinus* occur in North America and in the United States. *Pinus strobus* L., the white pine, is a familiar species in the northeastern part of the country and at high altitudes in the Appalachian chain. *Pinus virginiana* Miller, the scrub pine, is abundant in the eastern part of the country; *P. palustris* Miller, the long-leaved pine, is restricted to the coastal plain in the southeast and southwest. *Pinus ponder-osa* Dougl., the western yellow pine, is one of the largest species of the genus; *P. cembroides* Zucc. var. *edulis* Voss., the piñon of the western states, produces large edible seeds. The Bristlecone pine, *P. aristata* Engelm., along with *Sequoia*, is one of the longest-lived organisms known. Specimens from the Inyo National Forest in the White Mountains of California are more than 4600 years old. The reader no doubt will discover other species, either native or introduced, in the locality where he is living. The following account is based largely on *Pinus virginiana* and *P. taeda* as they develop in the southern United States.[1]

Vegetative Morphology

The habit of *Pinus* is sufficiently familiar to permit dispensing with extensive description. The trees are freely and excurrently branched and evergreen, and therefore conspicuous elements of the areas where they occur during the winter months when the surrounding deciduous trees are leafless. Like all woody perennials of the temperate zone, growth is seasonal and periodic. In the winter months, the delicate growing points of the stems and the young leaf primordia are protected by impermeable bud scales. The latter are shed early during renewal of growth in the spring.

Two kinds of branches and two kinds of leaves are produced in *Pinus*. In addition to the familiar needle leaves, less conspicuous leaves, the scale leaves, occur on the main

[1] The writer is indebted to Dr. Ruth B. Thomas for use of her microscopic preparations of *Pinus virginiana*.

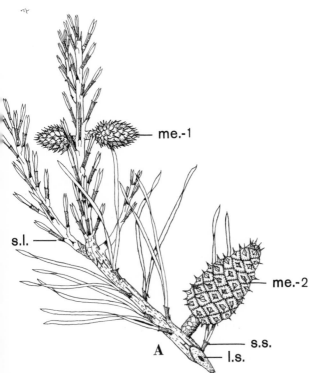

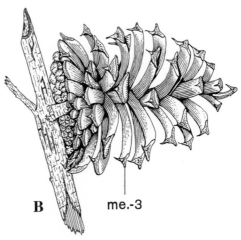

FIG. 27-1. *Pinus virginiana* Miller. A. Long shoot with megastrobili in spring, just after pollination. B. Megastrobilus shedding seed; l.s., long shoot; me.-1, megastrobilus of the season, just after pollination; me.-2, megastrobilus which was pollinated one year earlier; me.-3, megastrobilus pollinated 2 years before; s.l., scale leaf; s.s., spur shoot. X 1.

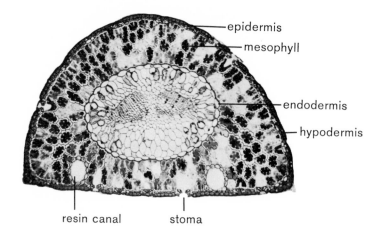

FIG. 27-2. *Pinus nigra* Arnold. Transection of leaf. X 30.

branches and at the bases of the branches that bear the needle leaves (Fig. 27-1). Only the needle leaves are photosynthetic. They occur singly or in groups that vary from one to eight in number in the several species. The short lateral branches on which the leaves arise are known as spur or dwarf shoots, as in *Ginkgo*. These arise in the axils of scale leaves of the long shoots (Fig. 27-1A), the latter increasing rapidly in length during the growing season. The spur shoots are lateral branches of determinate growth.

The needle leaves of species of *Pinus* have been observed to persist on the trees for peri-

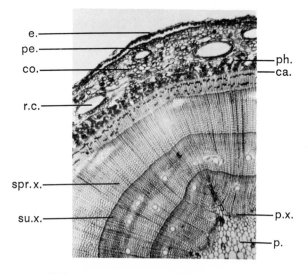

FIG. 27-3. *Pinus* sp. Sector of transection of a three-year-old stem; ca., cambium; co., cortex; e., epidermis; p., pith; pe., periderm; ph., phloem; p.x., primary xylem; r.c., resin canal; spr.x., spring xylem; su.x., summer xylem. X 30.

ods varying between 2 and 14 years, after which they are abscised with the spur shoots which bear them. They are shed gradually, so that their fall is not as striking as leaf fall is in deciduous plants. Although the needle leaves are small—in some species they have only a single unbranched vein—they are macrophyllous, as evidenced by the foliar gaps in the stem stele.

The needle leaves of *Pinus* exhibit striking xerophytic attributes (Fig. 27-2). The leaf surface is covered by a heavily cutinized epidermis within which there are one or more thick-walled hypodermal layers. The stomata lie beneath the leaf surface. The mesophyll is compact, with few air spaces; each mesophyll cell has trabecular projections on the walls on the surfaces of which numerous chloroplasts are arranged. Resin canals are present in the mesophyll. The central portion of the leaf is delimited by a conspicuous endodermis within which, depending on the species, one or two vascular groups are embedded in **transfusion tissue**. The latter sometimes is interpreted as secondarily simplified, hence reduced, xylem.

The multicellular apical meristem of the stem is active only during the spring and summer months, when the buds are developing the season's branches. The procambium differentiates into an endarch siphonostele which encloses the pith and is surrounded by pericycle, cortex, and epidermis. Young stems are green and photosynthetic. The vascular cylinder is interrupted by gaps above the points of departure of the traces which connect with the spur shoots. The cambium becomes active even

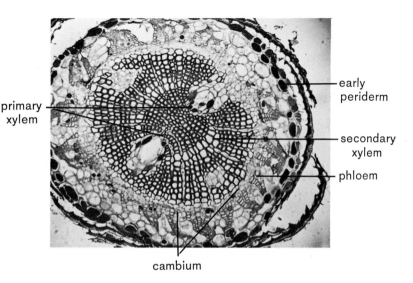

FIG. 27-4. *Pinus* sp. Sections of wood or secondary xylem. A. Transection at junction of two annual rings. B. Radial longisection; note tracheids with bordered pits in their radial walls. X 90.

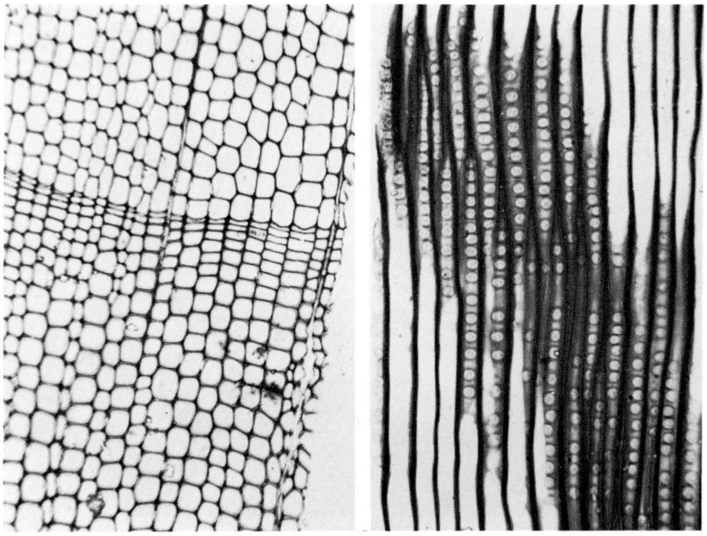

A   B

before primary differentiation has been completed (Fig. 27-3) and it adds abundant derivatives which mature internally into secondary xylem and externally into secondary phloem. The xylem of *Pinus* is very homogeneous, being composed mostly of elongate tracheids the prominent bordered pits (Fig. 27-4B) of which occur in single series on the radial walls. Narrow rays extend centrifugally through the xylem (Figs. 27-3, 27-4). Well-marked annual zones of secondary xylem are present in older stems; sieve elements of the primary and secondary phloem are crushed, except for those most recently added by the cambium (Fig. 27-3).

As the vascular cylinder is augmented by the cambium, a phellogen or cork cambium arises in the outermost layers of the cortex. Phellem (cork cells) and phelloderm (cork parenchyma or "secondary cortex") are added by this meristematic layer (Fig. 27-3). In older stems, phellogen strips arise progressively deeper in the cortex and finally in the secondary phloem; hence the bark of older limbs is composed largely of alternating layers of dead secondary phloem and periderm. **Resin canals** occur in the secondary xylem and in the cortex of the stem as well as in the root and leaf.

The root of *Pinus* (and other Coniferopsida) is a protostelic tap root and may be diarch, triarch, or tetrarch. The stele is sur-

FIG. 27-5. *Pinus virginiana.* Transection of a root in early secondary growth. X 50.

primary xylem

early periderm

secondary xylem

phloem

cambium

FIG. 27-6. *Pinus taeda.* Successive stages in development of microstobili from a tree in Bastrop, Texas. A. January 15. X 0.5. B. March 1; meiosis in progress. X 0.05. C. March 25; pollen being shed; note expansion of terminal bud in C. X 1.

rounded by a narrow pericycle, a prominent endodermis and extensive cortex, and an epidermis with root hairs. The root hair zone is very short in *Pinus*. The roots also undergo secondary growth and become extremely woody (Fig. 27-5). The younger portions of the root system frequently are infected with mycorrhizal fungi.

Reproduction

The microsporangia and megasporangia of *Pinus* occur in separate strobili, but both are borne on the same individual. Pine, therefore, is monoecious, in contrast with the cycads and *Ginkgo*. The microstrobili develop in clusters around the base of the terminal buds of most branches on mature individuals and are recognizable all through the winter preceding the spring in which they emerge. During the dormant season, the microstrobili are covered with brown bud scales (Fig. 27-6A) which are shed early in the spring as the stro-

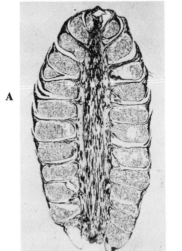

FIG. 27-7. *Pinus* sp. A. Median longisection of microstrobilus containing mature pollen; note abaxial position of microsporangia. X 3. B. Abaxial view of microsporophyll showing both microsporangia. X 5.

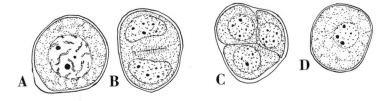

FIG. 27-8. *Pinus virginiana.* A–D. Sporogenesis. (Late March, near Nashville, Tennessee.) A. Microsporocyte. B. End of meiosis I. C. Tetrad of microspores. D. Microspore soon after dissociation of the tetrad. X 1000.

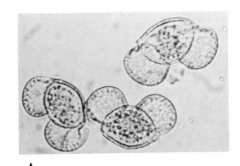

FIG. 27-9. Pine pollen. A. *Pinus virginiana.* X 350. B. *P. taeda.* X 100; note air bladders.

A   B

bili enlarge (Fig. 27-6B). The microstrobilus is simple, as in the cycads and *Ginkgo*, being composed of an axis bearing spirally arranged microsporophylls (Fig. 27-7A). To the abaxial surface of each of these are attached two elongate microsporangia (Fig. 27-7B). The microsporangia are eusporangiate in development; the sporangial wall is about four layers of cells thick, and a prominent tapetum is present. Dehiscence takes place by a longitudinal fissure along a region of thin-walled cells. The microsporocyte stage is attained early in the spring and microsporogenesis occurs as the strobili enlarge. In *P. virginiana*, the microsporophylls become purple-red as they protrude from the bud scales, and it is during this period that meiosis occurs. In the vicinity of Nashville, Tennessee, the meiotic process (Fig. 27-8) takes place between March 15 and April 1 each year. In *P. taeda* in central Texas it occurs two weeks earlier. Microsporogenesis in other species also is vernal, the dates varying with the species, latitude, and temperature. The microsporocytes contain abundant starch which is digested during sporogenesis. Cytokinesis is accomplished by furrowing at the conclusion of the meiotic nuclear divisions. The individual microspores (Fig. 27-8D) are liberated from the microsporocyte walls through predetermined thin areas. As the microspores enlarge and mature, they develop a two-layered wall composed of an intine and exine. The two layers subsequently separate at two points on the surface of the microspores, thus forming the characteristic winged cells (Figs. 27-9, 27-14). The haploid number of chromosomes in all species of *Pinus* so far investigated is $n = 12$.

In *Pinus*, the megastrobili are borne on short lateral branches near the apices of some of the younger green branches of the current season's growth (Figs. 27-1, 27-10). They are not visible clearly, therefore, until the terminal bud of such a branch has unfolded and elon-

FIG. 27-10. *Pinus taeda.* Two megastrobili at pollination. (March 25, in Bastrop, Texas). X 0.5.

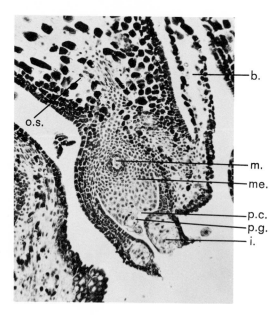

FIG. 27-11. *Pinus virginiana.* Median longitudinal section of ovule and associated structures soon after pollination; b., bract; i., integument; m., megasporocyte; me., megasporangium; o.s., ovuliferous scale; p.c., pollen chamber; p.g., pollen grains. X 50.

gated. When they first emerge, they are green and soft in texture. They begin to harden after pollination.

The ovules are not borne directly on the bractlike appendages which emerge from the strobilus axis; instead, they develop on **ovuliferous scales** (Fig. 27-11), which, in turn, are borne on the bracts. This arrangement has suggested, in light of comparison with fossil

conifers (p. 446), that the ovules are borne on reduced, fertile, spur shoots (= the ovuliferous scale) in the axile of a bract, much as are the vegetative spur shoots. The megastrobili of *Pinus* (and related genera) are, therefore, compound in organization.

Each ovule composed of a massive integument surrounding a small megasporangium (Figs. 27-11, 27-12). The integument is rather widely flaring at the apex where its arms surround the micropyle; it is attached only to the lower portion of the megasporangium of young ovules. From the apex of the integument two flaring wings project. As in *Zamia* and *Ginkgo*, a single cell of the megasporangium differentiates as a megasporocyte (Figs. 27-11, 27-12), enlarging somewhat before it undergoes meiosis to form a linear tetrad of megaspores. In some ovules, one of the daughter nuclei of the first division fails to divide a second time, so that a linear triad results (Fig. 27-13). In either case, however, only one of the megaspores functions, always the one farthest from the micropyle. The remainder degenerate and their remnants are resorbed. Occasionally, more than one megaspore in a given ovule may function, with the result that two female gametophytes develop.

The microspores begin their development into male gametophytes before they are shed from the microsporangia. As in *Zamia* and *Ginkgo*, the first stages in this process involve a series of intrasporal nuclear and cell divisions in which first and second prothallial

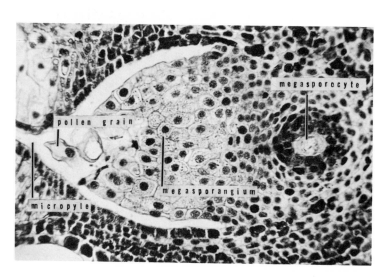

FIG. 27-12. *Pinus virginiana.* Enlarged view of portion of an ovule soon after pollination (mid-April). X 150.

cells, generative cell, and tube cell are produced, as shown in Fig. 27-14. The prothallial cells disintegrate rapidly, and their remains are incorporated in the wall as it thickens. The immature male gametophytes, the pollen grains, are shed in this four-celled condition (Fig. 27-14D) by the elongation of the internodes of the microstrobilus and the drying and longitudinal dehiscence of the microsporangia. The pollen grains are produced in enormous numbers and are carried great distances by air currents.

Pollination in *Pinus virginiana* occurs during April in the vicinity of Nashville, Tennessee, although the date varies within a period of approximately 2 weeks, depending on the temperature. Pollination and other life cycle stages are earlier further south and later northward in *P. virginiana* and other species. At the time

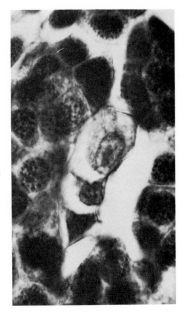

FIG. 27-13.
Pinus virginiana.
Linear triad;
functional megaspore
above. X 1400.

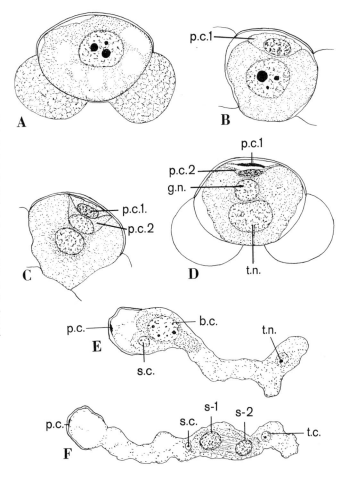

FIG. 27-14. *Pinus virginiana.* Stages in development of the ♂ gametophyte. A. Microspore with bladder-like exine. B, C. Delimitation of first and second prothallial cells. D. Microspore (pollen grain) with enclosed ♂ gametophyte at shedding (pollination) stage; note two aborting prothallial cells, small generative cell, and large tube cell. E. ♂ gametophyte within megasporangium, 14 months after pollination (compare with Fig. 26-18); note stalk, body and tube cells, and nuclei. F. Almost mature ♂ gametophyte; note division of body-cell nucleus into two sperm nuclei; b.c., body cell; g.n., generative nucleus; p.c., prothallial cell; s., sperm; s.c., stalk cell; t.c., tube cell: t.n., tube nucleus and cell. A–D. X 1030. E, F. X 410.

FIG. 27-15. *Pinus taeda.*
Enlarged views of megastrobilus at pollination (March
25). A. Note basal-scale
leaves and apices of ovuliferous scales. X 5. B. Note pollen grains wind-borne to
megastrobilus. X 15.

of pollination, the distal portions of adjacent ovuliferous scales are slightly separated. The windborne pollen grains thus are carried readily into the fissures (Fig. 27-15). The pollen grains sift between successive scales into the axillary chamber formed where the mega-sporophyll is attached to the axis of the strobilus. After pollination, the surface cells on adjacent ovuliferous scales undergo cell division and bridge the fissures between them, thus sealing the megastrobili. The arms of the integument and its cells lining the entrance to the micropyle are coated with a sticky sub-stance to which the grains adhere at pollina-tion. Observation of living ovules at this time has revealed that a prominent pollination drop-let develops at the orifice of the micropyle and that the pollen grains which make contact with the droplet float through it or are drawn up by its evaporation into a chamber between the base of the micropyle and the apex of the megasporangium[2] (Fig. 27-12). After the pollen grains have made contact with mega-sporangium tissue, the integumentary cells lining the micropyle elongate in a radial di-rection and decrease the diameter of the micropylar canal, thus "sealing" it. The in-tegumentary arms then wither.

[2] This is sometimes called a pollen chamber but differs from the depression formed by the disinte-gration of apical cells of the megasporangium in the cycads and *Ginkgo*. Only a very small chamber of the latter kind develops in *Pinus*.

Although it contains sugars, the micropylar fluid is ephemeral and seems to play only a mechanical, rather than nutritional, role in transporting pollen grains from the integu-mentary arms and micropyle to the apex of the megasporangium. Soon after the pollen grain has made contact with the megasporan-gium, a pollen tube emerges and begins para-sitic growth within the former.

At the time of pollination and germination of the pollen grains, the megasporangium of *P. virginiana* has arrived at the megasporocyte stage. Megasporogenesis follows about a month after pollination (mid-May), but the functional megaspore does not begin develop-ment into the female gametophyte for some months, often not until the following October or November. Both the megasporocyte and the functional megaspore apparently secrete sub-stances that diffuse into the tissues of the megasporangium which forms a nutritive, tapetumlike, spongy tissue (Fig. 27-12) as in *Ginkgo*. Development of the female gameto-phyte is extremely slow and is effected by a long-continued process of free-nuclear divi-sion which occupies approximately 6 months in *P. virginiana*. As the number of free nuclei increases, additional cytoplasm is produced. The large central vacuole of the early female gametophyte (Fig. 27-16) is in this way re-placed by watery cytoplasm. Meanwhile, the entire ovule and megastrobilus increase in

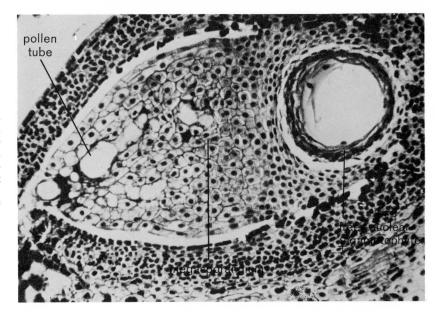

FIG. 27-16. *Pinus virginiana.* Longitudinal section of ovule 1 year after pollination; note free-nuclear ♀ gametophyte surrounded by disintegrating cells of megasporangium; pollen tubes within the latter. X 150.

size, and the exposed, distal portions of the ovuliferous scales harden (Fig. 27-17).

Early in May of the following year, about 13 months after pollination, the female gametophyte became cellular by the formation of delicate walls between the numerous[3] nuclei. The process of wall formation begins at the periphery of the gametophyte and gradually extends in a centripetal direction. A thickened megaspore wall is not demonstrable around the female gametophyte in *Pinus virginiana.* The thickened layer frequently visible on the

surface of the female gametophyte is made up, for the most part, of disintegrating cells and nuclei of the megasporangium.

As the gametophyte becomes cellular, several cells at its micropylar end function as archegonial initials (Fig. 27-18A). There are usually two or three archegonia in *Pinus virginiana.* As the initials enlarge, the vegetative cells of the gametophyte immediately surrounding them become modified and organized to form a jacket layer around each archegonium. Prior to extensive enlargement of the archegonial initials, each divides into a neck initial at the surface of the gametophyte, and

---

[3] Probably more than 2000.

FIG. 27-17. *Pinus taeda.* A, B. Megastrobili one year after pollination (March 25); note relation in position to terminal shoot in A. A. X 0.5. B. X 1.5.

A   B

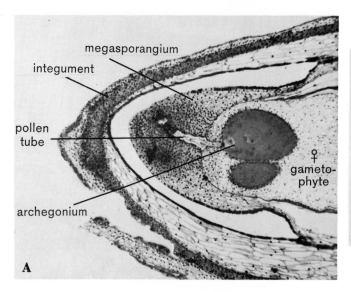

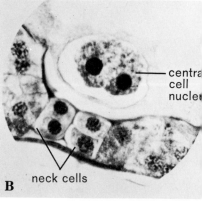

FIG. 27-18. *Pinus virginiana*. A. Longitudinal section of apex of ovule at fertilization (14 months after pollination); note course of pollen tubes through megasporangium to archegonia. X 30. B. Apex of archegonium showing central-cell nucleus, which will divide to form egg and ventral-canal nuclei, and neck cells. X 500.

a central cell. The neck initial divides to form a short neck (Fig. 27-18B) which may consist of as many as two tiers of four cells each; but frequently fewer neck cells are formed, the number varying. The central cell and its nucleus enlarge tremendously, as in the cycads and *Ginkgo*. Soon after they have attained their maximum size, early in June, the central cell nucleus migrates to the neck region of the archegonium and there divides, forming a ventral canal nucleus and an egg nucleus. These usually, but not always, are separated by a wall. The cell containing the ventral canal nucleus is very small and promptly disintegrates. The female gametophyte is now mature and ready for fertilization. A section of an ovule at this stage is shown in Fig. 27-18.

It will be recalled that the pollen grain or immature male gametophyte reached the micropyle and apex of the megasporangium (Fig. 27-12) of the ovule in a four-celled condition (Fig. 27-14D) and that the pollination of the ovule occurs more than a year before the ovule will contain a mature female gametophyte. In the middle of April, 12 months after pollination, the generative nucleus divides; this is followed by cytokinesis, forming a stalk and body cell (Fig. 27-14E). During the intervening year, the pollen tube, initiated soon after pollination, has developed into a branched haustorial organ (Figs. 27-16, 27-18A) which has digested its way through the elongate megasporangium toward the apex of the developing female gametophyte. The pollen tube nucleus lies near the tip of the pollen tube during its growth. Although

FIG. 27-19. *Pinus virginiana*. Fertilization (karyogamy): union of large egg nucleus and small sperm nucleus. X 400.

the pollen tube is branched and haustorial, as in the cycads and *Gingko*, it also serves as a conveyor which carries the male nuclei to the archegonium. This is in contrast with the pollen tubes of cycads and *Ginkgo*, which are solely haustorial. Several days before the pollen tube reaches the female gametophyte, the nucleus of the body cell divides to form two sperm nuclei which lie close together in the common cytoplasm of the body cell (Fig. 27-14F). Neither centrosomes nor granules appear during this division in *Pinus*, and the sperms consist largely of nuclear material without differentiated cytoplasm. Some time before fertilization, the two sperm nuclei and the stalk cell move nearer the tip of the pollen tube.

As the tube makes contact with the female gametophyte in the vicinity of an archegonium, it discharges some of its cytoplasm and generally all of its nuclei into the egg cell. One of the sperm nuclei migrates toward the egg

nucleus with which it unites (Fig. 27-19); the mechanism of this movement is not understood. The remaining nuclei of the male gametophyte disintegrate in the cytoplasm of the egg.

Reproduction: embryogeny

Usually the egg nuclei of all the archegonia of a single gametophyte are fertilized by sperms. In such cases, each zygote initiates embryo development and several embryos may begin to grow, although the mature seed usually contains only one. The development of several zygote nuclei into embryos is known as **simple polyembryony**; this seemingly occurs in the cycads but not in *Ginkgo*. Soon after fertilization, two successive nuclear divisions occur in the zygote to form four diploid nuclei of the **proembryo** (Fig. 27-20A,B). These nuclei, which correspond to the first four free nuclei in the embryogeny

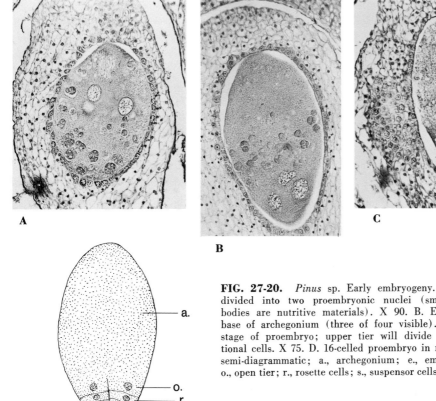

FIG. 27-20. *Pinus* sp. Early embryogeny. A. Zygote nucleus divided into two proembryonic nuclei (smaller, deep-staining bodies are nutritive materials). X 90. B. Embryonic nuclei at base of archegonium (three of four visible). X 90. C. 12-celled stage of proembryo; upper tier will divide to form four additional cells. X 75. D. 16-celled proembryo in median longisection, semi-diagrammatic; a., archegonium; e., embryo-forming cells; o., open tier; r., rosette cells; s., suspensor cells.

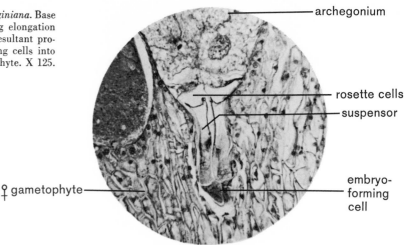

FIG. 27-21. *Pinus virginiana.* Base of archegonium, showing elongation of suspensor cells and resultant projection of embryo-forming cells into tissue of the ♀ gametophyte. X 125.

archegonium

rosette cells

suspensor

♀ gametophyte

embryo-forming cell

of *Zamia* and *Ginkgo*, migrate to the base of the egg cell where they arrange themselves in a tier of four, then undergo mitosis and cytokinesis (Fig. 27-20C). Successive nuclear and cell divisions result in the formation of sixteen cells arranged in four tiers (Fig. 27-20D). The tier of nuclei nearest the neck cells may or may not remain in continuity with the cytoplasm of the former egg cell.

In further development, the lowermost tier of four cells is directly involved in the formation of the embryo. The next upper tier of four cells elongates markedly, functioning as a **primary suspensor** which pushes the cells of the lowermost tier into the vegetative tissue of the female gametophyte (Fig. 27-21A). The four primary suspensor cells and the lowermost tier, the embryo-forming cells, often separate along their longitudinal walls. Inas-

much as each of the embryo-forming cells can initiate an embryo, this phenomenon is known as **cleavage polyembryony.** The lowermost embryo-forming cells cut off cells, often called **embryonal tubes,** which function as **secondary suspensors** (Fig. 27-22) between themselves and the primary suspensors. These with the primary suspensors exert pressure on the developing embryos in the direction of the vegetative cells of the female gametophyte which have become filled with stored metabolites. The gametophyte is digested and liquefied by the advancing embryos which lie in a cavity into which they have been thrust by the elongating suspensor system. One of the developing embryos outstrips the others, and by rapid nuclear and cell divisions organizes an embryo which occupies a major part of the cavity in the central portion of the female gametophyte (Fig. 27-23).

The embryo, as it enters the dormant period, has a radicle which lies in the region originally occupied by the archegonia. The remains of the latter and suspensors and embryonal tubes are compressed at the tip of the radicle. The remainder of the axis is the hypocotyl, which in some species of *Pinus* bears as many as eight needlelike cotyledons. Among their bases is the apex of the embryonic stem. The peripheral cells of the female gametophyte continue nuclear and cell divisions during the development of the embryo, so that, as the latter enters dormancy, considerable female gametophyte tissue remains (Fig. 27-24). Al-

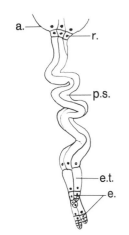

a.

r.

p.s.

e.t.

e.

FIG. 27-22. *Pinus banksiana* Lamb. Base of archegonium (above) and further elongation of suspensors, and divisions in embryo-forming cells; a., archegonium; e., embryo-forming cells; e.t., embryonal tube; p.s., primary suspensor; r., rosette cells. X 60. (*From Buchholz.*)

436   MORPHOLOGY OF PLANTS

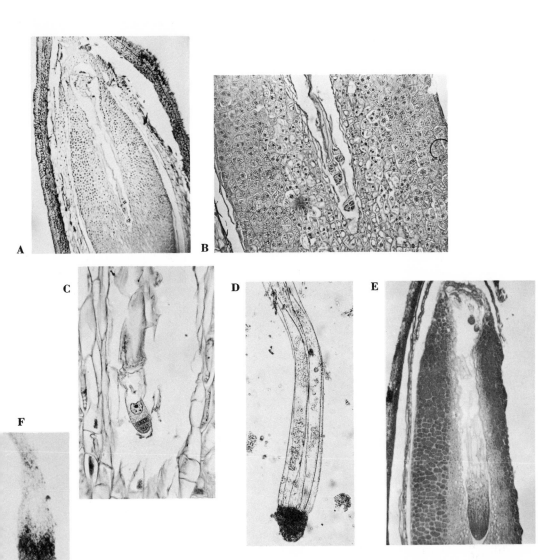

FIG. 27-23. *Pinus taeda.* Later embryogeny. A. Longisection of upper part of ovule in late July, 16 months after pollination and about six weeks after fertilization; note four young embryos with elongated suspensors in digested center of ♀ gametophyte; disintegrated archegonia, and at least two aborted embryos above. X 30. B. Embryos in A enlarged. X 90. C. Detail of suspensor, embryonal tube, and embryo-forming cells of one product only of cleavage polyembryo. X 120. D. Living proembryo showing embryonal tubes and embryo-forming cells. X 120. E. Longitudinal section of ovule on August 15, one month later than that in A. F. Note surviving embryo and suspensor at approximately the same stage as in E. D., E. X 120.

though three layers are distinguishable in the integument of the immature seed, the innermost and outermost are disorganized and vestigial by the time the seed is shed. The middle layer becomes hard and stony and actually serves as the seed coat.

In *Pinus virginiana* and many other species, the seeds are mature and are shed in the autumn of the second year following the ap-

pearance of the megastrobili. During this period the megastrobilus, which was soft and green at pollination, increases in size from approximately a half-inch to a hard, woody cone many times larger (Fig. 27-25A,B). The ovuliferous scales become separated and recurved, making possible the dissemination of the winged seeds (Fig. 27-26).

Germination of the pine seed is epigean.

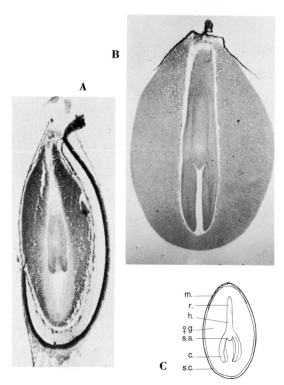

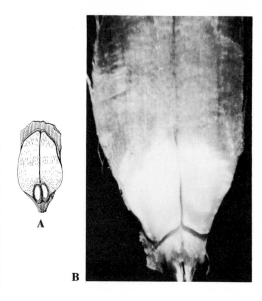

FIG. 27-26. *Pinus* sp. Winged seeds on adaxial surface of ovuliferous scale. A. *P. virginiana.* X 3. B. *P. taeda.* X 5.

FIG. 27-24. *Pinus* sp. A. Longisection of almost-mature seed; organization of cotyledons in embryo. X 30. B. *P. edulis.* Section of megasporangium (black cap), ♀ gametophyte, and embryo of mature seed; note hypocotyl, cotyledons, and plumule. X 30. C. *P. edulis.* Bisection of living seed; c., cotyledon; ♀ g., female gametophyte; h., hypocotyl; m., remains of megasporangium; r., radicle; s.a., stem apex or plumule; s.c., seed coat. X 2.

Other Abietaceae

The cotyledons remain within the seed some time after germination, absorbing the metabolites still present in the female gametophyte. Ultimately they emerge, shed the remains of the seed, and function as photosynthetic organs.

More than one-half of the coniferalean genera are members of the family Abietaceae, genera of which are well represented in North America, with concentration in the western part of the continent. The Douglas fir, *Pseudotsuga taxifolia* Britt. is one of the largest and most important of the western lumber trees. *Pinus*, with more than 80 species, is restricted to North America with few exceptions. *Larix*, the larch or tamarack, a northern genus is distinguished by its deciduous habit. *Abies* (fir), *Picea* (spruce), and *Tsuga* (Fig. 27-27A) (hemlock) are familiar genera of the

FIG. 27-25. *Pinus taeda.* A. Megastrobili in August, 17 months after pollination and two and a half months after fertilization; embryos, like those in Fig. 27-24A, are present within them. B. Opening of megastrobilus at the time of seed dissemination. X 0.75.

B

FIG. 27-27. A. *Tsuga canadensis.* Hemlock; branch with megastrobili shedding seeds. X 0.75. B. *Cedrus deodora*, a true cedar. C. Close-up of a branchlet of B. X 0.5.

C

temperate climates of the world. The true cedar, *Cedrus* (Fig. 27-27B,C), especially *C. deodara* Loud., native to the Mediterranean and Himalaya regions, is widely cultivated in the United States. In this family the scale-, needle leaves, and sporophylls are spirally arranged and the bract and ovuliferous scales are free from each other in part. Many Abietaceae have winged pollen. The Abietaceae are all monoecious. All have prothallial cells in their male gametophytes and the sperms seem to be naked, that is, without cytoplasmic sheaths. The archegonia are in a ring separated by vegetative cells of the female gametophyte.

FAMILY 2. TAXODIACEAE

Of *Taxodium* (United States and Mexico), *Sequoia* and *Sequoiadendron* (the western

U.S. redwoods), and *Metasequoia* (native to China), the first three are probably familiar examples. In these, leaves are spirally arranged, but the ovuliferous scales and bracts are closely fused. Winged pollen is absent. *Taxodium* (Fig. 27-28), the bald cypress, is the familiar tree of many swamps in the southern states. Like *Larix* (Abietaceae), *Taxodium* is deciduous. *Sequoiadendron gigantea* (Lindbl.) Buchholz is one of the giants among trees, up to 300 feet tall and larger than the coastal redwood, *Sequoia sempervirens* (Lamb.) Endl. Large specimens of *S. gigantea* are more than 4000 years old. *Metasequoia* (Fig. 27-29) (see p. 446) is truly a living fossil. The bracts of the megastrobilus of *Metasequoia* are decussate.[4] All Taxodia-

---

[4] That is, opposite but with successive pairs emerging 180° from the pair above and below.

A   **B**

FIG. 27-28. *Taxodium distichum*, cypress. A. Branch with maturing megastrobili. X 0.75. B. Portion of microsporangiate axis. X 5.

FIG. 27-29. *Metasequoia glyptostroboides.* A. One of the largest specimens in the United States (ca. 45 foot). B. Branchlet, enlarged, X 0.75. (A. *Courtesy of Dr. J. M. Fogg, Jr. and The Morris Arboretum.*)

ceae are monoecious. Many lack prothallial cells in the male gametophytes. In this family the sperms are cellular, large and cycadlike, except that they lack cilia. The archegonia are closely contiguous, forming a complex.

FAMILY 3. CUPRESSACEAE

The family Cupressaceae is represented by four genera in North America, namely, *Thuja* (eastern white cedar, including American arbor-vitae, *T. occidentalis*), *Cupressus* (*C. macrocarpa* Hartw., the Monterey cypress), *Chamaecyparis* (*C. thyoides* Brit., the white cedar), and *Juniperus* (juniper), including the red "cedar," *J. virginiana* L. The leaves and sporophylls of these are whorled or decussate. The wood of *J. virginiana* is used extensively for chests, closet linings, lead pencils, and fence posts. The leaves are of the scale type, only the juvenile leaves being of the needle type. The megastrobili are often fleshy at maturity, as in *Juniperus* (L. *Juniperus*, classic Latin name). *Juniperus* is dioecious (Fig. 27-30), but both monoecious and dioecious genera occur in the family. In some species, the microspores are shed in uninucleate condition, before any intrasporal divisions to form the male gametophyte. Here too the sperms are cellular and cycadlike, except for the absence of cilia. In *Cupressus*, there may be as many as 12 sperms in each male gametophyte. The archegonia, like those of Taxodiaceae, are closely associated to form a complex. There are between four and ten in *Juniperus*.

FAMILY 4. ARAUCARIACEAE

Leaves of Araucariaceae are spirally arranged, usually broad (nonneedlelike), and the ovuliferous scale and bract are closely united. The microsporangia (up to 13–15) are borne on a shield-shaped microsporophyll and the ovules are solitary. The two genera of this family, *Agathis* (Fig. 27-31) and *Araucaria*, are both restricted to the southern hemisphere and may reach 140 ft. in height. The trees are used as timber. *Araucaria* species are widely distributed in cultivation. The monkey-puzzle tree, *A. araucana* (Molina) K. Koch, is familiar through its bizarre

A

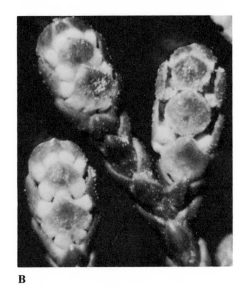

B

C

D

FIG. 27-30. *Juniperus ashei.* A. Branchlet with megastrobili at pollination (December–January, in Bertram, Texas). X 3. B. Microstrobili, the one at the right having shed pollen. X 10. C. Megastrobilus with single terminal ovule protruding. X 8. D. Megasporangiate branch with mature seed. X 0.75.

branching. The Norfolk Island "pine," *A. excelsa* (Lamb) R. Br., is widely cultivated because of the strikingly regular whorled symmetry of its branches.

The genus *Araucaria* is of special interest because as many as forty prothallial cells may develop in the male gametophytes.

Both monoecious and dioecious species are known. In *Araucaria* thirty-two free nuclei occur during embryogeny; in *Agathis*, there are sixty-four, the largest number in the Coniferales. Cleavage polyembryony seems not to occur in this family.

FAMILY 5. PODOCARPACEAE

The genera of this small family are confined to the southern hemisphere except for the genus *Podocarpus* (Gr. *pod-*, *pous*, foot or stalk + Gr. *karpos*, fruit) which extends north-

ward to the West Indies and Central America. The leaves of *Podocarpus* may be needlelike or broader (Fig. 27-32). The genus is widely cultivated as an ornamental shrub in the southern part of the United States where it is known in horticulture as "Yew"; it is of course, not at all the same as *Taxus*, the northern yew (see p. 442).

Podocarpus is dioecious. Numerous prothallial cells are present in the male gametophyte. *Podocarpus* is used for timber in Australasia.

Class 2. Taxopsida

Order 1. Taxales

The order Taxales is sometimes included in the Coniferales as the family Taxaceae. How-

FIG. 27-33. *Taxus canadensis* Marsh. Note ovules partially encased in fleshy arils. X 0.3 (*Courtesy of Dr. Raymond Lynn.*)

FIG. 27-31. *Agathis australis.* Model of Kauri pine or Dammara; branchlet with megastrobili. (*Courtesy of the Chicago Natural History Museum.*)

ever, its genera have attributes which seem sufficiently different from those of Coniferales to warrant higher rank; furthermore, the taxads are distinct from the conifers as far back as their fossil record can be followed. Foremost among their distinctive attributes is the absence of a megastrobilus, the ovules occurring terminally on short lateral branches (Fig. 27-33). Two genera, *Taxus* (L. *Taxus*) (Yew) and *Torreya* (after *John Torrey,* 1796–1873, American botanist) occur in the United States.

FIG. 27-32. *Podocarpus* sp. Branch. X 0.5.

Genera of Taxales are dioecious. The microsporophylls are shield-shaped with 6–8 microsporangia. The microsporophylls occur in strobili but the ovules are solitary and have a fleshy, cuplike structure, the **aril,** at the base, which surrounds the seed at maturity (Fig. 27-33).

The microspores are shed in the uninucleate stage, and the male gametophytes lack prothallial cells. The sperms are cellular in *Taxus* but markedly unequal in size. In *Torreya,* only a single archegonium occurs in each female gametophyte, and there are only four free nuclei during embryogeny, as in *Pinus.* Cleavage polyembryony apparently does not occur in this family.

Class 3. Cordaitopsida

One of the best-known coniferous fossils is the Paleozoic (Table 32-1) *Cordaites* (Fig. 27-34). *Cordaites,* unlike the pteridosperms and cycadeoids, was a tall (up to 100 feet), much-branched tree which formed extensive forests. Remains of *Cordaites* are widely distributed in Carboniferous strata. The leaves (Fig. 27-34C) of *Cordaites* were straplike and simple and attained a meter in length in some species. Venation was dichotomous from the base to the apex of the leaves. The latter were restricted to the tips of the youngest branches, the older axes being leafless.

The central portion of the *Cordaites* stem

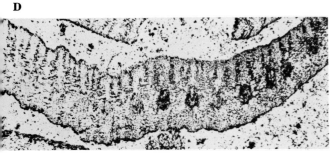

FIG. 27-34. *Cordaites* sp. A, *C. borasifolius*. Reconstruction. B, *C. borasifolius*. Reconstructed detail of fertile branch. C. *Cordaites* sp. Fertile branch. D. Transection of a leaf. X 30. (A, B. *Courtesy of the Chicago Natural History Museum*. C. *After Grand 'Eury, from Andrews.*)

was occupied by an extensive pith which was septate and contained a number of air-filled gaps. The primary xylem groups were endarch, or sometimes mesarch, and were augmented through cambial activity by a com-

plete cylinder of secondary xylem. The tracheids had several rows of circular bordered pits on their radial walls.

Callixylon (Fig. 27-35A) is a widely distributed fossil gymnosperm which also was

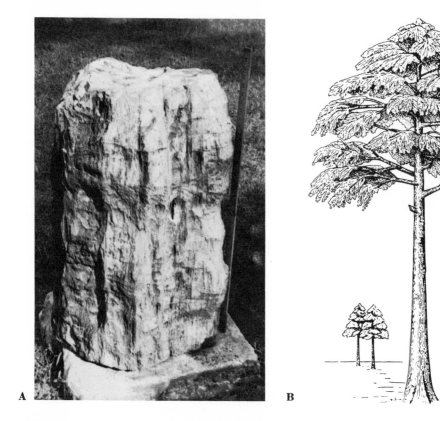

FIG. 27-35. A. *Callixylon newberryi.* Portion of trunk. X 0.05. B. *Archaeopteris.* Generalized reconstruction. (B. *After Beck.*)

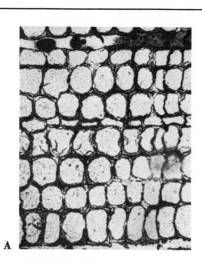

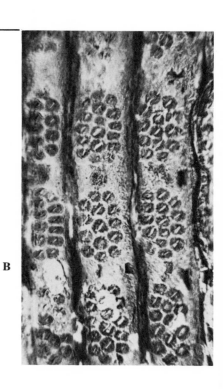

FIG. 27-36. *Callixylon newberryi.* A. Transverse section of
wood. X 125. B. Radial section of wood showing multiplicity of
pits. X 250.

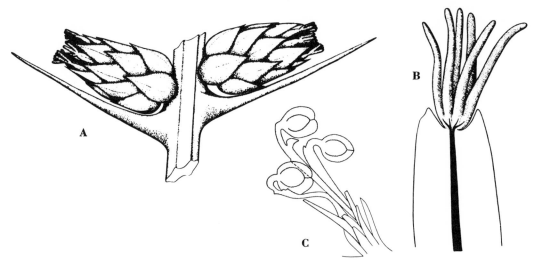

FIG. 27-37. *Cordaianthus concinnus*. A. Reconstruction of microsporangiate branch with two dwarf shoots in the axils of bracts. B. *C. penjoni*. Apex of microsporophyll with terminal microsporangia.

X 25. C. *C. pseudofluitans*. Dwarf shoot with ovules. X 1. (A. *After Delevoryas*. B, C. *After Florin, from Andrews*.)

treelike. Figure 27-36 shows the microscopic structure of its secondary xylem which has been remarkably well preserved. Recently, the fernlike foliage of a species of *Archaeopteris* (Fig. 27-35B) has been found attached to stems of *Callixylon*. It has been suggested that the organism was possibly an early gymnosperm type.

The roots of *Cordaites* contained either exarch protosteles or separate exarch strands. Secondary growth occurred also in the roots.

The fertile structures of *Cordaites* were first described as the form genus *Cordaianthus*. The microsporangia were borne on slender axes with two rows of small leaves or bracts (Figs. 27-34B, 27-37). In the axil of each of these developed a bud or strobiluslike struc-

ture composed of an axis with spirally arranged scales. At the tip, some of the scales, the microsporophylls, were fertile, bearing six elongate microsporangia (Fig. 27-37B). Early development of the male gametophytes was intrasporal, as in other seed plants.

The ovules were borne in similar axillary buds or strobili on lateral branches with two rows of reduced, bractlike leaves (Fig. 27-37C); these were up to 30 mm. long. Some of the terminal scales of the axillary buds were fertile. These fertile megasporophylls were dichotomously lobed, and each bore two or more terminal ovules or seeds or, as in one species, the megasporophylls were unbranched, each producing but one terminal ovule (Fig. 27-37C).

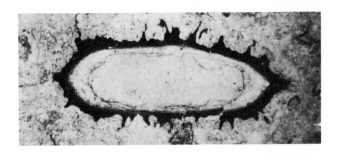

FIG. 27-38.
Cordaicarpus spinatus.
Longisection of a seed.

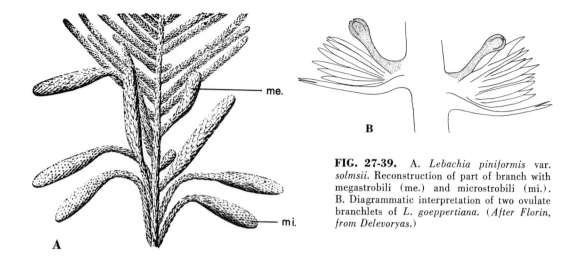

FIG. 27-39. A. *Lebachia piniformis* var. *solmsii*. Reconstruction of part of branch with megastrobili (me.) and microstrobili (mi.). B. Diagrammatic interpretation of two ovulate branchlets of *L. goeppertiana*. (*After Florin, from Delevoryas.*)

Immature cordaitean seeds containing female gametophytes with archegonia are known. A cordaitean seed is illustrated in Fig. 27-38.

Several Upper Carboniferous and Permian[5] form genera based on leafy axes have been described as belonging to the Coniferales. *Lebachia* (Fig. 27-39A) is an example of one of these. The ovule-bearing axes of *Lebachia* (Fig. 27-39B) resemble somewhat telescoped models of the more elongate ovulate branches of *Cordaianthus*, but in *Lebachia* the bracts are spirally arranged instead of in two rows. Those of *Lebachia*, accordingly, were cone-like and compact as in extant conifers. In the axil of each bract there occurs a budlike axis or dwarf shoot as in *Cordaianthus*. In *Lebachia*, however, the axillary dwarf shoot bore only a few scales, all sterile, except one which produced a single terminal ovule (Fig. 27-39B).

Other species of *Lebachia* and those of other Permian and more recently extinct genera indicate that further reduction in the ovulate dwarf shoot and inversion of the ovule have led to the condition of the latter which prevails in *Pinus* (Fig. 27-11) and other Abietaceae. The ovulate strobilus of these genera is the counterpart of the more extended compound ovulate axis of *Cordaites* (*Cordaianthus*) with its two-ranked bracts and axillary

dwarf shoots. Both ontogenetic and phylogenetic considerations suggest that the ovulate strobilus of conifers is a compound structure in which the remains of the dwarf shoot have become united to its subtending bract.

It is important to note that the microsporangiate strobili of modern conifers, in contrast to the ovulate, are simple structures (Fig. 27-7A) and that they, therefore, correspond to single, axillary dwarf shoots of *Cordaites* (*Cordaianthus*). In spite of the emphasis on the homologies between the modern Coniferales and Cordaitales, the fossil record indicates that the former could not have been derived from the latter, since both were contemporaneous. These homologies do, however, suggest a common origin from earlier precursors.

Genera corresponding to families of extant Coniferales have been traced back to the Jurassic (Taxodiaceae, Taxaceae) and Cretaceous (Abietaceae, Araucariaceae).

It is of interest to conclude this brief discussion of fossil conifers with a brief statement regarding a true "living fossil," *Metasequoia glyptostroboides* Hu and Cheng (Fig. 27-29). Described as a fossil *Sequoia*-like genus from the Pleiocene (Table 32-1) in 1941, living specimens of the organism were subsequently (1945) discovered to be growing in central China, and seeds and seedlings have since been distributed all over the world. This seems to have been a unique occurrence in the annals of plant science.

---

[5] Coniferous wood has been found as early as the Devonian.

Classification and Summary

The gymnosperms discussed or alluded to in this chapter may be classified as follows:

Division Coniferophyta
  Class 1. Cordaitopsida
    Order 1. Cordaitales
      Family 1. Cordaitaceae
        Genera: *Cordaites, Lebachia*
  Class 2. Coniferopsida
    Order 1. Coniferales
      Family 1. Abietaceae
        Genera: *Pinus, Cedrus, Larix, Picea, Tsuga, Pseudotsuga,* and *Abies*
      Family 2. Taxodiaceae
        Genera: *Sequoia, Sequoiadendron, Metasequoia,* and *Taxodium*
      Family 3. Cupressaceae
        Genera: *Thuja, Cupressus, Chamaecyparis,* and *Juniperus*
      Family 4. Araucariaceae
        Genera: *Agathis* and *Araucaria*
      Family 5. Podocarpaceae
        Genus: *Podocarpus*
  Class 3. Taxopsida
    Order 1. Taxales
      Family 1. Taxaceae
        Genera: *Taxus* and *Torreya*

Of the Coniferophyta, the Abietaceae, Taxodiaceae, and Taxaceae are almost exclusively northern hemisphere in their distribution, while most Podocarpaceae and Araucariaceae are southern-hemisphere genera. The Cupressaceae occur in both hemispheres. More than half of all the coniferous genera are members of the family Abietaceae. The Cordaitopsida are entirely extinct; comparative study of their microsporangium and ovule-bearing axes has illuminated our understanding of the corresponding structures in extant conifers.

Unlike the Cycadophyta and Ginkgophyta, the former with nine or ten living genera and the latter with only one, the Coniferophyta appear to be a flourishing group in which more than fifty living genera are known. Furthermore, many species of Coniferophyta grow in dense aggregations, forming vast forested areas in which they are the dominant organisms. Like *Ginkgo*, the stems of most genera are strongly branched and are either treelike or shrubby in habit. In the needle-leaved genera, long shoots and spur shoots are present. Strong secondary growth of the stems is characteristic of the group, as is the homogeneity of the xylem, which is composed largely of tracheids, as in *Pinus*.

The reproductive process in pine has been presented in some detail in this chapter. *Pinus* is monoecious. The microstrobili occur on the old wood in clusters at the base of the current season's expanding stems, and the megastrobili are on short lateral branchlets of the season's growth. The megastrobili are compound structures in which the ovules are borne on modified spur shoots (the ovuliferous scales); these, in turn, are borne in the axils of bracts. As in the cycads and *Ginkgo*, a number of months intervene between pollination and fertilization. The male gametophytes of *Pinus* and all Coniferophyta produce nonciliate sperms, in contrast with the cycads and *Ginkgo*. Their pollen tubes perform a dual role: in addition to their haustorial function, they convey the sperms to the archegonia. An archegonial chamber is absent.

The early embryogeny, although free-nuclear, is restricted to as few as four nuclei in conifers (*Pinus*), in comparison with the 256 free nuclei of *Zamia* and *Ginkgo*. Both simple polyembryony (development of more than one zygote) and cleavage polyembryony (vertical dissociation of the tiers of each proembryo) are of common occurrence in *Pinus*, but only one embryo is present in the mature seed, which is winged. Germination is epigean.

DISCUSSION QUESTIONS

1. With the aid of labeled diagrams, summarize reproduction in *Pinus,* giving careful attention to the time factor.

2. If you were to examine trees of pine as the terminal buds were unfolding, what types of strobili would be present, and where?

3. What functions can you ascribe to the pollen tube in *Zamia, Ginkgo,* and *Pinus?*

4. Why are the needles of pine, hemlock, and spruce not microphyllous?

5. Why are the megastrobili of pine considered to be compound?

6. How do the sperms of pine differ from those of *Zamia* and *Ginkgo?*

7. Distinguish between simple and cleavage polyembryony.

8. Diagram a median longitudinal section through a pine seed.

9. In what respects do the archegonia of *Pinus* differ from those of *Zamia* and *Ginkgo?*

10. What is the fate of the nuclei, other than the successful sperm, which are discharged into the archegonium by the pollen tube of *Pinus?*

11. Do you consider it appropriate to call microstrobili "male" and megastrobili "female"? Explain.

12. How does embryogeny in pine differ from that in *Zamia* and *Ginkgo?*

13. Describe the process of primary and secondary development in the pine stem, using labeled diagrams of successively older transverse sections.

14. What are resin canals? How are they distributed in the plant? Do corresponding cavities occur in *Zamia* and *Ginkgo?*

15. Ovules containing two female gametophytes occur with considerable frequency in *Pinus virginiana.* How do you explain their presence?

16. The megaspores of *Pinus, Zamia,* and *Ginkgo* are not markedly larger than microspores of the same plants. On what grounds are they called megaspores? Suggest possible reasons for their size relationship.

17. The megaspores of *Selaginella* and *Isoetes* have thick walls at maturity. Those of the seed plants lack thick walls. Can you suggest an explanation for this?

18. What genera of the Abietaceae and other families of Coniferales and Taxales are familiar to you?

19. What light do the reproductive branches of the Cordaitales shed on similar structures of living Coniferales?

CHAPTER 28

Division Gnetophyta

The final representatives of the gymnospermous seed plants to be considered in this text are *Ephedra* (L. *ephedra*, horsetail) (Fig. 28-1), *Gnetum* (Malay, *gnenom*) (Fig. 28-19), and *Welwitschia* (after *F. Welwitsch*, its discoverer) (Fig. 28-22). These plants are sometimes considered to comprise a single order, the Gnetales, which includes 71 species. Careful morphological comparisons of these three genera, however, indicate that there are a number of important divergences among them. This is reflected in a recent classification in which each of the genera is placed in a separate order, with a single family in each. *Ephedra* has been chosen for detailed discussion because it usually is more readily available for study than the other two genera.

FIG. 28-1. *Ephedra antisyphilitica* Meyer. Living plant. X 0.7.

Class 1. Gnetopsita

Order 1. Ephedrales

Ephedra, the only representative of the family Ephedraceae, is xerophytic. Approximately forty species of the genus have been described, all of them shrubby or trailing plants. *Ephedra antisyphilitica* Meyer has the habit of a small, shrubby tree, attaining a height of 9 to 15 feet in the Rio Grande valley. Approximately six species occur in the southwestern United States, among them *E. trifurca* Torr. and *E. antisyphilitica*. The following account is based on these and on *E. foliata* Boiss., an Indian species.

In the arid regions of the southwest and California, *Ephedra*, known as the **joint fir,** sometimes is important as a range plant and is grazed. The American and Mexican Indians used decoctions of the roots and stems of these plants for genitourinary ailments and as a cooling beverage, and they used the fruits (seeds) to make a bitter bread. The alkaloid, ephedrine, is prepared from *E. sinica* Stapf,

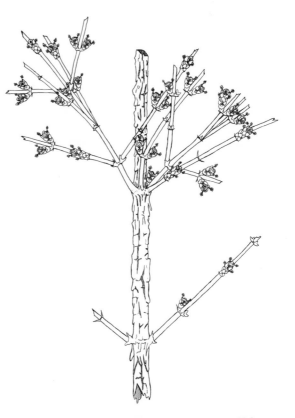

FIG. 28-2. *Ephedra antisyphilitica* Meyer. Habit of woody branch with photosynthetic shoots bearing microstrobili shedding pollen. X 1.

449

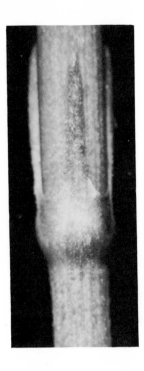

FIG. 28-3. *Ephedra anti-syphilitica.* Node with three leaves; minute white spots are stomata. X 5.

a Chinese species. The Chinese name of the drug is **Ma Huang.** The medicinal properties of species of *Ephedra* were known in China as early as 2737 B.C.

Vegetative morphology

The younger, green branches of *Ephedra* plants (Fig. 28-2) superficially resemble species of *Psilotum* and *Equisetum* because of the minuteness and ephemeral photosynthetic activities of the leaves. Many of the lateral branches arise in fasciculate whorls (Fig. 28-2). In *E. foliata*, the branching is quite variable. On the main excurrent leaders, it may be either opposite or alternate. In older, woody portions of the axes, the green shoots are fasciculate, and many of them are shed during dry periods by abscission layers which extend across the pith and wood. The minute leaves are either opposite or in whorls of three (Fig. 28-3). The younger branches are delicately ribbed and carry on most of the photosynthesis in these plants. The older stems are hard and woody because of secondary growth and are anchored to the substratum by a deep tap root and abundant adventitious roots.

The apices of the young axes are occupied by meristem cells which differentiate into primary meristems from which the primary, permanent tissues develop. The younger shoots of *E. foliata* contain an extensive parenchymatous pith surrounded by vascular bundles with endarch xylem (Fig. 28-4A). The cortex is composed of patches of photosynthetic parenchyma into which groups of sclerenchymatous cells beneath the ridges of the stem surface intrude as supporting areas. The stomata occur on the slopes of the ridges, as in *Equisetum*, and are sunken and overarched by accessory cells. The epidermis is heavily thickened. The presence of such an abundance of sclerotic tissue renders even the younger portions of *Ephedra* axes relatively hard and resistant.

Annual zones of secondary xylem are added by the activity of a continuous cambium (Fig. 28-4B). The wood is extremely hard and is traversed by multiseriate rays in older axes. The most significant feature in the secondary xylem of *Ephedra* is the perforation of the terminal walls of some of the tracheids (Fig. 28-5) to form vessels. It will be recalled that these are absent from the xylem of most cryptogams, the genera *Selaginella*, *Equisetum*, *Pteridium*, and *Marsilea* being notable exceptions. The wood of the Cycadophyta, Ginkgophyta, and Coniferophyta also lacks vessels, so that *Ephedra* (also *Gnetum* and *Welwitschia*) is unique in having them. Vessels are present in the xylem of most flowering plants (Anthophyta) but absent in certain primitive ones (p. 467). The tracheids of *Ephedra* are pitted with bordered pits on both the radial and tangential walls. Although the vessels, for the most part, are larger in diameter than tracheids, they are linked by a series of elements intermediate in size. Many stages transitional between tracheids and vessels may be observed in the xylem of *Ephedra*. The young seedling contains only tracheids at first. It is noteworthy that the perforations in the tracheid end walls (which result in vessels) arise from circular, rather than from scalariform, pits, the latter being the case in *Selaginella*, *Pteridium*, and flowering plants.

The primary steles of *Ephedra* roots are diarch. They increase by secondary thickening to form woody tap roots.

The rudimentary leaves of *Ephedra* are histologically simple; they are composed of a thickened midrib region and thin wings which

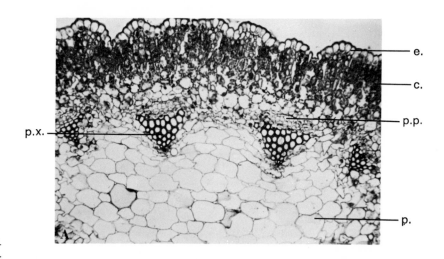

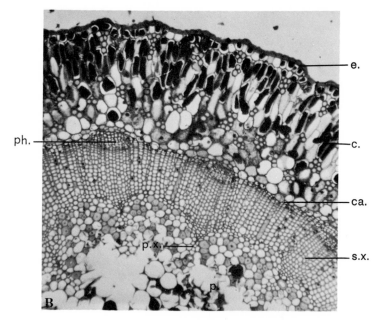

FIG. 28-4. *Ephedra californica.* A. Sector of transection of young branch. B. Sector of transection of stem which has undergone secondary growth. X 60; c., cortex; ca., cambium; e., epidermis; p., pith; ph., phloem; p.p., primary phloem; p.x, primary xylem; s.x., secondary xylem.

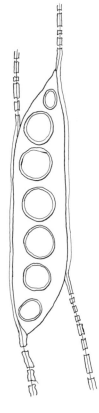

FIG. 28-5. *Ephedra antisyphilitica.* Slanting terminal wall of two tracheid-like vessel elements, showing perforations. X 325.

soon lose their chlorophyll and turn brown. Two unbranched veins traverse the leaves, which are macrophyllous in spite of their small size, as evidenced by the gaps above the points of departure of their traces from the stele. Stomata are present on the abaxial surface. The seedling leaves and those of younger branches are less reduced than those in mature specimens.

Reproduction: the sporophyte

Because of a superficial resemblance to angiosperm inflorescences, the reproductive structures of the gnetophytan sporophyte (especially *Gnetum*) are sometimes referred to as inflorescences or flowers. These terms, however, are inadmissible. Both monoecious and dioecious species are known in *Ephedra*; *E. antisyphilitica* is strictly dioecious (Figs. 28-2, 28-6). The microsporangiate strobili have rounded apices (Fig. 28-6B), while those of the ovulate strobili are acute (Fig. 28-6D). The strobili of *E. antisyphilitica* are already visible and well developed in the late autumn in the vicinity of Abilene[1] and elsewhere in Texas, at the nodes among the fasciculate, photosynthetic axes.

The ovulate strobilus (Figs. 28-6D, 28-7A,B) consists of between four and seven pairs of decussate bracts attached to an axis. These correspond to the bracts of the ovulate *Cordaianthus* axis (Fig. 27-34). The lower-

most pairs are sterile, but in the axil of one or occasionally both (Fig. 28-7A) of the terminal pairs of bracts a short-stalked ovule occurs. Sometimes two ovules are present, but one of these may be abortive. The ovule (Fig. 28-8) is surrounded by a fleshy cuplike structure, sometimes called an "outer integument," which is attached at the ovule base and free above. It probably represents a united pair of bracteoles. These correspond to the sterile scales of microsporangiate *Cordaianthus* dwarf shoots. A more delicate, inner (true) integument is prolonged at the time of pollination into a tubular process which projects beyond the bracts and bracteoles (Fig. 28-8). The inner integument is chlorophyllous at the time of pollination. Comparative study of a number of species of *Ephedra* indicates that the *apparently* terminal ovules are borne on lateral appendages of the strobilus axis. The ovulate strobilus, accordingly, is compound.

[1] The writer is indebted to Mr. and Mrs. Donald T. Knight for numerous excellent collections of reproductive stages of *E. antisyphilitica*.

C

B

D

A

FIG. 28-6. *Ephedra antisyphilitica.* A. Branch with microstrobili. X 0.75. B. Microstrobili. X 1.5. C. Microstrobili with protuberant microsporophylls. X 1.5. D. Megastrobili. X 3.

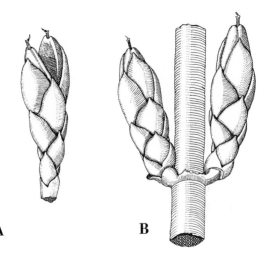

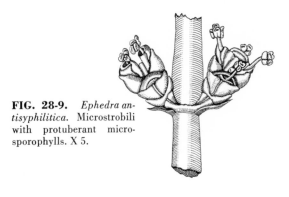

A

B

FIG. 28-7. *Ephedra antisyphilitica.* A, B. Megastrobili at pollination; note protuberant micropylar tubes. X 5.

FIG. 28-9. *Ephedra antisyphilitica.* Microstrobili with protuberant microsporophylls. X 5.

The microsporangiate strobilus also is compound. It consists of an axis that bears about seven pairs of decussate bracts (Figs. 28-6B, 28-9A), most of which subtend a short axis on which microsporangia are borne. Each microsporangiate axis is enclosed early in de-

velopment by two overlapping, transparent **bracteoles** (Fig. 28-10); these correspond to the sterile scales of microsporangiate *Cordaianthus* dwarf shoots. The microsporangiate axis of *E. antisyphilitica* is composed of several united microsporophylls, as indicated by anatomical evidence, to form a sterile portion, the **column.** In *E. antisyphilitica*, five two-chambered microsporangia are typically present at the apex of the column. When the pollen is about to be shed, the column elongates, carrying the microsporangia free of the bracteoles and subtending bracts (Fig. 28-10).

The young microsporangia have two-layered walls and a prominent tapetal layer surrounding the sporogenous tissue. The tapetal cells become binucleate during sporogenesis. At maturity, the biloculate microsporangium (Fig. 28-10) is covered only by a single layer of epidermal cells because of the degeneration of the remaining wall cells. Dehiscence of the microsporangium by an apical fissure occurs at maturity. During microsporogenesis, the microsporocytes separate from each other, become almost spherical, and undergo the meiotic process, which culminates in the usual tetrad of microspores (Fig. 28-11). Micro-

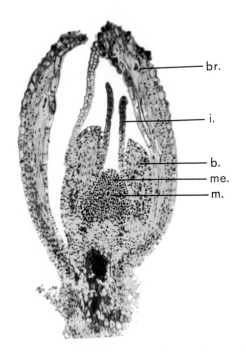

br.

i.

b.
me.
m.

FIG. 28-8. *Ephedra antisyphilitica.* Median longisection of apex of very young megastrobilus; b., bracteole; br., bract; i., integument; m., megasporocyte; me., megasporangium. X 45.

FIG. 28-10. *Ephedra antisyphilitica.* Two microsporophylls emerging from their transparent bracteoles. X 12½.

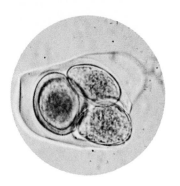

FIG. 28-11. *Ephedra antisyphilitica.* Microsporocyte containing tetrad of microspores; one being liberated. X 500.

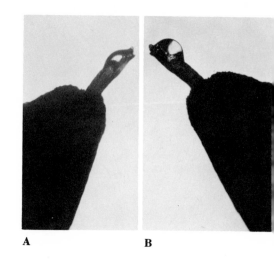

FIG. 28-13. *Ephedra antisyphilitica.* A. Micropylar orifice. B. The same with pollination droplet. X 125.

sporogenesis is not simultaneous in all the microsporangia of a given strobilus, those within the distal bracts being retarded. Microsporogenesis in *E. antisyphilitica* continues over a long period from December through early February, depending on the temperature. After the microspores have been liberated from the microsporocyte walls, they increase considerably in size and their walls become thickened with ribbed exines (Fig. 28-14C).

A single megasporocyte differentiates within the megasporangium of the ovule (Fig. 28-8). A linear tetrad is produced as a result of meiosis, and the chalazal megaspore alone usually is functional.

Reproduction: the gametophytes

Development of the female gametophyte is free-nuclear as in all seed plants. The number of nuclei so formed varies in the several species of *Ephedra*. In one, *E. trifurca*, wall for-

mation occurs when approximately 256 free nuclei have formed, in *E. foliata* after 500 nuclei have appeared, and in *E. distachya* after 1000 nuclei have developed. Two or three archegonia are organized at the micropylar pole of the female gametophyte (Fig. 28-12). The necks of the archegonia are the most massive of any among the gymnosperms; they may consist of 40 or more cells at maturity. The neck cells are arranged in tiers of four or more. The ventral canal nucleus and egg nucleus are rarely separated by cytokinesis in the developing archegonium. The cha-

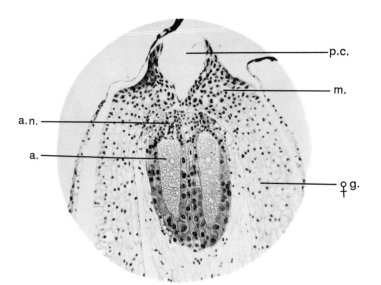

p.c.

m.

a.n.

a.

♀ g.

FIG. 28-12. *Ephedra antisyphilitica.* Median longisection of ovule apex just before fertilization; a., archegonium; a.n., archegonial neck; ♀ g., female gametophyte; m., megasporangium; p.c., pollen chamber. X 125.

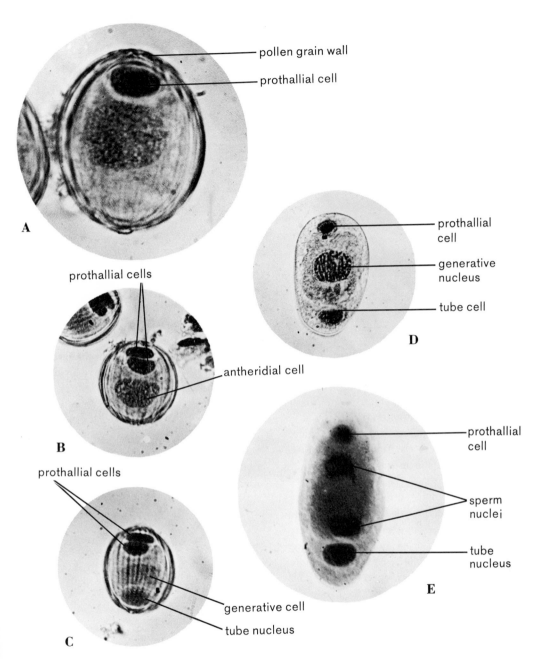

pollen grain wall
prothallial cell

A

prothallial cell
generative nucleus
tube cell

D

prothallial cells

antheridial cell

B

prothallial cell
sperm nuclei
tube nucleus

E

prothallial cells

generative cell
tube nucleus

C

FIG. 28-14. *Ephedra antisyphilitica.* Development of the ♂ gametophyte. A. Small, first prothallial cell and large cell. B. Two prothallial cells and antheridial cell. C. Two prothallial cells, generative cell, and tube nucleus (polar). D. Prophase of division of generative nucleus; second prothallial cell above, tube cell below. E. Telophase of division of generative nucleus; second prothallial cell above, tube nucleus below. A. X 1200. B–E. X 600.

lazal cells of the female gametophyte are dense and filled with stored metabolites, and those at the micropylar pole are watery and vacuolate. In *E. antisyphilitica*, polynucleate cells are present, particularly at the chalazal portion of the female gametophyte. The walls of the cells of the archegonial jacket are extremely delicate and the cells may be binucleate. As the female gametophyte develops, the cells at the apex of the megasporangium

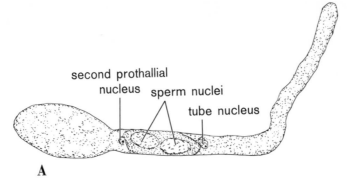

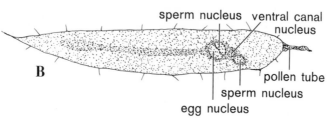

second prothallial
nucleus sperm nuclei
tube nucleus

A

sperm nucleus ventral canal
nucleus

B

pollen tube
sperm nucleus
egg nucleus

FIG. 28-15. A. *Ephedra anti-syphilitica.* Maturing male gametophyte. X 315. B. *Ephedra trifurca.* Longisection of archegonium at fertilization. X 125. (B. *From Land.*)

degenerate to form a deep pollen chamber (Fig. 28-12), which, unlike that in other gymnosperms described in earlier chapters, extends to the female gametophyte and archegonia. A prominent pollination droplet is visible at the subterminal orifice of the micropyle (Fig. 28-13) at the time of pollination. No thickening of the megaspore wall occurs in *Ephedra.*

As in most gymnosperms, the microspores begin their development into male gametophytes before they are shed from the microsporangia. The process may be followed readily in material collected during the winter and forced in laboratory or greenhouse. The microspore nucleus divides first to form a prothallial cell nucleus which is delimited from a larger cell by cytokinesis. The prothallial cell lies near one of the poles of the microspore (Fig. 28-14A). A small second prothallial nucleus and a larger nucleus then arise by mitosis of the nucleus of the large cell, but usually these are not segregated by a cell wall (Fig. 28-14B). The second prothallial nucleus is more persistent than the first, which gradually shrinks into oblivion. The large nucleus now divides to form the generative and tube nuclei (Fig. 28-14C), which are separated by cytokinesis to form a generative cell which is ovoidal. The generative nucleus is reported to

form a stalk and body nucleus in several species of *Ephedra,* but conclusive evidence of this has not been observed in *E. antisyphilitica.* On the contrary, the generative nucleus seems to form the two sperm nuclei directly (Fig. 28-14D,E), but further study is necessary to settle the point. In other species, of course, the body cell is said to give rise to the two sperm nuclei.

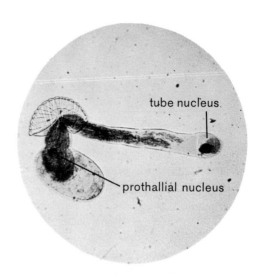

tube nucleus

prothallial nucleus

FIG. 28-16. *Ephedra antisyphilitica.* Rupture of exine and formation of pollen tube on 10 percent cane-sugar agar; note distal tube nucleus and second prothallial nucleus; other nuclei not visible. X 250.

Pollination occurs through the agency of wind, a number of pollen grains usually being present in the pollen chamber of each ovule. Adequate data on pollination and the interval between it and fertilization are lacking for *Ephedra*. Pollination in *E. trifurca* occurs about the time the archegonia are being organized and are maturing. The interval between pollination and fertilization in that species may be as short as 10 hours, one of the briefest among the gymnosperms.

Within the pollen chamber, the pollen grain protoplast emerges from the exine and the two male nuclei are formed (Fig. 28-15A). These may be slightly unequal in size. The pollen tube (Figs. 28-15A, 28-16) develops from the region of the male gametophyte to which the tube nucleus migrates. The tube grows down between the cells of the archegonial neck into the apex of the egg cell, into which it discharges its nuclei. One of the sperm nuclei moves toward the egg nucleus with which it unites, and the other nuclei of the pollen tube remain at the apex of the archegonium in the vicinity of the ventral canal nucleus (Fig. 28-15B).

Reproduction: embryogeny

Development of the embryo of *Ephedra* involves free-nuclear divisions as in other gymnosperms. In *E. trifurca*, the zygote nucleus usually undergoes three successive divisions to form eight nuclei which may be somewhat unequal in size and scattered in the egg cytoplasm. Several of these, usually those near the lower pole of each egg cell, become surrounded by delicate walls (Fig. 28-17A) by free-cell formation with residual cytoplasm; they are called proembryos. The small dividing nuclei observed in the neck region of the egg cell (Fig. 28-17A) have been interpreted as dividing nuclei descended from the second sperm nucleus and/or the ventral canal nucleus. The cells of the archegonial jacket break down after fertilization and their nuclei may mingle with the egg cytoplasm.

All of the proembryonic cells descended from the zygote may begin to develop into embryos, but those at the lower region of the egg cell develop more rapidly. Embryogeny is initiated by a nuclear division and the formation of a tube into which both nuclei migrate. They are separated later by a septum (Fig. 28-17B). The upper cell functions as a primary suspensor, and the lower forms the embryo by further nuclear and cell division. The several embryos of each archegonium are thrust into the vegetative tissue of the female gametophyte by elongation of the primary suspensors (Fig. 28-17C). Secondary suspensors are organized by the cells at the micropylar pole of the embryo. The developing embryos (Fig. 28-18A) gradually appropriate the delicate tissue in the center of the female gametophyte and grow at its expense, finally digesting and absorbing all but the most peripheral cells of the female gametophyte. Only one embryo is present in the mature seed (Fig. 28-18B), the others having disintegrated.

Just after fertilization, when the proembryos are developing, certain cells at the micropylar region of the female gametophyte are stimulated to divide and they form a plug which closes the pollen chamber of the megasporangium. It is interesting to note that although some binucleate cells are present in the vegetative tissue of the female gametophyte of *E. antisyphilitica* at the time of fertilization, the cells of this tissue contain from two to four or five nuclei when the embryo enters the dormant period. The significance of this phenomenon has not yet been ascertained.

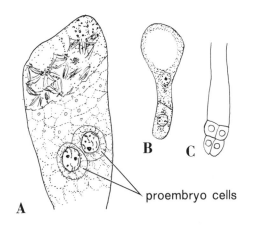

proembryo cells

FIG. 28-17. *Ephedra trifurca.* Embryogeny. A. Two (of eight) cells of proembryo near neck end of egg cell. X 250. B. Later stage in development of embryo. C. Suspensor and early embryo. B., C. X 125. (*From Land.*)

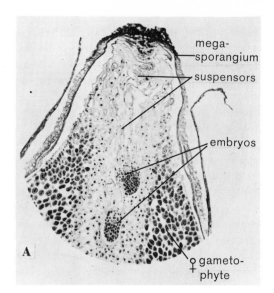

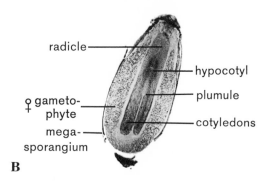

FIG. 28-18. *Ephedra antisyphilitica.* A. Median longisection of micropylar end of ovule after fertilization. X 30. B. Median longitudinal section of seed (outer integument removed before sectioning). X 12.5.

As the embryo becomes dormant (approximately mid-April in west Texas), the inner integument forms a hard seed coat. The seeds require about 5 months to reach maturity after the strobili are first recognizable. The fleshy bracts or the ovulate strobilus become scarlet as the seeds ripen, and the latter become black. Germination follows immediately, under favorable conditions. It is epigean and the two cotyledons are long-persistent and photosynthetic.

Orders 2 and 3.
Gnetales and Welwitschiales

Brief mention must be made at this point of two other genera of seed plants, namely, *Gnetum* and *Welwitschia*, which formerly were considered to be closely allied to *Ephedra*. *Gnetum* and *Welwitschia* are now classified in separate orders, each with a single family, as is *Ephedra*. On the basis of gradually accumulating knowledge of these genera, it now appears that they represent three independent lines of development (see below). It is regrettable that, because of their geographical distribution and the difficulties involved in cultivating them, these imperfectly known plants are usually unavailable for laboratory study, for what is known of them suggests that in some respects they are similar to the flowering plants.

Gnetum[2] (Fig. 28-19) is a genus which contains some thirty species of mostly vinelike woody plants that have broad leaves like dicotyledonous angiosperms. *Gnetum gnemon* is a tree about 30 feet tall. It is cultivated in Java where the young leaves and reproductive axes are eaten after being cooked in coconut milk. The bark yields strong fibers used for making rope.

The vessels of *Gnetum* are more highly developed than those of *Ephedra* in that they may have several or only single, terminal perforations between the segments in the secondary xylem. In the primary xylem there are several perforations as in *Ephedra*.

[2] For a recent summary see Maheshwari, P., and V. Vasil, *Gnetum*, Council of Scientific and Industrial Research, New Delhi, 1961.

FIG. 28-19. *Gnetum gnemon.* Young plant. X 0.3.

B

FIG. 28-20. *Gnetum gnenom.* A. Microsporangiate axis. B. Branch with ovules. A., B. X 0.5. (A. *After Madhulata, from Maheshwari and Vasil.*)

A

Plants of *Gnetum* are dioecious. The microsporophylls occur on vermiform axes (Fig. 28-20A) which arise from the axils of bract-like leaves. The fertile axis has prominent nodes with very short internodes. The nodal bracts form a circular collar or "cupule" above each of which are a number (25–30 in *G. ula* Brongn.) of microsporangiate units. Each of these consists of a microsporophyll with 2–4 microsporangia enclosed in a bell-like sheath. A single ring of abortive ovulate units sometimes is present near the tip of a microsporangiate axis (Fig. 28-20A).

Meiosis of the microsporocytes is followed by liberation of the microspores and their development into male gametophytes. At shedding, the pollen grain contains a single prothallial cell, a generative cell, and tube cell.

At pollination, which occurs during the early free-nuclear stages of the female gametophyte, the pollen grains reach the shallow pollen chamber, a depression at the apex of the megasporangium.

The ovules also occur on axes within nodal collars (Fig. 28-20B). Each ovule consists of a megasporangium enclosed within three structures. The innermost (integument) is prolonged into a micropylar tube as in *Ephedra.* The outermost is massive and its epidermis has stomata, as does that of the middle integument. In *G. ula,* it is reported that 8–10 megasporocytes differentiate. All these may undergo meiosis.

Usually only one megasporocyte persists, but on occasion several may do so and give rise to female gametophytes. The four postmeiotic nuclei are not separated by cell walls, and all four (megaspore) nuclei initiate free-nuclear divisions to form the female gametophyte. This is the only case known among gymnosperms where four megaspore nuclei are involved in the development of a single female gametophyte. (This occurs in angiosperms, however, as in lily, see p. 480.)

The lower portion of the female gametophyte becomes cellular, but the upper at first remains free-nucleate except for isolated clusters of 3–8 cells. One or two cells of each group function as an egg. This report of cellular eggs in *G. ula*[3] is at variance with accounts of other species in which the eggs are said to consist of free nuclei.

The pollen grains, meanwhile, have germinated in the pollen chamber, their tubes growing through the megasporangium toward

---

[3] Vasil, V., "Morphology and Embryology of *Gnetum ula* Brongn.," *Phytomorphology,* 9:167–215, 1959.

FIG. 28-21. *Gnetum* sp. Branch with mature and abortive seeds (left); younger ovulate branches at right. X 1.5.

the apex of the female gametophyte. The generative cells divide to form two sperm cells each as the pollen tubes penetrate the female gametophyte. Both eggs of a group may be fertilized and as many as four zygotes have been found in a singe female gametophyte.

Embryogeny is complex and does not involve a free-nuclear phase. Polyembryony occurs and suspensors function actively. The mature seeds, which are large and fleshy (Fig. 28-21) normally contain a single embryo.

Welwitschia (Fig. 28-22) is a truly remarkable plant. The enlarged, woody-fleshy inverted conical stem, which may attain a diameter of 4 feet, is extended below the soil as a long tap root. The mature plants bear only two enormous leaves which persist throughout the life of the plant through the activity of their basal meristems.

The compound microstrobili and megastrobili of *Welwitschia*, which is dioecious, occur on branching axes in the axils of the leaves

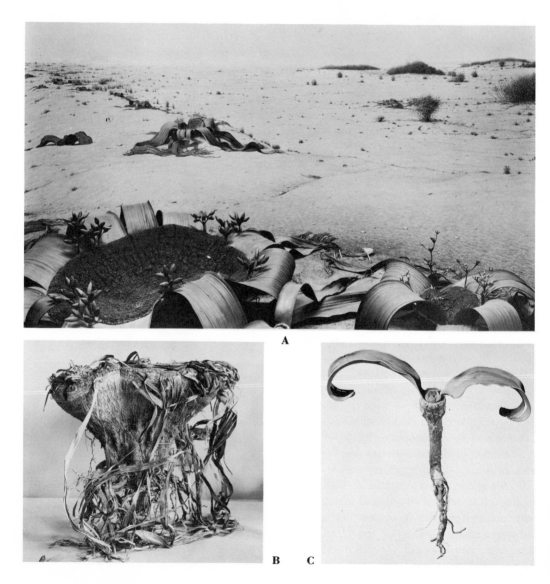

FIG. 28-22. *Welwitschia mirabilis.* A. Reconstruction of growth habit of plants in Mossandes Desert, Angola; note strobili. B. Actual plant; leaves in shreds. C. Young plant showing leaves and part of tap root. (*Courtesy of the Chicago Natural History Museum.*)

A

B

FIG. 28-23. *Welwitschia mirabilis.* A. Reconstructed microstrobili. B. Reconstructed megastrobili. (*Courtesy of the Chicago Natural History Museum.*)

(Fig. 28-23). The mature female gametophyte here too is free-nuclear, and no archegonia are organized. *Welwitschia* is endemic in the coastal region of Angola and southwest Africa where the annual rainfall approximates 1 inch and where there may be no precipitation for several years at a time. The plants are slow-growing and markedly xerophytic in organization.

Fertilization in *Welwitschia* is unique in that tubular processes from the eggs grow up toward and unite with the pollen tubes. Fertilization occurs within the united tubes.

Summary and Classification

Of the three genera of Gnetophyta, it is clear that *Ephedra* is the most primitive in its vegetative and reproductive features. A recent discussion of the relationship of *Ephedra*, *Gnetum*, and *Welwitschia* emphasizes that they are not closely related and recommends that they be classified in separate orders and families. In accordance with this, these genera are classified as follows:

Division Gnetophyta
  Class 1. Gnetopsida
    Order 1. Ephedrales
      Family 1. Ephedraceae
        Genus: *Ephedra*

Order 2. Gnetales
  Family 1. Gnetaceae
    Genus: *Gnetum*
Order 3. Welwitschiales
  Family 1. Welwitschiaceae
    Genus: *Welwitschia*

The fossil record of Gnetophyta is scanty. Pollen attributed to plants related to *Ephedra* has recently been found in Upper Cretaceous of Long Island, New York. It had been found previously in Tertiary strata from other parts of the world.

Ephedra is a genus of xerophytic seed-bearing plants which differs from other gymnosperms described in earlier chapters in a number of important attributes. First among these may be cited the occurrence of vessels in the secondary xylem. These arise by perforation of the circular bordered pits of the sloping terminal walls of tracheids. The leaves are reduced to minute, bractlike organs which function only early in development; they are macrophyllous, however. The delicate fasciculate branches are the chief photosynthetic organs of the *Ephedra* plant.

Furthermore, both the microstrobili and the megastrobili of *Ephedra* are compound structures in which the sporogenous organs are appendicular, not cauline. The male gametophytes are primitive in their production of two prothallial cells, but may be advanced, as compared with other gymnosperms, if further study indicates that the generative cells form sperm nuclei directly, without dividing to form a stalk and body cell. Development of the male gametophytes of *Ephedra*, as compared with those of *Zamia*, *Ginkgo*, and *Pinus*, is very rapid. The ovule of *Ephedra* is composed of the megasporangium surrounded by two envelopes. The inner or true integument is delicate, membranous, photosynthetic, and prolonged into a micropylar tube through which pollination is effected. The outer ovular envelope consists of two united bracts. Breakdown of the apical cells of the megasporangium gives rise to a pollen chamber, which, unlike that in the genera described in earlier chapters, is in direct contact with the female gametophyte and archegonia. The latter are primitive in having the largest number of neck cells known among gymnosperms, namely, 40 or more. The pollen tube performs no obviously haustorial function. Embryogeny includes a more limited free-nuclear period than that found in other gymnosperms.

Comparative study of the reproductive axes (strobili) of the various species of *Ephedra* reveals that they correspond more closely to those of the Cordaitales than they do to those of other conifers or to those of *Welwitschia* and *Gnetum*. With respect to vegetative attributes, the same general relationship seems to obtain. The stomata of *Ephedra*, like those of the Coniferophyta are simple, those of *Gnetum* and *Welwitschia* being complex.[4] Similarities in leaf form, venation, leaf trace number, and wood structure exist between *Ephedra* and the Coniferophyta. *Ephedra*, then, seems more closely related to the Coniferophyta than it does to *Gnetum* or to *Welwitschia*.

---

[4] This has recently been questioned for *Gnetum*; see Maheshwari, P., and V. Vasil, "The Stomata of *Gnetum*," *Am. Bot.*, 25:313–319, 1961.

DISCUSSION QUESTIONS

1. What vascular cryptogams are suggested superficially by the vegetative attributes of *Ephedra*? In what respects are they similar?

2. In what habitats would you seek *Ephedra*?

3. Discuss the medicinal uses of species of *Ephedra*.

4. By what macroscopically visible criteria could you distinguish the microstrobili from the megastrobili of *Ephedra*?

5. Describe the development of the male gametophyte of *Ephedra*.

6. In what genera, other than *Ephedra*, are long micropylar tubes present?

7. How does the pollen chamber of *Ephedra* differ from that in the seed plants discussed in earlier chapters?

8. What functions are ascribable to the pollen tube of *Ephedra*? How does it compare in function with that of *Zamia*, *Ginkgo*, and *Pinus*?

9. On the basis of supplementary reading, list features which the genera *Ephedra*, *Gnetum*, and *Welwitschia* share in common.

10. There is evidence that the sperm nuclei of certain gymnosperms differ in size. Can you cite any other examples of dimorphism in reproductive cells in the plant and animal kingdoms?

11. In what respects is the archegonium of *Ephedra* primitive?

12. How do the vessels of Gnetophyta differ from those of other vascular plants?

13. How do the female gametophytes of *Ephedra*, *Gnetum*, and *Welwitschia* differ?

14. What homologies exist between the sporogenous reproductive structures of *Ephedra* and those of the Cordaitales?

CHAPTER 29

Gymnosperms:
Recapitulation

The plants discussed in Chapters 25 through 28 all have in common the attribute of producing seeds. As was stated in the opening paragraphs of Chapter 25, in earlier classifications the seed habit served as a sufficiently important criterion for uniting a vast assemblage of plants into a single division, the **Spermatophyta.** This taxon often was divided further into two classes, the **Gymnospermae** (Gr. *gymnos*, naked + Gr. *sperma*, seed), and the **Angiospermae** (Gr. *angeion*, vessel + Gr. *sperma*). The Gymnospermae were delimited from the class Angiospermae because the seeds of the former usually are exposed on the appendages which bear them, while those of the Angiospermae develop within their subtending structures. In the present book, the plants formerly grouped in the class Gymnospermae have been interpreted as representing four independent divisions, namely, the Cycadophyta, Ginkgophyta, Coniferophyta, and Gnetophyta. The present chapter has been written in an effort to summarize comparatively the vegetative morphology and the reproductive processes of the gymnospermous seed plants described in earlier chapters.

Comparison of Vegetative Attributes

When one considers such extant genera as *Zamia* and *Cycas*, *Ginkgo*, *Pinus*, and other conifers, and the genera *Ephedra* and *Gnetum*, the striking divergences among them forcefully crowd their more subtle common attribute of gymnospermy almost into oblivion. The vegetative features of these plants are markedly diverse, although all are macrophyllous. In the Cycadophyta, the plant bodies

are relatively small, never exceeding the status of shrubs or small trees. They are strongly suggestive of the ferns, especially in their pinnately compound leaves. The sparingly branched stems are armored with old leaf bases and contain xylem interspersed with parenchyma tissue, even though they have active cambial layers. The leaflets in at least some genera of cycads, like those of pteridosperms, exhibit circinate vernation, another fernlike attribute. The Ginkgophyta and Coniferophyta stand in strong contrast to the Cycadophyta with respect to their vegetative organs. All are richly branched, usually large, trees in which the leaves are simple and broad-leaved and deciduous, as in *Ginkgo*, or scalelike, needlelike, or narrow and leathery as in the conifers. In these trees, the cambium becomes active in both stem and root during the first season of growth and adds cylinders of secondary xylem with little parenchyma each growing season, so that the stems and roots are woody, not fleshy as in the cycads. The stems are protected not by the remains of the leaf bases but by periderm layers generated by cork cambiums. Furthermore, the leaves of these trees often are borne in fasciculate fashion on short lateral shoots, the spur or dwarf shoots, which increase very slowly in length.

Finally, in the genera *Ephedra*, *Gnetum*, and *Welwitschia* of the Gnetophyta, the vegetative organization is extremely diverse and in each case is different from that in cycads, *Ginkgo*, and the conifers. *Ephedra*, the representative of the Gnetophyta emphasized in this text, is a shrubby or trailing xerophyte in which the leaves are reduced to scales that function only temporarily in photosynthesis. The ribbed internodes and the absence of well-developed leaves suggest the arthrophytan genus *Equisetum,* and the presence of vessels in the primary and secondary xylem is unique (except for those in *Gnetum* and *Welwitschia*) among living gymnosperms.

Additional evidence of diversity among the living gymnosperm types is not wanting, of course, but the features cited above should be sufficient to indicate the heterogeneity of the group with respect to vegetative attributes. It seems clear that abandonment of an inclusive taxon Gymnospermae has been justified.

Reproduction in the Gymnosperms

A comparative review of the reproductive features of gymnosperms reveals both common and divergent attributes. The sporogenous tissues of some representatives of the four gymnospermous divisions are localized in cones or strobili; in others strobili are absent. For example, the ovules of the genus *Cycas* are borne on pinnately divided sporophylls, while those of *Ginkgo* occur in terminal pairs on a branching peduncle. The microstrobili which produce the microspores are said to be simple because the spore-bearing appendages are borne directly on the axis of the strobilus, except in the Gnetophyta. In the latter, the microstrobili are compound; the microsporophylls and their enclosing bracteoles are produced in the axils of lateral bracts.

The megastrobili in the cycads are simple, but in *Pinus* and related genera and in *Ephedra* they are compound. The sporangia themselves are in all cases eusporangiate in development, the sporangial walls being relatively massive; the output of microspores in each sporangium is enormous.

In all the representative gymnosperms (and in all seed plants), a single megasporocyte[1] undergoes meiosis to form potential megaspores, three of which usually degenerate. The heterospory of seed plants is functional, not markedly morphological, as it is in vascular cryptogams. However, the megaspore increases greatly in volume during the devel-

opment of its enclosed female gametophyte.

The location, nutrition, and course of development of the megaspores into female gametophytes are quite uniform. In all seed plants, the permanent retention of the megaspore within the megasporangium and its intimate connection with the surrounding tissues (sterile megasporangium) make possible the seed habit. The megaspore of each genus develops into the female gametophyte after passing through a period of free-nuclear division. In a number of gymnosperms, the megaspore wall thickens during the development of the female gametophyte. This is considered to represent a vestigial attribute retained from free-spored precursors. The nutriment for the developing gametophyte diffuses *gradually* into it by the dissolution of the surrounding sporophytic tissues. This is in marked contrast, timewise, with the storage of metabolites in the megaspores of vascular cryptogams. Wall formation at the end of the free-nuclear period (except in *Gnetum* and *Welwitschia*) results in the organization of a completely cellular gametophyte. Archegonia, all reduced and less complex than those of the cryptogams, are organized in all genera except *Gnetum* and *Welwitschia*. In *Gnetum,*[2] as in the flowering plants (Chapter 30), one or more of the nuclei of the free-nuclear gametophyte function directly as eggs, and archegonia are lacking. In all the representative gymnosperm genera, breakdown of the apical tissues of the megasporangium results in the formation of a chamber for the reception of pollen and is accompanied by the secretion of a pollination droplet which facilitates the transfer of pollen to the apex of the megasporangium. The pollen chamber in the megasporangium of *Pinus* is extremely rudimentary. *Ephedra, Gnetum,* and *Welwitschia* are unique, among the types described, in that their pollen chambers extend to the tissues of the mature female gametophyte.

The development of the microspores into male gametophytes in the gymnosperms is quite uniform except for several variations, such as in number of prothallial cells and

---

[1] See, however, p. 430.

[2] Except in *G. ula,* page 459.

motility of male gametes. In all cases, the process begins before the microspores have been shed from the microsporangia. Flagellate sperms are produced in the cycads and *Ginkgo* but are absent in other living genera. In all divisions but the Gnetophyta, the growth of the pollen tube is slow and prolonged, and the pollen tube is obviously both haustorial and nutritive in function. In the Gnetophyta, however, the proximity of the pollen grain to the archegonia eliminates the circumstance which results in haustorial activities, and the pollen tube accordingly is short in length and ephemeral.

The development of the gymnosperm embryo is unlike that of the vascular cryptogams, on the one hand, and the flowering plants, on the other, for it always involves a period of free-nuclear division of variable duration.[3] In the cycads and *Ginkgo*, approximately 256 nuclei arise in the proembryo before wall formation occurs. In *Pinus*, the proembryo consists of only four free nuclei, and the number is often eight in *Ephedra*. In these genera, except *Ginkgo*, the embryo is thrust into the nutritive tissue of the female gametophyte by an active system of suspensors. In *Ginkgo*, a suspensor is absent, but

the embryo itself grows into the female gametophyte through the base of the egg cell. In gymnosperms, the ovule by the time of fertilization has achieved essentially the dimensions which will characterize the mature seed. Both simple polyembryony (the development of more than one zygote into an embryo within a single female gametophyte) and cleavage polyembryony (the division of the cellular progeny of a single zygote into several embryos) occur among the gymnosperms. Cleavage polyembryony, however, is confined to *Pinus* and other conifers. Normally, the mature seed contains only one functional embryo.

Both hypogean and epigean germination are represented in the gymnosperms. The two cotyledons in *Zamia* and *Ginkgo* remain within the seed at germination and serve as absorptive organs. *Pinus*, which is polycotyledonous, and *Ephedra*, which has two or three cotyledons, are both epigean.

Thus, in spite of the diversities in vegetative structure among the gymnospermous genera discussed in Chapters 25 to 28, there is considerable uniformity in the reproductive process. However, considering both living and fossil genera, it seems that a number of parallel lines of development have long existed among gymnospermous plants.

---

[3] Except *Gnetum*. See reference, page 460.

DISCUSSION QUESTIONS

1. Explain the term "gymnosperm." How do the terms "gymnosperm" and "Gymnospermae" differ?

(Questions 2 to 4 refer to *Zamia*, *Ginkgo*, *Pinus*, and *Ephedra*.)

2. Compare the vegetative features of these plants.

3. Compare the disposition of sporogenous tissue in these genera.

4. Discuss the ontogeny of the male gametophyte in these genera comparatively. What divergences are apparent in structure, function, and longevity?

5. How does heterospory in seed plants differ from that in vascular cryptogams?

6. How does the embryogeny of gymnosperms differ from that of vascular cryptogams? Are there exceptions?

7. If the formal class "Gymnospermae" is abandoned, may one still refer to a plant as a "gymnosperm"?

8. What attributes does *Ginkgo* have in common with Coniferopsida? with Cycadopsida?

CHAPTER 30

Division Anthophyta—I

The division Anthophyta, the flowering plants, includes the most recent and successful plants which have colonized the earth. It is the largest of the groups of vascular plants in number and in diversity of genera and species, approximately 300,000[1] species of 12,000 genera having been described. The range of these plants in both habit and habitat is extreme. They are represented by such diverse types as trees, shrubs, herbs, vines, floating plants, epiphytes, and even colorless parasites. They have populated a wide variety of xeric, mesic, and hydric habitats, and they form the major portion of the vegetation of many areas. With respect to longevity, they include annual, biennial, and perennial types. They perennate either as woody trees, shrubs, and vines (deciduous or evergreen) or as herbaceous types which survive seasons of dormancy by means of corms, bulbs, rhizomes, or other subterranean organs.

Because of the diversities mentioned above, and many others, it is not feasible to give an adequate description of the morphology of their vegetative organs in a volume of limited size which includes an account of plants other than Anthophyta, as well as of the latter. Indeed, in practice, such considerations have come to form much of the subject matter of a separate field of plant science, namely, **plant anatomy.** The present chapter, therefore, will summarize only a few of the salient features of vegetative organization. Others of these, it will be recalled, were treated in Chapter 17. The remainder of this chapter will deal largely with the reproductive process in the flowering plants, which occurs in the structure familiarly known as the "flower." The next Chapter (Chapter 31) will present a brief consideration of the problem of the

origin of the Anthophyta and their fossil record.

The Vegetative Organization of Anthophyta

The plant body of most Anthophyta consists of leaves, stems, and roots, as in all vascular cryptogams, except certain Psilophyta and *Salvinia.*

These organs are either primary (embryonic) in origin or adventitious in that they arise without connection with the embryo.

The embryonic axis of the seed shows polarity, consisting as it does, of an "open" terminal bud or plumule at one pole and a primary root or radicle at the other. The attachment of the leaves (cotyledon or cotyledons) to the axis is at such a level that an intermediate portion, the hypocotyl, occurs between stem and root. Branches of the radicle are **secondary roots;** all other roots are adventitious. The probable totipotency of most living cells of angiosperms—demonstrated in the case of carrot phloem (p. 251)—and their widespread powers of regeneration make the occurrence of adventitious organs commonplace.

The Leaf

Angiosperm leaves, which are macrophyllous, vary in size from the minute organs of certain cacti and spurges to the large ones of palms. A vast majority of leaves, of course, are intermediate in size. They may be arranged on the stems in spiral (hence alternate), opposite or, more rarely, whorled fashion. Inasmuch as the leaves have buds in their axils, branching is similar in pattern.

The leaf, in many cases, is differentiated into a **blade** or **lamina** and **petiole** or leaf

---

[1] Eames, A. J., *Morphology of the Angiosperms,* McGraw-Hill Book Co., New York, 1961.

stalk. The petiole arises from intercalary growth at the base of the lamina late in ontogeny. Other leaves, those of *Iris*, for example, are sessile, that is, they lack petioles. The blade may be simple (undivided), with plain (entire) or variously lobed and dentate margins. Compound leaves (with divided blades) occur in many angiosperms (Fig. 17-17). The leaflets may be arranged pinnately along an extension of the petiole (the rachis) or all may originate in digitate (palmate) fashion from the tip of the petiole.

In a number of cases, small, lateral appendages, **stipules,** arise near the leaf base either from the stem or petiole. Ligules occur at the bases of certain monocotyledonous leaves like those of grasses and in a few dicotyledons.

The venation of angiosperm leaves is dichotomous in a few species. In most dicotyledons, the main veins branch and rebranch frequently to form a network. In most, but not all, monocotyledons the main veins are prominent and arcuate or longitudinal; these may be connected by very minute, unbranched veins which are not conspicuous. There are intermediates between these two major patterns of venation.

The leaf blade does not differ markedly, histologically, from that in macrophyllous crytogams. In angiosperms, the stomata may occur on both leaf surfaces (*Iris*), only on the lower (*Ligustrum*) or only on the upper (waterlilies) leaf surface. In most angiosperms, the epidermal cells lack chloroplasts. The epidermis may consist of several cell layers.

The mesophyll in most dicotyledons is differentiated into palisade and spongy regions; the palisade layer usually occurs near the adaxial surface of the blade or, more rarely, on both surfaces, in this case, with the spongy mesophyll between.

The leaf veins contain both xylem and phloem, the xylem usually nearer the adaxial surface. The delicate vein endings may be composed solely of xylem tracheids. The xylem and phloem of the veins are often surrounded by a sheath of parenchyma, the **bundle sheath.** The latter may be composed of thick-walled cells.

The leaves of many angiosperms are separated from the stem by formation of a special layer, the **abscission layer,** which arises near the base of the petiole. Some leaves wither and are separated by mechanical breakage, without the formation of a special abscission layer.

The Stem

In angiosperms, the stem may be aerial (erect, decumbent, prostrate or climbing) or subterranean (including rhizomes,[2] tubers, bulbs,[3] and corms). They may be extremely woody because of addition of abundant xylem by the cambium, as in trees and shrubs, or they may have little or no secondary growth as in herbaceous genera. Secondary growth is absent from monocotyledons, except in certain genera like *Yucca* and *Agave*. Woody angiosperms are considered to be primitive and herbaceous types as derived from them by decrease in cambial activity.

The steles of dicotyledonous angiosperms are endarch eusteles or siphonosteles, while in monocotyledons they are eusteles with one or two concentric circles of vascular bundles or atactosteles with scattered bundles.

Of those angiosperms which have been investigated, vessels occur in the xylem of all but about 100. The genera which lack vessels are all members of the putatively primitive order Ranales or a few highly specialized, reduced parasites. Companion cells are associated with the sieve cells of angiospermous phloem, but lacking in those dicotyledons which lack vessels in the xylem.

The leaf traces and their associated gaps or lacunae follow several alternative patterns in angiosperms (Fig. 30-1). There may be (1) a single trace associated with a single gap; (2) three traces (a median and two laterals) associated with three gaps; (3) many traces subtending as many gaps; and (4) two or more traces may be associated with a single gap. Nodes may be described in terms of the number of leaf gaps as **unilacunar, trilacunar,** or **multilacunar.** In stems with

---

[2] Not all rhizomes are subterranean (see p. 253).

[3] Only a small portion of a bulb is stem; the major portion consists of fleshy leaf bases or entire fleshy leaves.

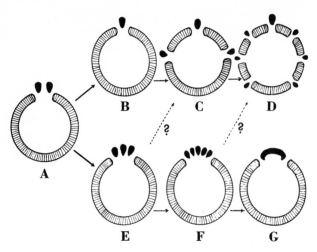

FIG. 30-1. Nodal anatomy in angiosperms; diagram showing proposed evolutionary relationship. A, B, E–G. Unilacunar, with varying number of traces. C. With three and D. with many traces and gaps. (*After Canright, from Eames.*)

eusteles, it is usually not possible to distinguish leaf gaps from the parenchyma between the several vascular bundles.

Although the trilacunar node with three associated leaf traces has often been considered the primitive type for angiosperms, the occurrence of single lacunae with two traces in certain primitive living angiosperms, at the cotyledonary node in many others, in *Ginkgo*, and in certain fossil gymnosperms, suggests that the two-trace-unilacunar relationship is more primitive.

The Root

A primary root or radicle is present in the embryo of angiosperms except in some arborescent monocotyledons. After germination, the emergent radicle may persist as a deep-growing fleshy or woody tap root, especially in dicotyledons. In many monocotyledons, the radicle stops growing soon after germination and a largely adventitious root system functions throughout the life of the plant. Branches of primary roots are called secondary roots. Unlike stem branches which arise superficially from axillary buds, root branches arise endogenously from the pericycle (Fig. 17-14). Mycorrhizal roots are present in a number of angiosperms. The regular occurrence of nitrogen-fixing bacteria in the root nodules of legumes is of great economic significance.

The apical meristem of the angiosperm root, as in all roots, is covered by a root cap. Its stele is clearly delimited from the cortex by the modified innermost layer of the latter, the endodermis (Fig. 17-15). In most dicotyledonous roots, the vascular tissue is organized as an exarch protostele, typically diarch or tetrarch (Fig. 17-15). The primary phloem, as in all roots, alternates with the primary xylem ridges. The vascular tissue is surrounded by a more-or-less prominent pericycle from which branch roots may arise opposite the protoxylem.

In many monocotyledonous and some dicotyledonous roots, the center of the stele is often parenchymatous and designated as pith. The primary xylem is often arranged as many discrete strands alternating with the primary phloem. The exarch protostele of the primary root is connected to the endarch stem stele (eustele or siphonostele) by a **transition zone** in the hypocotyl of seedlings.

Secondary growth occurs in varying degrees in the roots of dicotyledons but is absent from those of monocotyledons. In many roots, addition of abundant secondary xylem and phloem results early in the splitting and destruction of the endodermis, cortex, and epidermis. As this begins, the pericycle undergoes periclinal divisions; one of the outer derivative layers forms a cork-cambium (phellogen) which gives rise to an impervious periderm.

Reproduction

Gross Morphology of the Flower

In spite of the *apparently* limitless variation of floral structure observable in the numerous genera of flowering plants, a remarkable uniformity of basic organization prevails. This becomes clear on careful analysis, which reveals that the individual flower always is an axis that may have as many as four types of appendages (Fig. 30-2), two of which are fertile. Flowers may occur separately or in groups. The stalk of an individual flower is

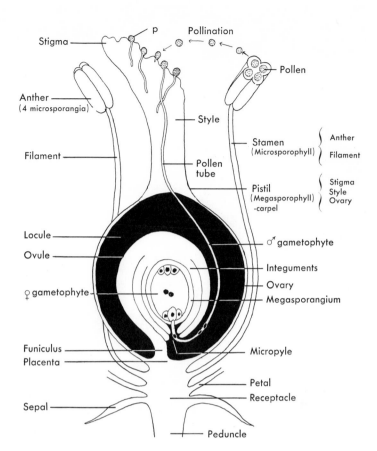

FIG. 30-2. Diagrammatic median longisection of a sample flower; component structures labeled.

known as a **peduncle.** When flowers are grouped in **inflorescences,** the stalk of the individual flower is called a **pedicel.** In the center of the flower and at the apex of the axis tip, the **receptacle** or **torus,** are one or more ovule-bearing structures, the **carpel, pistil,** or pistils (L. *pistillum,* pestle) (Fig. 30-2).[4] The fact that the ovules are enclosed during their development is recognized in the term **angiospermy,** as distinct from gymnospermy. Surrounding the pistil or pistils, a number of **stamens** (Fig. 30-2) emerge from the receptacle or from the **hypanthium,** the latter a tubular outgrowth of the receptacle, or they may arise from the corolla tube. The stamen is most often composed of a stalklike portion, the **filament,** and of sporangia which compose the **anther.** The stamens and pistils are spore-bearing, and, therefore, are **essential organs** of the flower. The great majority of flowers have sterile appendages

on the floral axis, the **petals** (Gr. *petalon,* leaf) and **sepals,** collectively known as the **corolla** (L. dim. of *corona,* crown) and the **calyx** (Gr. *kalix,* cup), respectively (Fig. 30-2). The petals and sepals usually, but not always, are distinguishable in both color and place of origin. Petals generally are colored other than green. Sepals arise lower on the floral axis than do petals. The calyx and corolla together comprise the **perianth** of the flower. In a number of flowers, both the petals and sepals are inconspicuous, green, or almost colorless. Flowers which have sepals, petals, stamens, and pistils are said to be **complete;** where one of these is absent they are **incomplete.**

In a great majority of flowering plants, both stamens and pistils are present in the same flower, which, therefore, is said to be **perfect.** However, in such flowers as those of corn (*Zea mays* L.) (Fig. 30-3), willow (*Salix* sp.) (Figs. 30-4, 30-5), and oak (*Quercus* sp.) (Fig. 30-6), the stamens and pistils occur in

[4] See page 473.

FIG. 30-3. *Zea mays* L. Corn. A. Tassel or staminate inflorescence. X 0.2. B. Single staminate flower with three stamens; white dots are pollen grains. X 3. C. Pollen grains. X 30. D. Young ear or branch of pistillate inflorescence at pollination. X 0.3. E. Branch of pistillate inflorescence; surrounding leaves removed. X 0.2. F. Details of young kernels or ovaries showing emergence of silk or style stigmas. X 9.

FIG. 30-4. *Salix niger.* Black willow. Stages in maturation of inflorescences. A. Staminate. B. Pistillate. X 1.

separate flowers, which are then said to be **staminate** or **pistillate** and **imperfect.** In both corn and oak, furthermore, staminate and pistillate flowers are borne on the same individual plant; this condition is known as **monoecism.** In the willow, on the other hand, staminate and pistillate flowers are distributed on different individuals; hence a state of **dioecism** prevails.

The floral organs are supplied with vascular tissues in the form of traces which depart from the receptacle. Study of the number, path, and arrangement of these traces has contributed much to our understanding of the fundamental patterns and variations of flower structure. It is apparent that a flower is an axis of limited growth with shortened internodes, and that it always bears spore-producing appendages and may bear sterile ones in addition. The extreme brevity of the floral axis in many flowers complicates analysis of their

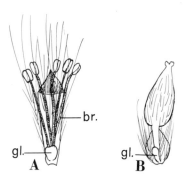

FIG. 30-5. *Salix* sp. A. Single staminate flower. B. Single pistillate flower. X 8; gl., gland; br., bract.

floral organization. The several sets of floral organs are supplied by traces which leave gaps in the stele of the receptacle just as the traces of foliage leaves do. The sepals are leaflike and usually receive the same number of traces as the foliage leaves of the species, three being a common number. Petals and stamens fre-

FIG. 30-6. *Quercus virginiana.* Live oak. A. Staminate inflorescences. X 0.5. B. Enlarged portion of inflorescence, showing individual staminate flowers. X 10. C. Pistillate flowers. X 10. D. Fruits or acorns. X 0.75.

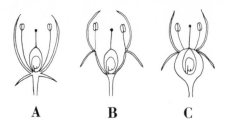

FIG. 30-7. Median longitudinal section of: A. An hypogynous, B. A perigynous, C. An epigynous flower; diagrammatic.

quently receive only single traces. Stamens with three traces occur in certain families such as those of the *Magnolia* group. The pistil (carpel) also receives three traces in many plants which are considered to be primitive. Fewer than three traces, in the past, have been interpreted as evidence of reduction, and more than three as a specialized condition.

The several floral organs exhibit variation in their arrangement on the receptacle and in relation to each other. In many flowers, a median longitudinal section or bisection of the flower (Figs. 30-2, 30-7A, 30-8) reveals that the pistil or pistils are borne at the apex of the receptacle, and that the stamens, petals, and sepals occur on it at lower levels. Such an arrangement exemplifies **hypogyny** (Gr. *hypo,* under + Gr. *gyne,* female). Epipetalous

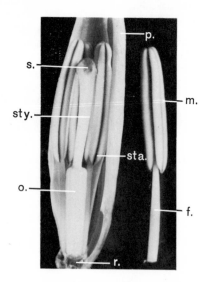

FIG. 30-8. *Lilium.* Lily. Longitudinal bisection of flower bud; a single stamen to the right; f., filament; m., microsporangia; o., ovary; p., petal; r., receptacle; s., stigma; sta., stamen; sty., style. X 1.

flowers, in which the stamens arise from a corolla tube, are still considered as hypogynous, inasmuch as the tube arises below the pistil on the receptacle. In many other flowers, however, it can be observed in longitudinal sections that the pistil, although borne at the apex of the floral axis, has its basal portion, the ovary, partially or wholly united with tissues which represent the bases of sepals, petals, and stamens (Fig. 30-7B). Such a flower is said to be **epigynous** (Gr. *epi,* upon + Gr. *gyne*). In many flowers of the rose alliance, the pistil or pistils occur at the base of a cuplike structure (Fig. 30-7C) upon the rim of which the stamens, petals, and sepals are borne. This type of organization is called **perigyny.**

Further attention will be devoted at this point to the structure and structural variations which occur in the organs of the flower. The individual floral organs may be approximately similar in size and arranged about the axis in radial fashion, a condition called **actinomorphy;** or they may vary in form and insertion so that the flower is **zygomorphic.**

The petals and sepals may be separately inserted on the floral axis (**polypetaly** and **polysepaly**), or they may be united at their bases (**sympetaly** and **synsepaly**). In flowers considered to be primitive, the stamens and pistils are indefinite in number, spirally inserted, and individually attached to the floral axis. In contrast with this is the cyclic type of flower in which the several organs appear to arise from the axis in whorls of definite number, members of a whorl alternating with those of succeeding whorls.

Crowding of the floral receptacle has also resulted in the phenomenon of **adnation,** the union of one type of floral appendages with another. Sepals and petals may be united to form a perianth tube like that in *Iris* which is adnate also to the ovary. Petals and stamens are often adnate, the stamens then being **epipetalous.**

The pistil is enlarged at the base to form an **ovary** which encloses the ovule or ovules (Figs. 30-2, 30-8, 30-10). From the apex of the ovary arise the **style** and **stigma** (Figs. 30-2, 30-8). The style may be either solid or hollow. The stigma may be simple or

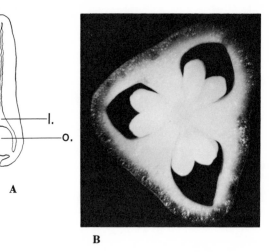

A

B

FIG. 30-9. A. *Pisum sativum* L. Garden pea. Transection of ovary of simple pistil. X 10. B. *Lilium* sp. Transection of compound ovary; note three carpels and axile placentation. X 4; l., locule; o., ovary.

branched, and variously modified as a receptive surface for pollen. Each pistil may have a single, undivided style and stigma, or both styles and stigmas may be multiple. The multiple condition is often an indication that the pistil is compound rather than simple. A **simple pistil** is one that is composed of a single ovule-bearing unit, known as the **carpel** (Gr. *karpos,* fruit). The carpel is by most morphologists considered to represent a phylogenetically folded megasporophyll which has enclosed one or more ovules (see p. 499). Evidence from external form and internal anat-

omy indicates that in many flowers a number of carpels have united and function as a unit, the **compound pistil.** A transverse section of the ovary usually[5] indicates whether the pistil is simple (Fig. 30-9A, 30-10 or compound (Fig. 30-9B) and, in the latter case the number of carpels involved in the fusion. Compound pistils may have several styles and stigmas or only one of each.

The portion of the ovary to which the ovules are attached, each by a **funiculus,** is known as the **placenta** (Figs. 30-2, 30-10). The point of attachment varies in different flowers. In many, the ovules are attached to the ovary wall, a condition known as **parietal**

[5] But not always—as in violet (*Viola*) and members of the family Compositae, for example.

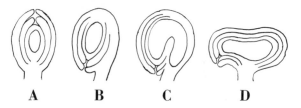

A   **B**   **C**   **D**

FIG. 30-11. Diagrammatic structure of ovules in median longitudinal section. A. Orthotropous. B. Anatropous. C. Amphitropous. D. Campylotropous.

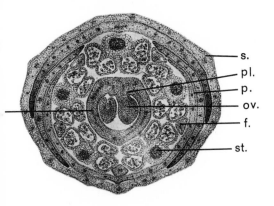

s.
pl.
p.
ov.
f.
st.

FIG. 30-10. *Pisum sativum.* Garden pea. Transection of flower bud; note simple ovary and parietal placentation; five stamens and the filaments of the other five are visible; f., filament; o., ovary; ov., ovule; p., petal; pl., placenta; s., sepal; st., stamen. X 125.

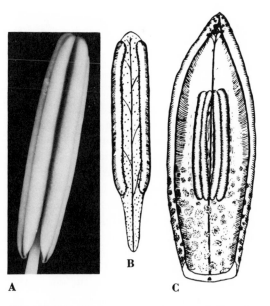

A   **B**   **C**

FIG. 30-12. Stamens or microsporophylls. A. *Lilium.* X 2. B. *Magnolia* sp. X 2. C. *Austrobaileya.* (B, C. *After Canright.*)

FIG. 30-13. *Magnolia grandiflora.* A. Single flower. X 0.25. B. Receptacle, enlarged; note stigmas of numerous pistils above, numerous stamens (some abscised, ovaries enlarging) below. X 1. C. Receptacle with pistils after pollination. X 1. D. Enlarging fruits (follicles); note their spiral arrangement. X 0.75. E. Dehiscent fruits. X 0.75.

placentation (Figs. 30-2, 30-9A, 30-10). In other flowers, the ovules are borne on the central axis of the compound ovary, a condition known as **axile placentation** (Fig. 30-9B). In still others, the floral axis at maturity is free from the upper portion of the ovary but attached at its base. In this case, the ovules may be borne on the distal portion of the axis as well as on its flanks. This last arrangement is described as **free-central placentation.**

The ovules themselves exhibit variations in form and in relation to their stalk, the funiculus. Orthotropous, amphitropous, anatropous, and campylotropous types are common (Fig. 30-11). **Orthotropous** (Fig. 30-11A) ovules are those in which the micropyle and funiculus lie on the same longitudinal axis. **Anatropous** ovules (Fig. 30-11B) are those in which greater growth of one surface of the funiculus, during development, inverts the body of the ovule so that the micropyle and base of the funiculus are adjacent and parallel. In **amphitropous** ovules (Fig. 30-11C), the body of the ovule itself is strongly curved. In **campylotropous** ovules (Fig. 30-11D) the funiculus is attached near the equator of the ovule body. Ovules with one or two integuments occur in most Anthophyta. A very few lack integuments.

Stamens have a stalklike axis, the filament,

at the tip of which the anther is borne (Figs. 30-2; 30-12). The filament may be stalk- or petallike. The anther is composed of four chambers, the microsporangia, supported by a zone of sterile tissue, the **connective,** which contains vascular tissue extending from the filament (Figs. 30-10, 30-17). As the spores mature, the two microsporangia on either side of the connective usually become confluent, so that only two **pollen sacs** are demonstrable in the dehiscent anther. The anthers may dehisce by longitudinal fissures or, less commonly, by apical pores.

Flowers may occur singly, as they do in *Magnolia* (Fig. 30-13), tulip and buttercups, or they may be grouped as **inflorescences.** The latter are of two major types, indeterminate and determinate. **Indeterminate inflorescences** keep developing new flowers over a long period, often as long as environmental conditions are favorable. **Spikes** (Fig. 30-14A), with sessile flowers, and **racemes** (Fig. 30-14B), with stalked pedicellate flowers on an elongate axis, are common types, among others, of indeterminate inflorescences. The youngest flowers, of course, are at the apex of the indeterminate inflorescence.

In **determinate inflorescences,** the apical meristem is "used up" or differentiated[6] in formation of a flower. Examples of these are **cymes** (Fig. 30-15A), **umbels** (Fig. 30-15B) and **heads** (Fig. 30-16). In umbels, the floral pedicels are of equal lengths and arise in whorls so that the inflorescence is flat-topped.

The head or **capitulum** (Fig. 30-16) is characteristic of the large family Compositae. In this type of inflorescence the axis is short-

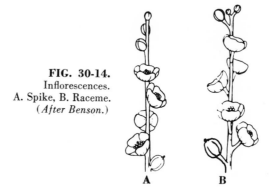

FIG. 30-14.
Inflorescences.
A. Spike, B. Raceme.
(*After Benson.*)

ened and in the form of a convex or flattened head on which many minute flowers are closely arranged. These may be of two kinds, the central **disc flowers** and the marginal **ray flowers** (Fig. 30-16). The disc flowers have bell-like corollas and are perfect, while the corollas of ray flowers are ligulate and the flowers usually lack stamens. In some genera with capitula, all the flowers may be ligulate or ray-type, while in others they may be all bell-like as in disc flowers.

Before entering into a discussion of the details of reproduction in the flowering plants, the student should familiarize himself with the gross aspects of floral morphology summarized in the preceding paragraphs. Examination of a number of types of living flowers will be helpful in this connection. It will be shown below that the spores that arise in the anther become pollen grains which contain immature male gametophytes. Similarly, each ovule produces a spore which develops into a female gametophyte. In the light of comparisons with other seed plants, the stamen of flowering plants often is regarded as a microsporophyll which bears four microsporangia that produce microspores, and the pistil or carpel as a megasporophyll enclosing one or

---

[6] Like that in acrogynous liverworts in forming archegonia.

FIG. 30-15.   Inflorescences.
A. Cyme. B. Umbel. (*After Benson.*)

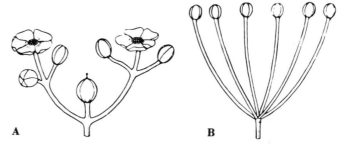

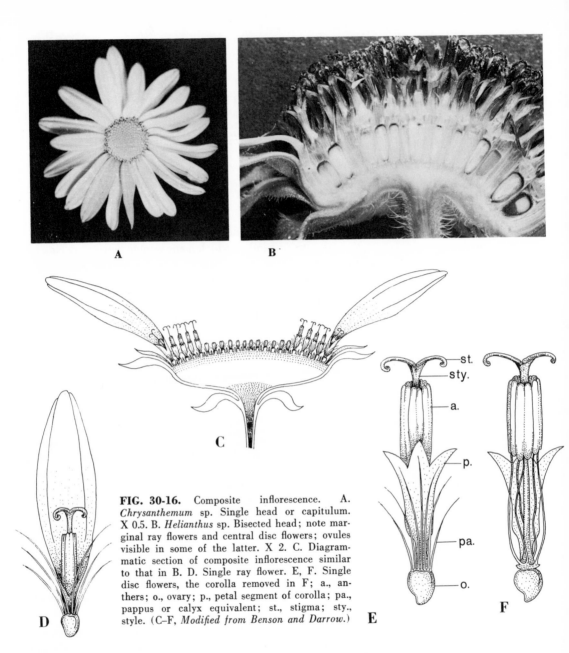

FIG. 30-16. Composite inflorescence. A. *Chrysanthemum* sp. Single head or capitulum. X 0.5. B. *Helianthus* sp. Bisected head; note marginal ray flowers and central disc flowers; ovules visible in some of the latter. X 2. C. Diagrammatic section of composite inflorescence similar to that in B. D. Single ray flower. E, F. Single disc flowers, the corolla removed in F; a., anthers; o., ovary; p., petal segment of corolla; pa., pappus or calyx equivalent; st., stigma; sty., style. (C–F, *Modified from Benson and Darrow.*)

more ovules, the latter, megasporangia surrounded by integuments.

In bringing to a close this discussion of the gross morphology of the flower we are brought finally to the problem of defining it. It is clear that a flower is essentially an axis with short internodes upon which spore-bearing appendages are borne. This statement, of course, also defines the strobilus and it is practically impossible to distinguish flowers and strobili by definition. If it is argued that flowers have colored petals and sepals, unlike strobili, numerous examples of incomplete flowers lacking these may be cited. The flower then, *of itself*, does not distinguish Anthophyta from other seed plants. More subtle characters are available, however, which make this distinction reliable (see p. 493).

The Reproductive Process

The process of reproduction in the flowering plants may be discussed conveniently under the following topical headings: (1) microsporogenesis; (2) megasporogenesis; (3)

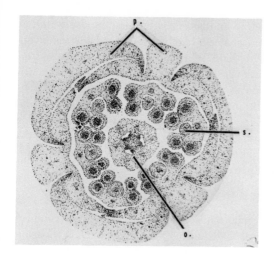

FIG. 30-17. *Lilium* sp. Transection of flower bud; o., ovary; p., perianth; s., stamen. X 12.5.

development of the male gametophyte; (4) development of the female gametophyte; (5) pollination and fertilization; and (6) development of the embryo, seed, and fruit.

(1) MICROSPOROGENESIS

Early stages in the development of the stamen (microsporophyll) may be found by dissecting or sectioning very young flower buds. In these, transverse sections of the anthers exhibit a rudimentary lobing into four parts, but the anther tissue is homogeneous except for slightly differentiated epidermal cells. Development of the microsporangia is eusporangiate. One or more deeply located cells in each lobe function in generating sporogenous tissue. In older anthers (Figs. 30-17, 30-18), the wall is composed of several layers of cells, as in typical eusporangiate sporangia, the outermost of which differentiates as an epidermis. The layer of cells immediately within the epidermis is known as the **endothecium.** As the

anther matures, the endothecial cells may develop fibrous bands on their walls. The innermost layer of the microsporangium wall functions as a well-differentiated **tapetum** (Fig. 30-18). The nuclei of tapetal cells frequently undergo either normal or modified mitoses, not followed by cytokinesis; hence binucleate cells result. The tapetum may disintegrate during microsporogenesis, or in some genera it may be organized as a **tapetal plasmodium,** as is the case in a number of vascular cryptogams.

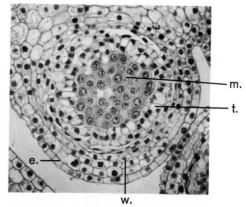

FIG. 30-18. *Lilium* sp. Transection of one immature anther lobe (microsporangium); e., epidermis; m., microsporocytes; t., tapetum; w., microsporangial wall. X 120.

As development proceeds, the sporogenous cells become differentiated as microsporocytes which ultimately separate from each other, become spherical, and suspended in fluid. The meiotic process follows, and tetrads of microspores are organized (Fig. 30-19). Cytokinesis may be by successive bipartition with the formation of cell plates after each division of the nuclei, or it may be by centripetal cleavage furrows which are initiated after the second nuclear division in the microsporocyte. The

FIG. 30-19. *Lilium* sp. Microsporogenesis. A. Microsporocyte. B. End of meiosis I. C. Tetrad of microspores. X 770.

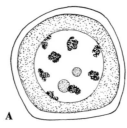

A

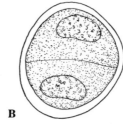

B

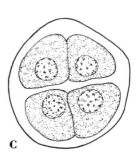

C

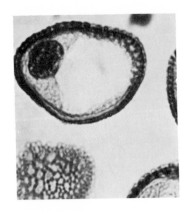

FIG. 30-20. *Lilium* sp. Microspores, sectional and surface view. X 600.

tetrads of uninucleate microspores are arranged in tetrahedral or quadrilateral fashion; occasionally they exhibit linear arrangement. Shortly after their formation, the tetrads separate into individual microspores. Each microspore contains a single haploid nucleus. The microspores enlarge as they separate from the tetrad and become sculptured by deposition of more or less highly ornamented surface layers (Fig. 30-20). In a few plants—*Rhododendron* and cat tail (*Typha*), for example—the microspores remain permanently in the tetrad condition like the spores of some species of the liverwort, *Sphaerocarpos*. In certain orchids and members of the milkweed family, the microspores adhere in a waxy mass, the **pollinium.**

(2) MEGASPOROGENESIS

The ovule, a megasporangium surrounded with integuments, develops by cell division from the superficial cells of its placenta (Figs. 30-9B, 30-17). The number of ovules in each ovary varies with the genus. There may be one, as in corn (*Zea mays* L.), buckwheat (*Fagopyrum esculentum* Gaertn.), sunflower (*Helianthus* sp.); or a small number as in pea (*Pisum sativum* L.) and sweet pea (*Lathyrus odoratus* L.) (Fig. 30-36C), or they may be very numerous and minute as in the orchids,

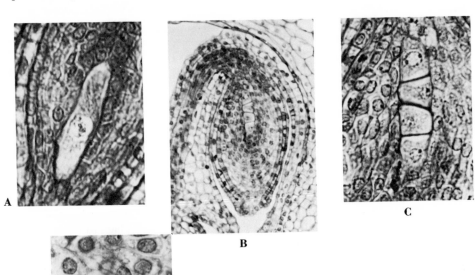

FIG. 30-21. *Oenothera* sp. Megasporogenesis. A. Megasporocyte. X 800. B. Longisection of ovule with linear tetrad. X 250. C. Linear tetrad of megaspores. X 800. D. Functional and degenerating megaspores. X 800.

begonias, and snapdragons (*Antirrhinum majus* L.). Each ovule is attached to its placenta by the funiculus, as noted above. The megasporangium tissue is covered with either one or two closely adpressed (to each other and to the megasporangium) integumentary layers except for a minute passageway, the micropyle (Figs. 30-2, 30-21).

Early in the development of each ovule, a subepidermal cell in the micropylar region differentiates into a **primary archesporial cell**. This may form several sporogenous cells or it may function directly as a megasporocyte (Figs. 30-21, 30-22, 30-26). The latter is readily recognizable because of its large size

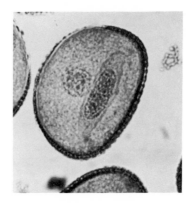

FIG. 30-23. *Lilium* sp. Intrasporal development of male gametophyte; note tube nucleus and cell and elongate generative nucleus and cell. X 900.

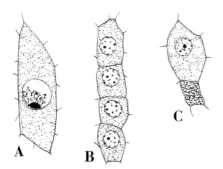

FIG. 30-22. *Oenothera* sp. Megasporogenesis. A. Megasporocyte. B. Linear tetrad. C. Functional megaspore and three abortive. X 770.

as compared with the sterile cells of the megasporangium. In a great majority of the flowering plants, the megasporocyte undergoes two successive nuclear and cell divisions, during which meiosis occurs. The products of these divisions are the four megaspores arranged in linear fashion (Figs. 30-21B,C, 30-22B). Several deviations[7] from this process are known. One of the daughter cells of the megaspore mother cell may fail to undergo division, so that three instead of four cells result. Furthermore, the megaspores are not always arranged in a strictly linear fashion. Normally, as in the gymnosperms, the three megaspores nearest the micropyle degenerate, and the chalazal megaspore persists and functions (Figs. 30-21D, 30-22B,C). This is permanently retained within the megasporangium, where it continues its development into the female gametophyte.

---

[7] See also page 481.

(3) DEVELOPMENT OF THE MALE GAMETOPHYTE

As in other seed plants, the uninucleate microspore (Fig. 30-20) begins its development into the male gametophyte before it is shed from the microsporangium, by undergoing nuclear division and cytokinesis. The two daughter nuclei and cells differ in size and often in form as well; the larger represents the **tube cell** and nucleus and the smaller the **generative cell** and nucleus (Fig. 30-23). The cytoplasm of the generative cell is usually dense. In many flowering plants the generative cell may be ellipsoid, lenticular, or somewhat elongate (Fig. 30-23). It should be noted that a prothallial cell is not formed in the male gametophyte of angiosperms. The generative

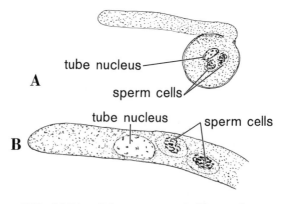

FIG. 30-24. *Polygonatum* sp. A. Mature ♂ gametophyte, tube nucleus, and two sperm cells in microspore. X 515. B. Tip of pollen tube showing detail of tube nucleus and two sperm cells. X 1030.

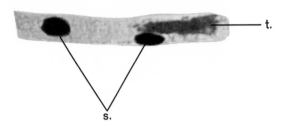

FIG. 30-25. *Hippeastrum belladona.* Segment of pollen tube near its tip showing two sperm nuclei (s.) and tube nucleus (t.). X 960. (*From a preparation by Dr. James Pipkin.*)

nucleus may divide to form two **sperm nuclei** before the pollen is shed, or this division may occur in the pollen tube. In that event, the sperm nuclei usually are surrounded by specially differentiated cytoplasm so they are, in fact, sperm cells (Figs. 30-24, 30-25).

Dehiscence of the anther results in dissemination of the immature male gametophytes or **pollen grains.** Depending on the species, some of these reach the receptive stigmatic surface of the pistil by means of gravity, wind, insects, rain, or water currents (Fig. 30-2).

The ornamentation of the surface of the pollen grain is a feature of taxonomic value. The pollen grains of angiosperms vary in size, shape, and ornamentation of the outer wall or **exine.** The pollen grains of most living angiosperms seem to range from 25 to 100 microns in greatest diameter; grains as small as 5 microns are known as well as those over 200 microns. Pollen may be radially or bilaterally symmetrical.

Pollen grains may have thin areas in their walls, either in the form of **germinal pores** or **germinal furrows,** or both. In pollen without furrows, the germinal pores are usually numerous (up to 30 in some cases). Pollen may be classified into two major types, the **monocolpate** with one germinal furrow, and the **tricolpate** with three. The monocolpate type is thought to be primitive and occurs in monocotyledons and primitive woody families of dicotyledons (and in cycads, cycadeoids, and Pteridosperms). The tricolpate type of pollen characterizes most dicotyledons.

The study of pollen grains and spores of other plants, known as **palynology,** has become an increasingly important phase of plant

science. Fossil pollen has been used by geologists as an aid in locating ancient shore lines, since deposits of pollen are more abundant near the shores of seas. Fossil pollen is used to identify coal beds through the relative abundance in the deposit of certain types of grains. Study of fossil pollen, of course, gives insight into the nature and diversity of extinct floras.

The identification of pollen of living plants is, of course, of paramount importance in diagnostic procedure and treatment of certain allergic conditions. Finally, the study of both extant and extinct pollen has provided helpful data regarding phylogenetic relationships among taxa.

(4) DEVELOPMENT OF THE FEMALE GAMETOPHYTE

The functional megaspore normally gives rise to a single female gametophyte as in gymnosperms. This process is usually accompanied by a series of three consecutive free-nuclear divisions within the functional megaspore, which enlarges during this period (Fig. 30-26 [1–8]); there is no evidence in angiosperms of thickening of the megaspore wall during gametogenesis. At the conclusion of these divisions, the developing female gametophyte contains a quartet of nuclei at each pole. Rearrangement, cell membrane formation, and differentiation of the resulting cells effect the maturation of the female gametophyte (Fig. 30-26), the size, duration, and organization of which are obviously much reduced, as compared with those of gymnospermous female gametophytes. Differentiated archegonia are

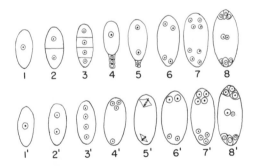

FIG. 30-26. Megasporogenesis and ontogeny of the ♀ gametophyte; 1–8, the "normal type"; 1'–8', *Lilium (Fritillaria)* type; diagrammatic.

FIG. 30-27. *Lilium* sp. A. Immature eight-nucleate ♀ gametophyte. B. Mature ♀ gametophyte and double fertilization. X 315; a., antipodal cells; e.n., egg nucleus; me., megasporangium; p.-1, haploid polar nucleus; p.-2, triploid polar nucleus; p.t., pollen tube; s.-1, s.-2, sperm nuclei; sy.n., synergid nuclei.

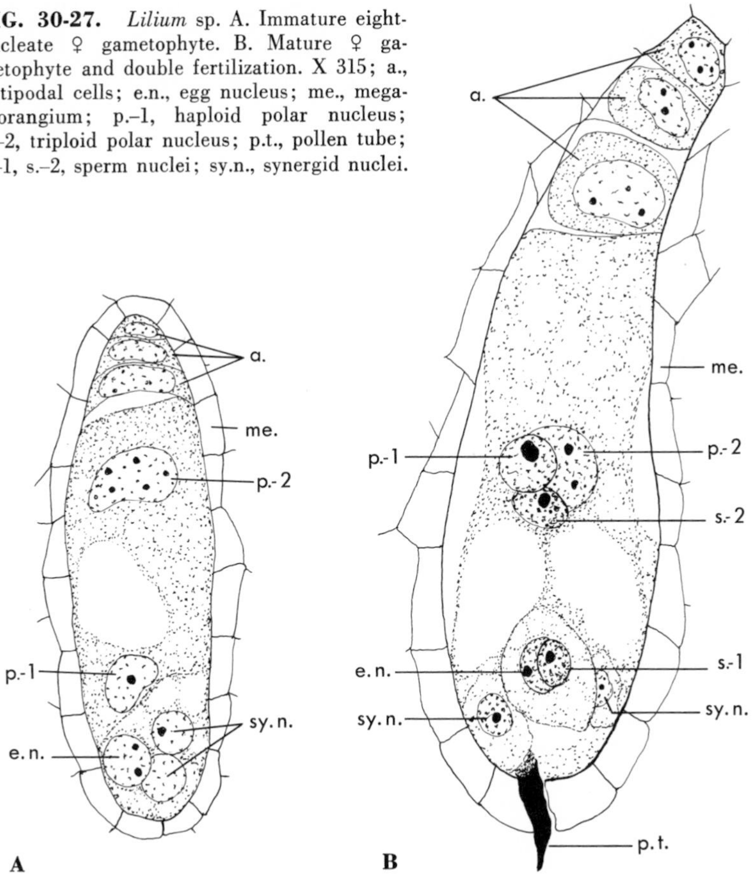

A

B

entirely lacking (as in *Gnetum* and *Welwitschia*).

Three of the four nuclei at the micropylar pole differentiate as the **"egg apparatus,"** consisting of an **egg cell** and two cellular **synergids** (Fig. 30-27B). Three of the four nuclei at the chalazal pole develop cell membranes and are known as **antipodal cells** (Fig. 30-27B). The remaining two nuclei, one from each pole, migrate toward each other away from the poles. They, therefore, are known as **polar nuclei** (Fig. 30-27B). The mature female gametophyte of most angiosperms thus is a seven-celled structure consisting of three uninucleate cells at each pole with a larger binucleate cell between them. As far as known, the egg and one synergid are always sister cells as are the other synergid and one polar nucleus.[8]

The process of female gametophyte develop-

ment just described is essentially that which occurs in more than 70 percent of the flowering plants. It should be noted, however, that a great many regularly recurring variations characteristic of specific genera have been described. The genus *Lilium*, usually used to illustrate reproduction in angiosperms because of the large size of its nuclei and female gametophyte, exhibits one of these deviations.[9] Inasmuch as this plant is still used in most laboratories and because the process of female gametophyte development can be readily demonstrated, the divergent ontogeny will be described at this point (Figs. 30-26[1'–8'], 30-28).

The first point at which the lily differs from the normal type of female gametophyte development is during the division and meiosis of

---

[8] This may be significant when one recalls that the egg and ventral canal cell are always sister cells.

[9] Although the development of the female gametophyte in lily is often spoken of as a "deviation" from the "normal" angiosperm type, it is, of course, quite "normal" in lily.

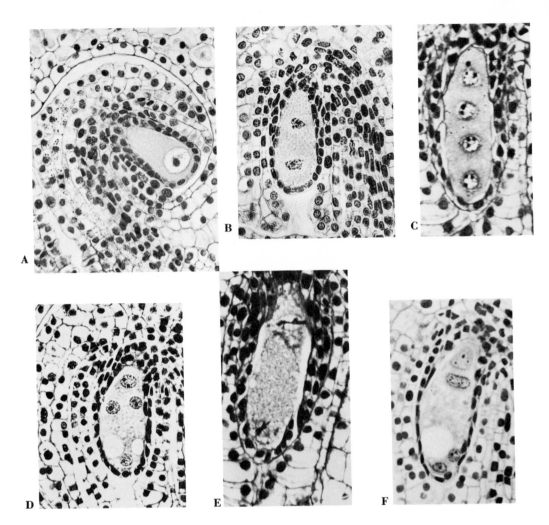

FIG. 30-28. *Lilium* sp. Development of the ♀ gametophyte. A. Median longitudinal section of ovule showing integuments, micropyle, megasporangium, and megasporocytes. B. End of meiosis I. C. Four haploid megaspore nuclei ("first four-nucleate stage"). D. Migration of three haploid nuclei to chalazal pole; prophases of division. E. Metaphase of triploid division, above; metaphase of haploid division, nearer micropyle. F. Two triploid nuclei, above; two haploid nuclei nearer micropyle ("second four-nucleate stage"). A. X 125. B–F. X 250.

the megasporocyte. Two successive nuclear divisions occur as usual, but these are not followed by cytokinesis (Figs. 30-26 [1'–3'], 30-28A-C). As a result, the four megaspore nuclei are embedded in common cytoplasm of the megasporocyte. A second deviation is that in *Lilium*, three of the four megaspore nuclei do not degenerate and, furthermore, all four are involved in the formation of the female gametophyte. The latter, therefore, is tetrasporic in origin. The linear arrangement of the megaspore nuclei is followed by a change in position in which one remains near the micro-

pylar pole of the developing female gametophyte and three migrate to the other (chalazal) end (Figs. 30-26 [4'], 30-28D). At this point, a third deviation becomes apparent, namely, as the three chalazal neclei enter mitosis, either in late prophase or in metaphase, they join together, making a single large division figure (Figs. 30-26 [5'], 30-28E. Inasmuch as each of the haploid nuclei had undergone chromosome reduplication in preparation for this mitosis, the single large spindle includes three haploid sets of dual chromosomes. The result is that two large triploid nuclei are organized at telophase (Figs. 30-26 [6'], 30-28F). The megaspore nucleus at the micropylar pole, meanwhile, has divided to form two haploid nuclei (Figs 30-26 [6'], 30-28F). This "second four-nucleate stage" is readily recognizable by the presence of two large (triploid) nuclei at the chalazal pole and two smaller (haploid) nuclei at the micropylar pole of the female gametophyte. Following this, a fourth mitosis takes place, resulting in the formation of four triploid nuclei and four haploid nuclei (Fig. 30-26 [7']). Further development is normal, one triploid nucleus and one haploid nucleus functioning as polar nuclei (Figs. 30-26 [8'], 30-27). In the mature female gametophyte of *Lilium*, the antipodal cells are triploid and the egg and synergids are haploid. One polar nucleus is triploid and one is haploid.

(5) POLLINATION AND FERTILIZATION

In many angiosperms, the maturation of the female gametophyte occurs just as the flower opens or just prior to its opening. Each ovule in the ovary contains a single mature gametophyte. The pollen grains, in reality immature male gametophytes, are transferred to the receptive surface of the stigma after the flower has opened, in the process of **pollination** (Fig. 30-2). Pollination here differs from that in gymnosperms in that in the latter the pollen is transferred directly to the vicinity of the micropyle of the ovule. A few flowering plants —many species of *Viola*, for example—produce **cleistogamous flowers**[10] which do not open. These are regularly self-pollinated; in *V. odorata* L. it has been shown that the pollen grains germinate within the anther and grow through its walls to the stigma. In a few angiosperms with hollow stigmas and styles, intracarpellary pollen grains have been observed; this suggests the pollination process in gymnosperms.

The agents of pollination may be wind, water (in certain aquatics), snails, insects, birds, or bats. In self-pollinated flowers, anthers and stigma may be in contact or the pollen may fall on the stigma, if the anthers are above it. Insect pollination is considered by some to be the primitive condition in angiosperms, while others have considered wind pollination to be so. Pollination by beetles, which occurs in certain ranalian and magnolialian genera, among others, is considered to be the most primitive type of insect pollination.

A number of specialized relationships between pollinating insects and certain species of angiosperms are well known. Among these are the wasp, *Blastophaga*, and the edible fig and the moth, *Pronuba*, on which *Yucca* depends for pollination.

The pollen of wind-pollinated species is small and dry, while insect-pollinated plants

[10] *Viola* has open or **chasmogamous** flowers as well; these are produced earlier in the season.

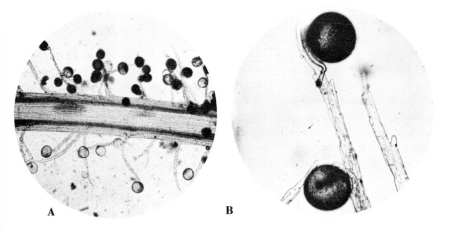

A   B

FIG. 30-29. *Zea mays.* Corn. A. "Silk" (stigma-style) with hairs and attached pollen. X 30. B. Hairs with germinating pollen grains. X 250.

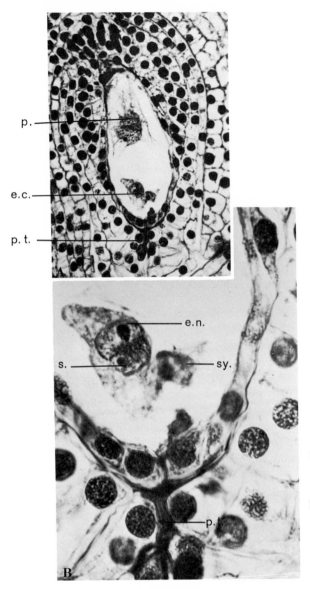

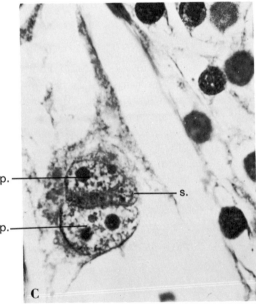

FIG. 30-30. *Lilium* sp. Double fertilization. A. X 200. B. Union of egg and sperm nuclei. X 1000. C. Triple fusion of two polar nuclei and sperm. X 1000; e.c., egg cell, containing egg and sperm nuclei (see B); e.n., egg nucleus; p., polar nucleus (see C); p.t., pollen tube remnant; s., sperm nucleus; sy., synergid.

have sticky, adherent pollen with a waxy or oily surface.

Pollen grains germinate on the stigmatic surface (Figs. 30-2, 30-29). In many cases, germination occurs through a predetermined germ pore, a thin place in the wall of the grain. A tubular process emerges from the pollen grain and grows into the stigma and through the style into the ovary (Fig. 30-2). There can be little doubt that part of the nutriment of the pollen tube and male gametophyte is absorbed from the stigma and style. Germination of the pollen grains in most angiosperms is relatively rapid, occurring soon after the pollen has reached the stigma. In some cases, pollen grains germinate readily in sugar solutions, the optimum concentration varying with the species. Normally, only one tube emerges from each pollen grain. However, in some species, as many as fourteen tubes have been observed developing from a single pollen grain. The style through which the pollen tube grows may be hollow, as in *Viola,* or solid, as in cotton (*Gossypium*). In the latter case, the pollen tube forces its way through the intercellular spaces of the stylar tissue.

It has been demonstrated experimentally that the stigma and upper style of lily[11] contain substances which stimulate pollen tubes to positive chemotropism. These substances may be extracted and retain their stimulatory properties. Furthermore, they increase the germination percentage of the pollen and stimulate growth of the tubes. In this connection, reports that pollen is deficient in boron but that stigmatic and stylar tissue contain relatively high levels of the element may be significant.

In most cases, the pollen tube enters the ovule through the micropyle (Figs. 30-2, 30-27B, 30-30), but it also may penetrate other points on the surface of the ovule. In ovaries containing more than one ovule, each is penetrated by one or more pollen tubes if pollination has been sufficiently heavy. The tip of the pollen tube enters through the wall of the female gametophyte. The synergids may disintegrate as it enters. Shortly after its contact with the female gametophyte, the pollen tube discharges the sperm cells, and sometimes the tube nucleus also, into the female gametophyte.

In spite of the great amount of study devoted to the process of reproduction in angiosperms, the details of nuclear union are not well known in most cases. This may indicate that once the sperm cells are discharged into the female gametophyte, nuclear union follows rapidly. One of the sperm cells approaches the egg and unites with it, while the other moves toward the two polar nuclei and unites with them (Figs. 30-27B, 30-30). In plants in which the polar nuclei have united to form the so-called **secondary nucleus** prior to fertilization, the second sperm unites with it. Thus, it is obvious that in the flowering plants, both sperms of a given male gametophyte are functional and involved in nuclear unions within the female gametophyte. These phenomena comprise **double fertilization;** the latter seems to be limited to angiosperms in which it was discovered in 1898. It is clear, in the female gametophytes that have developed in the "normal" fashion from one haploid megaspore, that union of the two haploid

polar nuclei with one sperm nucleus or of a secondary nucleus with a sperm nucleus, results in the formation of a triploid nucleus. The latter is called the **primary endosperm nucleus** because of its subsequent activity. In such a plant as *Lilium,* however, it will be recalled that one of the polar nuclei is triploid and one haploid. Union of these with the sperm nucleus produces a pentaploid primary endosperm nucleus.

(6) DEVELOPMENT OF THE EMBRYO, SEED, AND FRUIT

In most cases, the zygote, enclosed by a delicate membrane, remains undivided for some interval after fertilization. The primary endosperm nucleus, in contrast, soon enters upon a period of rapid division which may be free-nuclear (Fig. 30-31A,B), or the mitoses may be followed by successive cytokineses after each nuclear division. If free-nuclear division has occurred, walls are usually, but not always, developed between the free nuclei, and the tissue which contains them is called **endosperm.** The endosperm of *Lilium* passes through a free-nuclear period before cell walls are laid down (Fig. 30-31A,B). When the first and subsequent divisions of the primary endosperm nucleus are followed by cytokineses, the endosperm is cellular from its inception. This occurs in many plants, among them *Adoxa, Lobelia,* and *Nemophila.* The descendants of the primary endosperm nucleus give rise to a more or less extensive endosperm within the enlarging lumen of the female gametophyte, now perhaps most appropriately called the embryo sac. The endosperm cells are often filled with starch grains or other stored metabolites which have diffused into them from the parent sporophyte. The endosperm is a storage tissue which provides readily available nutriment to the developing embryo. It is a triploid tissue in a great majority of angiosperms, but a number of exceptions are known, such as the pentaploid type in *Lilium.* The origin and development of the endosperm and phenotypic attributes residing in it are involved in the phenomenon of **xenia.** This term denotes the direct influence of the male parent, as expressed in endosperm character-

---

[11] And, therefore, presumably other plants.

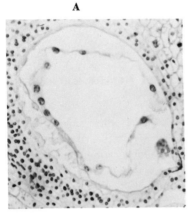

A

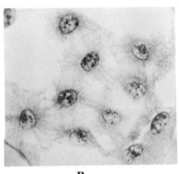

B

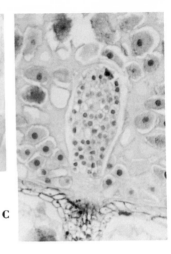

C

FIG. 30-31. *Lilium* sp. Embryogeny. A. Section of early post-fertilization ovule; note embryo at right, near micropyle, and ring of free endosperm nuclei. X 60. B. Surface view of free-nuclear endosperm. X 125. C. Micropylar region of dormant seed; note embryo (small cells) embedded in endosperm. X 60.

istics, an influence readily observable in certain maize hybridizations. For example, when varieties of white or light-yellow maize are pollinated by pollen from dark varieties, the kernels of the former are noticeably darker as they mature.

Some time after the initiation of endosperm formation, the zygote begins the nuclear and cell divisions which result in the formation of the embryonic sporophyte (Fig. 30-31C). The cytokinesis which follows the first nuclear division forms a two-celled embryo. Free-nuclear stages are absent from the embryogeny of angiosperms. The division product that lies more deeply within the female gametophyte is known as the **terminal cell,** and the other is called the **basal cell.** Considerable variation exists in the subsequent stages of development. The following account is based largely on the process as it occurs in the "shepherd's purse," *Capsella bursa-pastoris* (L.) Medic., a dicotyledonous weed with amphitropous ovules (Fig. 30-32).

This species is widespread in distribution, and microscopical preparations of the stages of embryogeny are readily obtainable. After the first division of the zygote, the basal cell divides in a transverse plane, and the terminal cell undergoes vertical division at right angles to the plane of division of the basal cell. A second vertical division in a plane perpendicular to the first results in the formation of a quartet of cells (quadrant stage) from the original terminal cell. This is followed by transverse divisions in all four cells to form an octant stage. The four cells of the octant farthest from the basal cell give rise to the cotyledons and stem apex of the embryo. The other four initiate an axis or hypocotyl. Periclinal divisions in each of the cells of the spherical eight-celled embryo segregate the eight superficial protodermal from eight inner cells.

While these changes have been taking place in the descendants of the terminal (embryo-forming) cell, the products of division of the basal cell have divided to form a short chain that functions as a **suspensor,** the basal cell of which is attached to the wall of the embryo sac (Fig. 30-32D). This cell enlarges markedly and possibly functions in absorption. By regular sequential divisions, the lowermost (nearest the embryo-forming cells) of the suspensor cells give rise to the root and root cap of the embryo. In subsequent development, the original octant region becomes organized into an elongate hypocotyl bearing two large cotyledons (Fig. 30-32E). Between their bases lies

486

the promeristem of the stem. The embryo is curved in later development in conformity with the amphitropy of the *Capsella* ovule.

The developing embryo digests the bulk of the endosperm and assimilates it. As the latter enters a period of dormancy, histological changes in the cells of the integuments result in the formation of seed coats, the inner known as the **tegmen** and the outer as the **testa**. It should be noted that in *Capsella* the antipodal

cells, having undergone several divisions, persist at the antipodal pole of the embryo sac (Fig. 30-32E). The embryos of *Capsella* are dicotyledonous.

Monocotyledonous embryos differ in their organization, having a single, large cotyledon and the axis or stem lateral (Fig. 30-33). In a number of flowering plants—many orchids, for example—the embryo remains minute and undifferentiated. In such seeds, further devel-

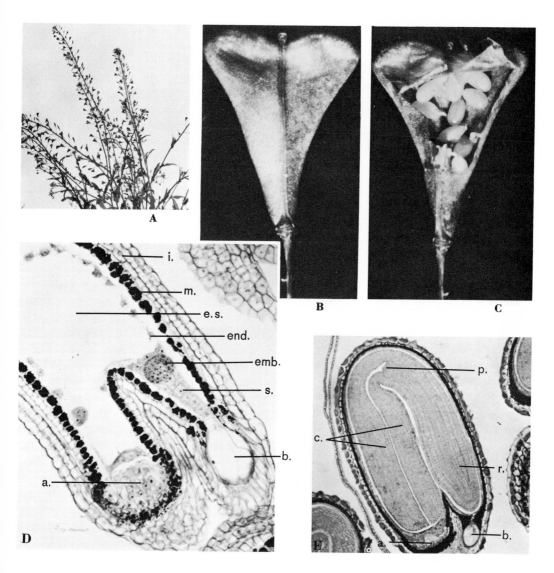

FIG. 30-32. *Capsella bursa-pastoris* (shepherd's purse). A. Plants in flower and fruit. X 0.1. B. Immature fruit containing ovules with embryos in stage shown in E. X 4. C. Fruit wall partially removed to show maturing seeds. X 4. D. Longisection of ovule with early embryo. X 150. E. Longisection of ovule with well-differentiated embryo. X 90; a., antipodal tissue; b., basal cell; c., cotyledons; emb., embryo; end., endosperm; e.s., embryo sac; i., integument; m., megasporangium; p., plumule; r., radicle; s., suspensor.

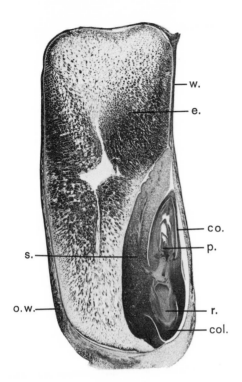

FIG. 30-33. *Zea mays.* Corn. Longisection of immature grain; co., coleoptile; col., coleorhiza; e., endosperm; o.w., ovary wall; p., plumule; r., radicle; s., scutellum or cotyledon; w., united integuments and ovary wall. X 25. (*Courtesy of Dr. J. E. Sass and the Iowa State University Press.*)

opment is delayed until after the seeds have been shed.

Although endosperm is produced in the development of almost all angiosperm seeds, the orchids being a notable exception, whether or not endosperm is present in the mature seed depends on the degree to which it has been absorbed by the developing embryo. In seeds that lack endosperm at maturity (Fig. 30-34),

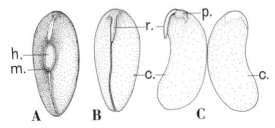

FIG. 30-34. *Phaseolus vulgaris* L. Garden bean. Seed morphology. A. External appearance. B. With seed coats removed. C. Embryo with cotyledons separated; c., cotyledon; h., hilum or funiculus scar; m., micropyle; p., plumule; r., radicle.

such as bean, peanut, and garden pea, the embryo is massive and its cotyledons are rich in stored metabolites. In seeds with endosperm, the cotyledons are more like foliage leaves, as in the castor bean (*Ricinus*) (Fig. 30-35), basswood (*Tilia*), corn (*Zea*), and *Magnolia*. The seed of the angiosperms, therefore, may be defined as an embryonic sporophyte often, but not always, in a dormant condition, either surrounded by endosperm or gorged with food (Figs. 30-34, 30-35); furthermore, the embryo is enclosed also by the remains of the megasporangium and by the matured integuments, the seed coats. The angiosperm seed differs fundamentally from that of gymnosperms in the origin of the tissue which nourishes the developing embryo. In the gymnosperms, the haploid vegetative tissue of the female gametophyte serves this purpose, whereas in the angiosperms, the food tissue or endosperm is a postfertilization development initiated and stimulated by the union of the sperm nucleus and the polar nuclei or secondary nucleus.

Fertilization (and sometimes pollination, alone) stimulates some of the cells of the ovary wall to multiply and to develop into the fruit wall or **pericarp.**

Soon after pollination and fertilization, the stamens and petals of most flowers wither and may be abscised from the receptacle. The ovary of the pistil, which contains the ovule or ovules and the latter with developing embryos, enlarges rapidly after pollination and fertilization (Fig. 30-36). This is in contrast to gymnosperms in which the ovule at fertilization is essentially the same size as the mature seed. The pistil, and in some cases the receptacle and other floral organs as well, matures into the structure known as the **fruit.** The structure of the mature fruit varies in the families of angiosperms with respect to form, texture, and dehiscence, if any. These variations serve, in part, as criteria for the delimitation of various taxonomic categories.

The fruit then, is the matured pistil or pistils of the angiosperm flower along with, in some types, certain associated accessory structures.

Fruits are often classified in three categories on the basis of origin, namely, **simple, ag-**

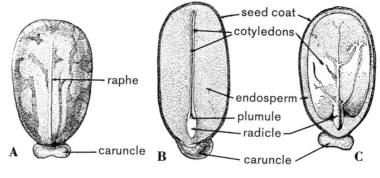

FIG. 30-35. *Ricinus communis.* Castor-oil plant. Seed structure. A. External view. B. Median sagittal section. C. Longisection parallel to flat surface. X 1.5. (*After Holman and Robbins.*)

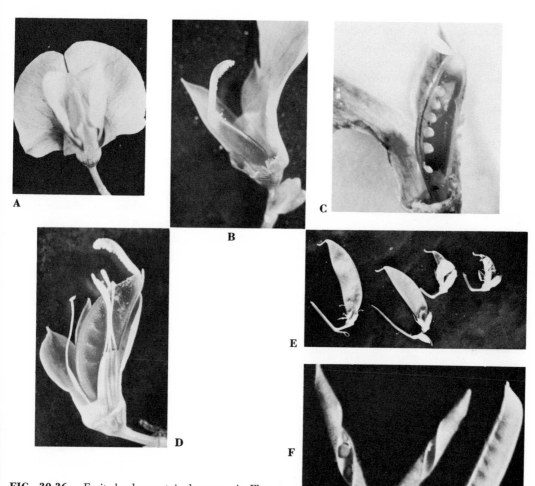

FIG. 30-36. Fruit development in legumes. A. Flower; stamens and pistil concealed by two petals which form the keel. X 0.75. B. Pistil at flowering; note ovary, style, and hairy stigma. X 2.5. C. Ovary, one wall removed; note locule of simple ovary containing ovules; note also parietal placentation. X 2. D. Post-pollination and enlargement of pistil, early fruit. X 2. E. Successively older stages of fruit development (right to left). X 0.50 F. Fruits, one dehiscent showing remaining seed. X 1. A, C, and F are of sweet pea, *Lathyrus odoratus*. The remainder are from garden pea, *Pisum sativum*.

gregate, and **multiple.** Some examples of these are presented in the following abbreviated treatment.

I. Simple Fruits

These arise from the pistil of a single flower; the pistil may be simple or compound. Simple fruits may be subdivided into those which are dry when their contained seeds mature and those which are moist and fleshy.

A. DRY FRUITS

1. Dehiscent types: these open and shed their seed at maturity. Here are included, among others, **follicles** (Fig. 30-37A) (opening along one side), like those of willow and columbine; **pods** or **legumes** (Fig. 30-37B) (opening along two sides) as in peas, beans and many other legumes; and **capsules** (like those of *Iris*) with various loci of dehiscence (Fig. 30-37C). Both follicles and pods arise from simple pistils, while capsules are matured compound ones.

2. Indehiscent types: here the seeds are permanently retained within the fruit. The **cary-**

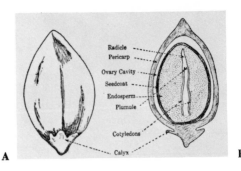

FIG. 30-38. Achene of *Fagopyrum esculentum* Moench. Buckwheat. Fruit (achene). A. External features. B. Median longisection. X 7. (*After Robbins, from Holman and Robbins.*)

opsis or **grain** (Fig. 30-33) and **achene** (Fig. 30-38) are well-known examples of this type. The seed of caryopsis is nowhere free from the fruit wall; in the achene, the seed is attached to the fruit wall at but one point.

B. FLESHY FRUITS

In fleshy fruits, the wall of the ovary increases markedly in thickness after pollination and fertilization. It is called the pericarp and often has three component layers termed **exocarp, mesocarp,** and **endocarp.** The berry, drupe, and pome are familiar examples of simple fleshy fruits.

In the **berry** (grape and tomato, for example) the exocarp is skinlike, the mesocarp fleshy, and the endocarp succulent or slimy. Berries may arise from either simple or compound pistils (Fig. 30-39A).

Drupes (Fig. 30-39B) are much like berries except that here the endocarp is stony.

Pomes (Fig. 30-39C) arise from a compound pistil embedded in the receptacle and other accessory parts of epigynous flowers. Here, the edible portion is not part of the fruit (*sensu stricto*) or core.

II. Aggregate Fruits

These arise from several simple pistils of a single flower and its receptacle. Strawberries, raspberries, and blackberries are familiar examples. Their differences are described in Fig. 30-40A and its legends.

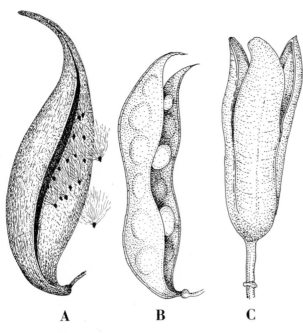

A   B   C

FIG. 30-37. Simple dehiscent fruits. A. *Asclepias tuberosa.* Follicle of milkweed. B. *Robinia pseudoacacia.* Pod or legume of locust. C. *Iris* sp. Capsule.

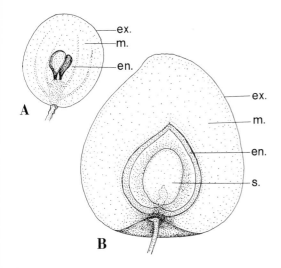

A

B

C

FIG 30-39. Simple fleshy fruits, bisected. A. *Vitis* sp. Grape, a berry. B. *Prunus armeniaca* L. Apricot, a drupe. C. *Pyrus malus* L. Apple, a pome; c., cortex of receptacle; en., endocarp; ex., exocarp; m., mesocarp; p., periderm; s., seed; v.b., vascular bundle of receptacle.

III. *Multiple Fruits*

These arise from an inflorescence axis and the pistils of a number of associated flowers. An "ear" of corn, a pineapple, and a mulberry all exemplify this type of fruit (Fig. 30-40C).

Seed germination in angiosperms varies both morphologically and physiologically over a wide range of conditions. To some extent, rapidity of germination is correlated with the degree of development of the embryo at the time the seed is freed from the parent plant. Seed dormancy may be morphological, occasioned by incomplete differentiation of the embryo,[12] as in the coconut and a number of other angiosperms, both mono- and dicotyledons. Completion of embryo development after the seed has been shed is known as **after-ripening.** In general, seeds with fully developed embryos develop more rapidly than those

[12] As in the cycads, *Gnetum* and *Ginkgo*.

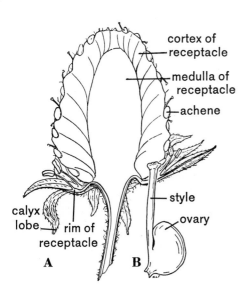

A   B

C   D

FIG. 30-40. Aggregate fruits. A, B. *Fragaria* sp. Strawberry; note enlarged receptacle bearing the true fruits which are achenes. C. *Rubus* sp. Blackberries; the receptacle bears a number of minute, fleshy drupes. D. *Morus alba*. Multiple fruit of mulberry. A. X 1.5. B. X 5. C. X 0.5. D. X 2. (*After Holman and Robbins.*)

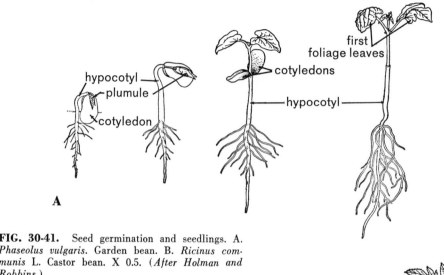

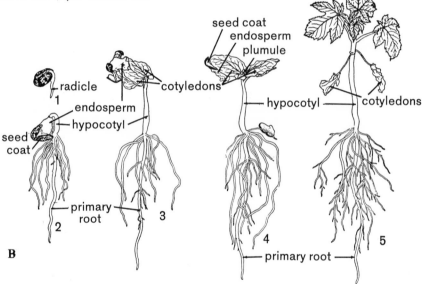

FIG. 30-41. Seed germination and seedlings. A. *Phaseolus vulgaris.* Garden bean. B. *Ricinus communis* L. Castor bean. X 0.5. (*After Holman and Robbins.*)

with rudimentary embryos, although such factors as seed coat texture, temperature, humidity, and light may have a bearing on the speed of the germination process. In some angiosperms, including a number of tropical forms, no dormant period occurs so that embryogeny is continuous into the seedling stages.

As in gymnosperms, both epigean and hypogean germination occur in angiosperms (Figs. 30-41, 30-42). A majority of dicotyledons are epigeal, while most monocotyledons are hypogeal. Epigeal germination is considered to be more primitive than hypogeal. Germination and seedling stages of four common angiosperms are illustrated in Figs. 30-41 and 30-42.

In bringing to a close this brief account of reproduction in Anthophyta, it should be emphasized, as would be expected in such a large and diversified assemblage of plants, that there are many variations in detail from the general account presented above. Furthermore, as was indicated previously both in the Bryophyta and in certain vascular cryptogams, deviations from normal sexual reproduction also occur in angiosperms, both spontaneously and as a result of artificial stimulation. These deviations in angiosperms also may be grouped

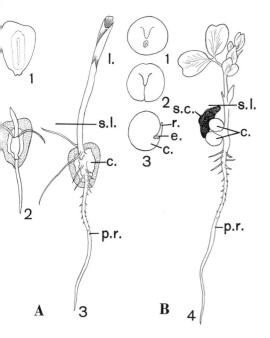

FIG. 30-42. Seed germination and seedlings. A. *Zea mays.* Corn. 1. Ungerminated grain; embryo with large scutellum visible. 2. Early germination. 3. Six-day-old seedlings. B. *Pisum sativum.* Garden pea. 1. Seed covered with seed coats; embryonic root barely visible; 2. Seed coat removed showing two fleshy cotyledons and radicle; 3. Hemisected seed; 4. Eight-day-old seedling; c., cotyledon; e., epicotyl; l., leaf; p.r., primary root; r., radicle; s.c., seed coat; s.l., soil line. (*After Bold.*)

under the phenomena of apogamy or **apomixis** and apospory. Among them may be mentioned the development of haploid embryos from unfertilized egg cells, development of haploid embryos from cells of the female gametophyte other than the egg, development of diploid embryos because of parthenogenetic development of diploid eggs in aposporously produced female gameto-phytes, and development of diploid embryos from the megasporangium or integument. Details of these deviations are beyond the scope of this account, but they are mentioned as examples of similar phenomena seen in other plant groups.

Summary

Because of the tremendous range in their diversity, organization of the vegetative organs of the angiosperms has been given only cursory consideration in the present chapter. Instead, this chapter contains a brief discussion of the gross morphology of the flower and the details of the reproductive process. The latter may be considered to consist of microsporogenesis and megasporogenesis, maturation of the male and female gametophytes, double fertilization, embryogeny, and development of the seed and fruit. Brief reference to deviations from the usual reproductive cycle has been made. The flowering plants differ from other seed plants in having the seeds enclosed in the megasporophylls (angiospermy), in their pollination, in their double fertilization and postfertilization endosperm. Unlike those of gymnosperms, angiospermous ovules enlarge markedly after fertilization until the seed matures. Except for peony (*Paeonia*), angiosperms lack the free-nuclear phases in embryogeny characteristic of gymnosperms other than *Gnetum*. Embryogeny does not involve free-nuclear stages which characterize the process in gymnosperms. The widespread occurrence of vessels in their xylem is a characteristic they share only with the Gnetophyta among seed plants.

DISCUSSION QUESTIONS

1. What reasons can you suggest to explain the fact that the flowering plants exceed any other group of plants in number of species?

2. In what respects are flowers and strobili similar? In what respects do they differ?

3. What attributes do angiosperms and gymnosperms have in common?

4. In what respects do they differ?

5. How do the seeds of gymnosperms and angiosperms differ?

6. Botanists used to group all seed plants in a single division, Spermatophyta. Give reasons for and against such a disposition of these plants.

7. On what basis are the spores of angiosperms called microspores and megaspores? Express your opinion regarding the propriety of this practice.

8. What evidence can you cite that sepals and petals differ in origin?

9. What evidence can you cite that a carpel (simple pistil) is foliar in origin? Are there alternate possibilities?

10. Summarize the terms used to describe the gross morphology of the flower and explain each in a single complete sentence.

11. Explain the use of the terms perfect and imperfect; monoecious and dioecious.

12. Distinguish between hypogynous, perigynous, and epigynous flowers, citing familiar examples of each.

13. What is meant by the term fruit?

14. What effect does epigyny have on the fruit?

15. Explain the term seed as it applies to angiosperms, and describe types of seed structure and variations in seed germination.

16. Obtain seeds of corn, pea, garden bean, and castor bean and follow their germination in moist peat moss or sand.

17. Outline the major phenomena in the reproductive process of the flowering plant and then prepare an account of the process, using this outline and making appropriate drawings.

18. What is an ovule? What variations in ovular form occur? Give an example of a plant with each type.

19. Are the Anthophyta unique, among seed plants, in lacking archegonia? Explain.

20. How are the gametophytes of flowering plants nourished?

21. What interval may elapse between pollination and fertilization in Anthophyta? How does this compare with gymnosperms?

22. Distinguish between pollination and fertilization in both angiosperms and gymnosperms.

23. How does the reproductive cycle of *Lilium* deviate from the "normal" type? Why has the word normal been enclosed in quotation marks?

24. Compare the mature male and female gametophytes of the flowering plants with those of the several genera of gymnosperms described in an earlier chapter.

25. What is meant by cleistogamy? Give examples. Of what genetic significance is this phenomenon?

26. Comment on the possible benefits which accrue to plants through cross-pollination.

27. What is meant by xenia? Give an example?

28. With the aid of labeled diagrams, describe the embryogeny of *Capsella*.

29. In what area of plant science is the structure of the vegetative organs of the flowering plants considered in great detail?

30. What criteria are employed in the classification of flowering plants?

31. What book (manual) summarizes the flora (vascular plants) of the region in which you live? Consult its keys.

32. What branch of plant science involves detailed consideration of the characteristics of the orders and families of flowering plants?

33. How would you demonstrate the germination of angiosperm pollen?

CHAPTER 31

Division Anthophyta—II

From the preceding chapter it should be evident that the flower, of itself, is an inadequate criterion by which to differentiate between Anthophyta and other seed plants. The differentiating attributes of Anthophyta are, in fact, their angiospermy, site of pollination, double fertilization, postfertilization endosperm and lack of free nuclear embryogeny.[1] This chapter will discuss briefly some of the important problems concerning the origin, possible precursors, and evolution of the flowering plants.

The Origin and Fossil Record of Angiosperms

About a century ago, Charles Darwin wrote that the sudden appearance in abundance of

the flowering plants in relatively recent rock strata (Cretaceous, Table 32-1), was "an abominable mystery." In spite of advances in our knowledge of comparative floral morphology and of the fossil record, and in spite of the publication of many pages of speculation on this subject, Darwin's words still eloquently summarize the current state of our knowledge.

The sudden appearance of an abundant and diverse angiosperm flora in the Cretaceous (Table 32-1) has suggested both that they must have had a long period of evolution in the earlier Mesozoic or even in the Paleozoic or that, once primitive angiosperms had evolved, their evolutionary diversification was extremely rapid.

Recent critical appraisal of the fossil record emphasizes that there at present is little convincing paleobotanical evidence of the existence of pre-Cretaceous flowering plants. An-

---

[1] Except in *Paeonia*, as far as is known.

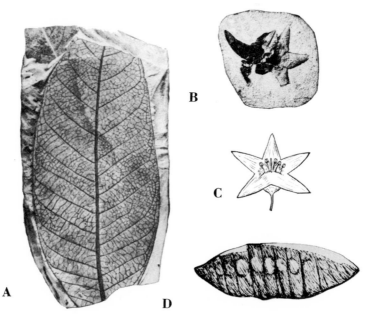

FIG. 31-1. Eocene angiosperm fossils. A. Leaf of *Diospyros wilcoxiana* Berry. B. Flowers of *Solanites saportana* Berry. C. Restoration of same. D. A leguminous fruit, *Gleditsiophyllum hilgardianum* Berry. (*After Berry.*)

A

giosperm remains in Cretaceous and later strata are in the form of pollen, leaves, fruits, axes, and, least frequently, flowers. Angiosperm fossils are usually assigned to genera and families with extant members with the implication that they differ little from modern flowering plants. This is especially true of extinct genera based on leaves. However, the reliability of using leaves in assessing rela-tionships has recently been challenged, and it is quite possible that Cretaceous angiosperms, in fact, differed more profoundly than these taxonomic practices would imply. Furthermore, pollen from the Cretaceous is in many cases unassignable to genera of extant angiosperms, and it is definitely known that some types of pollen did not appear until Tertiary (Table 32-1).

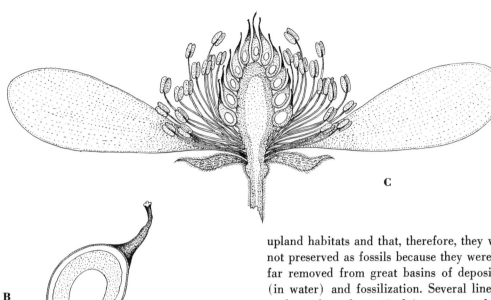

C

B

A

FIG. 31-2. *Ranunculus macranthus.* Floral structure. A. Single flower; note numerous petals, stamens, and pistils; at right, receptacle with numerous one-ovuled simple pistils (carpels) enlarging after pollination and fertilization. B. Bisection of flower; note massive, elongate receptacle to which are attached (in order of base to apex): sepals, petals, stamens, and pistils. C. Single pistil with ovary bisected longitudinally; note parietal placentation of single ovule.

To account for the absence of pre-Cretaceous fossils, there have been several hypotheses. The suggestion that such forms may not have been preserved because of their herbaceous nature is vitiated by the widespread preservation of soft, hydrophytic angiosperms. One hypothesis postulates that the first angiosperms (either a monophyletic or a polyphyletic series) originally evolved in upland habitats and that, therefore, they were not preserved as fossils because they were too far removed from great basins of deposition (in water) and fossilization. Several lines of evidence have been cited in support of this view. Careful study of the whole fossil record indicates that in each successive plant formation the newer, more complex types, which gradually replace the older forms, are migrants from uplands where they first developed. Furthermore, although the first angiosperms (and other plants) may have been preserved in small, upland fossil basins, these basins would have eroded away and their fossilized remains would thus have been lost. Finally, there is evidence that more abrupt and pronounced environmental extremes of upland environments may favor successful evolution of a new adaptive type. These lines of evidence support the hypothesis that the primitive angiosperms may have arisen in upland habitats and suggest an explanation for the gap in the fossil record.

However, it has been pointed out in criticism of this hypothesis that certain plant remains (pollen, fruits, seed, and wood) have been transported great distances from point of origin to site of deposition and fossilization. The fossil record indicates quite clearly the absence of angiosperm pollen, readily transportable, from pre-Cretaceous deposits. Furthermore, it is argued, there is evidence available that the origin and diversification of angiosperms are probably centered in moist tropical regions where conditions would have been favorable for their preservation as fossils. An additional argument in favor of the rapid evolutionary diversification of angiosperms is the rapid appearance and increase of angiosperm leaves and pollen in Lower Cretaceous deposits. In such deposits, furthermore, both "upland" pollens and pollens from other diverse habitats are intermingled.

In summary, a quotation from a recent discussion[2] of the origin and fossil record of angiosperms seems singularly appropriate: "The time of origin of the angiosperms, whether Paleozoic, Cretaceous, or, as is more probable, intermediate between them, is not known. The fascinating potentialities of the paleontological record make it possible and even more likely that tomorrow's discoveries will outmode today's speculation. Despite its vagaries and imperfections, the fossil record remains our best index to relationship involving geologic time; and it does not bear out speculations on the origin of the angiosperms in the Paleozoic era."

Remains of clearly angiospermous plants (Fig. 31-1) are abundant in Late Cretaceous strata and continue to the present, but they appear to be much like extant genera and provide no convincing clues regarding their progenitors. Most of the remains are of vegetative organs such as leaves and stems. Flowers and fruits are not abundant, although pollen has been well preserved under certain circumstances. As far as is known, the fossil flowering plants which have been studied were not markedly different from extant genera to which many of them may be assigned with confidence. Although there is possible evidence that flowering plants existed in the late Triassic of the Mesozoic[3] (Table 32-1), the fossil record has not contributed convincing evidence regarding their progenitors.

However, botanists have not failed to speculate on the problem of angiosperm origin and almost every one of the gymnosperm series has been suggested as a possible point of origin for the flowering plants. The cycadeoids, the *Gnetum-Ephedra* alliance, the seed ferns (Pteridosperms), and, among others, a hypothetical group, the "Hemiangiospermae," have featured prominently in such discussions.

The origin of the "perfect" condition (having both stamens and pistils, or microsporophylls and megasporophylls) of the majority of flowers has been postulated by some to have been the fertile structures of the cycadeoids. The latter have been viewed with favor as a possible ancestral line of the angiosperms by those who consider the dicotyledonous ranalian and magnoliaceous flowers (Figs. 30-13, 31-2) to be the most primitive type among the flowering plants. The aggregation of ovule-bearing appendages on a central axis surrounded by microspore-bearing appendages in cycadeoids (Fig. 25-34) has suggested the organization of a primitive flower (Fig. 31-2), in spite of the absence of true angiospermy and the massive, compound structure of the microspore-bearing organ of cycadeoids.

In the complete absence of a fossil record in support, the Gnetophyta have been suggested as angiosperm precursors for a number of reasons, especially by those who consider the inconspicuous, imperfect type of flower (Figs. 30-3, 30-6) to represent the primitive condition in angiosperms. The presence of vessels in the secondary xylem and the absence of archegonia and the free-nuclear female gametophyte of two of the genera (*Gnetum* and *Welwitschia*) are often cited in support of this suggestion.

The Origin of Angiospermy

The problem of recognizing angiosperm precursors is complex. In the search for them it is important to realize that angiosperms differ from other seed plants in a number of attributes in addition to their angiospermy. These include the flower (however difficult of definition); its typical production of *both*

[2] R. A. Scott, E. S. Barghoorn and Estella B. Leopold, "How Old Are the Angiosperms?" *Amer. Journ. Science.* Bradley Volume, 258 A:284–299, 1960. For a somewhat different discussion see: A. D. J. Meeuse, "Angiosperms—Past and Present," *Advancing Frontiers of Plant Science,* vol. 11, Institute for Advancement of Science and Culture, New Delhi, 1965.

[3] Palmlike leaves have been found in such strata in Colorado. There is no certainty, however, that they belonged to angiosperms.

microsporangia and megasporangia; method of pollination in which pollen does not reach the ovule; double fertilization; postfertilization endosperm formation; and absence of free-nuclear stages during embryogeny. Furthermore, there is some difference of opinion regarding which extant angiosperms represent the primitive type (see p. 500).

With reference to the origin of angiospermy, there are two prominent hypotheses, as follows: (1) On the basis of paleobotanical evidence, it has been suggested that the origin of angiospermy lies in the Pteridospermopsida and their cupules; that is, the cupule is looked upon as the precursor of the angiosperm carpel or pistil (Fig. 31-3). (2) Alternately it has been suggested that the angiosperm carpel has arisen by longitudinal folding (conduplication) of an ovule-bearing leaf (see below, p. 500).

Very rudimentary, pteridosperm cuplike enclosures around seeds are known from the Lower Carboniferous. *Eurystoma angulare* and *Stamnostoma huttonense* are examples of these. In the former (Fig. 31-3A,B), the cupule is formed by dichotomously branching cylindrical axes. In the latter, the enveloping axes are more cuplike in arrangement. In some pteridosperms, like *Calathospermum scoticum* Walton (Fig. 31-3C), the cupule enclosed more than one seed. The saclike enclosures of the ovules in *Caytonia* (Fig. 25-32) have also been suggested as possible near precur-

sors to the angiospermous state, for their phylogenetic closure is not difficult to envisage.

Because of the lack of strong evidence from paleobotany, clues to the origin of the angiosperms have been sought in the ontogeny and morphology of their flowers, especially those of supposed primitive types in the order Ranales. In this order, long considered to be primitive on the basis of the gross structure of the flower (Fig. 31-2) (elongate floral axis, spirally arranged appendages, and indefinite number and separate attachment of the latter and also because of presence of some of its members in early strata) there occur a number of genera (about 100 species) with vesselless xylem, a gymnosperm attribute, and others with a primitive type of carpel (Fig. 31-4) and stamen (Fig. 30-12). In some species both primitive attributes are present.

The primitive carpel is clearly a longitudinally folded (conduplicate), three-veined leaf blade that is not firmly sealed along the line of union of the margins, until the initiation of fruit formation; the margins may then be merely appressed. These margins bear interlocking glandular hairs which function as stigmatic surfaces for the reception of pollen (Fig. 31-4A,B). There is no style or localized stigma, but the entire edge of the conduplicate carpel is stigmatic. A progressive series in modification of such primitive carpels has been traced in certain of these genera. This involves local-

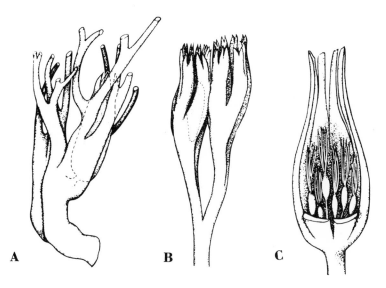

FIG. 31-3. A. *Eurystoma angulare.* B. *Stamnostoma huttonense.* C. *Calathospermum scoticum.* Seed-bearing structures; position of seeds indicated (in part) by dotted lines. (A, B. *After Long.* C. *After Walton. All from Andrews.*)

A B C

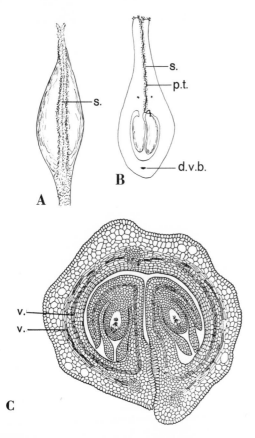

FIG. 31-4. Primitive angiosperm carpel, diagrammatic. A. Ventral view showing paired stigmatic areas (s), running the full length of the carpel. B. Transverse section showing dorsal (d.v.b.) and two lateral vascular bundles; stigmatic area traversed by a pollen tube (p.t.). C. *Cananga* sp. Transection of conduplicate carpel; note closure by interlocking of epidermal cells; v., vascular bundle. (A, B. *From Bailey and Swamy*. C. *After Periasamy and Swamy, from Eames.*)

ization of the stigmatic surface to form a stigma, formation of a style, and firm closure of the carpels with formation of a locule.

The ovules in these primitive ranalian carpels are laminar (i.e., not marginal) in origin (Fig. 31-4B). In modifications of the primitive conduplicate carpel, loss of the sterile portions of the lamina lateral to the ovules, and sealing of the carpel give the false appearance that the ovules arise at the *margins* of the blade, but they are truly laminar in origin. In spite of such evidence from comparative morphology regarding the origin of carpels from leaves, there is no clear evidence of the derivation of this type of angiospermy from gymnospermous types.

Is it possible that angiospermy also arose by the enclosure of ovules (hence seeds) by the overgrowth of pteridospermous cupules? Were such the case, angiosperms would be at least biphyletic and their carpels would not be strictly homologous.

The Nature of Primitive Flowers

As noted earlier, it is difficult, if not impossible, to formulate a definition of the flower which would delimit it from the cone or strobilus. Both are, essentially, determinate[4] axes with appendicular organs bearing sporangia. Sepals and petals, present in most (but not all) flowers but absent in strobili, are clearly modified leaves which seem to have several possible origins. It has been suggested that the perianth represents a modified continuation of the sterile bracts associated with certain strobili. Another hypothesis holds that sepals and petals represent secondarily sterilized sporophylls. Evidence for this is available in petaloid stamens of water lilies and certain "double" flowers. Still another suggestion is that the perianth was a new development which appeared with the angiosperms. According to this, primitive flowers lacked a perianth and the latter evolved from protective scales and bracts. Only later did some of the perianth segments (petals) develop color. Some of these suggested steps in development seem, indeed, to be present in the order Ranales, in such genera as *Liriodendron* (tulip tree) and *Magnolia*.

Inasmuch as the fossil record has not yet provided us with clear and unequivocal evidence regarding the nature of primitive angiosperms and their precursors, data from the comparative morphology of living angiosperms have been marshaled from time to time in attempts to decide which of the extant angiosperms show primitive attributes. That this practice involves difficulties is clear from lack of complete agreement regarding which living angiosperms are, indeed, primitive. An eminent student[5] of the group has written as

[4] Growth-limited.

[5] G. H. M. Lawrence, *Taxonomy of Vascular Plants*, Macmillan Co., New York (p. 95) 1951.

follows, in this connection: "The primitive characters of contemporary, and presumedly phylogenetic, systems of angiosperm classification are not often based on paleobotanical evidence illustrative of ancestral conditions, and for the most part their primitiveness may be a matter of personal opinion or of judgments based on circumstantial evidence. Many of the so-called primitive characters in published lists . . . are alleged to be primitive because they occur in members of primitive taxa, and the taxa are primitive because they have primitive characters. It is difficult to find, by objective methods, devices to break this cyclic reasoning, and, among the angiosperms at least, there is inadequate paleobotanical evidence to support one view and reject the other."

There are two (among other) quite different major hypotheses regarding which extant angiosperms are most primitive. According to one, imperfect flowers[6] which lack petals and which have cyclic arrangement of the floral members are considered to be primitive. This would be supported by the occurrence of microsporangia and megasporangia on different axes or in different strobili in all gymnosperms except the Cycadeoidopsida. Examples of such allegedly primitive flowers are those of the Salicales (willow order), Fagales (beech order), and Juglandales (walnut order), among others. The minute apetalous flowers of willow (*Salix*) (Figs. 30-4, 30-5), oak (*Quercus*) (Fig. 30-6), and Pecan (*Carya illinoensis*) are exemplified by familiar genera in these orders. In *Salix*, both the staminate and pistillate flowers are very simple, consisting of a few stamens or a pistil subtended by a bract. The flowers of *Quercus* and *Carya* are equally simple. The staminate flowers (and the pistillate ones in *Salix*) are borne in pendulous inflorescences known as **aments**.[7] The simple pistillate flowers of *Quercus* and *Carya* are borne in terminal clusters of a few flowers. The conclusion that flowers of this type are primitive has been challenged, however, on the basis of anatomical evidence

which seems to indicate that their apetalous condition represents secondary simplification or reduction from petaliferous precursors. Furthermore, the xylem of these ament-bearing angiosperms is relatively highly specialized, not primitive.

A more widely accepted (at present) view is that the flowers of many members of the Ranales and Magnoliales exhibit primitive attributes and that certain attributes of the vegetative plant body are correspondingly primitive. The floral attributes considered to be primitive include: (1) an elongate receptacle to which (2) are attached separately in spiral arrangement an indefinite (large) number of stamens and pistils (Figs. 30-13, 31-2); (3) the presence of unfused perianth segments, often not differentiated as sepals and petals; (4) radially symmetrical flowers; (5) the occurrence of leaflike stamens with microsporangia embedded in the blade; (6) the presence of simple pistils (carpels), in some cases not completely closed or closing only relatively late in ontogeny (Figs.

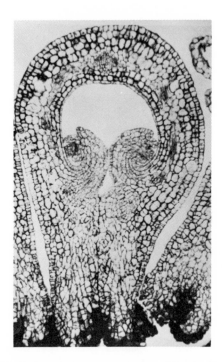

FIG. 31-5. *Drimys winteri* var. *chilensis*. Transection of carpel; note line of appression of carpel margins; dark cells below are stigmatic area. X 115. (*After Tucker.*)

---

[6] Having either microsporophylls (stamens) or megasporophylls (pistils), not both.

[7] Hence the group name "Amentiferae" for these orders.

31-5, 31-6) ; (7) seeds with two integuments; (8) seeds with vascularized integuments.

Among supposedly primitive attributes of the vegetative plant body may be cited: (1) the woody habit; (2) absence of vessels from the xylem; (3) spirally (alternately) arranged leaves; (4) glandular and stipulate leaves.

The fossil record supports this second (ranalian and magnolialian) hypothesis with respect to the primitive nature of spiral and separate attachment of appendages, as contrasted with the whorled or cyclic one. According to this same hypothesis, shortening of the receptacle has resulted in crowding and a change to a cyclic condition of the floral organs. Other results have been the reduction in number of the floral organs and, in some cases, their union to form compound structures.

With respect to stamens, certain magnoliacean flowers bear leaflike microsporophylls

(Fig. 30-12B,C) in which the two pairs of microsporangia are embedded near the midvein of the microsporophyll. Reduction in the vegetative tissue of the microsporophyll has resulted in the type of stamen with a slender filament and distal anther (Fig. 30-12A).

Certain ranalian and magnoliaceous carpels are considered primitive because of their seemingly incipient closure and their lack of a localized stigma (p. 499). The genus *Aquilegia* and many other genera provide ontogenetic evidence that carpels are infolded megasporophylls (Fig. 31-6).

The Origin of Other Angiospermous Attributes

The origin of double fertilization, a unique common attribute of angiosperms, has recently been under discussion. The fossil record here is of little help inasmuch as the delicate reproductive tissues are not preserved to provide sufficient details for cytological study. It has been suggested that the beginnings of double fertilization must be sought in the seed plants in which both sperms of a given pollen tube were discharged into or engulfed by the cytoplasm of one archegonium. This seems to occur with frequency in the conifers and Gnetophyta. In *Gnetum*, it will be recalled, the female gametophyte is free-nuclear at fertilization in at least some species, and two sperms usually are discharged into it. One unites with one of the potential egg nuclei and the other sperm may, on occasion, also unite with another free nucleus of the female gametophyte. However, only one zygote may represent a precursor to the fusion which leads to the primary endosperm nucleus in angiosperms.

This brings us now to a consideration of the origin of the endosperm of angiosperms. Here again, the fossil record is of little value. It is perhaps significant to note that although double fertilization probably occurs in all angiosperms, the formation of a primary endosperm nucleus does not always result in development of endosperm. It has been

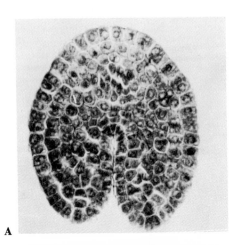

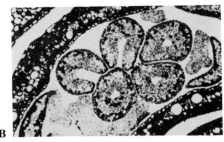

FIG. 31.6. A. *Aquilegia formosa* var. *truncata*. Transection of carpel primordium; note closure due to activity of marginal cells. X 500. B. Transection of (five) slightly older carpels; the margins of some are appressed to form a locule, but others are still open. X 75. (*After Tepfer.*)

suggested that lack of endosperm is a primitive condition in such organisms.

Finally, the absence of free-nuclear stages in angiosperm embryogeny seems to have no counterpart in a majority of extant gymnosperms and is, clearly, an attribute which became fixed early in angiosperm evolution. It is noteworthy, however, that comparative embryology of the Coniferales reveals a series with decreasing numbers of free embryonic nuclei, culminating in *Pinus* which has only four and *Sequoia sempervirens* which has none. Furthermore, it has been reported that in the embryogeny of certain species of *Paeonia* a free-nuclear phase does, indeed, occur. These exceptions indicate the need for caution in considering distinguishing attributes as universal and absolute.

Not only does the origin of angiosperms remain in the realm of speculation, but the true relationship of the numerous orders and families of angiosperms to each other is conjectural. There are those who raise the question of whether the angiosperms are truly monophyletic. Whether monophyletic or polyphyletic in origin, the relation of the monocotyledons and dicotyledons to each other is a further perplexing problem. The monocotyledons are sometimes considered to be primitive and sometimes interpreted as derived from dicotyledonous forms in the ranalian series. That woody genera in each family are primitive and that herbaceous ones have arisen from woody forms by curtailment of cambial activity has been proposed on the basis of comparative anatomy and other considerations. This point of view has found wide acceptance.

If this brief discussion of the possible origin of the angiosperms seems somewhat nebulous and unsubstantial, it will correspond quite appropriately to the state of our knowledge about the problem. Inasmuch as there are such a large number of orders and families of flowering plants, an eloquent manifestation of the great range of variation and complexity, no summary of their classification will be presented in the present text. This aspect of the flowering plants usually is treated in texts and courses in plant taxonomy.

In the preceding pages an attempt has been made to present a glimpse of plants of the past and their significance in relation to our extant flora. The data in this chapter will be drawn upon as the basis for certain conclusions presented in the next, and final, chapter.

DISCUSSION QUESTIONS

1. What conditions favor the preservation of plants as fossils?

2. Are any plants being so preserved at the present time? If so, suggest locations.

3. Summarize the eras of geologic time and their component epochs or periods. In which were the exposed strata in your vicinity deposited?

4. Define or explain petrifaction, case, and impression. Which is most valuable to the morphologist? Why?

5. Briefly define the peel method of preparing fossil plants for microscopic study.

6. On what basis have cycadeoids been suggested as angiosperm precursors?

7. On what basis have Gnetophyta been suggested as angiosperm precursors?

8. On what basis have pteridosperms been suggested as angiosperm precursors?

9. What explanation has been suggested for the absence of angiosperms from fossiliferous strata earlier than Cretaceous?

10. What attributes have been cited as those of primitive extant flowers? On what basis?

CHAPTER 32

General Summary

Introduction

The preceding chapter brought to a conclusion the discussion of representative types, both extant and extinct, of the various divisions of the plant kingdom. Although the treatment of these plants has not been exhaustive in scope, thoughtful reading of it, along with study of the relevant laboratory materials and collateral reading, will have provided a substantial basis upon which to formulate some generalizations and conclusions. The purpose of this final chapter, therefore, is to emphasize some of the more important principles and phenomena that have been alluded to in earlier pages. These are discussed under three categories, namly: (1) vegetative organization; (2) reproduction; and (3) phylogeny and classification. The discussion which follows presupposes that the reader is familiar with the more important attributes of the type genera described up to this point.

Vegetative Organization

Form and Growth

With respect to form of the plant body, the plant kingdom includes a rather wide range of organisms. The simplest are those in which the organism exists as a single cell, the great multiplicity of vital processes taking place within an extremely minute unit of protoplasm. This concept of the unicellular organism, as exemplified by such an assemblage as certain bacteria, and algae like *Chlamydomonas*, *Chlorella*, and *Pinnularia*, among others, is here restricted in scope. It does not include such siphonaceous and coenocytic organisms as *Bryopsis*, the Myxomycota, and *Rhizopus*, for example, which may, perhaps, be interpreted more properly as acellular organisms in which partition into cells has not accompanied nuclear multiplication.

Increasing complexity of body form probably first arose when single-celled organisms remained together after division, either in the form of colonies in which the cells are remote from each other and separated by colloidal secretions (*Volvox*), or in the form of chains of cells, namely, filaments. That such colonies and filaments are relatively loosely organized assemblages of cells is attested by the ease with which fragments survive and regenerate. Other types of colonies with contiguous cells are illustrated by *Pediastrum* and *Hydrodictyon*, among others.

It is doubtful, however, that the colonial type of organism was the precursor from which the more complex bodies of the higher plants have developed. Instead, the simple filament may well have been their origin. Ontogeny furnishes us with the clue that unbranched filaments preceded branched types as well as membranous, parenchymatous types of plant bodies. In the development of the germlings of such membranous plants as *Ulva* and *Laminaria*, the reproductive cells pass through an unbranched, filamentous stage before forming a parenchymatous plant body. The same phenomenon occurs also in developing gametophytes of liverworts and ferns, in the protonemata of mosses, in the sporophyte of *Sphagnum*, and even in the development of the embryonic sporophyte of *Capsella* and other Anthophyta.

The fungi, of course, and many siphonaceous algae have remained permanently filamentous, although they often consist of complex pseudoparenchymatous plant bodies (as in *Codium*, for example) which result from interweaving of their filaments. This type of construction, however, like the colonial one, probably was not involved in the ancestry of parenchymatous organisms.

By continuous cell division in more than two directions, the unbranched filament may have given rise to another type of plant body, the solid cylindrical axis, exemplified by such green algae as *Schizomeris* and many genera of brown algae. A parenchymatous cylindrical type of construction occurs widely in the plant kingdom, as, for example, in the axes of mosses and vascular plants.

Another aspect of filamentous algae must be emphasized in discussing the origin of plant body types, namely, the phenomenon of heterotrichy, in which a much-branched or even disclike prostrate system supports an erect filamentous one (*Stigeoclonium*, Fig. 3-28, p. 46). There are numerous examples of algae in which the erect system has been almost entirely suppressed, so that the prostrate system expands as a membranous parenchymatous layer. It is possible that some of the early hepatophytan land plants may have arisen from such prostrate algae, and the cylindrical axes of other land plants may have been derived from the erect portions of algal ancestors. The green algae, *Prasiolopsis* and *Fritschiella* (Fig. 32-1), consist of epiterranean

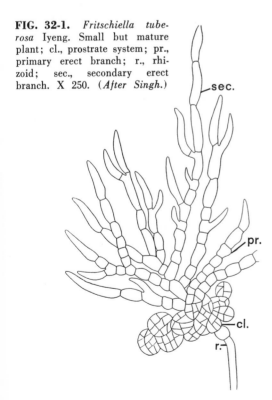

FIG. 32-1. *Fritschiella tuberosa* Iyeng. Small but mature plant; cl., prostrate system; pr., primary erect branch; r., rhizoid; sec., secondary erect branch. X 250. (*After Singh.*)

parenchymatous branches, some rhizomelike in the former and some subterranean with rhizoids in the latter.

Whatever its origin, the plant body increases in size throughout its individual existence by the process known as **growth.** The latter has been defined as increase in mass usually accompanied by differentiation. Increase in mass without differentiation occurs in the plasmodial phase of the Myxomycota and in algae with generalized growth (see below). Increase in mass of multicellular organisms is expressed by increase in cell number and cell size, and these, in turn, are made possible by the synthesis of additional protoplasm. Increase in cell number and size may be entirely separate processes, as illustrated by the rapid enlargement of the fruiting bodies of fleshy fungi after a rain or the rapid increase in length of the *Pellia* seta, by increase in the size (only) of their component cells, and the final phase of growth in all organs of vascular plants.

In the plant kingdom, growth may be **generalized,** as in free-floating filamentous algae and noncoenobic colonies, or **localized.** The growing region may be **apical, basal, intercalary,** or **peripheral,** the last type exemplified by the cambium of the vascular plants. Representative plants displaying one or another type of localization of growth have been referred to repeatedly in the preceding pages. Growth also may be classified as determinate or indeterminate and as continuous or periodic. **Determinate growth** is illustrated by the acrogynous liverworts, the differentiation of branches of algae and fungi into sporangia or gametangia, and by strobili and flowers in which the axis usually differentiates completely, thus "using up" the meristem. **Indeterminate growth,** that is, continuing increase in size, is manifested in vegetative apices of many plants in all divisions of the plant kingdom. **Periodic,** as contrasted with **continuous,** growth involves periods of inactivity. Although this may occur in all plants, it is most strikingly manifested in woody perennial plants of the temperate zone with their closed or dormant buds. Differentiation, which usually accompanies growth, will be discussed in the next paragraphs.

Differentiation

In unicellular organisms, differentiation is entirely intracellular, except for the cell wall. Special portions of the protoplasm and cell wall perform all the functions which support the individual and maintain the species. Similarly, in many colonial algae, the individual cells of the aggregate differ little from each other in structure or function. In other colonies, however, the cells are differentiated into so-called **vegetative** (somatic) and **reproductive** (germ) cells. The implications of these terms in these and similar cases often are misunderstood. Vegetative activities are those that are involved in the maintenance of the individual; reproduction results in the maintenance of the species or race. The difference between vegetative and reproductive cells probably arose when cells which originally performed both types of functions lost during subsequent evolutionary specialization the capacity for reproduction. All cells are vegetative in the sense that they carry on the functions essential to the life of the individual cell. Although this segregation of function seems quite absolute in such a plant as *Volvox* and annual vascular plants because the vegetative cells survive for only one generation, segregation of vegetative from reproductive activities in other plants seems to be less complete. This is evidenced by the widespread occurrence of vegetative reproduction and regeneration from specialized tissues, a phenomenon which will be discussed below.

In addition to this primary dichotomy into vegetative and reproductive phases, further differentiation and specialization are manifest in plant bodies. Differentiation of a variety of vegetative tissues and functions in multicellular organisms with resulting complexity is a measure of degree of advancement in the plant kingdom. This has resulted in the concepts of "lower" and "higher" plants, the adjectives by implication indicating different levels in the evolutionary hierarchy. The terms are unfortunate in view of the almost universally similar ultraorganization of all plants[1] and because they are relative terms with indefinable limits.

------

[1] Except bacteria and blue-green algae.

As a group, the fungi offer few indications that differentiation of the vegetative system, their mycelium, has progressed to any marked degree. The algae, on the other hand, include an instructive series in this connection. The colonial forms have already been cited. In the filamentous and membranous green algae, the plant bodies are histologically uniform except for the lower holdfast or rhizoidal cells. In many Rhodophycophyta and Phaeophycophyta, however, the plant bodies are differentiated into a medullary region composed of cells with few or no plastids, presumably a storage region, and more superficial, chlorophyllous cells which form the photosynthetic cortex. Histological simplicity, of course, characterizes algae, the plant bodies of which are immersed in a solution containing the elements essential for metabolism. No part of the plant body is far removed from the source of water and the inorganic salts dissolved in it. But in the larger, longer-lived kelps, among the Phaeophycophyta, there has developed a specialized conducting system (phloem) which, it is assumed, transports organic materials from the site of their manufacture to more remote portions of the plant. It is of interest, but hardly surprising, that no water-conducting system has been discovered in such algae. That extensive development of water-conducting tissues does not usually occur in plants with aquatic habitats is indicated also by the paucity of xylem in submerged aquatic representatives of the vascular plants.

The differentiation of a water-conducting system and other specializations have made possible plant life on land. It is true that a number of terrestrial plants are scarcely more differentiated than membranous green algae. Such liverworts as *Sphaerocarpos* and *Pellia*, for example, are not markedly more complex internally than *Ulva*. It is noteworthy, however, that such simple terrestrial plants as the liverworts, as a group, are restricted mostly to moist habitats, although there are such conspicuous exceptions as the corticolous *Frullania* and *Porella*. The evolutionary change from a habitat in which the entire plant surface is bathed in a solution containing its required raw materials to one in which at least one surface is exposed to the atmosphere was probably an important force in selecting differentiations and specializations of survival value. Special cells and tissues for absorption, cuticular mechanisms and stomata, some types of epidermal hairs, and silicification are all manifestations of adaptation to a terrestrial habitat. The development of supporting tissues and of those for the efficient conduction of water and solutes and organic substances throughout the plant body resulted in the possibility of increase in size and extension of plant habitats to less hydric surroundings.

Differentiation in the plant kingdom occurred not only at the cellular level but also in the grouping and arrangement of the cells and tissues in plant bodies as specialized organs, namely, roots, stems, and leaves. True roots, stems, and leaves are those which have vascular tissues, xylem and phloem. However, rootlike organs, leaves, and stems, all lacking vascular tissues, are present in certain algae, in the liverworts, and in the mosses. Although these vascularized and nonvascularized structures differ, there is every indication of parallelism in function. The unicellular rhizoids of *Botrydium* among the algae, of the liverworts, of the fern gametophyte, the root hairs of the vascular plants, the multicellular rhizoids of mosses, and vascularized roots all perform the functions of anchorage and absorption. Similarly, the bladelike branches of *Sargassum* and the kelps, those of the leafy liverworts and mosses, the microphyllous leaves of *Lycopodium*, *Selaginella*, and *Isoetes*, and the macrophyllous leaves of other plants all represent expanded surfaces which function primarily in photosynthesis. The axis of *Chara*, that of the kelps, those of leafy liverworts and mosses, and the stems of vascular plants all are organs supporting photosynthetic appendages, performing translocation, and are also themselves actively photosynthetic. The several series just cited indicate that differentiation may follow diverse paths in relation to a given function.

Nutrition and Habitat

Growth and differentiation of living organisms involve syntheses of additional protoplasm and its nonliving adjuncts from basic materials of their environment. The preceding chapters have referred to organisms which vary in the materials they require and the pathways by which syntheses are accomplished, and these will be reviewed briefly at this point.

Autotrophic organisms are those which synthesize their protoplasm from entirely inorganic sources. Their enzyme systems, therefore, are the most extensive and complex in the world of living things. As noted in Chapter 9, autotrophism has been interpreted both as a primitive and as a derived attribute. Autotrophic organisms obtain their primary energy either from light, as in photoautotrophism, or from chemical processes, as in chemoautotrophism. Although most organisms which have chlorophyll are assumed to be photoautotrophic, there are relatively few in which this has actually been demonstrated by cultivation in a controlled environment. On the other hand, in such organisms as *Euglena* and probably many other flagellates, in spite of the presence of chlorophyll, one or more organic substances may be required. It seems probable, too, that although organisms can grow in a completely autotrophic environment in the laboratory, such conditions rarely prevail in natural habitats, and it is probable that syntheses from inorganic sources may be augmented by the organic materials of the surrounding medium.

Organisms which are not autotrophic are heterotrophic. Of the plants considered in this text, the fungi and bacteria which lack chlorophyll are heterotrophic, with the exception of certain chemosynthetic bacteria. Parasitism, saprophytism, and phagotrophism are exemplified in the various groups of these colorless organisms. Heterotrophic nutrition is not confined exclusively to fungi and bacteria, however. Parasitism and lack of chlorophyll are found in the angiosperms in such a plant as dodder (*Cuscuta*); such saprophytic plants as Indian pipe (*Monotropa*) are widely distributed.

Finally, it should be noted that both photoautotrophic and heterotrophic nutrition may prevail in different phases of the same organism. The nutrition of the developing carpospore-producing filaments of the red algae and the embryos of the vascular cryptogams and seed plants is certainly heterotrophic during early stages of development, although the parent plants are photoautotrophic. Similarly, the gametophytes of heterosporous plants are either saprophytic, in those in which the spores are shed, or parasitic, in those in which the spores are retained, although the mature sporophytes are presumably photoautotrophic. Whatever the methods and pathways of syntheses, they culminate in the production of additional protoplasm and its subsequent differentiation.

The representative genera described in this text are found in a wide range of natural habitats. As a group, the algae are predominantly aquatics, although a number occur both in the soil and in moist aerial habitats. A majority of fungi must be classified as hydrophytes, for they cannot grow actively except in the presence of abundant moisture. Most liverworts and mosses also are plants with high moisture requirements, although many are able to withstand desiccation for long periods during which they remain dormant. A few grow exclusively under xeric situations. The vascular plants, probably primarily because of the efficiency of their absorbing, conducting, and epidermal systems, are less restricted and occur in a wide range of habitats, insofar as available water is involved. There is every indication that morphological adaptations for absorbing, conducting, and conserving water are correlated closely with the habitats in which the various plant types can survive. For example, many xerophytes at times become quite dehydrated. It is the abundance of their supporting tissues which holds them in position and masks their wilting. It is likely that this role of the supporting tissues in maintaining the organism's shape and in preventing mechanical damage to flaccid tissues makes it possible for the organisms to survive in xeric habitats.

Reproduction

Once generated, the plant body ultimately reaches a degree of maturity at which the phenomenon of reproduction begins. Reproduction is simply the reduplication of the individual and it results in increase in numbers, directly or indirectly. The various reproductive processes cited in earlier chapters have been treated as examples of two basic types, sexual and asexual reproduction. The former usually involves the union of cells and nuclei, the association of chromosomes and genes in a zygote from which a new individual sooner or later arises; meiosis is inevitably involved. In contrast to the unions involved in sexual reproduction, asexual reproduction includes methods of reduplication of individuals in which no such cell and nuclear union takes place.

Perhaps the simplest type of asexual reproduction is that of unicellular organisms in which the division of the cell duplicates the individual. In colonial aggregates and multicellular organisms, however, cell division results only in the reduplication of the component cells and in growth of the plant body. In these, a variety of reproductive phenomena have been described. One of the most widespread may be designated as fragmentation; it occurs throughout the whole plant kingdom. It involves the separation of the original plant body into segments, often specialized parts, and their distribution and subsequent development into new individuals. It is illustrated, for example, in the breaking up of colonial algae, in hormogonium formation in Cyanophycophyta, in the separation of branches by posterior decay in liverworts and rhizomatous plants, and by the natural and artificial propagation of segments of leaves, stems, and roots. In a number of cases, special portions of the plant body are set aside as reproductive fragments. This is exemplified by the gemmae of certain fungi, liverworts, and mosses, by the soredia of lichens and the bulbils of *Lycopodium* and certain ferns, and by the formation of bulbs, rhizomes, and stolons in many vascular plants.

Asexual reproduction is accomplished in the cryptogams also by the formation of special bodies usually known as spores. These may be unicellular or few-celled; in the latter case, they are not very different from certain types of gemmae. Such structures as zoospores, aplanospores, autospores, and the many types of fungal spores all may be classified as asexual because they continue their development without prior union with other reproductive cells. According to this concept, the spermatia of rusts and the uniting basidiospores of certain smuts would not be interpreted as asexual spores. Although many spores are asexual in the sense that they develop without union, they are in many cases more or less closely related to the sexual process. Examples of this are seen in the auxospores of diatoms, the dormant zygotes and the carpospores of algae, the ascospores and basidiospores of fungi, and especially the spores of the land plants.

The origin of sexual reproduction remains obscure in spite of numerous investigations of the lower algae where sexuality seems to be incipient. Sexuality in such organisms is thought to be incipient both because the individual vegetative cells themselves may function directly as gametes without special morphological differentiation, and because the gametes may develop into new individuals whether or not they undergo sexual union. There is good evidence that even in such organisms, in the absence of morphological differentiations, the process of sexual union is regulated by a complex series of hormones, and that disturbances in their functioning prevent the culmination of sexuality. Regarding the actual origin of sexuality, however, nothing is known with certainty.

In some organisms, although sexuality is present potentially, the race is maintained through many generations by asexual means, and sexuality may be considered a purely genetic phenomenon, a sporadic opportunity for gene combination and segregation. The plant kingdom includes organisms which exhibit a high degree of differentiation in the sexual process. Examples of a supposedly primitive type of sexual reproduction are plants like *Chlamydomonas eugametos* and *Spirogyra*, in which there is no morphological differentiation of vegetative cells from gametes. In other plants, special reproductive cells are differentiated when the individual attains maturity. These may be scattered in the plant body, as in certain filamentous green algae (*Ulothrix, Stigeoclonium*), or they may be restricted to certain regions where they are borne in special structures called gametangia

(*Codium, Ectocarpus, Chara, Allomyces*, etc.).

The gametes may be *apparently* similar to each other, as in isogamy, or differentiated, as in heterogamy and its advanced form, oogamy. The compatible isogamous gametes, male or female sex cells, may both be borne on the same individual (bisexuality) or they may be segregated on different individuals which are unisexual. The application of the terms "monoecious" and "dioecious" to describe the distribution of sexes on gametophytes is unfortunate, inasmuch as the terms first referred to the distribution of the spore-bearing organs of the plant sporophyte. In this connection it is noteworthy that although stamens (microsporophylls) and pistils (megasporophylls) of seed plants are spore-producing organs rather than gametophores, they have long been interpreted as manifestations of sexuality.

The segregation of plants into Cryptogams and Phanerogams was based originally on the premise that stamens and pistils are sex organs. Allen[2] has called attention succinctly to this problem in the following sentences: "Any genetic analysis of sex in Angiosperms must deal almost exclusively with characters of the so-called asexual generation, since those of the much reduced haploid 'sexual' generation have yet afforded little material for genetic study. To speak of sexual characters in an asexual generation is paradoxical; but the paradox inheres in the terminology, not in the facts. The diploid sporophyte helps through various devices to effect union of gametes produced by the filial gametophytes, and to provide for the shelter and nutrition of the embryonic grand-filial sporophyte; and such devices are sexual characters under any usable definition of the term." In some plants such as *Fucus* and angiosperms, in which the gametophytic phases are reduced almost to oblivion, it is *almost* true that the *sporophyte* has become sexual.

The advent of the meiotic process must have been coincident with the evolution of sexuality. As pointed out almost 70 years ago by the German botanist Strasburger, for every act of sexuality in which two chromosome complements (and genotypes) are brought together,

[2] C. E. Allen, "Sex Inheritance and Sex Determination," *American Naturalist*, 66:97–107, 1932.

there is a preceding or following meiosis in which the chromosomes and the genes they bear are again segregated. The relation between these two phenomena, in time, differs in various plants (and animals). Three fundamental types of life cycles based on these differences have been described. In the first, the vegetative phase is haploid and potentially sexual and is designated as the gametophyte. Gametic union produces a zygote, the only diploid cell in the life cycle. This zygote is interpreted by some to represent the precursor of and to be the homologue of the sporophyte of other types of life cycles. Zygotic meiosis restores the haploid gametophytic phase; hence alternation of generations is absent in a morphological sense, although cytological alternation is present.

At the other extreme lies a second type of life cycle, characteristic of most members of the animal kingdom, but occurring also in certain algae. In this type, the sexual individual is diploid and meiosis is gametic. The gametes alone in the life cycle are haploid, and here again morphological alternation is absent.

Many algae, certain fungi and all the land plants are characterized by a third type of life cycle which involves morphological as well as cytological alternation of generations. In these, the gametophytic and sporophytic phases both exceed a single cell generation (gamete or zygote) in duration and complexity. The diploid zygote gives rise to the sporophyte in which meiosis occurs at sporogenesis. The products of meiosis (spores) develop into haploid gametophytes. The two alternants may be free-living (diplobiontic cycle) or one may be physically associated with the other. Furthermore, the alternants may be morphologically equivalent (isomorphic alternation) or divergent (heteromorphic alternation). Both generations may be propagated indefinitely either by naturally occurring reproductive cells or by artificial manipulation. That the chromosome number of itself is not responsible for the divergence of the alternants in ontogeny is clear from the phenomena of apogamy and apospory discussed in Chapter 23. The causal factors in heteromorphic alternation of generations remain to be elucidated.

Sexuality is present almost universally in the plant kingdom. Only the Cyanophycophyta[3] and Euglenophycophyta seem to lack it entirely, as do most bacteria. It is quite possible that some subtle mechanism of gene interchange will yet be discovered in these organisms, as in certain bacteria, where it seemingly is a rare event in a very few species. The significance of sexuality, quite aside from its role in maintaining the species, is the opportunity it affords for originating new genetic combinations at meiosis and gametic union. Sexual reproduction is one of the mechanisms by which evolution proceeds.

In bringing to a conclusion this summary of reproductive processes in the plant kingdom, brief consideration must again be given to the phenomena which culminate in the production of seeds. The initiation of seed formation has certainly changed the face of the earth, for the seed plants, especially modern flowering plants, constitute its dominant vegetation and seed-eating animal species (including man) are correspondingly abundant.

A number of coordinated morphological phenomena are associated in the formation of the seed. A seed consists of an embryonic sporophyte embedded within a female gametophyte (in gymnosperms) which is surrounded by the delicate remains of the megasporangium tissue and covered by an integumentary layer. In angiospermous seeds, an additional nutritive tissue, the postfertilization endosperm, which replaces the nutritive female gametophyte in function, may persist. Among these coordinated phenomena may be cited the permanent retention of a single functional spore that produces the female gametophyte within the tissues of its sporangium and surrounding integument and the transportation of the male gametophyte to the proximity of the female gametophyte. The latter is known as pollination. In relation to pollination and proximity of the gametophytes, several further correlated phenomena may occur. In gymnosperms, these include the formation of a pollen chamber at the apex of the megasporangium for the reception of pollen grains and the formation of a pollen tube. The latter may be

---

[3] See, however, p. 21.

long or short, branched or unbranched. It is chiefly haustorial in the cycads and *Ginkgo* but also a mechanism for sperm transfer in other gymnosperms and the angiosperms. Pollen chambers are absent in the latter, the receptive function residing in the stigma of the megasporophyll.

Although chlorophyll is present in the female gametophyte of *Ginkgo*, the gametophytes of other seed plants are colorless, and their nutrition is based ultimately on the materials synthesized by the parent sporophyte. The nutrition of the male gametophyte of such genera as *Zamia*, *Ginkgo*, and *Pinus*, which involves breakdown of megasporangium tissue through enzymic activity, probably should be classified as parasitism. In *Ephedra* and many angiosperms, however, the pollen tube is so ephemeral that there is little probability of its absorbing much nutriment, unless it be from the mucilaginous secretions present in the micropyle or style. In other angiosperms, however, where the pollen tube grows slowly or over a great distance, parasitism may prevail.

The origin and steps in the development of these coordinated processes associated in seed formation remain in the realm of speculation, since the most trustworthy area of evidence, the fossil record, is eloquent in its silence. As far as is known, these phenomena characterize both extinct and extant seeds and their development. A great majority of botanists cite still another morphological attribute, namely, heterospory, as the inevitable concomitant of the seed habit. It will be recalled that this term is applied to such plants as *Selaginella*, *Isoetes*, and *Marsilea*, and to certain fossil genera, in which the spores that produce male gametophytes are markedly smaller than those that develop into female gametophytes. This is the reason for the terms microspores and megaspores.

Careful measurements of the microspores and megaspores of gymnosperms and angiosperms, however, supply no evidence that so-called megaspores are consistently larger than microspores. In fact, the contrary is true in a number of genera. This is in striking contrast to such heterosporous cryptogams as *Selaginella scandens*, for example, in which the ratio, by volume, of megaspore to microspore is in the order of 30,000 to 1. It is probable that permanent retention of the megaspore within the sporangium has been responsible for the initial reduction in its size. As evidence of its pristine free existence, some botanists emphasize the thickness of the megaspore membrane which surrounds the female gametophyte in such genera as *Ginkgo* (8 microns thick). However, the essential factor which distinguishes the heterospory of seed plants from that of cryptogams seems to be the timing of possible nutritional inflow: in cryptogams, food for the anticipated development of the female gametophyte is very early stored in the megaspore with resulting increase in the size of the latter. In seed plants, by contrast, provision of the nutriment is delayed until the initiation of the gametophyte development. Here the megaspore does, in fact, enlarge, but only later.

The Fossil Record, Classification and Phylogeny

The somewhat detailed discussion of living or extant representatives of the twenty-five plant divisions has been supplemented in the preceding pages of this text with brief treatments of certain extinct organisms presumably related to the living plant species. It now becomes essential to summarize briefly our knowledge regarding the course of evolution of the plant kingdom, as this is revealed in the fossil record.

Table 32-1 summarizes the various divisions of geologic time together with the interval during which the various plant groups have been represented in the earth's flora.

A number of significant facts emerge from examination of Table 32-1:

1. There was a long prebiotic period in the earth's history, the so-called period of chemical evolution, before the first recognizable living organisms[4] appeared, approximately 3,000,000,000 years ago.

2. There is good evidence, reviewed in more detail earlier in this text, that algae, bacteria,

---

[4] Not life, it should be noted.

TABLE 32-1

Major Stratigraphic and Time Divisions as Related to the Development of Major Plant Groups[a]

Era	System or Period	Series or Epoch	Estimated Age of Time Boundaries in Millions of Years	Duration of Existence of Plant Groups
Cenozoic	Quaternary	Recent		
		Pleistocene	1	
	Tertiary	Pliocene	10	
		Miocene	25	
		Oligocene	40	
		Eocene	60	
		Paleocene	63	
Mesozoic	Cretaceous	Upper (Late)		
		Lower (Early)	125	
	Jurassic	Upper (Late)		
		Middle (Middle)		
		Lower (Early)	150	
	Triassic	Upper (Late)		
		Middle (Middle)		
		Lower (Early)	180	
Paleozoic	Permian		205	
	Pennsylvanian	Upper (Late)		
		Middle (Middle)		
		Lower (Early)		
	Mississippian	Upper (Late)		
		Lower (Early)	255	
	Devonian	Upper (Late)		
		Middle (Middle)		
		Lower (Early)	315	
	Silurian	Upper (Late)		
		Middle (Middle)		
		Lower (Early)	350	
	Ordovician	Upper (Late)		
		Middle (Middle)		
		Lower (Early)	430	
	Cambrian	Upper (Late)		
		Middle (Middle)		
		Lower (Early)	510	
			3000	
	Pre-Cambrian[b]			

Plant groups shown as vertical ranges (Duration of Existence of Plant Groups): Algae and Fungi[c], Liverworts, Mosses, Psilophytes, Lycopods, Arthrophytes, Ferns, Cycadophytes, Ginkgophytes, Coniferophytes, Gnetophytes, Angiosperms.

[a] In use by the U.S. Geological Survey.
[b] Informal subdivisions such as upper, middle, and lower, or upper and lower, or younger and older, may be used locall
[c] Algae, 1.9 billion years; bacteria, 3 billion years.

and other fungi were present in this ancient period (mid-Pre-Cambrian) and that some of their descendants have persisted with little modification until the present.

3. Land plants did not become significant in the earth's flora until the Devonian, approximately 2.7 billion years after the algae, fungi, and bacteria had evolved.

4. The various groups of vascular cryptogams seem to have been contemporaneous in early development and could scarcely have evolved from each other.

5. Their origin must have been from an earlier, hopefully, still-to-be-discovered, precursor group.

6. The vascular cryptogams probably did not have hepatophytan[5] or bryophytan progenitors.

7. Gymnospermous seed plants arose in the Carboniferous, although certain progymnosperms[6] were probably present in the Devonian.

8. The angiosperms are the most recent (and successful) plants to appear in the earth's flora; recognizable precursors have yet to be discovered.

9. The fossil record does not reveal unequivocal evidences of common ancestry. This is evident in Table 32-1 in which the lines of development of the several plant groups are not represented as convergent; that, in fact, they must have been so, is indicated from the evidences cited on page 515.

Because we lack conclusive evidence, at present, regarding the *course* of evolution and the exact lineage of extant plants, we speak of the several groups or series in Tables 32-1 and 2 and their component taxa, as being "polyphyletic." Again, it seems to the writer that this term, in light of the seemingly incontrovertible evidences of the unity of origin and monophyletic development of living organisms, presented on page 515, is best interpreted as a negative and unrealistic one; in reality, there is little room for doubt that all living things are related—the term polyphyletic never gives the real or final answer—it is a *tentative term*, signifying our current ignorance of the actual course of evolution.

Finally, seed size and certain changes in the protective layers (integuments and/or megasporophylls) are correlated with the phenomena of pollination and fertilization in that they take place only when stimulated chemically by these latter occurrences. The possession of the seed habit together with a wide range of adaptive vegetative features certainly explains the extensive colonization of the earth by angiosperms.

In concluding this volume on the morphology of representative plants, reference must be made again to the problem of classifying the groups of which the type plants discussed are representatives. The problem of classification was alluded to in Chapter 1, when it was stated that fruitful discussion of systems of classification should be deferred until one has become familiar with the plants to be classified. It is assumed that the reader is now in this position, at least to some degree.

In initiating such a discussion, a word of caution from an eminent morphologist seems particularly appropriate. He writes: "Once a system of classification becomes widely adopted, it takes on many of the attributes of a creed. Not only does it constitute the framework about which the botanist does his thinking, but it rapidly becomes a substitute for it. It comes to be looked upon as having emanated from some authoritative and inspired source."[7]

The old saying, "a little knowledge is a dangerous thing," is an appropriate and chastening thought for anyone who attempts to erect a phylogenetic system of classification of plants and animals. A phylogenetic classification, it will be recalled, is one in which the organisms are arranged in categories or taxa in an order which describes their supposed relationship based on evolutionary development. As expressed by a distinguished taxonomist: "A phylogenetic system classifies organisms according to their evolutionary sequence, it reflects genetic relationships, and

---

[5] The reverse has been suggested (see p. 221).
[6] *Archaeopteris-Callixylon.*

[7] C. A. Arnold, "Classification of the Gymnosperms from the Viewpoint of Paleobotany," *Bot. Gaz.*, 110: 2–12, 1948.

it enables one to determine at a glance the ancestors or derivatives (when present) of any taxon."[8] Attempts at phylogenetic classification multiplied after Darwin's *Origin of Species* was published in 1859. In spite of the paucity of evidence from paleobotany and comparative morphology of living plants, faith that plants could be arranged in phylogenetic systems apparently was unbounded, and in some cases enthusiasm outstripped critical judgment. One might well assume, therefore, that, as rich as they have been in scientific inquiry, the intervening decades, almost a century, would have provided firm and convincing data on which to erect *the one* definitive, phylogenetic scheme. Actually, many such schemes have been presented, and although incontrovertible evidence of evolution and kinship has been educed at the species level and below it, increasing knowledge has counseled caution regarding the degree of assurance with which we should postulate relationship and the course of evolution among the higher categories. This caution is reflected in a marked increase in the number and degree of polyphyletic systems of the plant kingdom which have been suggested in the recent literature.

Table 32-2 presents in comparative fashion a summary of the widely used system of Eichler,[9] somewhat modified by others, the system of Tippo,[10] and the system used in the first (and slightly modified in the present) edition of this text. The legend of the table explains the mechanics of comparison. It is clear at once that the number of divisions has increased from Eichler's four, through Tippo's twelve, to the twenty-five of the present volume. The table shows the progressive subdivision of earlier categories. Classification of the old Eichlerian class Algae into seven or eight separate taxa, raised to divisional rank, was the first manifestation of a more polyphyletic viewpoint and first appeared in an American textbook in 1933. The partition of the Eichlerian Pteridophyta, which included the ferns and their "allies" (Table 32-2) came later. Abandonment of the class name Gymnospermae was proposed still more recently and is accepted in the present volume. The classification here presented differs mainly in that plants other than algae also have been classified polyphyletically. These innovations will now be considered.

The Phycomycota, Ascomycota, and Basidiomycota, still included in the single division Eumycophyta in other systems (Table 32-2), here are raised to the rank of divisions for reasons already presented in Chapter 14. Similarly, the liverworts and mosses have been treated here as separate divisions, the Hepatophyta and Bryophyta, as explained at the end of Chapter 16. Doubt that liverworts and mosses are closely related was expressed many years ago by Goebel. In the opinion of the writer, no convincing evidence to contradict Goebel's view has yet been educed.

The most striking departures of the author's system are apparent in his disposition of the vascular plants, often widely conceived as comprising a single division, Tracheophyta (Table 32-2), although several recent texts have abandoned this concept. As noted in Chapter 17, uniting such a large and diverse assemblage of morphological types in a single division on the basis of a single common attribute, namely, the possession of xylem and phloem, is open to question. "The result of the widespread practice of classifying plants on single sets of characters has been to encourage overemphasis on certain morphological phenomena, to the neglect or exclusion of others of equal significance, and to try to construct phylogenetic lines on them alone."[11]

The division Tracheophyta is subject to this very criticism, in the writer's opinion. Accordingly, the vascular plants have been reclassified here in a number of separate divisions. This has occasioned raising the subdivisions Psilopsida, Lycopsida, and Sphenopsida to divisional rank and has required changing the

[8] G. H. M. Lawrence, *Taxonomy of Vascular Plants*, The Macmillan Company, New York, p. 13, 1951.

[9] G. M. Smith (*Cryptogamic Botany*, vol. 1, 1955) has presented evidence that this system was used, at least in part, before Eichler.

[10] O. Tippo, "A Modern Classification of the Plant Kingdom," *Chronica Botanica*, 7:203–206, 1942. (Tippo calls divisions "phyla.")

[11] C. A. Arnold, "Classification of the Gymnosperms from the Viewpoint of Paleobotany," *Bot. Gaz.*, 110:2–12, 1948.

suffixes of the group names.[12] The quite meaningless name Lycopsida ("having the appearance of a wolf") has been replaced by the designation Microphyllophyta, an allusion to an important attribute of the group. Arthrophyta, an older name, here is used as the divisional name to replace Sphenopsida, because the latter is based on a fossil genus not well known to many students.

The treatment of the macrophyllous vascular plants in the present text (Table 32-2) also deviates from previous practice. To unite in the same taxon spore-bearing plants with free-living gametophytes and seed-bearing plants with retained gametophytes on the basis of their single common attribute of macrophylly seems questionable. In this volume, therefore, the subdivision Pteropsida (Table 32-2) has been abandoned and has been replaced by six divisions, namely, the Pterophyta (now restricted to macrophyllous plants lacking seeds), Cycadophyta, Ginkgophyta, Coniferophyta, Gnetophyta, and Anthophyta. The reasons for this arrangement have been presented in earlier chapters and need not be repeated.

Although the number of divisions has been increased by these changes to twenty-five, the author is strongly of the opinion that in light of the available evidence a tentatively "polyphyletic" view really is the properly conservative one. His opinion in this connection and the system of classification used in this volume should not be considered as representing the final solution to the question of plant relationship. The author himself at present looks upon the suggested classification as, at best, a tentative approximation.

Does the classification presented in the present volume then imply or deny that there is evidence available for the relationship through common lineage of living plants to each other and to extinct plants? Quite the contrary, as stated in the introductory chapter (p. 4) to this volume and earlier in this chapter (p. 513). Such attributes as the cellular organization of protoplasm (at both the light-

microscopic and ultrastructural levels), methods of nuclear and cell replication, biochemical patterns in metabolism, and the mechanisms of genetic interchange, recombination, and segregation, among others, are so universal that they seemingly cannot be explained satisfactorily on any basis other than that of a common origin of all plants and animals.

It is, however, when we come to consider the actual course or lineage in the subsequent diversification of organisms, both extinct and extant, as this can be expressed in a system of classification, that we meet with disappointment and frustration if we rigorously distinguish between *evidence* and *speculation*. This becomes increasingly true as we consider taxa successively higher than species. The writer, after carefully weighing the currently available evidence of comparative morphology, cytology, biochemistry, and the fossil record, is *at present* unwilling to amalgamate any two or more of the twenty-five divisions in which he has tentatively classified the organisms of the plant kingdom. When and if additional relevant data become available, such amalgamations will undoubtedly be required, but at this time there are no known living or fossil forms which unequivocally link any two of the proposed divisions.

On the other hand, when one reviews the attributes of the twenty-five divisions, three seemingly natural series emerge, as indicated by the grouping of the divisions within three subkingdoms in Table 32-3, namely, the Prokaryota, Chlorota, and Achlorota. Let us examine the attributes which suggest these groupings.

The Prokaryota (Gr. *pro*, before + Gr. *karyon*, nut, hence nucleus) are organisms possessing cells in which the DNA is not delimited from the cytoplasm by double membranes as it is in all other plant and animal cells. These organisms (blue-green algae and bacteria), furthermore, lack certain cellular organelles—membrane-bounded plastids, mitochondria, Golgi apparatus, and endoplasmic reticulum—which characterize the cells of all other members of the plant kingdom. Animal cells are more similar to those of the latter in their organization than the cells of both animals and plants are to the Prokaryota. Fur-

---

[12] International Code of Botanical Nomenclature; adopted by the Ninth International Botanical Congress, Montreal, 1959. *Regnum Vegetabile* 23, Kemink en Zoon, N. V., Utrecht.

TABLE 32-2. A Comparative Summary of Some Classifications of the Plant Kingdom[a]

Eichler, 1883 (and modifications)	Tippo, 1942	Present Text
PLANT KINGDOM	PLANT KINGDOM	PLANT KINGDOM
A. Cryptogamae	Abandoned	
Division 1. Thallophyta	Sub-kingdom 1. Thallophyta	
Class 1. Algae	Abandoned	
Cyanophyceae	Phylum[b] 1. Cyanophyta	Division 1. Cyanophycophyta
Chlorophyceae	Phylum 2. Chlorophyta	Division 2. Chlorophycophyta
	Phylum 3. Euglenophyta	Division 3. Euglenophycophyta
		Division 4. Charophyta
Phaeophyceae	Phylum 4. Phaeophyta	Division 5. Phaeophycophyta
Rhodophyceae	Phylum 5. Rhodophyta	Division 6. Rhodophycophyta
Diatomeae	Phylum 6. Chrysophyta	Division 7. Chrysophycophyta
	Phylum 7. Pyrrophyta	Division 8. Pyrrophycophyta
Class 2. Fungi	Abandoned.	
Schizomycetes	Phylum 8. Schizomycophyta	Division 9. Schizomycota
	Phylum 9. Myxomycophyta	Division 10. Myxomycota
Eumycetes	Phylum 10. Eumycophyta	Abandoned
	Class 1. Phycomycetes	Division 11. Phycomycota
	Class 2. Ascomycetes	Division 12. Ascomycota
Lichens	Class 3. Basidiomycetes	Division 13. Basidiomycota
		Division 14. Deuteromycota
	Sub-kingdom 2. Embryophyta	Abandoned
	Phylum 11. Bryophyta	
Division 2. Bryophyta	Class 1. Hepaticae	Division 15. Hepatophyta
Class 1. Hepaticae		Division 16. Bryophyta
Class 2. Musci	Class 2. Musci	
Division 3. Pteridophyta	Abandoned	
	Phylum 12. Tracheophyta	Abandoned
	Sub-phylum 1. Psilopsida	Division 17. Psilophyta
Class 1. Lycopodinae	Sub-phylum 2. Lycopsida	Division 18. Microphyllophyta
Class 2. Equisetinae	Sub-phylum 3. Sphenopsida	Division 19. Arthrophyta
	Sub-phylum 4. Pteropsida	Abandoned
	Class 1. Filices	Division 20. Pterophyta

MORPHOLOGY OF PLANTS

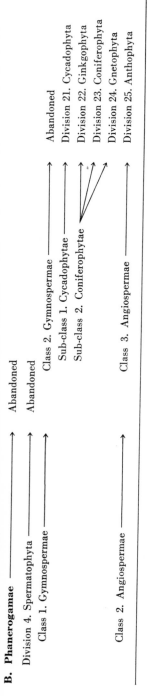

[a] The arrows indicate the fate of taxa in successively more modern systems of classification.
[b] Although approximately equivalent to "Division," "Phylum" is not recognized as a category by the International Code of Botanical Nomenclature.

thermore, mitosis, meiosis, and sexuality are essentially different or lacking in Prokaryota. It seems clear that the Prokaryota have not evolved beyond an algal (Cyanophycophyta) or fungal (Schizomycota) level of organization. It is argued by some biologists that the Prokaryota differ so markedly from both plants and animals that they should be classified in a completely separate kingdom.

The Chlorota have diverged the most widely morphologically in evolution from their postulated green algal (chlorophycophytan) progenitors (Table 32-3). The cells of all Chlorota contain chlorophyll a and have double-membrane-bounded plastids and nuclei as well as mitochondria, Golgi apparatus, and endoplasmic reticulum. Like most members of the animal kingdom, their nuclei divide mitotically, and meiosis and sexual reproduction are widespread.

One series of evolutionary development within the Chlorota, represented in Table 32-3 by Division 1a–f, while remaining at an algal level of organization,[13] became diversified cytologically (with respect to wall composition and flagellar insertion and organization) and biochemically (with respect to accessory pigmentation and stored metabolites). In contrast, a second series, exemplified by Divisions 1a–13 in Table 32-3, while retaining essentially the same cytological organization (including possession of stacked or grouped chloroplast lamellae, either granoids or grana) also have conservatively retained the same chlorophyll pigments (a and b), storage of starch, and cellulosic wall composition. The evolutionary diversification here was in the direction of increasingly complex gross morphology, as is apparent in such subseries as the liverworts, mosses, vascular cryptogams, gymnosperms, and angiosperms. The Chlorophycophyta, of all the algae, are here considered to have been the most likely progenitors of the remaining divisions of Chlorota. Certainly all available evidence supports that conclusion.

The Mycota, characterized by lack of chlorophyll and, accordingly, by heterotrophic nutrition, in general have cellular and ultra-

---

[13] See page 9 for definition of algae.

TABLE 32-3. **A Phylogenetic Grouping of the Divisions of the Plant Kingdom**[a]

Subkingdom I. Chlorota

Division 1a. Chlorophycophyta
Division 1b. Euglenophycophyta
Division 1c. Phaeophycophyta
Division 1d. Chrysophycophyta
Division 1e. Pyrrophycophyta
Division 1f. Rhodophycophyta
Division 2. Charophyta
Division 3. Hepatophyta
Division 4. Bryophyta
Division 5. Psilophyta
Division 6. Microphyllophyta
Division 7. Arthrophyta
Division 8. Pterophyta
Division 9. Cycadophyta
Division 10. Ginkgophyta
Division 11. Coniferophyta
Division 12. Gnetophyta
Division 13. Anthophyta

Subkingdom II. Mycota[b]

Division 1. Myxomycota
Division 2. Phycomycota
Division 3. Ascomycota
Division 4. Basidiomycota
Division 5. Deuteromycota

Subkingdom III. Prokaryota[c]

Division 1. Cyanophycophyta
Division 2. Schizomycota

[a] Of the Chlorota, Divisions 1a–f are algae; Division 2 contains the stoneworts or brittleworts; Divisions 3 and 4, the liverworts and mosses, respectively.
Divisions 5–8 are the vascular cryptogams; Divisions 9–12 are gymnospermous and Division 13, angiospermous seed plants.
[b] The Mycota contain the fungi (*sensu lato*).
[c] The Prokaryota contain the blue-green algae and bacteria.

structural organization similar to that of Chlorota. They differ, of course, in lacking plastids, often in the chemical composition of their walls, and in other less obvious attributes. Most mycologists classify divisions 2–5 of the Mycota as a single division (Eumycota), a practice not followed here by the author because of his conviction that the differences among these several divisions of fungi are

certainly of as great magnitude as those which have resulted in the classification of algae as seven separate divisions.

Certain criticisms of the classification, as here presented, have been expressed by several colleagues. The strongest of these held that it is a negative, retrogressive system which overlooks evidences of relationship and separates subdivisions of plants grouped together in other classifications.[14] This criticism has been directed especially against the treatment of the vascular plants and the author's abandonment of the "phylum" Tracheophyta. Similar criticisms were voiced when the Eichlerian division Thallophyta, and also its component classes, the Algae and Fungi, were dismembered a number of years ago. We still, however, meaningfully speak of "thallophytes," "algae," and "fungi," and one can continue to refer to "tracheophytes" or "vascular plants," "seed plants," "gymnosperms," and "angiosperms" in informal designation of groups of taxa, even if he is reluctant to use these names as proper nouns in the system of classification, thereby formalizing relationships.

In final defense of his proposals, the writer can only reiterate that the appraisal and interpretation of the evidence of evolutionary development and phylogeny vary with the appraiser and interpreter. The translation of their conclusions into a system of classification will, therefore, vary accordingly. Variations in and prolonged consideration of diverse systems of classification should serve as the inspiration for discussion and should not detract from the reader's understanding of the plants themselves, as they have been presented in earlier chapters.

After all, nature mocks at human categories, and our present series of classifications represent only our current, subjective appraisals of the significance of available data and their bearing on phylogeny. "No single system (of classification) can be accepted as final as long as a single fact concerning any kind of plant remains unknown."[15]

[14] "You have not *reclassified* the plant kingdom but *declassified* it" wrote one outraged colleague.
[15] C. A. Arnold, "Classification of the Gymnosperms from the Viewpoint of Paleobotany, *Bot. Gaz.,* 110:2–12, 1948.

Glossary

Abscission layer: a zone of cells at the base of an appendage (petiole, fruit stalk, etc.) which results in the separation of that appendage from another organ.

Achene: a dry, indehiscent, one-seeded fruit in which the seed is free from the pericarp except at the point of attachment of the seed.

Acrasin: a secretion of amoebae of cellular slime molds which is effective in evoking aggregation.

Acrogynous: having the apical cell of an axis "used up" or differentiated in archegonium formation, as in *Porella*, etc.

Actinomorphy: radial symmetry.

Actinostele: a protostele with a ridged surface.

Adnation: fusion of one organ to another, as in epipetalous stamens.

Advanced: derived or descended with modification from the primitive.

Adventitious root: one neither primary nor secondary nor arising therefrom.

Aeciospore: the spore produced in the aecial stage of a rust.

Aecium: conglomeration of hyphae by which aeciospores are produced.

Agar: a gel-forming polysaccharide, a polymer of galactose, derived from certain red algae and used in microbiology as a solidifying agent in culture media.

Aggregate fruit: a receptacle bearing a number of matured pistils (fruits) of a single flower.

Akaryota: organisms lacking membrane-bounded nuclei, plastids, Golgi apparatus, and mitochondria.

Akinete: a vegetative cell transformed by wall thickening into a nonmotile spore.

Alga: a photosynthetic eukaryotic organism lacking sex organs; or with unicellular ones; or, if the gametangium is multicellular, having every cell fertile.

Allophycocyanin: a blue biliprotein pigment of the blue-green algae.

Alternation of generations: a reproductive cycle in which a haploid organism (or tissue) gives rise sexually to a diploid organism (or tissue): the meiotic products of the latter grow directly into a haploid organism (or tissue).

Ament: a spike of apetalous flowers, either staminate or pistillate, as in willow.

Amphigastrium: the ventral leaf (often reduced in size) of leafy liverworts.

Amphiphloic: having phloem on both sides of the xylem.

Amphithecium: an external or superficial cell layer or layers differentiated in embryonic sporophytes from an internal endothecium.

Amphitropous ovule: one in which the ovular body itself is bent in the form of a "U."

Anacrogynous: not having the apical cell of an axis involved in archegonium formation.

Anatomy: in botany, that area which deals with the organization of the organs of vascular plants.

Anatropous ovule: one in which the ovule is inverted with respect to its funiculus; the micropyle, accordingly, at the same level as the base of the funiculus.

Androspore: a motile zoospore of the Oedogoniales which generates a dwarf-male plant.

Angiosperm: a seed plant with ovules and seeds enclosed in a carpel, pistil, or fruit.

Anisophyllous: having dimorphic leaves.

Annulus: a specialized or differentiated layer of cells in the moss capsule or in the sporangial wall of vascular cryptogams.

Antheridial cell: the larger product of internal division (along with the smaller prothallial cell) of the microspore.

Antheridiophore: a fertile branch bearing antheridia.

Antheridium: a multicellular, sperm-producing organ consisting of spermatogenous tissue and a sterile jacket in plants other than algae or fungi; in the latter, a unicellular sperm-forming organ.

Antherozoid: a sperm.

Anticlinal: perpendicular to the surface.

Antipodal cell: one or more cells of the mature female gametophyte of angiosperms, located at the opposite end from the micropyle.

Apical cell: a prominently differentiated meristem cell, derivatives of which organize the plant body or organ.

Apical growth: growth localized in an apical meristem.

Aplanospore: a nonmotile spore (in algae, with the potentiality of motility, i.e., a nonmotile zoospore).

Apogamy: formation of an organism without gametic union.

Apogeotropic: negatively geotropic.

Apomixis: a collective term for absence of sexual union and failure of meiosis.

Apophysis: basal region of moss capsule, enlarged in some.

Apospory: formation of the gametophyte in a manner other than from spores.

Apothecium: an open ascocarp, often cup- or saucer-like.

Appressorium: a flattened hypha from which a minute process may enter a host cell.

Archegonial chamber: a cavity or groove at the apex of the female gametophyte in certain gymnosperms; the archegonial neck cells are on its surface.

Archegoniophore: a branch bearing archegonia.

Archegonium: a multicellular, egg-producing gametangium with a jacket of sterile cells.

Ascocarp: the ascus-containing body of Ascomycota.

Ascospore: a spore produced by free-cell formation following meiosis in an ascus.

Ascus: a sac-like cell of the Ascomycota in which karyogamy is followed immediately by meiosis and in which ascospores of definite number arise by free-cell formation.

Asexual reproduction: reproduction not involving plasmogamy and karyogamy.

Atactostele: a scattered arrangement of xylem and phloem groups (vascular bundles).

Autocolony: a miniature daughter colony formed by coenobic algae.

Autoecious: completing the life cycle on a single host species as in certain rusts.

Autospore: a nonmotile, asexual daughter cell which lacks the ontogenetic potentiality of motility.

Autotrophic: capable of synthesizing protoplasm from entirely inorganic substances.

Auxiliary cell: that cell to which the zygote nucleus migrates in certain red algae.

Auxospore: the zygote of diatoms.

Axenic culture: one which contains a population of only one species.

Axile placentation: attachment of ovules to central axis of a compound ovary.

Axillary bud: one borne in the axil of the leaf.

Axis: the stem and root (if present) of a plant.

Bacillus: a rod-shaped bacterium.

Basidiocarp: the basidiospore-containing structure of certain Basidiomycota.

Basidiospores: a spore borne outside of a basidium and arising after meiosis.

Basidium: a nonseptate or septate hypha bearing (usually) four basidiospores exogenously following karyogamy and meiosis.

Berry: a simple, fleshy indehiscent fruit with a skin-like exocarp, fleshy mesocarp, and slimy or juicy endocarp.

Biochemistry: the chemistry of living matter.

Body cell: that cell of the male gametophyte of gymnosperms which divides to form the sperm cells.

Bracteole: the inner of two appendages surrounding the microsporophylls in *Ephedra*.

Bryology: the study of liverworts and mosses.

Bud: a minute stem with short internodes bearing the primordia of vegetative leaves or sporophylls.

Bud scale: a modified basal leaf which encloses the more delicate leaf or sporophyll primordia.

Budding: abscission of a cellular protuberance resulting in multiplication as in certain yeasts.

Bulb: a short, vertical subterranean stem covered by fleshy leaf bases or scales as in lily and onion.

Bulbil: a gemma or miniature plantlet produced in the leaf axils of certain species of *Lycopodium*.

Bundle sheath: differentiated tissue, often thick-walled, surrounding a leaf vein.

Callus: undifferentiated tissue which heals a wound or which may be grown in tissue culture.

Calyptra: the enlarged and modified archegonium which for awhile encloses the embryonic sporophyte of liverworts, mosses, and vascular cryptogams.

Calyx: the collective term for the sepals of a flower.

Cambium: a zone of meristematic cells, between primary xylem and phloem, the division products of which differentiate as secondary xylem and phloem.

Campylotropous ovule: an ovule in which the funiculus is perpendicular to the long axis of the ovular body.

Capillitium: thread-like structures among the spores of Myxomycetes and certain puff balls.

Capitulum: the head-like inflorescence of composite flowers, as in daisy.

Capsule: the sporangium of liverworts and mosses; or the colloidal sheath in algae and bacteria.

Carinal canal: a cavity within the arthrophytan stem lying on the same radius as a ridge, as in *Equisetum*.

Carotene: a red and orange pigment (oxygen-free hydrocarbon).

Carotenoid: collective term which includes both carotenes and xanthophylls.

Carpel: enclosing structure of angiospermous ovules often considered to represent a folded megasporophyll.

Carpogonium: the female gametangium of red algae.

Carposporangium: a carpospore-containing cell in red algae.

Carpospore: the single protoplast contained within a carposporangium.

Carposporophyte: a group of carposporangia and carpospores in red algae which arise directly or indirectly from the zygote.

Carrageenin: polysaccharides extracted by hot water from certain red algae, composed of D-galactose units and sulfate groups.

Caryopsis: a dry, indehiscent, one-seed fruit in which the seed coat is completely fused to the pericarp.

Cauline: pertaining to the stem.

Central canal: the central cavity in the internodes of arthrophytes.

Central cell: the precursor of the egg and ventral canal cells which arise by its division.

Central nodule: a complex, thickened region in the center of the valves of motile, pennate diatoms.

Centrarch: a pattern of primary xylem differentiation in which the protoxylem is central and surrounded by metaxylem.

Chalaza: the base of an ovule, often conspicuous as the region below the point of union of integuments with the megasporangium.

Chasmogamous flower: a flower which opens for pollination and reproduction.

Chemosynthetic: autotrophic and using chemical energy for synthesis.

Chemotaxis: movement of cells to or away from a chemical stimulus.

Chlamydospore: a hyphal cell which becomes thick-walled, segregated from the parent mycelium and functions as a spore (probably equivalent to an algal akinete).

Chlorenchyma: parenchyma containing chloroplasts.

Chlorophyll: the green pigment complex in plants; several types are known; tetrapyrrolic compounds containing a magnesium atom.

Chloroplast: a membrane-bounded area of cytoplasm containing photosynthetic lamellae.

Chromoplast: a chloroplast low in chlorophyll content and high in carotenoid content.

Chrysolaminarin: a polysaccharide composed of glucose units in β-1:3-linkage (synonym, leucosin).

Circinate vernation: curled arrangement of leaves and leaflets in the bud occasioned by their more rapid growth on one surface.

Clamp connection: a lateral connection between adjacent cells of the secondary mycelium of Basidiomycota.

Cleavage polyembryony: the formation of as many as four proembryos from a single zygote by separation of the cleavage products.

Cleistogamous flower: one which does not open for pollination but is fertilized by germination of pollen within the closed system.

Cleistothecium: an ascocarp which does not open.

Clonal culture: a population descended from a single individual.

Coccus: a spherical bacterium.

Coenobium: a colony with the cell number fixed at origin and not subsequently augmented.

Coenocyst: a multinucleate cyst or dormant spore.

Coenocyte: a multinucleate mass of protoplasm lacking internal septa.

Column: (1) the anterior protuberance of the female gametophyte in *Ginkgo*; (2) the stalk which bears the microsporangia in *Ephedra*.

Companion cell: a small nucleated cell associated with some sieve cells.

Complete flower: one having sepals, petals, stamens, and pistil(s).

Compound leaf: one with a divided blade.

Compound pistil: one composed of several united simple pistils or carpels.

Conceptacle: a chamber in a receptacle of the rockweeds in which gametangia are borne.

Conidium: an asexual fungus spore borne apically or laterally on a hypha.

Conjugation: union of gametes and/or gametangia in certain algae and fungi.

Connective: the tissue between the pairs of microsporangia in an anther.

Contractile vacuole: one which excretes liquid after previous dilation by the same.

Cork cambium: the phellogen, a layer of meristematic cells which function in secondary growth forming cork cells (phellem) to the periphery and cork parenchyma (phelloderm) internally.

Corm: a short, vertical, fleshy, subterranean stem.

Corolla: collective term for petals.

Corona: the crown cells on the oogonia of Charophyta.

Corpus: the portion of the apical meristem internal to the tunica.

Cotyledon: a primary embryonic leaf.

Crozier: the configuration of the ultimate, penultimate and antepenultimate cells during ascus formation.

Cryoflora: plants of ice and snow.

Cryptoblast: a sterile invagination of the surface in rockweeds.

Cryptogam: a seedless plant.

Culture: a laboratory population of (usually) microorganisms.

Cyanophycean starch: amylopectin fraction of starch produced by blue-green algae.

Cyme: an inflorescence in which the apex differentiates with the result that lateral branches differentiate later to produce younger flowers.

Cystidium: an enlarged sterile cell in the hymenium of Basidiomycota.

Cystocarp: the carposporangia and associated sterile covering cells in red algae.

Cytological alternation of generations: term applied to that type of life cycle ($H + h$ or $H + d$) in which one generation is represented only by reproductive cells of different chromosome number.

Cytology: the study of cellular organization.

Derived: descended or modified from an older, more primitive precursor.

Desmid: one of a group of green algae in which the cells are composed of mirror-image halves; their reproduction is by union of amoeboid gametes.

Diarch: having two sites of protoxylem differentiation.

Dichotomous: branching into two equal parts.

Dictyostele: a siphonostele or solenostele dissected by leaf gaps.

Dikaryotic: binucleate.

Dioecious: having microspores and megaspores produced on separate individuals.

Diplanetism: having two periods of motility.

Diploid: having two complements of haploid chromosomes.

Disc flower: one of the central, symmetrical flowers of the capitulum of composites.

DNA: deoxyribonucleic acid.

Double fertilization: in angiosperms, union of one sperm with the egg and the other with two polar nuclei or a secondary nucleus.

Drupe: a simple, fleshy, indehiscent fruit with stony endocarp, fleshy mesocarp, and skin-like exocarp.

Diplobiontic: having two free-living alternants (organisms) in the life cycle.

Ecology: the study of the interrelationships between organism and environment.

Ectophloic: having phloem external to the xylem.

Egg: a large, nonflagellate female gamete.

Egg apparatus: the egg cell and synergids in angiosperms.

Elater: (1) a sterile, hygroscopic cell in the capsule of certain liverworts; (2) the appendages formed from the outer spore wall in *Equisetum*.

Elaterophore: region of attachment of elaters in certain liverworts.

Embryonal tube: secondary suspensor-like cells in the proembryos of certain gymnosperms.

Endarch: differentiation of primary xylem centrifugally.

Endocarp: the innermost layer of the ovary wall at the fruit stage.

Endodermis: the innermost, differentiated layer of the cortex, present in roots, rhizomes, and certain cryptogamous stems.

Endophyte: a plant living within another plant.

Endoplasmic reticulum: lamellar or tubular system in the colorless cytoplasm.

Endosperm: nutritive tissue for the embryo in angiosperms.

Endospore: an internally formed, thick-walled spore of bacteria and certain blue-green algae.

Endothecium: (1) the internal tissue of an embryonic sporophyte surrounded by amphithecium; (2) the inner portion of an anther wall.

Epidermis: the surface tissue of plant organs, composed of living parenchyma cells.

Epigean: having the cotyledons emerging from the seed and raised above the soil.

Epigyny: the overgrowth of the ovary by the receptacle and/or bases of other floral organs.

Epipetalous: Borne upon the petals.

Epiplasm: Residual cytoplasm resulting from free-cell formation.

Epitheca: the larger of the two valves in the diatom frustule.

Essential organ: stamens and pistils of a flower.

Eukaryotic: organisms having membrane-bounded nuclei, plastids, Golgi apparatus, and mitochondria.

Eusporangiate: having the sporangial wall develop from superficial cells and the sporogenous tissue from internal cells of the sporophyll or sporangiophore.

Eustele: arrangement of primary xylem and phloem in discrete strands but separated by parenchymatous tissue occasioned by leaf gaps.

Evolution: descent with modification.

Exarch: differentiation of primary xylem centripetally.

Exine: outer layer of the wall of a spore or pollen grain.

Exocarp: the outermost layer of the ovary wall in the fruit stage.

Eyespot: stigma, the hypothetical site of light perception.

False branching: branching originating by rupture of an unbranched trichome from its sheath.

False indusium: the unrolled leaf margin when it covers marginal sporangia.

Fertile spike: the spore-bearing axis in the Ophioglossales.

Fertilization tube: a protuberance from the antheridium which penetrates each egg in water molds.

Fiber: an elongate, pointed, thick-walled, usually nonliving, supporting cell of the sclerenchyma.

Filament: (1) a chain of cells; (2) the stalk of the angiosperm stamen.

Flagellum: an extension of the protoplasm, the beating of which propels the cell.

Floridean starch: extra-plastid polysaccharides of red algae similar to the branched amylopectin fraction of other plant starches.

Follicle: a simple, dry, dehiscent fruit originating from a simple pistil which dehisces along one line.

Foot: the absorbing organ of the embryonic sporophyte in liverworts, mosses, and vascular cryptogams.

Free cell formation: cytokinesis within a cell to form one or more cells, leaving residual cytoplasm or epiplasm.

Free central placentation: attachment of ovules to a central axis, the latter joined only at its base to the compound ovary.

Free-nuclear division: mitoses without cytokineses.

Frond: the fern leaf.

Fruit: the matured ovary or ovaries of one or more flowers and associated structures.

Frustule: the siliceous cell wall of diatoms.

Fucoxanthin: a xanthophyll produced in brown algae and Chrysophycophyta.

Functional megaspore: the surviving megaspore of the linear tetrad in seed plants which produces the female gametophyte.

Fungi: in a broad sense, all achlorophyllous non-vascular cryptogams.

Funiculus: the stalk of the ovule which attaches it to the placenta.

Gametangium: a structure containing gametes.

Gamete: a sex cell which unites with another to form a zygote.

Gametic meiosis: meiosis occurring during the production of gametes.

Gametophore: a branch bearing gametes.

Gametophyte: a plant which produces gametes.

Gamone: a chemical substance involved in effecting sexual union.

Gemma: a bud or fragment of an organism which functions in asexual reproduction.

Generalized growth: increase in size, not localized.

Generative cell: (1) in many gymnosperms, the cell which gives rise to the stalk and body cells; (2) in angiosperms, the cell which divides to form two sperms.

Genetics: the science of heredity and variation.

Germinal pore: a thin place in the wall of a pollen grain through which the tube emerges.

Germ tube: the protruding tubiform protoplast of a germinating spore.

Gill: the radiating lamellae in certain basidiocarps.

Girdle band: in diatoms, the structures to which hypotheca and epitheca are attached.

Golgi apparatus: cellular organelles consisting of stacks of sacs or cisternae, probably secretory in function.

Gonidium: an asexual reproductive cell.

Gonimoblast: a filament which arises after fertilization in red algae, giving rise to carposporangia.

Gradate: an arrangement of sporangia on the fern receptacle, the oldest at the apex and younger ones lateral.

Ground meristem: the primary meristematic tissue other than protoderm and procambium.

Gymnosperm: a seed plant with seeds not enclosed by a megasporophyll or pistil.

Haplobiontic: having one free-living organism in the life cycle.

Haploid: having a single chromosome complement.

Haplostele: a cylindrical protostele with a smooth margin in transection.

Haustorium: an absorptive hypha which penetrates a host cell.

Heterocyst: transparent, thick-walled, blue-green algal cell.

Heteroecious: requiring two living hosts to complete its life cycle, as in certain rusts.

Heterogamy: male and female gametes morphologically distinct, both flagellate.

Heteromorphic alternation: having alternants which differ morphologically.

Heterospory: production of microspores which grow into male gametophytes and megaspores which develop into female gametophytes; the two kinds of spores may or may not differ in size (see p. 393).

Heterothallism: self-incompatibility, thus requiring two compatible strains or organisms in sexual reproduction.

Heterotrophic: nutrition based on organic compounds, in contrast to autotrophic nutrition.

Homothallism: sexual reproduction occurring in a self-compatible individual or strain.

Hormogonium: a segment (usually motile) of a trichome of a blue-green alga which can grow into a new trichome.

Histology: the study of tissues.

Holdfast: an attaching organ in certain algae.

Holozoic: phagotrophic, i.e., ingesting solid food particles.

Homospory: condition of producing monomorphic spores.

Hydrophyte: a plant living in water or in a very moist habitat.

Hymenium: the fertile layer of asci on the surface of an ascocarp, or of basidia on or in a basidiocarp.

Hypha: one branch of mycelium in a fungus.

Hypocotyl: the portion of the axis between the cotyledonary node and primary root.

Hypodermis: a layer or layers of thick-walled cells below the epidermis.

Hypogean: germination in which the cotyledons are not elevated but remain in the seed within the soil.

Hypogyny: floral organization in which the pistil is at the apex of the receptacle, the other floral organs originating below it.

Hypothallus: a thin deposit under the fruiting body in certain Myxomycota.

Hypotheca: the smaller valve of a diatom frustule.

Imperfect flower: one lacking either stamens or pistils.

Incomplete flower: one lacking one of the four types of floral organs.

Indusium: the thin covering layer of a group of sporangia in ferns.

Inflorescence: an axis bearing flowers.

Integument: the tissues covering the megasporangium in ovules.

Intercalary growth: growth localized (sometimes at intervals) between base and apex of an organism.

Internode: the region of the stem between two nodes.

Intine: the inner layer of the spore or pollen grain wall.

Involucre: (1) tissue which encloses a group of archegonia and hence a sporophyte in liverworts; (2) the bracts below a capitulum.

Isogamy: the type of sexual reproduction in which the gametes are morphologically indistinguishable.

Isomorphic alternation of generations: a life cycle in which the two alternants are morphologically similar.

Isophyllous: producing one type of leaf.

Jacket layer: (1) the wall of an antheridium in cryptogams; (2) the cells surrounding the egg in gymnosperms.

Karyogamy: nuclear union.

Lacuna: a chamber or air space.

Laminarin: a polymer of glucose and mannitol with 1:6-glucosidic linkages; a storage product in brown algae.

Lateral conjugation: union of two algal cells of the same filament by formation of lateral protuberances near common transverse septa.

Leaf gap: a parenchymatous interruption in a stele associated with departure of a leaf trace.

Leaf primordium: a miniature leaf in the bud.

Leaf trace: xylem and phloem connecting that of the petiole with that of the stele.

Legume: (1) a member of the legume family; (2) a simple, dry, fruit which dehisces along two sutures at maturity (fruits in some genera of the family indehiscent).

Lenticel: a region in the bark of woody stems where gaseous interchange occurs.

Leptosporangiate: the development of an entire sporangium from the outer product of a periclinal division of a superficial cell.

Leucosin: see Chrysolaminarin.

Ligule: a minute, membranous appendage at the base of grass leaves and those of certain Microphyllophyta.

Linear tetrad: arrangement of four spores in a single series.

Lip cells: thin-walled cells which interrupt the annulus in certain fern sporangia.

Localized growth: growth occurring in one or more definite regions of an organism.

Long shoot: in certain woody plants branches which increase rapidly in length during the first season in which they emerge from the bud (in contrast to spur shoots).

Macroconidium: a conidium of certain ascomycetous molds, as distinct from a microconidium.

Macrocyclic: long-cycled; a rust which produces one or more types of binucleate spores in addition to teliospores.

Macrophyllous: having leaves with branching veins, the traces of which leaves are associated with gaps in the stem stele.

Mannitol: an alcoholic storage product of brown algae.

Manubrium: a prismatic cell which bears capitula and antheridial filaments in Charophyta.

Marginal meristem: the meristem which gives rise to the leaf blade in ontogeny.

Medulla: pith or central region.

Megasporangium: the sporangium in which megaspores are produced.

Megaspore: a spore arising by meiosis in which all four products potentially can grow female gametophytes; often, but not always, larger than microspores.

Megasporocyte: the megaspore mother cell which forms megaspores after meiosis.

Megasporophyll: a leaf bearing one or more megasporangia or ovules.

Meiosis: two successive nuclear divisions in which the chromosome number is halved and genetic segregation occurs.

Meiosporangium: a sporangium in which meiosis occurs.

Meristem: a tissue composed of embryonic, unspecialized cells.

Merozygote: a bacterial cell which has conjugated with another with resulting change in its genic complement.

Mesarch: pattern of primary xylem differentiation in which metaxylem surrounds the protoxylem.

Mesocarp: the layer of a fruit between exocarp and endocarp.

Mesome: an internode proximal to a telome.

Mesophyll: tissue other than veins between lower and upper epidermis of a leaf.

Mesophyte: a plant intermediate in moisture requirements and habitats between a hydrophyte and xerophyte.

Metabolism: the chemical processes occurring in living organisms.

Metaphloem: primary phloem which differentiates from procambium later than the protophloem and after elongation of the organ has ceased.

Metaxylem: that primary xylem which differentiates from procambium after elongation of the organ has ceased and after the protoxylem has matured.

Microconidium: a small conidium of ascomycetous molds which acts like a spermatium.

Microcyclic: short-cycled; a rust in which the teliospore is the only binucleate spore.

Micron: equivalent of 0.001 mm. or 1/25,000 in.

Microphyllous: having leaves with single unbranched veins, the leaf traces not leaving gaps in the stem stele.

Micropyle: a passageway between the apices of the integument or integuments.

Microsporangium: a sporangium producing microspores.

Microsporocyte: the microspore mother cell which forms four microspores after meiosis.

Microspore: a product of a microsporocyte, often, but not always, smaller than the megaspore of the species, and producing a male gametophyte.

Microsporophyll: a leaf bearing one or more microsporangia.

Midrib: the differentiated midaxis of a thallus or leaf.

Mitochondrion: a double-membrane-bounded cytoplasmic organelle, site of energy release in cellular respiration.

Mitosis: nuclear division involving chromosomes which are replicated and distributed equally between the daughter nuclei.

Mitosporangium: a sporangium in which the spores arise by mitotic, rather than meiotic, nuclear divisions.

Mixed: a fern sorus in which the sporangia are in varying stages of development at a given time.

Monarch: having one protoxylem group.

Monocolpate: pollen grains having one germ furrow.

Monoecious: producing both microspores and megaspores on one individual.

Monophyletic: representing a single or direct line of evolutionary descent.

Morphological alternation of generations: having two morphologically recognizable phases (plants or tissues) in the life cycle.

Morphology: the study of organization and development, both ontogenetic and phylogenetic.

Multiple fruit: one developing from the maturing ovaries of more than one flower.

Mutation: a sudden change in an organism which is transmitted to offspring.

Mycelium: the collective term for the hyphae of a fungus; the somatic or vegetative thallus of a fungus.

Mycobiont: the fungal member of a lichen.

Mycology: the study of fungi.

Mycorrhiza: an association of root and/or rhizome with a fungus which may be superficial or internal.

Neck: the slender portion of an archegonium.

Neck canal cells: cells which fill the center of an immature archegonial neck.

Nitrogen fixation: use of gaseous nitrogen in metabolism.

Node: point of attachment of a leaf; also point of branch emergence.

Oidium: a thin-walled sporelike hyphal cell.

Ontogeny: development of an individual.

Oogamy: sexual union of a large nonmotile egg and a small, motile sperm.

Oogonium: a unicellular gametangium which contains an egg.

Open-dichotomous venation: dichotomous venation with free vein endings.

Operculum: the cover-like apex of a moss capsule freed by rupture at the annulus.

Orthotropous ovule: an ovule in which the micropyle is 180° from the point of attachment of the funiculus to the ovule.

Ostiole: opening of a conceptacle, perithecium, or pycnidium.

Ovary: the ovule-bearing region of a pistil.

Overtopping: dominance of one fork of a dichotomy.

Ovule: a megasporangium covered by an integument.

Ovuliferous scale: the appendage to which the ovule is attached in certain conifers.

Paleobotany: the study of extinct plants.

Palmella stage: a nonmotile stage of motile algae embedded in a colloidal sheath.

Palynology: the study of spores and pollen grains.

Paraphysis, (es): a sterile structure among reproductive cells or organs.

Parasexuality: a process in which plasmogamy, karyogamy and haploidization occur in sequence but not at specified points in the life cycle of the individual.

Parasite: an organism which lives upon and at the expense of another.

Parenchyma: thin-walled living cells with large vacuoles; photosynthetic or storage cells.

Parietal placentation: attachment of ovules to the ovary wall.

Parthenogenesis: development of an embryo without gamete union.

Pedicel: the stalk which attaches a flower to the axis of the inflorescence.

Perfect flower: one which has both stamens and pistils.

Perianth: (1) the collective term for sepals and petals; (2) in liverworts, leaves or other tissue surrounding a group of archegonia.

Periclinal: parallel to the surface.

Pericycle: a thin zone of living cells just within the endodermis.

Peridium: the wall of a fructification in fungi.

Perigyny: a condition in certain flowers in which the sepals, petals, and stamens are borne on the rim of a cup-like receptacle, the pistil being at its base.

Periphyses: sterile filaments protruding from an ostiole.

Periplast: a complex and (often) ornamented plasma membrane.

Peristome: cellular or acellular structures at the mouth of the capsule in many mosses.

Perithecium: an ascocarp with a terminal ostiole.

Petal: a colored (usually) sterile appendage of the angiospermous flower.

Petiole: the stalk which attaches the leaf blade to the stem.

Phagotrophic: ingesting solid food particles.

Phanerogam: a seed plant.

Phellem: cork tissue.

Phellogen: cork cambium.

Phloem: living, thin-walled cells, typified by sieve areas in the walls of some of the cells; food-conducting in function.

Photoautotrophic: using light energy in synthesizing protoplasm from inorganic compounds.

Photosynthesis: the synthesis in light from carbon dioxide and water of carbohydrates with the liberation of oxygen in chlorophyllous plants.

Phototaxis: movement as stimulated positively or negatively by light.

Phycobilin: a protein-linked algal pigment of blue-green and red algae.

Phycobiont: the algal member of a lichen.

Phycocyanin: a blue phycobilin pigment of blue-green and red algae.

Phycoerythrin: a red phycobilin pigment of blue-green and red algae.

Phycology: the study of algae.

Phylogeny: the real relationships of organisms through evolutionary descent.

Physiology: the study of the functioning of organisms.

Phytogeography: the study of plant distribution.

Pileus: the cap of the mushroom basidiocarp and that of certain ascocarps.

Pinnule: the ultimate unit or division of a bipinnately compound leaf.

Pistil: a megasporophyll, carpel, or group of united megasporophylls in angiosperms.

Pistillate flower: one having only pistils, not stamens.

Pit connection: a modification in the common wall between contiguous cells in red algae.

Placenta: the region to which ovules are attached.

Placental cell: a cell in red algae which gives rise to carposporangia.

Placentation: the pattern of ovular attachment.

Planation: flattening of branches.

Plankton: suspended, free-floating, aquatic microorganisms.

Plasmodium: an unwalled, amoeboid, multinucleate mass of protoplasm.

Plasmogamy: union of sex cells or gametes.

Plectostele: a protostele in which xylem and phloem are intermingled in zones.

Plumule: the terminal bud of an embryo.

Plurilocular: a multicellular structure, each cell of which produces a reproductive cell.

Pod: see legume.

Polar nodule: the polar wall thickening in heterocysts and certain diatom frustules.

Polar nuclei: the nuclei of the angiosperm female gametophyte which migrates to its center from the poles.

Pollen chamber: a depression at the apex of the megasporangium formed by cellular breakdown.

Pollen grain: a microspore containing a mature or miniature male gametophyte.

Pollen tube: the tubular protuberance of maturing male gametophytes in seed plants.

Pollination: the transfer of pollen from the microsporangium to the micropyle of the ovule (in gymnosperms) or to the stigma of the pistil (in angiosperms).

Pollination droplet: a droplet of fluid at the micropyle at pollination.

Pollinium: a cohesive mass of pollen grains.

Polyeder: a tetrahedral cell in *Hydrodictyon* and *Pediastrum* which forms zoospores.

Polypetaly: having separate unfused petals.

Polyphyletic: descended from more than one phyletic line.

Polysepaly: having separate, unfused sepals.

Polystelic: containing more than one or two steles.

Pome: a simple, fleshy, indehiscent fruit formed from an epigynous flower, of which the true fruit is surrounded by enlarged floral tube and fleshy receptacle.

Primary archesporial cell: the earliest recognizable differentiated sporogenous cell.

Primary endosperm nucleus: the nucleus formed by the union of two polar nuclei (or a secondary nucleus) with a sperm in angiosperms.

Primary germination: nuclear and cell divisions within the spore wall.

Primary meristem: the three meristematic derivatives (protoderm, procambium, and ground meristem) of the apical meristem.

Primary permanent tissue: one differentiated from a primary meristem

Primary phloem: that phloem derived from procambium.

Primary suspensor: the tier of cells above the embryo-forming cells in certain conifers.

Primary xylem: that xylem derived from procambium.

Primitive: ancient; not changed or modified with time or in evolution.

Primordium: precursor of an organ.

Procambium: that primary meristem which differentiates into vascular tissue and cambium (if present).

Proembryo: a mass of cells produced by division of the zygote before organization of the organs of the embryo.

Progamone: the precursor of a sexual substance.

Progressive cleavage: gradual cytokinesis of multinucleate protoplasm ultimately into uninucleate or few-nucleate segments.

Prokaryota: organisms lacking membrane-bounded nuclei, plastids, Golgi apparatus, and mitochondria.

Proliferation: repeated development of spores from the same sporangium.

Promeristem: the apical meristematic region of an axis.

Prosporangium: precursor of the zoosporangium in certain chytrids.

Protandrous: earlier production of male than of female gametes in bisexual individuals.

Prothallial cell: the small, often lenticular, cell or cells produced in primary germination of microspores, thought to represent vestigial vegetative tissue of the male gametophyte.

Prothallium: the gametophyte of vascular cryptogams.

Protoderm: that primary meristem which is the precursor of epidermis.

Protogynous: earlier production of female than of male gametes in bisexual individuals.

Protonema: the product of spore germination in mosses and certain liverworts; the precursor of the leafy gametophores.

Protoperithecium: the precursor of the perithecium in certain ascomycetous molds.

Protophloem: the first-differentiated primary phloem.

Protostele: a solid core of xylem surrounded by phloem.

Protoxylem: the first-differentiated primary xylem, usually in a region where the organ is increasing in length.

Pseudoelater: the sterile cells among the spores of Anthocerotopsida.

Pseudoparenchymatous: giving the appearance of parenchyma, when sectioned, through interweaving of filaments.

Pseudoperianth: an envelope surrounding a single archegonium.

Pseudoplasmodium: an aggregate of amoebae in cellular slime molds.

Pseudopodium: the elongating portion of the gametophore axis which elevates the sporophyte in *Sphagnum* and *Andreaea*.

Pure culture: see Axenic culture.

Pyrenoid: a differentiated region of the plastid in certain algae: in green algae, a region of condensation of glucose into starch.

Raceme: an elongate inflorescence in which the short-pedicellate flowers are arranged with the youngest at the apex.

Rachis: the axis of a compound leaf on which the leaflets are borne.

Radicle: the primary or embryonic root.

Raphe: a longitudinal fissure in the frustules of motile pennate diatoms.

Ray flower: a ligulate flower at the margin of a capitulum.

Receptacle: a fertile area on which reproductive organs are borne.

Reduced: secondarily simplified in evolution.

Reproduction: replication or multiplication of individuals.

Resin canal: a secretory-cell-bounded tube in conifers into which resin is secreted.

Reticulate venation: branching, rebranching, and anastomosis of veins.

Rhizine: rope like-strands of absorptive hyphae in lichens.

Rhizome: a fleshy, elongate nonerect stem often, but not always, subterranean.

Rhizomorph: rope-like, twisted hyphal strands.

Rhizophore: a root-bearing organ or region.

Root cap: a covering of parenchymatous cells over the apical meristem of the root.

Root hair: an absorptive unicellular protuberance of the epidermal cells of the root.

Sagittal section: one cut parallel to the long axis of a dorsiventral structure and perpendicular to its surface.

Scalariform conjugation: formation of conjugation tubes laterally producing a ladder-like configuration in certain algae.

Sclerenchyma: lignified supporting tissue.

Sclerotium: a hard, dormant stage of certain fungi.

Secondary growth: that derived from a secondary meristem.

Secondary meristem: a lateral meristem such as cambium and phellogen.

Secondary nucleus: the nucleus formed by precocious union of the polar nuclei.

Secondary phloem: that derived from the cambium.

Secondary root: a branch of the primary root.

Secondary suspensor: elongating cells formed by division of the primary suspensors.

Secondary xylem: that derived from the cambium.

Seed: an embryonic sporophyte embedded in the female gametophyte (in gymnosperms) or in the endosperm, or gorged with digested products of the latter (in angiosperms), within the remains of the megasporangium and covered with one or more integuments.

Sepal: the lowermost sterile appendages, usually green, on a floral receptacle.

Serology: the study of immunological phenomena.

Seta: the stalk of the sporophyte in liverworts and mosses.

Sexual reproduction: reproduction involving nuclear union and meiosis and often plasmogamy.

Sheath: a colloidal capsule about a cell or trichome.

Shoot: the leaf-bearing portion of the axis.

Sieve element: a simple cell with sieve plates or areas.

Sieve plate: an aggregate of sieve areas in the wall of sieve cells.

Sieve tube: a series of sieve cells.

Simple fruit: one derived from a single pistil (simple or compound) of a single flower.

Simple leaf: one with an undivided blade.

Simple pistil: one derived from one megasporophyll or composed of one carpel.

Simple polyembryony: development of more than one embryo through formation of several zygotes.

Siphonogamous: having pollen tubes.

Siphonostele: a hollow cylinder composed of xylem and phloem.

Sirenin: a sexual substance attracting male gametes in *Allomyces*.

Solenostele: an amphiphloic siphonostele.

Somatogamy: union of vegetative hyphae.

Soredia: clusters of hyphae and algal cells of lichens.

Sorocarp: the fruiting structure of cellular slime molds.

Sorus: a group or cluster.

Specialized: derived; modified.

Sperm: the motile male gamete (or nucleus).

Spermagonium: the structure producing spermatia in rust fungi.

Spermatangium: the cell which produces a spermatium in red algae.

Spermatium: a minute nonflagellate male gamete.

Spermatogenous cells: those which will give rise to sperms.

Spherule: a segment of a myxomycetous sclerotium.

Spike: an elongate inflorescence with sessile flowers, the youngest at the apex.

Spirillum: a spirally twisted bacterium.

Spongy layer: specialized nutritive tissue of the megasporangium surrounding the developing female gametophyte in gymnosperms.

Sporangiophore: (1) in phycomycetous fungi, a hypha bearing a sporangium at its apex; (2) in vascular cryptogams, a branch bearing sporangia.

Sporangium: a structure containing spores.

Spore mother cell: a sporocyte.

Sporic meiosis: meiosis during sporogenesis.

Sporidium: the basidiospore of smuts.

Sporocarp: a hard, nut-like structure containing sori of heterosporous sporangia in ferns.

Sporocyte: the cell which gives rise meiotically to a tetrad of spores.

Sporophyll: a leaf bearing one or more sporangia.

Sporophyte: the spore-producing alternant.

Spur shoot: a lateral, dwarf shoot in certain woody plants.

Stalk cell: one of the products of division of the generative cell in gymnosperms, said to be the homologue of the antheridial stalk.

Staminate flower: one containing only stamens.

Stele: the vascular tissue of axes.

Sterile cell: see Stalk cell.

Sterile jacket: the cells covering an antheridium.

Stigma: (1) the "red eyespot" of algae; (2) in angiosperms, the receptive region of the pistil.

Stipe: (1) the stalk of a basidiocarp; (2) the portion of a kelp between blade and base.

Stoma (stomata): a minute, intercellular fissure in the epidermis surrounded by guard cells.

Stomium: the lip cell region of the sporangium in ferns.

Striate venation: having a series of arcuate or parallel main veins, mostly not interconnected.

Strobilus: a stem with short internodes and spore-bearing appendages.

Style: the portion of a pistil between stigma and ovary.

Supporting cell: that cell which bears the carpogonial branch in red algae.

Suspensor: (1) a sterile cell adjacent to the gametangium in phycomycetous molds; (2) a cell or cells which by elongation project the embryo into nutritive tissue.

Sympetaly: condition of having petals united.

Synangium: united sporangia.

Synergid: sterile cell associated with the angiosperm egg.

Synsepaly: union of sepals.

Tapetal plasmodium: a multinucleate mass of protoplasm arising by the breakdown of the tapetal walls.

Tapetum: a nutritive layer within sporangia.

Taxis: a movement toward or away from a stimulus.

Taxon (taxa): a category in classification.

Taxonomy: the science of classification.

Teliospore: a thick-walled spore in which karyogamy occurs, produced late in the rust-life cycle.

Telium: a group of binucleate hyphae which produce teliospores

Telome: a hypothetical unit of organization consisting of the ultimate segment of a dichotomously branched axis, either fertile or sterile.

Telome truss: a combination of a fertile and sterile telome.

Terminal bud: that one at the apex of an axis.

Tetrad: a group of four (often used to designate spore tetrad).

Tetrasporangium: a sporangium in red algae which gives rise to four spores after meiosis.

Tetraspore: the meiotic products of a tetrasporangium.

Tetrasporophyte: in the red algae, the diploid plant which produces tetraspores.

Tinsel flagellum: one with filiform appendages.

Trabecula: (1) a beam-like structure in certain large sporangia (*Isoetes*); (2) bridging lacunae in siphonalean algae and their stems and those of *Selaginella*.

Tracheid: a single-celled, lignified, nonliving water-conducting element of xylem.

Trama: interwoven fungal hyphae on which basidia are borne.

Transduction: genetic modification (in bacteria) effected by the DNA of viruses (bacteriophages).

Transformation: genetic modification in bacteria effected by their incorporation of DNA from another strain.

Transfusion tissue: tissue surrounding a leaf vein within the endodermis in gymnosperm leaves.

Transition zone: that portion of the axis between root and stem in which the xylem-phloem arrangement changes from radial to collateral.

Translocation: movement of substances in plants.

Transpiration: the loss of water in vapor form from the aerial parts of a plant.

Triarch: having three protoxylem groups.

Trichoblast: a sterile, branching, colorless filament in red algae.

Trichogyne: (1) a chain of cells (in blue-green algae); or (2) an epidermal hair (in vascular plants).

Trichothallic: intercalary growth at the base of a hair.

Tricolpate: having three germ furrows, as in pollen grains.

Tropism: a growth response or bending toward or away from a stimulus.

True indusium: an epidermal outgrowth covering receptacle and sporangia in certain ferns.

Trumpet hyphae: elongate, hypha-like cells inflated near the transverse septa.

Tube cell: the precursor of the pollen tube in male gametophytes.

Tuberculate rhizoid: one with peg-like thickenings.

Tunica: superficial layer or layers of meristematic cells covering the corpus.

Umbel: a flat-topped, cymose inflorescence.

Unilocular: having a single cavity.

Urediniospore: a binucleate spore in rusts.

Uredinium: a mass of binucleate cells forming urediniospores.

Vallecular canal: a canal opposite the valleys between the ridges of an arthrophytan stem.

Valve: (1) one-half of a diatom frustule; (2) a segment of the capsule wall of liverworts and hornworts at dehiscence.

Vascular plant: one containing xylem and phloem.

Vegetative: somatic; usually not reproductive.

Vein: xylem and phloem strand in a leaf.

Venation: pattern of vein arrangement in leaves.

Venter: the enlarged basal portion of an oogonium which contains an egg.

Ventral canal cell: the sister cell of the egg, derived with it by division of the central cell.

Ventral scale: a multicellular, monostromatic appendage in certain liverworts.

Vernation: arrangement of leaves in the bud.

Vessel: a series of perforate, lignified, conducting cells of xylem.

Vessel element: one cellular component of a vessel.

Volva: a cup at the base of the stipe in certain mushrooms.

Water bloom: a dense population of planktonic algae.

Webbing: hypothetical filling of areas between branches with parenchyma tissue.

Whiplash flagellum: one which is sheathed except for a free tip; lacking fibrillar appendages.

Xanthophyll: a carotenoid pigment, differing from carotene in containing oxygen.

Xenia: direct influence of pollen on seed or fruit.

Xerophyte: a plant of dry habitats.

Xylem: lignified water-conducting tissue.

Zoosporangium: a sporangium which produces zoospores.

Zoospore: a motile, asexual reproductive cell formed by a nonmotile organism.

Zygomorphy: the condition of being bilaterally symmetrical.

Zygote: the cell produced by the union of two gametes.

Zygotic meiosis: meiosis at zygote germination.

Index

Boldface numbers indicate pages on which illustrations appear.

Set in Linotype Bodoni Book

Format by Frances Torbert Tilley

Composition by American Book–Stratford Press, Inc.

Printed by The Murray Printing Company

Manufactured by American Book–Stratford Press, Inc.